Glyn James

Advanced Modern Engineering Mathematics

Taken from:

Advanced Modern Engineering Mathematics, Third Edition
by Glyn James

Custom Publishing

New York Boston San Francisco
London Toronto Sydney Tokyo Singapore Madrid
Mexico City Munich Paris Cape Town Hong Kong Montreal

Cover Art: *Pattern 10/Data Strategies*, by Angela Sciaraffa.

Taken from:

Advanced Modern Engineering Mathematics, Third Edition
by Glyn James

Published by Prentice Hall
Upper Saddle River, New Jersey 07458

This special edition published in cooperation with Pearson Custom Publishing.

Printed in the United States of America

10 9 8 7 6 5 4 3 2

2008360795

KW

www.pearsonhighered.com

ISBN 10: 0-555-00475-9
ISBN 13: 978-0-555-00475-3

Contents

Chapter 4 Fourier Series 265

Preface

Throughout the course of history, engineering and mathematics have developed in parallel. All branches of engineering depend on mathematics for their description and there has been a steady flow of ideas and problems from engineering that has stimulated and sometimes initiated branches of mathematics. Thus it is vital that engineering students receive a thorough grounding in mathematics, with the treatment related to their interests and problems. As with the previous editions, this has been the motivation for the production of this third edition – a companion text to the third edition of *Modern Engineering Mathematics*, this being designed to provide a first-level core studies course in mathematics for undergraduate programmes in all engineering disciplines. Building on the foundations laid in the companion text, this book gives an extensive treatment of some of the more advanced areas of mathematics that have applications in various fields of engineering, particularly as tools for computer-based system modelling, analysis and design. Feedback, from users of the previous editions, on subject content has been highly positive indicating that it is sufficiently broad to provide the necessary second-level, or optional, studies for most engineering programmes, where in each case a selection of the material may be made. Whilst designed primarily for use by engineering students, it is believed that the book is also suitable for use by students of applied mathematics and the physical sciences.

Although the pace of the book is at a somewhat more advanced level than the companion text, the philosophy of learning by doing is retained with continuing emphasis on the development of students' ability to use mathematics with understanding to solve engineering problems. Recognizing the increasing importance of mathematical modelling in engineering practice, many of the worked examples and exercises incorporate mathematical models that are designed both to provide relevance and to reinforce the role of mathematics in various branches of engineering. In addition, each chapter contains specific sections on engineering applications, and these form an ideal framework for individual, or group, study assignments, thereby helping to reinforce the skills of mathematical modelling, which are seen as essential if engineers are to tackle the increasingly complex systems they are being called upon to analyse and design. The importance of numerical methods in problem solving is also recognized, and its treatment is integrated with the analytical work throughout the book.

Much of the feedback from users relates to the role and use of software packages, particularly symbolic algebra packages. Without making it an essential requirement the authors have attempted to highlight throughout the text situations where the user could make effective use of software. This also applies to exercises and, indeed, a limited number have been introduced for which the use of such a package is essential. Whilst any appropriate piece of software can be used, the authors recommend the use of MATLAB (incorporating the Symbolic Math Toolbox) and MAPLE. These two software packages are widely referenced within the text, with basic commands introduced and illustrated. When indicated, students are strongly recommended to use these packages to check their solutions to exercises. This is not only to help develop proficiency in their use, but also to enable students to appreciate the necessity of having a sound knowledge of the underpinning mathematics if such packages are to be used effectively. Throughout the book two icons are used:

- An open screen indicates that the use of a software package would be useful (e.g. for checking solutions) but not essential.
- A closed screen indicates that the use of a software package is essential or highly desirable.

As indicated earlier, feedback on content from users of previous editions has been favourable, and consequently no new chapter has been introduced. However, in response to feedback individual chapters have been reviewed and updated accordingly. In addition to strengthening the links with MATLAB and MAPLE, additional worked examples and exercises have been incorporated and the treatment of some of the numerical methods, particularly the treatment of finite elements, has been extended.

A comprehensive Solutions Manual is available free of charge to lecturers adopting this textbook. It will also be available for download via the Web at: www.booksites.net/james.

Acknowledgements

The authoring team is extremely grateful to all the reviewers and users of the text who have provided valuable comments on previous editions of this book. Most of this has been highly constructive and very much appreciated. The team has continued to enjoy the full support of a very enthusiastic production team at Pearson Education and wishes to thank all those concerned. Finally I would like to thank my wife, Dolan, for her full support throughout the preparation of this text and its previous editions.

Glyn James
Coventry University
February 2003

About the Authors

Glyn James retired as Dean of the School of Mathematical and Information Sciences at Coventry University in 2001 and is now Emeritus Professor in Mathematics at the University. He also has a position as an Adjunct Professor in the Department of Mathematics at Curtin University of Technology, Perth, Australia. He graduated from the University College of Wales, Cardiff in the late 1950s, obtaining first class honours degrees in both Mathematics and Chemistry. He obtained a PhD in Engineering Science in 1971 as an external student of the University of Warwick. He has been employed at Coventry since 1964 and held the position of Head of Mathematics Department prior to his appointment as Dean in 1992. His research interests are in control theory and its applications to industrial problems. He also has a keen interest in mathematical education, particularly in relation to the teaching of engineering mathematics and mathematical modelling. He was co-chairman of the European Mathematics Working Group established by the European Society for Engineering Education (SEFI) in 1982, a past chairman of the Education Committee of the Institute of Mathematics and its Applications (IMA), and a member of the Royal Society Mathematics Education Subcommittee. In 1995 he was chairman of the Working Group that produced the report 'Mathematics Matters in Engineering' on behalf of the professional bodies in engineering and mathematics within the UK. He is also a member of the editorial/advisory board of three international journals. He has published numerous papers and is co-editor of five books on various aspects of mathematical modelling. He is a past Vice-President of the IMA and has also served a period as Honorary Secretary of the Institute. He is a Chartered Mathematician and a Fellow of the IMA.

David Burley has recently retired from the University of Sheffield. He graduated in mathematics from King's College, University of London in 1955 and obtained his PhD in mathematical physics. After working in the University of Glasgow, he spent most of his academic career in the University of Sheffield, being Head of Department for six years. He has long experience of teaching engineering students and has been particularly interested in encouraging students to construct mathematical models in physical and biological contexts to enhance their learning. His research work has ranged through statistical mechanics, optimization and fluid mechanics. Current interests involve the flow of molten glass in a variety of situations and the application of results in the glass industry.

Dick Clements is Reader in the Department of Engineering Mathematics at Bristol University. He read for the Mathematical Tripos at Christ's College, Cambridge in the late 1960s. He went on to take a PGCE at Leicester University School of Education before returning to Cambridge to research a PhD in Aeronautical Engineering. In 1973 he was appointed Lecturer in Engineering Mathematics at Bristol University and has taught mathematics to engineering students ever since. He has undertaken research in a wide range of engineering topics but is particularly interested in mathematical modelling and the development of new ways of teaching mathematics to engineers. He has published numerous papers and one previous book, *Mathematical Modelling: A Case Study Approach*. He is a Chartered Engineer, a Member of the Royal Aeronautical Society, a Chartered Mathematician, a Fellow of the Institute of Mathematics and its Applications, an Associate Fellow of the Royal Institute of Navigation and a Member of the Institute of Learning and Teaching.

Phil Dyke is Professor of Applied Mathematics and Head of School of Mathematics and Statistics at the University of Plymouth. After graduating with first class honours in Mathematics from the University of London, he gained a PhD in coastal sea modelling at Reading in 1972. Since then, he has been a full-time academic initially at Heriot-Watt University teaching engineers followed by a brief spell at Sunderland. He has been at Plymouth since 1984. He still engages in teaching and is actively involved in building mathematical models relevant to environmental issues.

John Searl is Director of the Edinburgh Centre for Mathematical Education at the University of Edinburgh. As well as lecturing on mathematical education, he teaches service courses for engineers and scientists. His current research concerns the development of learning environments that make for the effective learning of mathematics for 16–20 year olds. As an applied mathematician who has worked collaboratively with (among others) engineers, physicists, biologists and pharmacologists, he is keen to develop the problem solving skills of the students and to encourage them to think for themselves.

Nigel Steele is Professor and Head of Mathematics at Coventry University. He graduated in Mathematics from Southampton University in 1967, receiving his Master's degree in 1969. He has been a member of the Mathematics Department at Coventry University since 1968. He has a particular interest in teaching Engineering Mathematics, and is joint editor of the European Society for Engineering Education (SEFI) report 'A Common Core Curriculum in Mathematics for the European Engineer'. He has published numerous papers and contributed to several books. His current research interests are in the application of neurocomputing techniques, fuzzy logic and in control theory. He is a Member of the Royal Aeronautical Society, a Chartered Mathematician and a Fellow of the Institute of Mathematics and its Applications. He is Honorary Secretary of the Institute with responsibility for Education matters.

Jerry Wright is Technology Consultant at the AT&T Shannon Laboratory, New Jersey, USA. He graduated in Engineering (BSc and PhD at the University of Southampton) and in Mathematics (MSc at the University of London) and worked at the National Physical Laboratory before moving to the University of Bristol in 1978. There he acquired wide experience in the teaching of mathematics to students of engineering, and became Senior Lecturer in Engineering Mathematics. He held a Royal Society Industrial Fellowship for 1994, and is a Fellow of the Institute of Mathematics and its Applications. In 1996 he moved to AT&T Labs (originally part of Bell Labs) to continue his research in spoken language understanding and human/computer dialogue systems.

1 Functions of a Complex Variable

Chapter 1 Contents

1.1 Introduction

In the theory of alternating currents, the application of quantities such as complex impedance involves functions having complex numbers as independent variables. There are many other areas in engineering where this is the case; for example, the motion of fluids, the transfer of heat or the processing of signals. Some of these applications are discussed later in this book.

Traditionally, complex variable techniques have been important, and extensively used, in a wide variety of engineering situations. This has been especially the case in areas such as electromagnetic and electrostatic field theory, fluid dynamics, aerodynamics and elasticity. With the rapid developments in computer technology and the consequential use of sophisticated algorithms for analysis and design in engineering there has, in recent years, been less emphasis on the use of complex variable techniques and a shift towards numerical techniques applied directly to the underlying full partial differential equations model of the situation being investigated. However, even when this is the case there is still considerable merit in having an analytical solution, possibly for an idealized model, in order both to develop a better understanding of the behaviour of the solution and to give confidence in numerical estimates for the solution of enhanced models. Modern software packages, such as CFX, FLUENT and PHOENICS, are frequently used to solve fluid flow and heat transfer engineering problems in real situations often related to health and safety and other situations involving risk. To make the best use of such software requires knowledge of mappings and use of complex variables. Another example of where the theory has made a significant contribution is the design of aerofoil sections for aircraft and other lifting bodies. The strength of the theory in such applications is its ability to generate mappings which transform complicated shapes, such as an aerofoil section, into a simpler shape, typically a circle in the case of an aerofoil. The idealized airflow around the transformed shape (the circle) is relatively easy to calculate and, by reversing the transformation, the flow around the aerofoil, and hence its lifting capabilities, can be deduced. An application at the end of the chapter illustrates the technique applied to simplifying the geometry for the solution of a problem in the flow of heat.

Throughout engineering, transforms in one form or another play a major role in analysis and design. An area of continuing importance is the use of Laplace, z, Fourier and other transforms in areas such as control, communication and signal processing. Such transforms are considered later in this book, where it will be seen that functions of a complex variable play a key role. This chapter is devoted to developing an understanding of the standard techniques of complex variables so as to enable the reader to apply them with confidence in application areas.

1.2 Complex functions and mappings

The concept of a function involves two sets X and Y and a rule that assigns to each element x in the set X (written $x \in X$) precisely one element $y \in Y$. Whenever this situation arises, we say that there is a **function** f that **maps** the set X to the set Y, and represent this symbolically by

$$y = f(x) \quad (x \in X)$$

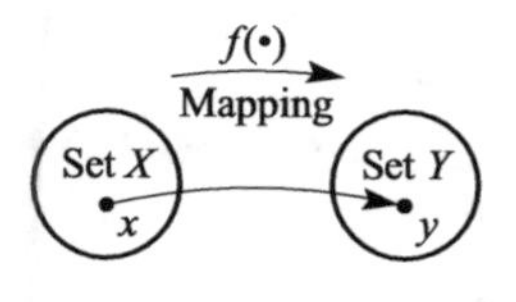

Figure 1.1 Real mapping $y = f(x)$.

Schematically we illustrate a function as in Figure 1.1. While x can take any value in the set X, the variable $y = f(x)$ depends on the particular element chosen for x. We therefore refer to x as the **independent** variable and y as the **dependent** variable. The set X is called the **domain** of the function, and the set of all images $y = f(x)$ $(x \in X)$ is called the **image set** or **range** of f. Previously we were concerned with real functions, so that x and y were real numbers. If the independent variable is a complex variable $z = x + \text{j}y$, where x and y are real and $\text{j} = \sqrt{(-1)}$, then the function $f(z)$ of z will in general also be complex. For example, if $f(z) = z^2$ then, replacing z by $x + \text{j}y$ and expanding, we have

$$f(z) = (x + \text{j}y)^2 = (x^2 - y^2) + \text{j}2xy = u + \text{j}v \quad \text{(say)}$$

where u and v are real. Such a function $f(z)$ is called a **complex function**, and we write

$$w = f(z)$$

where, in general, the dependent variable $w = u + \text{j}v$ is also complex.

The reader will recall that a complex number $z = x + \text{j}y$ can be represented on a plane called the **Argand diagram**, as illustrated in Figure 1.2(a). However, we cannot plot the values of x, y and $f(z)$ on one set of axes, as we were able to do for real functions $y = f(x)$. We therefore represent the values of

$$w = f(z) = u + \text{j}v$$

on a second plane as illustrated in Figure 1.2(b). The plane containing the independent variable z is called the z plane and the plane containing the dependent variable w is called the w plane. Thus the complex function $w = f(z)$ may be regarded as a **mapping** or **transformation** of points P within a region in the z plane (called the **domain**) to corresponding image points P′ within a region in the w plane (called the **range**).

It is this facility for mapping that gives the theory of complex functions much of its application in engineering. In most useful mappings the entire z plane is mapped onto the entire w plane, except perhaps for isolated points. Throughout this chapter the domain will be taken to be the entire z plane (that is, the set of all complex numbers, denoted by $\mathbb{C}$). This is analogous, for real functions, to the domain being the entire real line (that is, the set of all real numbers $\mathbb{R}$). If this is not the case then the complex function is termed 'not well defined'. In contrast, as for real functions, the range of the complex function may well be a proper subset of $\mathbb{C}$.

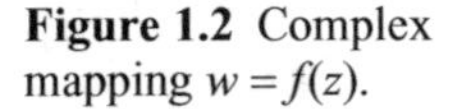
Figure 1.2 Complex mapping $w = f(z)$.

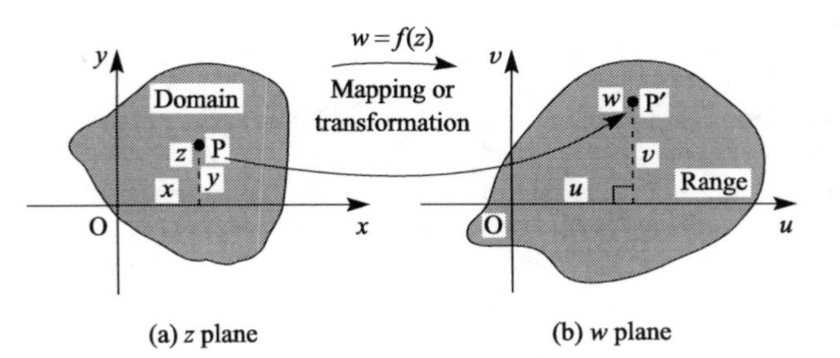

Example 1.1 Find the image in the w plane of the straight line $y = 2x + 4$ in the z plane, $z = x + jy$, under the mapping

$$w = 2z + 6$$

Solution Writing $w = u + jv$, where u and v are real, the mapping becomes

$$w = u + jv = 2(x + jy) + 6$$

or

$$u + jv = (2x + 6) + j2y$$

Equating real and imaginary parts then gives

$$u = 2x + 6, \qquad v = 2y \tag{1.1}$$

which, on solving for x and y, leads to

$$x = \tfrac{1}{2}(u - 6), \qquad y = \tfrac{1}{2}v$$

Thus the image of the straight line

$$y = 2x + 4$$

in the z plane is represented by

$$\tfrac{1}{2}v = 2 \times \tfrac{1}{2}(u - 6) + 4$$

or

$$v = 2u - 4$$

which corresponds to a straight line in the w plane. The given line in the z plane and the mapped image line in the w plane are illustrated in Figures 1.3(a) and (b) respectively.

Note from (1.1) that, in particular, the point $P_1(-2 + j0)$ in the z plane is mapped to the point $P_1'(2 + j0)$ in the w plane, and that the point $P_2(0 + j4)$ in the z plane is mapped to the point $P_2'(6 + j8)$ in the w plane. Thus, as the point P moves from P_1 to P_2 along the line $y = 2x + 4$ in the z plane, the mapped point P′ moves from P_1' to P_2' along the line $v = 2u - 4$ in the w plane. It is usual to indicate this with the arrowheads as illustrated in Figure 1.3.

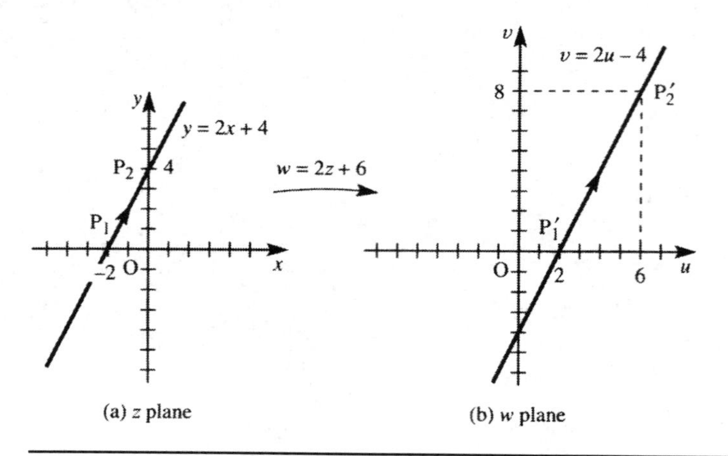

Figure 1.3 The mapping of Example 1.1.

1.2.1 Linear mappings

The mapping $w = 2z + 6$ in Example 1.1 is a particular example of a mapping corresponding to the general complex linear function

$$w = \alpha z + \beta \quad (1.2)$$

where w and z are complex-valued variables, and α and β are complex constants. In this section we shall investigate mappings of the z plane onto the w plane corresponding to (1.2) for different choices of the constants α and β. In so doing we shall also introduce some general properties of mappings.

Case (a) $\alpha = 0$

Letting $\alpha = 0$ (or $\alpha = 0 + \mathrm{j}0$) in (1.2) gives

$$w = \beta$$

which implies that $w = \beta$, no matter what the value of z. This is quite obviously a degenerate mapping, with the entire z plane being mapped onto the one point $w = \beta$ in the w plane. If nothing else, this illustrates the point made earlier in this section, that the image set may only be part of the entire w plane. In this particular case the image set is a single point. Since the whole of the z plane maps onto $w = \beta$, it follows that, in particular, $z = \beta$ maps to $w = \beta$. The point β is thus a **fixed point** in this mapping, which is a useful concept in helping us to understand a particular mapping. A further question of interest when considering mappings is that of whether, given a point in the w plane, we can tell from which point in the z plane it came under the mapping. If it is possible to get back to a unique point in the z plane then the mapping is said to have an **inverse mapping**. Clearly, for an inverse mapping $z = g(w)$ to exist, the point in the w plane has to be in the image set of the original mapping $w = f(z)$. Also, from the definition of a mapping, each point w in the w plane image set must lead to a single point z in the z plane under the inverse mapping $z = g(w)$. (Note the similarity to the requirements for the existence of an inverse function $f^{-1}(x)$ of a real function $f(x)$.) For the particular mapping $w = \beta$ considered here the image set is the single point $w = \beta$ in the w plane, and it is clear from Figure 1.4 that there is no way of getting back to just a single point in the z plane. Thus the mapping $w = \beta$ has no inverse.

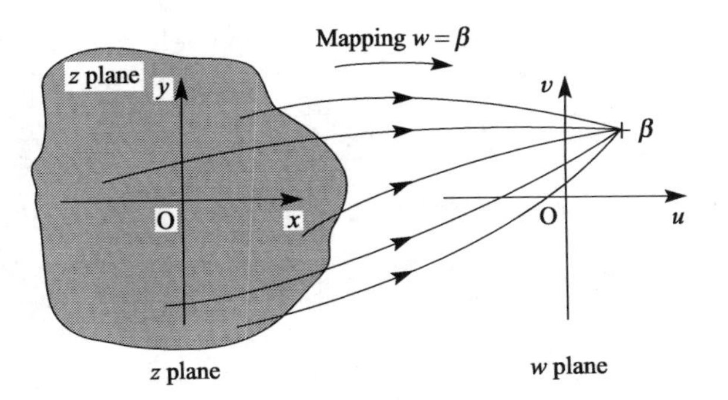

Figure 1.4 The degenerate mapping $w = \beta$.

Case (b) $\beta = 0, \alpha \neq 0$

With such a choice for the constants α and β, the mapping corresponding to (1.2) becomes

$$w = \alpha z$$

Under this mapping, the origin is the only fixed point, there being no other fixed points that are finite. Also, in this case there exists an inverse mapping

$$z = \frac{1}{\alpha}w$$

that enables us to return from the w plane to the z plane to the very same point from which we started under $w = \alpha z$. To illustrate this mapping at work, let us choose $\alpha = 1 + \mathrm{j}$, so that

$$w = (1 + \mathrm{j})z \tag{1.3}$$

and consider what happens to a general point z_0 in the z plane under this mapping. In general, there are two ways of doing this. We can proceed as in Example 1.1 and split both z and w into real and imaginary parts, equate real and imaginary parts and hence find the image curves in the w plane to specific curves (usually the lines $\mathrm{Re}(z)$ = constant, $\mathrm{Im}(z)$ = constant) in the z plane. Alternatively, we can rearrange the expression for w and deduce the properties of the mapping directly. The former course of action, as we shall see in this chapter, is the one most frequently used. Here, however, we shall take the latter approach and write $\alpha = 1 + \mathrm{j}$ in polar form as

$$1 + \mathrm{j} = \sqrt{2}\mathrm{e}^{\mathrm{j}\pi/4}$$

Then, if

$$z = r\mathrm{e}^{\mathrm{j}\theta}$$

in polar form it follows from (1.3) that

$$w = r\sqrt{2}\mathrm{e}^{\mathrm{j}(\theta + \pi/4)} \tag{1.4}$$

We can then readily deduce from (1.4) what the mapping does. The general point in the z plane with modulus r and argument θ is mapped onto an image point w, with modulus $r\sqrt{2}$ and argument $\theta + \frac{1}{4}\pi$ in the w plane as illustrated in Figure 1.5.

It follows that in general the mapping

$$w = \alpha z$$

maps the origin in the z plane to the origin in the w plane (fixed point), but effects an expansion by $|\alpha|$ and an anticlockwise rotation by arg α. Of course, arg α need not be positive, and indeed it could even be zero (corresponding to α being real). The mapping can be loosely summed up in the phrase 'magnification and rotation, but no translation'. Certain geometrical properties are also preserved, the most important being that straight lines in the z plane will be transformed to straight lines in the w plane. This is readily

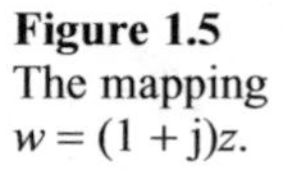

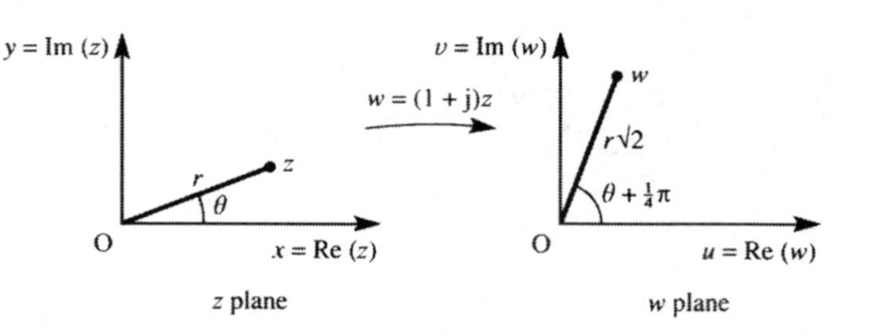

Figure 1.5 The mapping $w = (1 + \mathrm{j})z$.

confirmed by noting that the equation of any straight line in the z plane can always be written in the form

$$|z - a| = |z - b|$$

where a and b are complex constants (this being the equation of the perpendicular bisector of the join of the two points representing a and b on the Argand diagram). Under the mapping $w = \alpha z$, the equation maps to

$$\left|\frac{w}{\alpha} - a\right| = \left|\frac{w}{\alpha} - b\right| \quad (\alpha \neq 0)$$

or

$$|w - a\alpha| = |w - b\alpha|$$

in the w plane, which is clearly another straight line.

We now return to the general linear mapping (1.2) and rewrite it in the form

$$w - \beta = \alpha z$$

This can be looked upon as two successive mappings: first,

$$\zeta = \alpha z$$

identical to $w = \alpha z$ considered earlier, but this time mapping points from the z plane to points in the ζ plane; secondly,

$$w = \zeta + \beta \tag{1.5}$$

mapping points in the ζ plane to points in the w plane. Elimination of ζ regains equation (1.2). The mapping (1.5) represents a translation in which the origin in the ζ plane is mapped to the point $w = \beta$ in the w plane, and the mapping of any other point in the ζ plane is obtained by adding β to the coordinates to obtain the equivalent point in the w plane. Geometrically, the mapping (1.5) is as if the ζ plane is picked up and, without rotation, the origin placed over the point β. The original axes then represent the w plane as illustrated in Figure 1.6. Obviously *all* curves, in particular straight lines, are preserved under this translation.

We are now in a position to interpret (1.2), the general linear mapping, geometrically as a combination of mappings that can be regarded as fundamental, namely

- translation
- rotation, and
- magnification

that is,

$$z \xrightarrow[\text{rotation}]{} e^{j\theta}z \xrightarrow[\text{magnification}]{} |\alpha|e^{j\theta}z \xrightarrow[\text{translation}]{} |\alpha|e^{j\theta}z + \beta = \alpha z + \beta = w$$

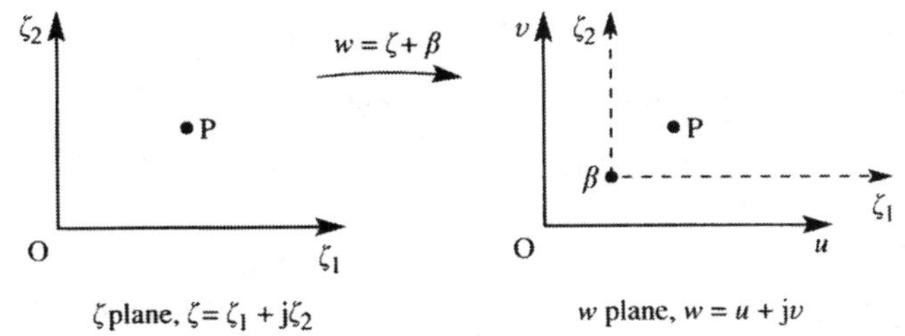

Figure 1.6 The mapping $w = \zeta + \beta$.

It clearly follows that a straight line in the z plane is mapped onto a corresponding straight line in the w plane under the linear mapping $w = \alpha z + \beta$. A second useful property of the linear mapping is that circles are mapped onto circles. To confirm this, consider the general circle

$$|z - z_0| = r$$

in the z plane, having the complex number z_0 as its centre and the real number r as its radius. Rearranging the mapping equation $w = \alpha z + \beta$ gives

$$z = \frac{w}{\alpha} - \frac{\beta}{\alpha} \quad (\alpha \neq 0)$$

so that

$$z - z_0 = \frac{w}{\alpha} - \frac{\beta}{\alpha} - z_0 = \frac{1}{\alpha}(w - w_0)$$

where $w_0 = \alpha z_0 + \beta$. Hence

$$|z - z_0| = r$$

implies

$$|w - w_0| = |\alpha| r$$

which is a circle, with centre w_0 given by the image of z_0 in the w plane and with radius $|\alpha| r$ given by the radius of the z plane circle magnified by $|\alpha|$.

We conclude this section by considering examples of linear mappings.

Example 1.2

Examine the mapping

$$w = (1 + \text{j})z + 1 - \text{j}$$

as a succession of fundamental mappings: translation, rotation and magnification.

Solution

The linear mapping can be regarded as the following sequence of simple mappings:

$$z \xrightarrow[\substack{\text{anticlockwise} \\ \text{by } \frac{1}{4}\pi}]{\text{rotation}} e^{\text{j}\pi/4} z \xrightarrow[\text{by } \sqrt{2}]{\text{magnification}} \sqrt{2}e^{\text{j}\pi/4} z \xrightarrow[\substack{0 \to 1-\text{j or} \\ (0,0) \to (1,-1)}]{\text{translation}} \sqrt{2}e^{\text{j}\pi/4} z + 1 - \text{j} = w$$

Figure 1.7 illustrates this process diagrammatically. The shading in Figure 1.7 helps to identify how the z plane moves, turns and expands under this mapping. For example, the line joining the points $0 + \text{j}2$ and $1 + \text{j}0$ in the z plane has the cartesian equation

$$\tfrac{1}{2}y + x = 1$$

Taking $w = u + \text{j}v$ and $z = x + \text{j}y$, the mapping

$$w = (1 + \text{j})z + 1 - \text{j}$$

becomes

$$u + \text{j}v = (1 + \text{j})(x + \text{j}y) + 1 - \text{j} = (x - y + 1) + \text{j}(x + y - 1)$$

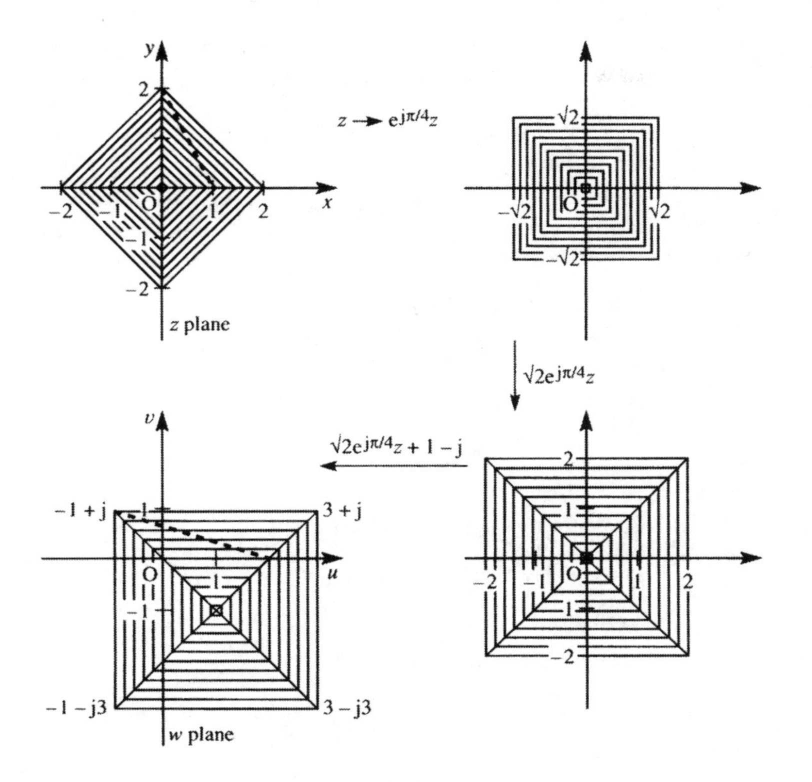

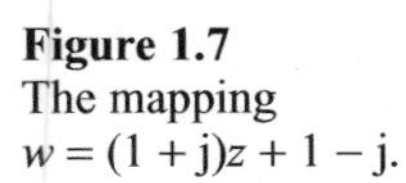

Figure 1.7
The mapping
$w = (1 + j)z + 1 - j$.

Equating real and imaginary parts then gives

$$u = x - y + 1, \qquad v = x + y - 1$$

which on solving for x and y gives

$$2x = u + v, \qquad 2y = v - u + 2$$

Substituting for x and y into the equation $\frac{1}{2}y + x = 1$ then gives the image of this line in the w plane as the line

$$3v + u = 2$$

which crosses the real axis in the w plane at 2 and the imaginary axis at $\frac{2}{3}$. Both lines are shown dashed, in the z and w planes respectively, in Figure 1.7.

Example 1.3

The mapping $w = \alpha z + \beta$ (α, β constant complex numbers) maps the point $z = 1 + j$ to the point $w = j$, and the point $z = 1 - j$ to the point $w = -1$.

(a) Determine α and β.

(b) Find the region in the w plane corresponding to the right half-plane $\text{Re}(z) \geqslant 0$ in the z plane.

(c) Find the region in the w plane corresponding to the interior of the unit circle $|z| < 1$ in the z plane.

(d) Find the fixed point(s) of the mapping.

In (b)–(d) use the values of α and β determined in (a).

Solution (a) The two values of z and w given as corresponding under the given linear mapping provide two equations for α and β as follows: $z = 1 + j$ mapping to $w = j$ implies

$$j = \alpha(1 + j) + \beta$$

while $z = 1 - j$ mapping to $w = -1$ implies

$$-1 = \alpha(1 - j) + \beta$$

Subtracting these two equations in α and β gives

$$j + 1 = \alpha(1 + j) - \alpha(1 - j)$$

so that

$$\alpha = \frac{1 + j}{j2} = \tfrac{1}{2}(1 - j)$$

Substituting back for β then gives

$$\beta = j - (1 + j)\alpha = j - \tfrac{1}{2}(1 - j^2) = j - 1$$

so that

$$w = \tfrac{1}{2}(1 - j)z + j - 1 = (1 - j)(\tfrac{1}{2}z - 1)$$

(b) The best way to find specific image curves in the w plane is first to express $z\ (= x + jy)$ in terms of $w\ (= u + jv)$ and then, by equating real and imaginary parts, to express x and y in terms of u and v. We have

$$w = (1 - j)(\tfrac{1}{2}z - 1)$$

which, on dividing by $1 - j$, gives

$$\frac{w}{1 - j} = \tfrac{1}{2}z - 1$$

Taking $w = u + jv$ and $z = x + jy$ and then rationalizing the left-hand side, we have

$$\tfrac{1}{2}(u + jv)(1 + j) = \tfrac{1}{2}(x + jy) - 1$$

Equating real and imaginary parts then gives

$$u - v = x - 2, \qquad u + v = y \tag{1.6}$$

The first of these can be used to find the image of $x \geqslant 0$. It is $u - v \geqslant -2$, which is also a region bordered by the straight line $u - v = -2$ and shown in Figure 1.8. Pick one point in the right half of the z plane, say $z = 2$, and the mapping gives $w = 0$ as the image of this point. This allays any doubts about which side of $u - v = -2$ corresponds to the right half of the z plane, $x \geqslant 0$. The two corresponding regions are shown 'hatched' in Figure 1.8.

Note that the following is always true, although we shall not prove it here. If a curve cuts the z plane in two then the corresponding curve in the w plane also cuts the w plane in two, and, further, points in one of the two distinct sets of the z plane partitioned by the curve correspond to points in just one of the similarly partitioned sets in the w plane.

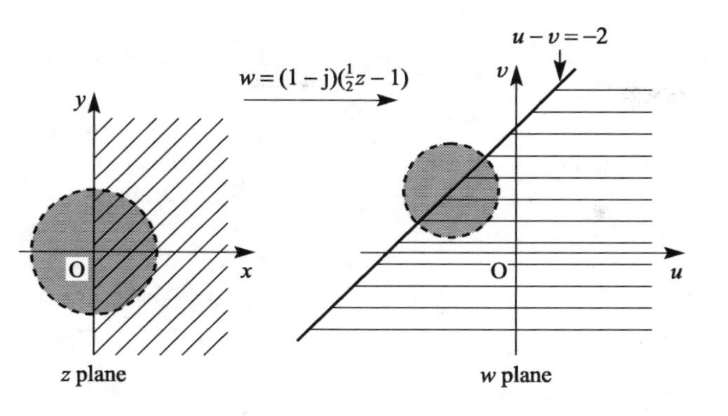

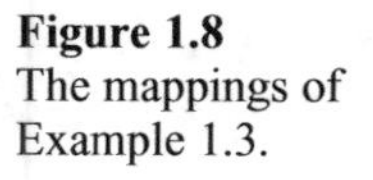
Figure 1.8 The mappings of Example 1.3.

(c) In cartesian form, with $z = x + jy$, the equation of the unit circle $|z| = 1$ is

$$x^2 + y^2 = 1$$

Substituting for x and y from the mapping relationships (1.6) gives the image of this circle as

$$(u - v + 2)^2 + (u + v)^2 = 1$$

or

$$u^2 + v^2 + 2u - 2v + \tfrac{3}{2} = 0$$

which, on completing the squares, leads to

$$(u + 1)^2 + (v - 1)^2 = \tfrac{1}{2}$$

As expected, this is a circle, having in this particular case centre (−1, 1) and radius $\sqrt{\tfrac{1}{2}}$. If $x^2 + y^2 < 1$ then $(u + 1)^2 + (v - 1)^2 < \tfrac{1}{2}$, so the region inside the circle $|z| = 1$ in the z plane corresponds to the region inside its image circle in the w plane. Corresponding regions are shown shaded in Figure 1.8.

(d) The fixed point(s) of the mapping are obtained by putting $w = z$ in $w = \alpha z + \beta$, leading to

$$z = (\tfrac{1}{2}z - 1)(1 - j)$$

that is,

$$z = \tfrac{1}{2}z - \tfrac{1}{2}jz - 1 + j$$

so that

$$z = \frac{-1 + j}{\tfrac{1}{2} + \tfrac{1}{2}j} = j2$$

is the only fixed point.

One final point is in order before we leave this example. In Figure 1.8 the images of $x = 0$ and $x^2 + y^2 = 1$ can also be seen in the context of translation, rotation (the line in Figure 1.8 rotates about $z = 2j$) and magnification (in fact, shrinkage, as can be seen by the decrease in diameter of the circle compared with its image in the w plane).

1.2.2 Exercises

1. Find in the cartesian form $y = mx + c$ (m and c real constants) the equations of the following straight lines in the z plane, $z = x + jy$:

   (a) $|z - 2 + j| = |z - j + 3|$

   (b) $z + z^* + 4j(z - z^*) = 6$

   where * denotes the complex conjugate.

2. Find the point of intersection and the angle of intersection of the straight lines

   $$|z - 1 - j| = |z - 3 + j|$$

   $$|z - 1 + j| = |z - 3 - j|$$

3. The function $w = jz + 4 - 3j$ is a combination of translation and rotation. Show this diagrammatically, following the procedure used in Example 1.2. Find the image of the line $6x + y = 22$ ($z = x + jy$) in the w plane under this mapping.

4. Show that the mapping $w = (1 - j)z$, where $w = u + jv$ and $z = x + jy$, maps the region $y > 1$ in the z plane onto the region $u + v > 2$ in the w plane. Illustrate the regions in a diagram.

5. Under the mapping $w = jz + j$, where $w = u + jv$ and $z = x + jy$, show that the half-plane $x > 0$ in the z plane maps onto the half-plane $v > 1$ in the w plane.

6. For $z = x + jy$ find the image region in the w plane corresponding to the semi-infinite strip $x > 0$, $0 < y < 2$ in the z plane under the mapping $w = jz + 1$. Illustrate the regions in both planes.

7. Find the images of the following curves under the mapping

   $$w = (j + \sqrt{3})z + j\sqrt{3} - 1$$

   (a) $y = 0$ (b) $x = 0$

   (c) $x^2 + y^2 = 1$ (d) $x^2 + y^2 + 2y = 1$

   where $z = x + jy$.

8. The mapping $w = \alpha z + \beta$ (α, β both constant complex numbers) maps the point $z = 1 + j$ to the point $w = j$ and the point $z = -1$ to the point $w = 1 + j$.

   (a) Determine α and β.
   (b) Find the region in the w plane corresponding to the upper half-plane $\text{Im}(z) > 0$ and illustrate diagrammatically.
   (c) Find the region in the w plane corresponding to the disc $|z| < 2$ and illustrate diagrammatically.
   (d) Find the fixed point(s) of the mapping.

   In (b)–(d) use the values of α and β determined in (a).

1.2.3 Inversion

The inversion mapping is of the form

$$w = \frac{1}{z} \tag{1.7}$$

and in this subsection we shall consider the image of circles and straight lines in the z plane under such a mapping. Clearly, under this mapping the image in the w plane of the general circle

$$|z - z_0| = r$$

in the z plane, with centre at z_0 and radius r, is given by

$$\left|\frac{1}{w} - z_0\right| = r \tag{1.8}$$

but it is not immediately obvious what shaped curve this represents in the w plane. To investigate, we take $w = u + jv$ and $z_0 = x_0 + jy_0$ in (1.8), giving

$$\left|\frac{u - \mathrm{j}v}{u^2 + v^2} - x_0 - \mathrm{j}y_0\right| = r$$

Squaring we have

$$\left(\frac{u}{u^2 + v^2} - x_0\right)^2 + \left(\frac{v}{u^2 + v^2} + y_0\right)^2 = r^2$$

which on expanding leads to

$$\frac{u^2}{(u^2 + v^2)^2} - \frac{2ux_0}{u^2 + v^2} + x_0^2 + \frac{v^2}{(u^2 + v^2)^2} + \frac{2vy_0}{(u^2 + v^2)} + y_0^2 = r^2$$

or

$$\frac{u^2 + v^2}{(u^2 + v^2)^2} + \frac{2vy_0 - 2ux_0}{u^2 + v^2} = r^2 - x_0^2 - y_0^2$$

so that

$$(u^2 + v^2)(r^2 - x_0^2 - y_0^2) + 2ux_0 - 2vy_0 = 1 \tag{1.9}$$

The expression is a quadratic in u and v, with the coefficients of u^2 and v^2 equal and no term in uv. It therefore represents a circle, unless the coefficient of $u^2 + v^2$ is itself zero, which occurs when

$$x_0^2 + y_0^2 = r^2, \quad \text{or} \quad |z_0| = r$$

and we have

$$2ux_0 - 2vy_0 = 1$$

which represents a straight line in the w plane.

Summarizing, the inversion mapping $w = 1/z$ maps the circle $|z - z_0| = r$ in the z plane onto another circle in the w plane unless $|z_0| = r$, in which case the circle is mapped onto a straight line in the w plane that does not pass through the origin.

When $|z_0| \neq r$, we can divide the equation of the circle (1.9) in the w plane by the factor $r^2 - x_0^2 - y_0^2$ to give

$$u^2 + v^2 + \frac{2x_0u}{r^2 - x_0^2 - y_0^2} - \frac{2y_0v}{r^2 - x_0^2 - y_0^2} = \frac{1}{r^2 - x_0^2 - y_0^2}$$

which can be written in the form

$$(u - u_0)^2 + (v - v_0)^2 = R^2$$

where (u_0, v_0) are the coordinates of the centre and R the radius of the w plane circle. It is left as an exercise for the reader to show that

$$(u_0, v_0) = \left(-\frac{x_0}{r^2 - |z_0|^2}, \frac{y_0}{r^2 - |z_0|^2}\right), \qquad R = \frac{r}{r^2 - |z_0|^2}$$

Next we consider the general straight line

$$|z - a_1| = |z - a_2|$$

in the z plane, where a_1 and a_2 are constant complex numbers with $a_1 \neq a_2$. Under the mapping (1.7), this becomes the curve in the w plane represented by the equation

$$\left|\frac{1}{w} - a_1\right| = \left|\frac{1}{w} - a_2\right| \tag{1.10}$$

Again, it is not easy to identify this curve, so we proceed as before and take

$$w = u + jv, \qquad a_1 = p + jq, \qquad a_2 = r + js$$

where p, q, r and s are real constants. Substituting in (1.10) and squaring both sides, we have

$$\left(\frac{u}{u^2 + v^2} - p\right)^2 + \left(\frac{v}{u^2 + v^2} + q\right)^2 = \left(\frac{u}{u^2 + v^2} - r\right)^2 + \left(\frac{v}{u^2 + v^2} + s\right)^2$$

Expanding out each term, the squares of $u/(u^2 + v^2)$ and $v/(u^2 + v^2)$ cancel, giving

$$-\frac{2up}{u^2 + v^2} + p^2 + \frac{2vq}{u^2 + v^2} + q^2 = -\frac{2ur}{u^2 + v^2} + r^2 + \frac{2vs}{u^2 + v^2} + s^2$$

which on rearrangement becomes

$$(u^2 + v^2)(p^2 + q^2 - r^2 - s^2) + 2u(r - p) + 2v(q - s) = 0 \tag{1.11}$$

Again this represents a circle *through the origin* in the w plane, unless

$$p^2 + q^2 = r^2 + s^2$$

which implies $|a_1| = |a_2|$, when it represents a straight line, also through the origin, in the w plane. The algebraic form of the coordinates of the centre of the circle and its radius can be deduced from (1.11).

We can therefore make the important conclusion that the inversion mapping $w = 1/z$ takes circles or straight lines in the z plane onto circles or straight lines in the w plane. Further, since we have carried out the algebra, we can be more specific. If the circle in the z plane passes through the origin (that is, $|z_0| = r$ in (1.9)) then it is mapped onto a straight line that does *not* pass through the origin in the w plane. If the straight line in the z plane passes through the origin ($|a_1| = |a_2|$ in (1.11)) then it is mapped onto a straight line through the origin in the w plane. Figure 1.9 summarizes these conclusions.

To see why this is the case, we first note that the fixed points of the mapping, determined by putting $w = z$, are

$$z = \frac{1}{z}, \quad \text{or} \quad z^2 = 1$$

so that $z = \pm 1$.

We also note that $z = 0$ is mapped to infinity in the w plane and $w = 0$ is mapped to infinity in the z plane and vice versa in both cases. Further, if we apply the mapping a second time, we get the identity mapping. That is, if

$$w = \frac{1}{z}, \quad \text{and} \quad \zeta = \frac{1}{w}$$

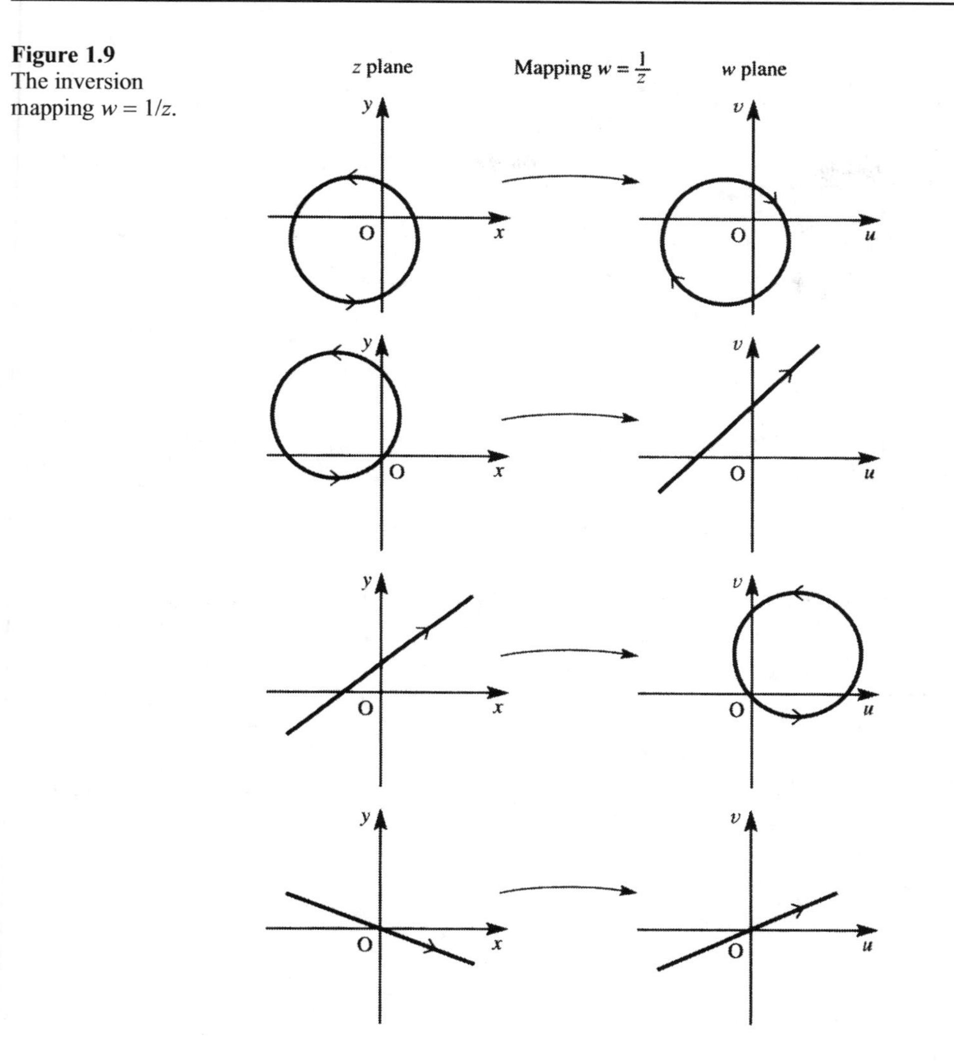

Figure 1.9 The inversion mapping $w = 1/z$.

then

$$\zeta = \frac{1}{1/z} = z$$

which is the identity mapping.

The inside of the unit circle in the z plane, $|z| < 1$, is mapped onto $|1/w| < 1$ or $|w| > 1$, the outside of the unit circle in the w plane. By the same token, therefore, the outside of the unit circle in the z plane $|z| > 1$ is mapped onto $|1/w| > 1$ or $|w| < 1$, the inside of the unit circle in the w plane. Points actually on $|z| = 1$ in the z plane are mapped to points on $|w| = 1$ in the w plane, with ± 1 staying fixed, as already shown. Figure 1.10 summarizes this property.

It is left as an exercise for the reader to show that the top half-boundary of $|z| = 1$ is mapped onto the bottom half-boundary of $|w| = 1$.

For any point z_0 in the z plane the point $1/z_0$ is called the **inverse of z_0 with respect to the circle $|z| = 1$**; this is the reason for the name of the mapping. (Note the double meaning of inverse; here it means the reciprocal function and not the 'reverse'

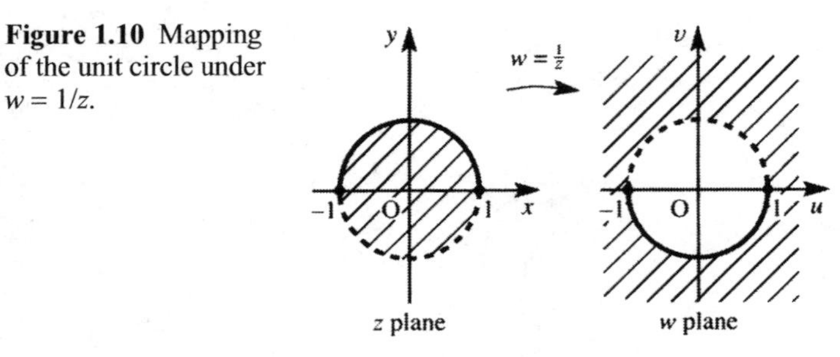

Figure 1.10 Mapping of the unit circle under $w = 1/z$.

mapping.) The more general definition of inverse is that for any point z_0 in the z plane the point r^2/z_0 is the inverse of z_0 with respect to the circle $|z| = r$, where r is a real constant.

Example 1.4

Determine the image path in the w plane corresponding to the circle $|z - 3| = 2$ in the z plane under the mapping $w = 1/z$. Sketch the paths in both the z and w planes and shade the region in the w plane corresponding to the region inside the circle in the z plane.

Solution

The image in the w plane of the circle $|z - 3| = 2$ in the z plane under the mapping $w = 1/z$ is given by

$$\left|\frac{1}{w} - 3\right| = 2$$

which, on taking $w = u + jv$, gives

$$\left|\frac{u - jv}{u^2 + v^2} - 3\right| = 2$$

Squaring both sides, we then have

$$\left(\frac{u}{u^2 + v^2} - 3\right)^2 + \left(\frac{-v}{u^2 + v^2}\right)^2 = 4$$

or

$$\frac{u^2 + v^2}{(u^2 + v^2)^2} - \frac{6u}{u^2 + v^2} + 5 = 0$$

which reduces to

$$1 - 6u + 5(u^2 + v^2) = 0$$

or

$$(u - \tfrac{3}{5})^2 + v^2 = \tfrac{4}{25}$$

Thus the image in the w plane is a circle with centre $(\frac{3}{5}, 0)$ and radius $\frac{2}{5}$. The corresponding circles in the z and w planes are shown in Figure 1.11.

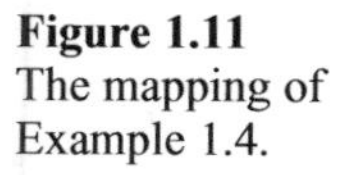

Figure 1.11
The mapping of Example 1.4.

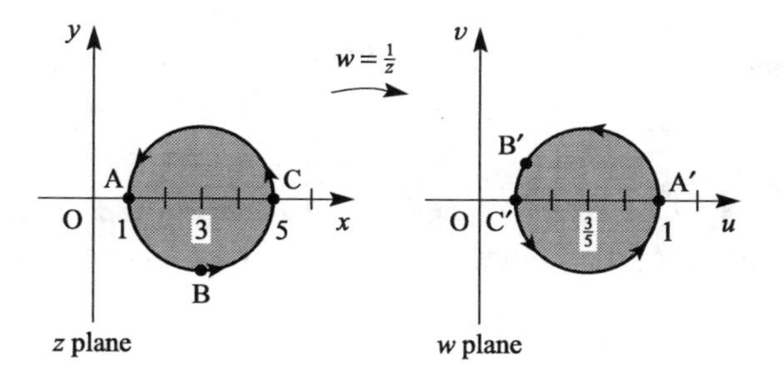

Taking $z = x + jy$, the mapping $w = 1/z$ becomes

$$u + jv = \frac{1}{x + jy} = \frac{x - jy}{x^2 + y^2}$$

which, on equating real and imaginary parts, gives

$$u = \frac{x}{x^2 + y^2}, \qquad v = \frac{-y}{x^2 + y^2}$$

We can now use these two relationships to determine the images of particular points under the mapping. In particular, the centre (3, 0) of the circle in the z plane is mapped onto the point $u = \frac{1}{3}$, $v = 0$ in the w plane, which is inside the mapped circle. Thus, under the mapping, the region inside the circle in the z plane is mapped onto the region inside the circle in the w plane.

Further, considering three sample points A($1 + j0$), B($3 - j2$) and C($5 + j0$) on the circle in the z plane, we find that the corresponding image points on the circle in the w plane are A′(1, 0), B′($\frac{3}{13}$, $\frac{2}{13}$) and C′($\frac{1}{5}$, 0). Thus, as the point z traverses the circle in the z plane in an anticlockwise direction, the corresponding point w in the w plane will also traverse the mapped circle in an anticlockwise direction as indicated in Figure 1.11.

1.2.4 Bilinear mappings

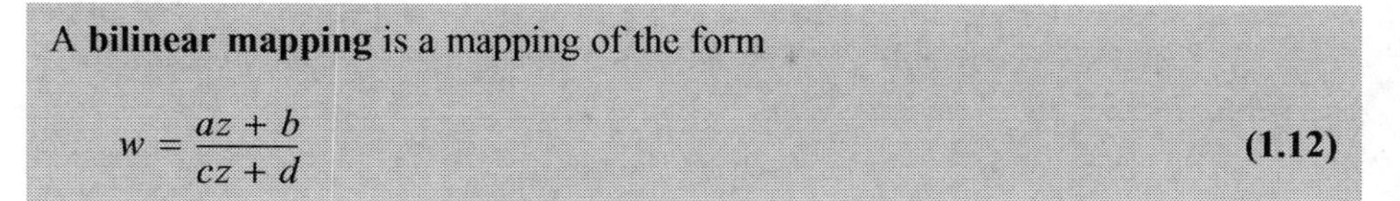

A **bilinear mapping** is a mapping of the form

$$w = \frac{az + b}{cz + d} \tag{1.12}$$

where a, b, c and d are prescribed complex constants. It is called the bilinear mapping in z and w since it can be written in the form $Awz + Bw + Cz + D = 0$, which is linear in both z and w.

Clearly the bilinear mapping (1.12) is more complicated than the linear mapping given by (1.2). In fact, the general linear mapping is a special case of the bilinear mapping, since setting $c = 0$ and $d = 1$ in (1.12) gives (1.2). In order to investigate the bilinear mapping, we rewrite the right-hand side of (1.12) as follows:

$$w = \frac{az + b}{cz + d} = \frac{\frac{a}{c}(cz + d) - \frac{ad}{c} + b}{cz + d}$$

so that

$$w = \frac{a}{c} + \frac{bc - ad}{c(cz + d)} \tag{1.13}$$

This mapping clearly degenerates to $w = a/c$ unless we demand that $bc - ad \neq 0$. We therefore say that (1.12) represents a bilinear mapping provided the determinant

$$\begin{vmatrix} a & b \\ c & d \end{vmatrix} = ad - bc$$

is non-zero. This is sometimes referred to as the **determinant of the mapping**. When the condition holds, the inverse mapping

$$z = \frac{-dw + b}{cw - a}$$

obtained by rearranging (1.12), is also bilinear, since

$$\begin{vmatrix} -d & b \\ c & -a \end{vmatrix} = da - cb \neq 0$$

Renaming the constants so that $\lambda = a/c$, $\mu = bc - ad$, $\alpha = c^2$ and $\beta = cd$, (1.13) becomes

$$w = \lambda + \frac{\mu}{\alpha z + \beta}$$

and we can break the mapping down into three steps as follows:

$$z_1 = \alpha z + \beta$$

$$z_2 = \frac{1}{z_1}$$

$$w = \lambda + \mu z_2$$

The first and third of these steps are linear mappings as considered in Section 1.2.1, while the second is the inversion mapping considered in Section 1.2.3. The bilinear mapping (1.12) can thus be generated from the following elementary mappings:

$$z \xrightarrow[\substack{\text{rotation}\\ \text{and}\\ \text{magnification}}]{} \alpha z \xrightarrow[\text{translation}]{} \alpha z + \beta \xrightarrow[\text{inversion}]{} \frac{1}{\alpha z + \beta}$$

$$\xrightarrow[\substack{\text{magnification}\\ \text{and}\\ \text{rotation}}]{} \frac{\mu}{\alpha z + \beta} \xrightarrow[\text{translation}]{} \lambda + \frac{\mu}{\alpha z + \beta} = w$$

We saw in Section 1.2.1 that the general linear transformation $w = \alpha z + \beta$ does not change the shape of the curve being mapped from the z plane onto the w plane. Also, in Section 1.2.3 we saw that the inversion mapping $w = 1/z$ maps circles or straight lines in the z plane onto circles or straight lines in the w plane. It follows that the bilinear mapping also exhibits this important property, in that it also will map circles or straight lines in the z plane onto circles or straight lines in the w plane.

Example 1.5 Investigate the mapping

$$w = \frac{z-1}{z+1}$$

by finding the images in the w plane of the lines $\text{Re}(z) = \text{constant}$ and $\text{Im}(z) = \text{constant}$. Find the fixed points of the mapping.

Solution Since we are seeking specific image curves in the w plane, we first express z in terms of w and then express x and y in terms of u and v, where $z = x + jy$ and $w = u + jv$. Rearranging

$$w = \frac{z-1}{z+1}$$

gives

$$z = \frac{1+w}{1-w}$$

Taking $z = x + jy$ and $w = u + jv$, we have

$$x + jy = \frac{1+u+jv}{1-u-jv}$$

$$= \frac{1+u+jv}{1-u-jv}\,\frac{1-u+jv}{1-u+jv}$$

which reduces to

$$x + jy = \frac{1-u^2-v^2}{(1-u)^2+v^2} + j\frac{2v}{(1-u)^2+v^2}$$

Equating real and imaginary parts then gives

$$x = \frac{1-u^2-v^2}{(1-u)^2+v^2} \tag{1.14a}$$

$$y = \frac{2v}{(1-u)^2+v^2} \tag{1.14b}$$

It follows from (1.14a) that the lines $\text{Re}(z) = x = c_1$, which are parallel to the imaginary axis in the z plane, correspond to the curves

$$c_1 = \frac{1-u^2-v^2}{(1-u)^2+v^2}$$

where c_1 is a constant, in the w plane. Rearranging this leads to

$$c_1(1 - 2u + u^2 + v^2) = 1 - u^2 - v^2$$

or, assuming that $1 + c_1 \neq 0$,

$$u^2 + v^2 - \frac{2c_1u}{1+c_1} + \frac{c_1-1}{c_1+1} = 0$$

which, on completing squares, gives

$$\left(u - \frac{c_1}{1 + c_1}\right)^2 + v^2 = \left(\frac{1}{1 + c_1}\right)^2$$

It is now clear that the corresponding curve in the w plane is a circle, centre ($u = c_1/(1 + c_1)$, $v = 0$) and radius $(1 + c_1)^{-1}$.

In the algebraic manipulation we assumed that $c_1 \neq -1$, in order to divide by $1 + c_1$. In the exceptional case $c_1 = -1$, we have $u = 1$, and the mapped curve is a straight line in the w plane parallel to the imaginary axis.

Similarly, it follows from (1.14b) that the lines $\text{Im}(z) = y = c_2$, which are parallel to the imaginary axis in the z plane, correspond to the curves

$$c_2 = \frac{2v}{(1 - u)^2 + v^2}$$

where c_2 is a constant, in the w plane. Again, this usually represents a circle in the w plane, but exceptionally will represent a straight line. Rearranging the equation we have

$$(1 - u)^2 + v^2 = \frac{2v}{c_2}$$

provided that $c_2 \neq 0$. Completing the square then leads to

$$(u - 1)^2 + \left(v - \frac{1}{c_2}\right)^2 = \frac{1}{c_2^2}$$

which represents a circle in the w plane, centre ($u = 1$, $v = 1/c_2$) and radius $1/c_2$.

In the exceptional case $c_2 = 0$, $v = 0$ and we see that the real axis $y = 0$ in the z plane maps onto the real axis $v = 0$ in the w plane.

Putting a sequence of values to c_1 and then to c_2, say -10 to $+10$ in steps of $+1$, enables us to sketch the mappings shown in Figure 1.12. The fixed points of the mapping are given by

$$z = \frac{z - 1}{z + 1}$$

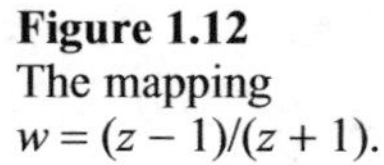

Figure 1.12
The mapping
$w = (z - 1)/(z + 1)$.

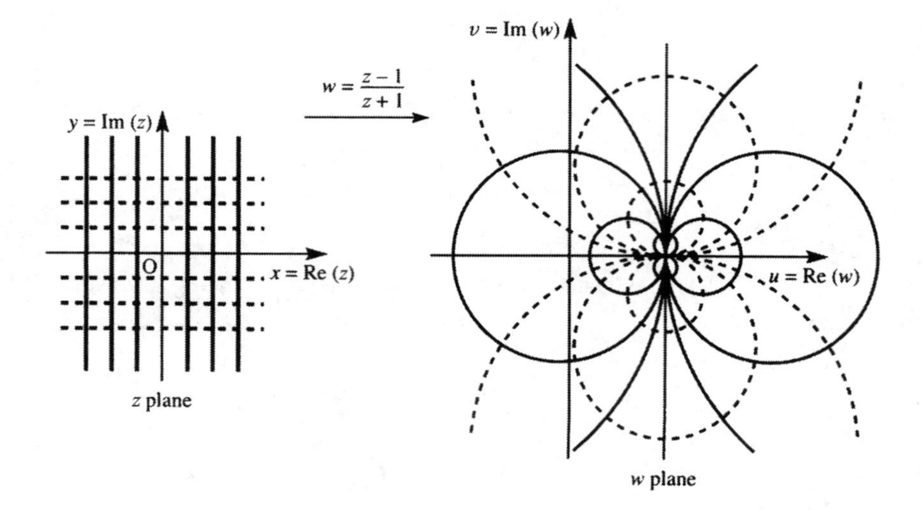

that is,

$$z^2 = -1, \quad \text{or} \quad z = \pm\text{j}$$

In general, all bilinear mappings will have two fixed points. However, although there are mathematically interesting properties associated with particular mappings having coincident fixed points, they do not impinge on engineering applications, so they only deserve passing reference here.

Example 1.6 Find the image in the w plane of the circle $|z| = 2$ in the z plane under the bilinear mapping

$$w = \frac{z - \text{j}}{z + \text{j}}$$

Sketch the curves in both the z and w planes and shade the region in the w plane corresponding to the region inside the circle in the z plane.

Solution Rearranging the transformation, we have

$$z = \frac{\text{j}w + \text{j}}{1 - w}$$

so that the image in the w plane of the circle $|z| = 2$ in the z plane is determined by

$$\left|\frac{\text{j}w + \text{j}}{1 - w}\right| = 2 \qquad \textbf{(1.15)}$$

One possible way of proceeding now is to put $w = u + \text{j}v$ and proceed as in Example 1.4, but the algebra becomes a little messy. An alternative approach is to use the property of complex numbers that $|z_1/z_2| = |z_1|/|z_2|$, so that (1.15) becomes

$$|\text{j}w + \text{j}| = 2|1 - w|$$

Taking $w = u + \text{j}v$ then gives

$$|-v + \text{j}(u + 1)| = 2|(1 - u) - \text{j}v|$$

which on squaring both sides leads to

$$v^2 + (1 + u)^2 = 4[(1 - u)^2 + v^2]$$

or

$$u^2 + v^2 - \tfrac{10}{3}u + 1 = 0$$

Completing the square of the u term then gives

$$(u - \tfrac{5}{3})^2 + v^2 = \tfrac{16}{9}$$

indicating that the image curve in the w plane is a circle centre ($u = \frac{5}{3}$, $v = 0$) and radius $\frac{4}{3}$. The corresponding circles in the z and w planes are illustrated in Figure 1.13. To identify corresponding regions, we consider the mapping of the point $z = 0 + \text{j}0$ inside the circle in the z plane. Under the given mapping, this maps to the point

$$w = \frac{0 - j}{0 + j} = -1 + j0$$

in the w plane. It then follows that the region inside the circle $|z| = 2$ in the z plane maps onto the region outside the mapped circle in the w plane.

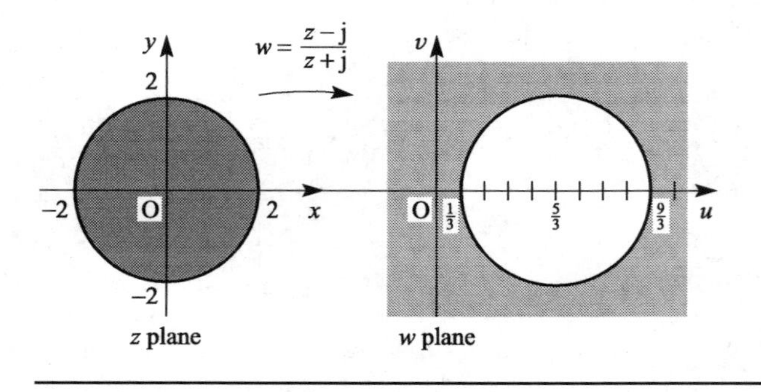

Figure 1.13 The mapping $w = (z - j)/(z + j)$.

An interesting property of (1.12) is that there is just one bilinear transformation that maps three given distinct points z_1, z_2 and z_3 in the z plane onto three specified distinct points w_1, w_2 and w_3 respectively in the w plane. It is left as an exercise for the reader to show that the bilinear transformation is given by

$$\frac{(w - w_1)(w_2 - w_3)}{(w - w_3)(w_2 - w_1)} = \frac{(z - z_1)(z_2 - z_3)}{(z - z_3)(z_2 - z_1)} \qquad (1.16)$$

The right-hand side of (1.16) is called the cross-ratio of z_1, z_2, z_3 and z. We shall illustrate with an example.

Example 1.7 Find the bilinear transformation that maps the three points $z = 0$, $-j$ and -1 onto the three points $w = j$, 1, 0 respectively in the w plane.

Solution Taking the transformation to be

$$w = \frac{az + b}{cz + d}$$

on using the given information on the three pairs of corresponding points we have

$$j = \frac{a(0) + b}{c(0) + d} = \frac{b}{d} \qquad (1.17a)$$

$$1 = \frac{a(-j) + b}{c(-j) + d} \qquad (1.17b)$$

$$0 = \frac{a(-1) + b}{c(-1) + d} \qquad (1.17c)$$

From (1.17c) $a = b$; then from (1.17a)

$$d = \frac{b}{j} = -jb = -ja$$

and from (1.17b) $c = \text{j}a$. Thus

$$w = \frac{az + a}{\text{j}az - \text{j}a} = \frac{1}{\text{j}}\frac{z + 1}{z - 1} = -\text{j}\frac{z + 1}{z - 1}$$

Alternatively, using (1.16) we can obtain

$$\frac{(w - \text{j})(1 - 0)}{(w - 0)(1 - \text{j})} = \frac{(z - 0)(-\text{j} + 1)}{(z + 1)(-\text{j} - 0)}$$

or

$$w = -\text{j}\frac{z + 1}{z - 1}$$

as before.

1.2.5 Exercises

9 Show that if $z = x + \text{j}y$, the image of the half-plane $y > c$ (c constant) under the mapping $w = 1/z$ is the interior of a circle, provided that $c > 0$. What is the image when $c = 0$ and when $c < 0$? Illustrate with sketches in the w plane.

10 Determine the image in the w plane of the circle

$$\left|z + \tfrac{3}{4} + \text{j}\right| = \tfrac{7}{4}$$

under the inversion mapping $w = 1/z$.

11 Show that the mapping $w = 1/z$ maps the circle $|z - a| = a$, with a being a positive real constant, onto a straight line in the w plane. Sketch the corresponding curves in the z and w planes, indicating the region onto which the interior of the circle in the z plane is mapped.

12 Find a bilinear mapping that maps $z = 0$ to $w = \text{j}$, $z = -\text{j}$ to $w = 1$ and $z = -1$ to $w = 0$. Hence sketch the mapping by finding the images in the w plane of the lines $\text{Re}(z) = \text{constant}$ and $\text{Im}(z) = \text{constant}$ in the z plane. Verify that $z = \frac{1}{2}(\text{j} - 1)(-1 \pm \sqrt{3})$ are fixed points of the mapping.

13 The two complex variables w and z are related through the inverse mapping

$$w = \frac{1 + \text{j}}{z}$$

(a) Find the images of the points $z = 1$, $1 - \text{j}$ and 0 in the w plane.
(b) Find the region of the w plane corresponding to the interior of the unit circle $|z| < 1$ in the z plane.
(c) Find the curves in the w plane corresponding to the straight lines $x = y$ and $x + y = 1$ in the z plane.
(d) Find the fixed points of the mapping.

14 Given the complex mapping

$$w = \frac{z + 1}{z - 1}$$

where $w = u + \text{j}v$ and $z = x + \text{j}y$, determine the image curve in the w plane corresponding to the semicircular arc $x^2 + y^2 = 1$ ($x \leqslant 0$) described from the point $(0, -1)$ to the point $(0, 1)$.

15 (a) Map the region in the z plane ($z = x + \text{j}y$) that lies between the lines $x = y$ and $y = 0$, with $x < 0$, onto the w plane under the bilinear mapping

$$w = \frac{z + \text{j}}{z - 3}$$

(*Hint*: Consider the point $w = \frac{2}{3}$ to help identify corresponding regions.)
(b) Show that, under the same mapping as in (a), the straight line $3x + y = 4$ in the z plane corresponds to the unit circle $|w| = 1$ in the w plane and that the point $w = 1$ does not correspond to a finite value of z.

16 If $w = (z - \text{j})/(z + \text{j})$, find and sketch the image in the w plane corresponding to the circle $|z| = 2$ in the z plane.

17 Show that the bilinear mapping

$$w = \text{e}^{\text{j}\theta_0}\frac{z - z_0}{z - z_0^*}$$

where θ_0 is a real constant $0 \leqslant \theta_0 < 2\pi$, z_0 a fixed complex number and z_0^* its conjugate, maps the upper half of the z plane ($\text{Im}(z) > 0$) onto the inside of the unit circle in the w plane ($|w| < 1$). Find the values of z_0 and θ_0 if $w = 0$ corresponds to $z = \text{j}$ and $w = -1$ corresponds to $z = \infty$.

18 Show that, under the mapping

$$w = \frac{2\text{j}z}{z + \text{j}}$$

circular arcs or the straight line through $z = 0$ and $z = \text{j}$ in the z plane are mapped onto circular arcs or the straight line through $w = 0$ and $w = \text{j}$ in the w plane. Find the images of the regions $|z - \frac{1}{2}| < \frac{1}{2}$ and $|z| < |z - \text{j}|$ in the w plane.

19 Find the most general bilinear mapping that maps the unit circle $|z| = 1$ in the z plane onto the unit circle $|w| = 1$ in the w plane and the point $z = z_0$ in the z plane to the origin $w = 0$ in the w plane.

1.2.6 The mapping $w = z^2$

There are a number of other mappings that are used by engineers. For example, in dealing with Laplace and z transforms, the subjects of Chapters 2 and 3 respectively, we are concerned with the polynomial mapping

$$w = a_0 + a_1 z + \ldots + a_n z^n$$

where $a_0, a_1, \ldots, a_n$ are complex constants, the rational function

$$w = \frac{P(z)}{Q(z)}$$

where P and Q are polynomials in z, and the exponential mapping

$$w = a\,\text{e}^{bz}$$

where $\text{e} = 2.718\,28\ldots$, the base of natural logarithms. As is clear from the bilinear mapping in Section 1.2.4, even elementary mappings can be cumbersome to analyse. Fortunately, we have two factors on our side. First, very detailed tracing of specific curves and their images is not required, only images of points. Secondly, by using complex differentiation, the subject of Section 1.3, various facets of these more complicated mappings can be understood without lengthy algebra. As a prelude, in this subsection we analyse the mapping $w = z^2$, which is the simplest polynomial mapping.

Example 1.8 Investigate the mapping $w = z^2$ by plotting the images on the w plane of the lines $x = \text{constant}$ and $y = \text{constant}$ in the z plane.

Solution There is some difficulty in inverting this mapping to get z as a function of w, since square roots lead to problems of uniqueness. However, there is no need to invert here, for taking $w = u + \text{j}v$ and $z = x + \text{j}y$, the mapping becomes

$$w = u + \text{j}v = (x + \text{j}y)^2 = (x^2 - y^2) + \text{j}2xy$$

which, on taking real and imaginary parts, gives

$$\left.\begin{aligned} u &= x^2 - y^2 \\ v &= 2xy \end{aligned}\right\} \quad (1.18)$$

If $x = \alpha$, a real constant, then (1.18) becomes

$$u = \alpha^2 - y^2, \qquad v = 2\alpha y$$

which, on eliminating y, gives

$$u = \alpha^2 - \frac{v^2}{4\alpha^2}$$

or

$$4\alpha^2 u = 4\alpha^4 - v^2$$

so that

$$v^2 = 4\alpha^4 - 4\alpha^2 u = 4\alpha^2(\alpha^2 - u)$$

This represents a parabola in the w plane, and, since the right-hand side must be positive, $\alpha^2 \geqslant u$ so the 'nose' of the parabola is at $u = \alpha^2$ on the positive real axis in the w plane.

If $y = \beta$, a real constant, then (1.18) becomes

$$u = x^2 - \beta^2, \qquad v = 2x\beta$$

which, on eliminating x, gives

$$u = \frac{v^2}{4\beta^2} - \beta^2$$

or

$$4\beta^2 = v^2 - 4\beta^4$$

so that

$$v^2 = 4\beta^2 u + 4\beta^4 = 4\beta^2(u + \beta^2)$$

This is also a parabola, but pointing in the opposite direction. The right-hand side, as before, must be positive, so that $u > -\beta^2$ and the 'nose' of the parabola is on the negative real axis. These curves are drawn in Figure 1.14.

Figure 1.14
The mapping $w = z^2$.

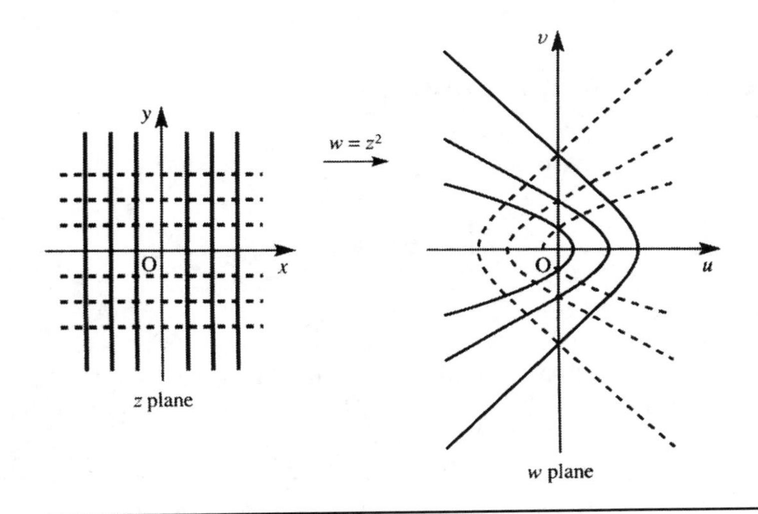

We shall not dwell further on the finer points of the mapping $w = z^2$. Instead, we note that in general it is extremely difficult to plot images of curves in the z plane, even the straight lines parallel to the axes, under polynomial mappings. We also note that we do not often need to do so, and that we have done it only as an aid to understanding.

The exercises that follow should also help in understanding this topic. We shall then return to examine polynomial, rational and exponential mappings in Section 1.3.4, after introducing complex differentiation.

1.2.7 Exercises

20. Find the image region in the w plane corresponding to the region inside the triangle in the z plane having vertices at $0 + j0$, $2 + j0$ and $0 + j2$ under the mapping $w = z^2$. Illustrate with sketches.

21. Find the images of the lines $y = x$ and $y = -x$ under the mapping $w = z^2$. Also find the image of the general line through the origin $y = mx$. By putting $m = \tan\theta_0$, deduce that straight lines intersecting at the origin in the z plane map onto lines intersecting at the origin in the w plane, but that the angle between these image lines is double that between the original lines.

22. Consider the mapping $w = z^n$, where n is an integer (a generalization of the mapping $w = z^2$). Use the polar representation of complex numbers to show that

    (a) Circles centred at the origin in the z plane are mapped onto circles centred at the origin in the w plane.

    (b) Straight lines passing through the origin intersecting with angle θ_0 in the z plane are mapped onto straight lines passing through the origin in the w plane but intersecting at an angle $n\theta_0$.

23. If the complex function

$$w = \frac{1 + z^2}{z}$$

is represented by a mapping from the z plane onto the w plane, find u in terms of x and y, and v in terms of x and y, where $z = x + jy$, $w = u + jv$. Find the image of the unit circle $|z| = 1$ in the w plane. Show that the circle centred at the origin, of radius r, in the z plane ($|z| = r$) is mapped onto the curve

$$\left(\frac{r^2 u}{r^2 + 1}\right)^2 + \left(\frac{r^2 v}{r^2 - 1}\right)^2 = r^2 \quad (r \neq 1)$$

in the w plane. What kind of curves are these? What happens for very large r?

1.3 Complex differentiation

The derivative of a real function $f(x)$ of a single real variable x at $x = x_0$ is given by the limit

$$f'(x_0) = \lim_{x \to x_0} \left[\frac{f(x) - f(x_0)}{x - x_0}\right]$$

Here, of course, x_0 is a real number and so can be represented by a single point on the real line. The point representing x can then approach the fixed x_0 either from the left or from the right along this line. Let us now turn to complex variables and functions depending on them. We know that a plane is required to represent complex numbers, so z_0 is now a fixed point in the Argand diagram, somewhere in the plane. The definition of the derivative of the function $f(z)$ of the complex variable z at the point z_0 will thus be

$$f'(z_0) = \lim_{z \to z_0} \left[\frac{f(z) - f(z_0)}{z - z_0} \right]$$

It may appear that if we merely exchange z for x, the rest of this section will follow similar lines to the differentiation of functions of real variables. For real variables taking the limit could only be done from the left or from the right, and the existence of a unique limit was not difficult to establish. For complex variables, however, the point that represents the fixed complex number z_0 can be approached along an infinite number of curves in the z plane. The existence of a unique limit is thus a very stringent requirement. That most complex functions can be differentiated in the usual way is a remarkable property of the complex variable. Since $z = x + jy$, and x and y can vary independently, there are some connections with the calculus of functions of two real variables, but we shall not pursue this connection here.

Rather than use the word 'differentiable' to describe complex functions for which a derivative exists, if the function $f(z)$ has a derivative $f'(z)$ that exists at all points of a region R of the z plane then $f(z)$ is called **analytic** in R. Other terms such as **regular** or **holomorphic** are also used as alternatives to analytic. (Strictly, functions that have a power series expansion – see Section 1.4.1 – are called **analytic functions**. Since differentiable functions have a power series expansion they are referred to as analytic functions. However, there are examples of analytic functions that are not differentiable.)

1.3.1 Cauchy–Riemann equations

The following result is an important property of the analytic function.

If $z = x + jy$ and $f(z) = u(x, y) + jv(x, y)$, and $f(z)$ is analytic in some region R of the z plane, then the two equations

$$\frac{\partial u}{\partial x} = \frac{\partial v}{\partial y}, \qquad \frac{\partial u}{\partial y} = -\frac{\partial v}{\partial x} \tag{1.19}$$

known as the **Cauchy–Riemann equations**, hold throughout R.

It is instructive to prove this result. Since $f'(z)$ exists at any point z_0 in R,

$$f'(z_0) = \lim_{z \to z_0} \left[\frac{f(z) - f(z_0)}{z - z_0} \right]$$

where z can tend to z_0 along any path within R. Examination of (1.19) suggests that we might choose paths parallel to the x direction and parallel to the y direction, since these will lead to partial derivatives with respect to x and y. Thus, choosing $z - z_0 = \Delta x$, a real path, we see that

$$f'(z_0) = \lim_{\Delta x \to 0} \left[\frac{f(z_0 + \Delta x) - f(z_0)}{\Delta x} \right]$$

Since $f(z) = u + jv$, this means that

$$f'(z_0) = \lim_{\Delta x \to 0} \left[\frac{u(x_0 + \Delta x, y_0) + jv(x_0 + \Delta x, y_0) - u(x_0, y_0) - jv(x_0, y_0)}{\Delta x} \right]$$

or, on splitting into real and imaginary parts,

$$f'(z_0) = \lim_{\Delta x \to 0} \left[\frac{u(x_0 + \Delta x, y_0) - u(x_0, y_0)}{\Delta x} + \mathrm{j} \frac{v(x_0 + \Delta x, y_0) - v(x_0, y_0)}{\Delta x} \right]$$

giving

$$f'(z_0) = \left[\frac{\partial u}{\partial x} + \mathrm{j} \frac{\partial v}{\partial x} \right]_{x=x_0, y=y_0} \tag{1.20}$$

Starting again from the definition of $f'(z_0)$, but this time choosing $z - z_0 = \mathrm{j}\Delta y$ for the path parallel to the y axis, we obtain

$$f'(z_0) = \lim_{\mathrm{j}\Delta y \to 0} \left[\frac{f(z_0 + \mathrm{j}\Delta y) - f(z_0)}{\mathrm{j}\Delta y} \right]$$

Once again, using $f(z) = u + \mathrm{j}v$ and splitting into real and imaginary parts, we see that

$$f'(z_0) = \lim_{\mathrm{j}\Delta y \to 0} \left[\frac{u(x_0, y_0 + \Delta y) + \mathrm{j}v(x_0, y_0 + \Delta y) - u(x_0, y_0) - \mathrm{j}v(x_0, y_0)}{\mathrm{j}\Delta y} \right]$$

$$= \lim_{\Delta y \to 0} \left[\frac{1}{\mathrm{j}} \frac{u(x_0, y_0 + \Delta y) - u(x_0, y_0)}{\Delta y} + \frac{v(x_0, y_0 + \Delta y) - v(x_0, y_0)}{\Delta y} \right]$$

giving

$$f'(z_0) = \left[\frac{1}{\mathrm{j}} \frac{\partial u}{\partial y} + \frac{\partial v}{\partial y} \right]_{x=x_0, y=y_0} \tag{1.21}$$

Since $f'(z_0)$ must be the same no matter what path is followed, the two values obtained in (1.20) and (1.21) must be equal. Hence

$$\frac{\partial u}{\partial x} + \mathrm{j} \frac{\partial v}{\partial x} = \frac{1}{\mathrm{j}} \frac{\partial u}{\partial y} + \frac{\partial v}{\partial y} = -\mathrm{j} \frac{\partial u}{\partial y} + \frac{\partial v}{\partial y}$$

Equating real and imaginary parts then gives the required Cauchy–Riemann equations

$$\frac{\partial u}{\partial x} = \frac{\partial v}{\partial y}, \qquad \frac{\partial v}{\partial x} = -\frac{\partial u}{\partial y}$$

at the point $z = z_0$. However, z_0 is an arbitrarily chosen point in the region R; hence the Cauchy–Riemann equations hold throughout R, and we have thus proved the required result.

It is tempting to think that should we choose more paths along which to let $z - z_0$ tend to zero, we could derive more relationships along the same lines as the Cauchy–Riemann equations. It turns out, however, that we merely reproduce them or expressions derivable from them, and it is possible to prove that satisfaction of the Cauchy–Riemann equations (1.19) is a necessary condition for a function $f(z) = u(x, y) + \mathrm{j}v(x, y)$, $z = x + \mathrm{j}y$, to be analytic in a specified region. At points where $f'(z)$ exists it may be obtained from either (1.20) or (1.21) as

$$f'(z) = \frac{\partial u}{\partial x} + \mathrm{j} \frac{\partial v}{\partial x}$$

or

$$f'(z) = \frac{\partial v}{\partial y} - \mathrm{j}\frac{\partial u}{\partial y}$$

If z is given in the polar form $z = r\,\mathrm{e}^{\mathrm{j}\theta}$ then

$$f(z) = u(r, \theta) + \mathrm{j}v(r, \theta)$$

and the corresponding polar forms of the Cauchy–Riemann equations are

$$\frac{\partial u}{\partial r} = \frac{1}{r}\frac{\partial v}{\partial \theta}, \qquad \frac{\partial v}{\partial r} = -\frac{1}{r}\frac{\partial u}{\partial \theta} \tag{1.22}$$

At points where $f'(z)$ exists it may be obtained from either of

$$f'(z) = \mathrm{e}^{-\mathrm{j}\theta}\left(\frac{\partial u}{\partial r} + \mathrm{j}\frac{\partial v}{\partial r}\right) \tag{1.23a}$$

or

$$f'(z) = \mathrm{e}^{-\mathrm{j}\theta}\left(\frac{1}{r}\frac{\partial v}{\partial \theta} - \frac{\mathrm{j}}{r}\frac{\partial u}{\partial \theta}\right) \tag{1.23b}$$

Example 1.9 Verify that the function $f(z) = z^2$ satisfies the Cauchy–Riemann equations, and determine the derivative $f'(z)$.

Solution Since $z = x + \mathrm{j}y$, we have

$$f(z) = z^2 = (x + \mathrm{j}y)^2 = (x^2 - y^2) + \mathrm{j}2xy$$

so if $f(z) = u(x, y) + \mathrm{j}v(x, y)$ then

$$u = x^2 - y^2, \qquad v = 2xy$$

giving the partial derivatives as

$$\frac{\partial u}{\partial x} = 2x, \qquad \frac{\partial u}{\partial y} = -2y$$

$$\frac{\partial v}{\partial x} = 2y, \qquad \frac{\partial v}{\partial y} = 2x$$

It is readily seen that the Cauchy–Riemann equations

$$\frac{\partial u}{\partial x} = \frac{\partial v}{\partial y}, \qquad \frac{\partial u}{\partial y} = -\frac{\partial v}{\partial x}$$

are satisfied.

The derivative $f'(z)$ is then given by

$$f'(z) = \frac{\partial u}{\partial x} + \mathrm{j}\frac{\partial v}{\partial x} = 2x + \mathrm{j}2y = 2z$$

as expected.

Example 1.10 Verify that the exponential function $f(z) = e^{\alpha z}$, where α is a constant, satisfies the Cauchy–Riemann equations, and show that $f'(z) = \alpha e^{\alpha z}$.

Solution

$$f(z) = u + jv = e^{\alpha z} = e^{\alpha(x+jy)} = e^{\alpha x} e^{j\alpha y} = e^{\alpha x}(\cos \alpha y + j \sin \alpha y)$$

so, equating real and imaginary parts,

$$u = e^{\alpha x} \cos \alpha y, \qquad v = e^{\alpha x} \sin \alpha y$$

The partial derivatives are

$$\frac{\partial u}{\partial x} = \alpha e^{\alpha x} \cos \alpha y, \qquad \frac{\partial v}{\partial x} = \alpha e^{\alpha x} \sin \alpha y$$

$$\frac{\partial u}{\partial y} = -\alpha e^{\alpha x} \sin \alpha y, \qquad \frac{\partial v}{\partial y} = \alpha e^{\alpha x} \cos \alpha y$$

confirming that the Cauchy–Riemann equations are satisfied. The derivative $f'(z)$ is then given by

$$f'(z) = \frac{\partial u}{\partial x} + j\frac{\partial v}{\partial x} = \alpha e^{\alpha x}(\cos \alpha y + j \sin \alpha y) = \alpha e^{\alpha z}$$

so that

$$\frac{d}{dz} e^{\alpha z} = \alpha e^{\alpha z} \tag{1.24}$$

As in the real variable case, we have (see Section 1.4.3)

$$e^{jz} = \cos z + j \sin z \tag{1.25}$$

so that $\cos z$ and $\sin z$ may be expressed as

$$\left.\begin{aligned} \cos z &= \frac{e^{jz} + e^{-jz}}{2} \\ \sin z &= \frac{e^{jz} - e^{-jz}}{2j} \end{aligned}\right\} \tag{1.26a}$$

Using result (1.24) from Example 1.10, it is then readily shown that

$$\frac{d}{dz}(\sin z) = \cos z$$

$$\frac{d}{dz}(\cos z) = -\sin z$$

Similarly, we define the hyperbolic functions $\sinh z$ and $\cosh z$ by

$$\left.\begin{aligned} \sinh z &= \frac{e^{z} - e^{-z}}{2} = -j \sin jz \\ \cosh z &= \frac{e^{z} + e^{-z}}{2} = \cos jz \end{aligned}\right\} \tag{1.26b}$$

from which, using (1.24), it is readily deduced that

$$\frac{d}{dz}(\sinh z) = \cosh z$$

$$\frac{d}{dz}(\cosh z) = \sinh z$$

We note from above that e^z has the following real and imaginary parts:

$$\text{Re}(e^z) = e^x \cos y$$

$$\text{Im}(e^z) = e^x \sin y$$

In real variables the exponential and circular functions are contrasted, one being monotonic, the other oscillatory. In complex variables, however, the real and imaginary parts of e^z are (two-variable) combinations of exponential and circular functions, which might seem surprising for an exponential function. Similarly, the circular functions of a complex variable have unfamiliar properties. For example, it is easy to see that $|\cos z|$ and $|\sin z|$ are unbounded for complex z by using the above relationships between circular and hyperbolic functions of complex variables. Contrast this with $|\cos x| \leqslant 1$ and $|\sin x| \leqslant 1$ for a real variable x.

In a similar way to the method adopted in Examples 1.9 and 1.10 it can be shown that the derivatives of the majority of functions $f(x)$ of a real variable x carry over to the complex variable case $f(z)$ at points where $f(z)$ is analytic. Thus, for example,

$$\frac{d}{dz} z^n = nz^{n-1}$$

for all z in the z plane, and

$$\frac{d}{dz} \ln z = \frac{1}{z}$$

for all z in the z plane except for points on the non-positive real axis, where $\ln z$ is non-analytic.

It can also be shown that the rules associated with derivatives of a function of a real variable, such as the sum, product, quotient and chain rules, carry over to the complex variable case. Thus,

$$\frac{d}{dz}[f(z) + g(z)] = \frac{df(z)}{dz} + \frac{dg(z)}{dz}$$

$$\frac{d}{dz}[f(z)g(z)] = f(z)\frac{dg(z)}{dz} + \frac{df(z)}{dz}g(z)$$

$$\frac{d}{dz}f(g(z)) = \frac{df}{dg}\frac{dg}{dz}$$

$$\frac{d}{dz}\left[\frac{f(z)}{g(z)}\right] = \frac{g(z)f'(z) - f(z)g'(z)}{[g(z)]^2}$$

1.3.2 Conjugate and harmonic functions

A pair of functions $u(x, y)$ and $v(x, y)$ of the real variables x and y that satisfy the Cauchy–Riemann equations (1.19) are said to be **conjugate functions**. (Note here the different use of the word 'conjugate' to that used in complex number work, where $z^* = x - jy$ is the complex conjugate of $z = x + jy$.) Conjugate functions satisfy the orthogonality property in that the curves in the (x, y) plane defined by $u(x, y) = \text{constant}$ and $v(x, y) = \text{constant}$ are orthogonal curves. This follows since the gradient at any point on the curve $u(x, y) = \text{constant}$ is given by

$$\left[\frac{\mathrm{d}y}{\mathrm{d}x}\right]_u = -\frac{\partial u}{\partial y}\bigg/\frac{\partial u}{\partial x}$$

and the gradient at any point on the curve $v(x, y) = \text{constant}$ is given by

$$\left[\frac{\mathrm{d}y}{\mathrm{d}x}\right]_v = -\frac{\partial v}{\partial y}\bigg/\frac{\partial v}{\partial x}$$

It follows from the Cauchy–Riemann equations (1.19) that

$$\left[\frac{\mathrm{d}y}{\mathrm{d}x}\right]_u \left[\frac{\mathrm{d}y}{\mathrm{d}x}\right]_v = -1$$

so the curves are orthogonal.

A function that satisfies Laplace's equation in two dimensions is said to be **harmonic**; that is, $u(x, y)$ is a harmonic function if

$$\frac{\partial^2 u}{\partial x^2} + \frac{\partial^2 u}{\partial y^2} = 0$$

It is readily shown (see Example 1.12) that if $f(z) = u(x, y) + jv(x, y)$ is analytic, so that the Cauchy–Riemann equations are satisfied, then both u and v are **harmonic** functions. Therefore u and v are **conjugate harmonic functions**. Harmonic functions have applications in such areas as stress analysis in plates, inviscid two-dimensional fluid flow and electrostatics.

Example 1.11

Given $u(x, y) = x^2 - y^2 + 2x$, find the conjugate function $v(x, y)$ such that $f(z) = u(x, y) + jv(x, y)$ is an analytic function of z throughout the z plane.

Solution

We are given $u(x, y) = x^2 - y^2 + 2x$, and, since $f(z) = u + jv$ is to be analytic, the Cauchy–Riemann equations must hold. Thus, from (1.19),

$$\frac{\partial v}{\partial y} = \frac{\partial u}{\partial x} = 2x + 2$$

Integrating this with respect to y gives

$$v = 2xy + 2y + F(x)$$

where $F(x)$ is an arbitrary function of x, since the integration was performed holding x constant. Differentiating v partially with respect to x gives

$$\frac{\partial v}{\partial x} = 2y + \frac{dF}{dx}$$

but this equals $-\partial u/\partial y$ by the second of the Cauchy–Riemann equations (1.19). Hence

$$\frac{\partial u}{\partial y} = -2y - \frac{dF}{dx}$$

But since $u = x^2 - y^2 + 2x$, $\partial u/\partial y = -2y$, and comparison yields $F(x) =$ constant. This constant is set equal to zero, since no conditions have been given by which it can be determined. Hence

$$u(x, y) + jv(x, y) = x^2 - y^2 + 2x + j(2xy + 2y)$$

To confirm that this is a function of z, note that $f(z)$ is $f(x + jy)$, and becomes just $f(x)$ if we set $y = 0$. Therefore we set $y = 0$ to obtain

$$f(x + j0) = f(x) = u(x, 0) + jv(x, 0) = x^2 + 2x$$

and it follows that

$$f(z) = z^2 + 2z$$

which can be easily checked by separation into real and imaginary parts.

Example 1.12 Show that the real and imaginary parts $u(x, y)$ and $v(x, y)$ of a complex analytic function $f(z)$ are harmonic.

Solution Since

$$f(z) = u(x, y) + jv(x, y)$$

is analytic, the Cauchy–Riemann equations

$$\frac{\partial v}{\partial x} = -\frac{\partial u}{\partial y}, \qquad \frac{\partial u}{\partial x} = \frac{\partial v}{\partial y}$$

are satisfied. Differentiating the first with respect to x gives

$$\frac{\partial^2 v}{\partial x^2} = -\frac{\partial^2 u}{\partial x \partial y} = -\frac{\partial^2 u}{\partial y \partial x} = -\frac{\partial}{\partial y}\left(\frac{\partial u}{\partial x}\right)$$

which is $-\partial^2 v/\partial y^2$, by the second Cauchy–Riemann equation. Hence

$$\frac{\partial^2 v}{\partial x^2} = -\frac{\partial^2 v}{\partial y^2}, \quad \text{or} \quad \frac{\partial^2 v}{\partial x^2} + \frac{\partial^2 v}{\partial y^2} = 0$$

and v is a harmonic function.

Similarly,

$$\frac{\partial^2 u}{\partial y^2} = -\frac{\partial^2 v}{\partial y \partial x} = -\frac{\partial}{\partial x}\left(\frac{\partial v}{\partial y}\right) = -\frac{\partial^2 u}{\partial x^2}$$

so that

$$\frac{\partial^2 v}{\partial x^2} + \frac{\partial^2 v}{\partial y^2} = 0$$

and u is also a harmonic function. We have assumed that both u and v have continuous second-order partial derivatives, so that

$$\frac{\partial^2 u}{\partial x \partial y} = \frac{\partial^2 u}{\partial y \partial x}, \qquad \frac{\partial^2 v}{\partial x \partial y} = \frac{\partial^2 v}{\partial y \partial x}$$

1.3.3 Exercises

24 Determine whether the following functions are analytic, and find the derivative where appropriate:

(a) $z\mathrm{e}^z$ (b) $\sin 4z$

(c) zz^* (d) $\cos 2z$

25 Determine the constants a and b in order that

$$w = x^2 + ay^2 - 2xy + \mathrm{j}(bx^2 - y^2 + 2xy)$$

be analytic. For these values of a and b find the derivative of w, and express both w and $\mathrm{d}w/\mathrm{d}z$ as functions of $z = x + \mathrm{j}y$.

26 Find a function $v(x, y)$ such that, given $u = 2x(1 - y)$, $f(z) = u + \mathrm{j}v$ is analytic in z.

27 Show that $\phi(x, y) = \mathrm{e}^x(x\cos y - y\sin y)$ is a harmonic function, and find the conjugate harmonic function $\psi(x, y)$. Write $\phi(x, y) + \mathrm{j}\psi(x, y)$ as a function of $z = x + \mathrm{j}y$ only.

28 Show that $u(x, y) = \sin x \cosh y$ is harmonic. Find the harmonic conjugate $v(x, y)$ and express $w = u + \mathrm{j}v$ as a function of $z = x + \mathrm{j}y$.

29 Find the orthogonal trajectories of the following families of curves:

(a) $x^3y - xy^3 = \alpha$ (constant α)

(b) $\mathrm{e}^{-x}\cos y + xy = \alpha$ (constant α)

30 Find the real and imaginary parts of the functions

(a) $z^2\mathrm{e}^{2z}$

(b) $\sin 2z$

Verify that they are analytic and find their derivatives.

31 Give a definition of the inverse sine function $\sin^{-1} z$ for complex z. Find the real and imaginary parts of $\sin^{-1} z$. (*Hint*: put $z = \sin w$, split into real and imaginary parts, and with $w = u + \mathrm{j}v$ and $z = x + \mathrm{j}y$ solve for u and v in terms of x and y.) Is $\sin^{-1} z$ analytic? If so, what is its derivative?

32 Establish that if $z = x + \mathrm{j}y$, $|\sinh y| \leqslant |\sin z| \leqslant \cosh y$.

1.3.4 Mappings revisited

In Section 1.2 we examined mappings from the z plane to the w plane, where in the main the relationship between w and z, $w = f(z)$ was linear or bilinear. There is an important property of mappings, hinted at in Example 1.8 when considering the mapping $w = z^2$. A mapping $w = f(z)$ that preserves angles is called **conformal**. Under such a mapping, the angle between two intersecting curves in the z plane is the same as the angle between the corresponding intersecting curves in the w plane. The sense of the angle is also preserved. That is, if θ is the angle between curves 1 and 2 taken in the anticlockwise sense in the z plane then θ is also the angle between the image of curve 1 and the image of curve 2 in the w plane, and it too is taken in the anticlockwise sense.

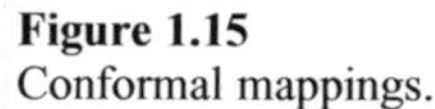

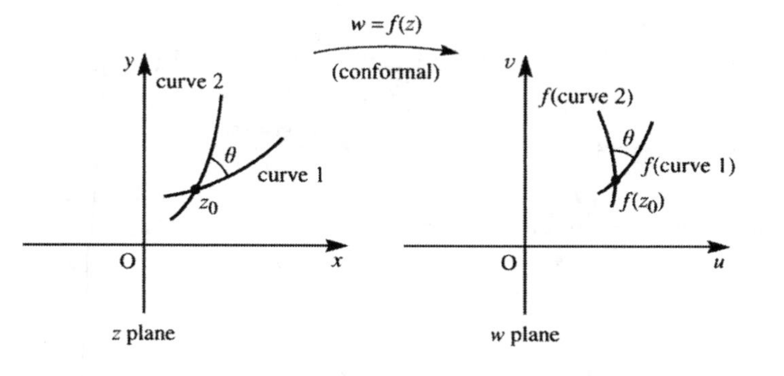

Figure 1.15
Conformal mappings.

Figure 1.15 should make the idea of a conformal mapping clearer. If $f(z)$ is analytic then $w = f(z)$ defines a conformal mapping except at points where the derivative $f'(z)$ is zero.

Clearly the linear mappings

$$w = \alpha z + \beta \quad (\alpha \neq 0)$$

are conformal everywhere, since $\mathrm{d}w/\mathrm{d}z = \alpha$ and is not zero for any point in the z plane. Bilinear mappings given by (1.12) are not so straightforward to check. However, as we saw in Section 1.2.4, (1.12) can be rearranged as

$$w = \lambda + \frac{\mu}{\alpha z + \beta} \quad (\alpha, \mu \neq 0)$$

Thus

$$\frac{\mathrm{d}w}{\mathrm{d}z} = -\frac{\mu\alpha}{(\alpha z + \beta)^2}$$

which again is never zero for any point in the z plane. In fact, the only mapping we have considered so far that has a point at which it is not conformal everywhere is $w = z^2$ (cf. Example 1.8), which is not conformal at $z = 0$.

Example 1.13

Determine the points at which the mapping $w = z + 1/z$ is not conformal and demonstrate this by considering the image in the w plane of the real axis in the z plane.

Solution

Taking $z = x + \mathrm{j}y$ and $w = u + \mathrm{j}v$, we have

$$w = u + \mathrm{j}v = x + \mathrm{j}y + \frac{x - \mathrm{j}y}{x^2 + y^2}$$

which, on equating real and imaginary parts, gives

$$u = x + \frac{x}{x^2 + y^2}$$

$$v = y - \frac{y}{x^2 + y^2}$$

The real axis, $y = 0$, in the z plane corresponds to $v = 0$, the real axis in the w plane. Note, however, that the fixed point of the mapping is given by

$$z = z + \frac{1}{z}$$

or $z = \infty$. From the Cauchy–Riemann equations it is readily shown that w is analytic everywhere except at $z = 0$. Also, $dw/dz = 0$ when

$$1 - \frac{1}{z^2} = 0, \quad \text{that is} \quad z = \pm 1$$

which are both on the real axis. Thus the mapping fails to be conformal at $z = 0$ and $z = \pm 1$. The image of $z = 1$ is $w = 2$, and the image of $z = -1$ is $w = -2$. Consideration of the image of the real axis is therefore perfectly adequate, since this is a curve passing through each point where $w = z + 1/z$ fails to be conformal. It would be satisfying if we could analyse this mapping in the same manner as we did with $w = z^2$ in Example 1.8. Unfortunately, we cannot do this, because the algebra gets unwieldy (and, indeed, our knowledge of algebraic curves is also too scanty). Instead, let us look at the image of the point $z = 1 + \varepsilon$, where ε is a small real number. $\varepsilon > 0$ corresponds to the point Q just to the right of $z = 1$ on the real axis in the z plane, and the point P just to the left of $z = 1$ corresponds to $\varepsilon < 0$ (Figure 1.16).

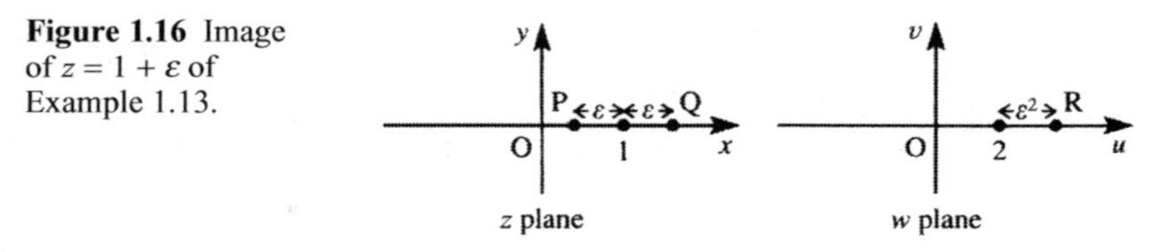

Figure 1.16 Image of $z = 1 + \varepsilon$ of Example 1.13.

If $z = 1 + \varepsilon$ then

$$\begin{aligned} w &= 1 + \varepsilon + \frac{1}{1 + \varepsilon} \\ &= 1 + \varepsilon + (1 + \varepsilon)^{-1} \\ &= 1 + \varepsilon + 1 - \varepsilon + \varepsilon^2 - \varepsilon^3 + \dots \\ &\simeq 2 + \varepsilon^2 \end{aligned}$$

if $|\varepsilon|$ is much smaller than 1 (we shall discuss the validity of the power series expansion in Section 1.4). Whether ε is positive or negative, the point $w = 2 + \varepsilon^2$ is to the right of $w = 2$ in the w plane as indicated by the point R in Figure 1.16. Therefore, as $\varepsilon \to 0$, a curve (the real axis) that passes through $z = 1$ in the z plane making an angle $\theta = \pi$ corresponds to a curve (again the real axis) that approaches $w = 2$ in the w plane along the real axis from the right making an angle $\theta = 0$. Non-conformality has thus been confirmed. The treatment of $z = -1$ follows in an identical fashion, so the details are omitted. Note that when $y = 0$ ($v = 0$), $u = x + 1/x$ so, as the real axis in the z plane is traversed from $x = -\infty$ to $x = 0$, the real axis in the w plane is traversed from

$u = -\infty$ to -2 *and back to* $u = -\infty$ *again* (when $x = -1$, u reaches -2). As the real axis in the z plane is traversed from $x = 0$ through $x = 1$ to $x = +\infty$, so the real axis in the w plane is traversed from $u = +\infty$ to $u = +2$ ($x = 1$) *back to* $u = \infty$ *again*. Hence the points on the real axis in the w plane in the range $-2 < u < 2$ do not correspond to real values of z. Solving $u = x + 1/x$ for x gives

$$x = \tfrac{1}{2}[u \pm \sqrt{(u^2 - 4)}]$$

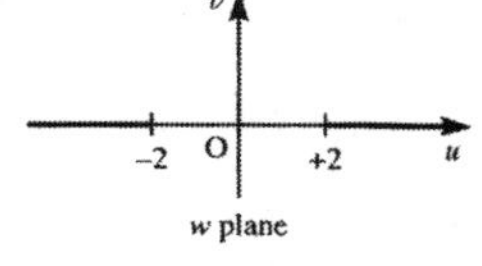

Figure 1.17 Image in w plane of the real axis in the z plane for Example 1.13.

which makes this point obvious. Figure 1.17 shows the image in the w plane of the real axis in the z plane. This mapping is very rich in interesting properties, but we shall not pursue it further here. Aeronautical engineers may well meet it again if they study the flow around an aerofoil in two dimensions, for this mapping takes circles centred at the origin in the z plane onto meniscus (lens-shaped) regions in the w plane, and only a slight alteration is required before these images become aerofoil-shaped.

Example 1.14

Examine the mapping

$$w = e^z$$

by (a) finding the images in the w plane of the lines x = constant and y = constant in the z plane, and (b) finding the image in the w plane of the left half-plane ($x < 0$) in the z plane.

Solution Taking $z = x + jy$ and $w = u + jv$, for $w = e^z$ we have

$$u = e^x \cos y$$

$$v = e^x \sin y$$

Squaring and adding these two equations, we obtain

$$u^2 + v^2 = e^{2x}$$

On the other hand, dividing the two equations gives

$$\frac{v}{u} = \tan y$$

We can now tackle the questions.

(a) Since $u^2 + v^2 = e^{2x}$, putting x = constant shows that the lines parallel to the imaginary axis in the z plane correspond to circles centred at the origin in the w plane. The equation

$$\frac{v}{u} = \tan y$$

shows that the lines parallel to the real axis in the z plane correspond to straight lines through the origin in the w plane ($v = u \tan \alpha$ if $y = \alpha$, a constant). Figure 1.18 shows the general picture.

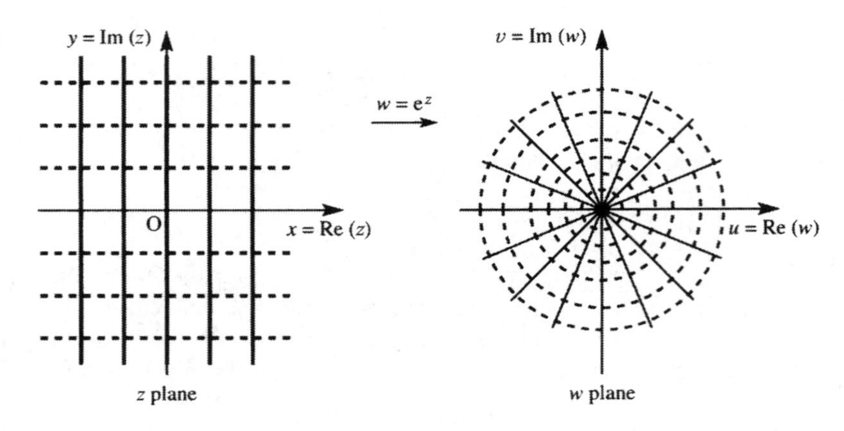

Figure 1.18 Mapping of lines under $w = e^z$.

(b) Since $u^2 + v^2 = e^{2x}$, if $x = 0$ then $u^2 + v^2 = 1$, so the imaginary axis in the z plane corresponds to the unit circle in the w plane. If $x < 0$ then $e^{2x} < 1$, and as $x \to -\infty$, $e^{2x} \to 0$, so the left half of the z plane corresponds to the interior of the unit circle in the w plane, as illustrated in Figure 1.19.

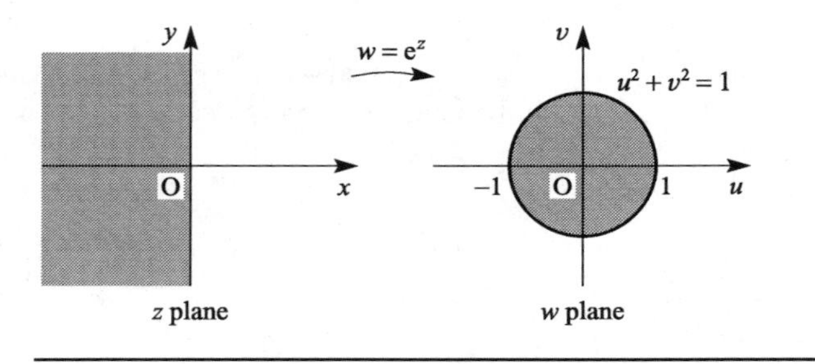

Figure 1.19 Mapping of half-plane under $w = e^z$.

1.3.5 Exercises

33 Determine the points at which the following mappings are *not* conformal:

(a) $w = z^2 - 1$ (b) $w = 2z^3 - 21z^2 + 72z + 6$

(c) $w = 8z + \dfrac{1}{2z^2}$

34 Follow Example 1.13 for the mapping $w = z - 1/z$. Again determine the points at which the mapping is not conformal, but this time demonstrate this by looking at the image of the *imaginary* axis.

35 Find the region of the w plane corresponding to the following regions of the z plane under the exponential mapping $w = e^z$:

(a) $0 \leqslant x < \infty$ (b) $0 \leqslant x \leqslant 1, 0 \leqslant y \leqslant 1$

(c) $\frac{1}{2}\pi \leqslant y \leqslant \pi, 0 \leqslant x < \infty$

36 Consider the mapping $w = \sin z$. Determine the points at which the mapping is not conformal. By finding the images in the w plane of the lines x = constant and y = constant in the z plane ($z = x + jy$), draw the mapping along similar lines to Figures 1.14 and 1.18.

37 Show that the transformation

$$z = \zeta + \frac{a^2}{\zeta}$$

where $z = x + jy$ and $\zeta = R e^{j\theta}$ maps a circle, with centre at the origin and radius a, in the ζ plane, onto a straight line segment in the z plane. What is the length of the line? What happens if the circle in the ζ plane is centred at the origin but is of radius b, where $b \neq a$?

1.4 Complex series

In *Modern Engineering Mathematics* we saw that there were distinct advantages in being able to express a function $f(x)$, such as the exponential, trigonometric and logarithmic functions, of a real variable x in terms of its power series expansion

$$f(x) = \sum_{n=0}^{\infty} a_n x^n = a_0 + a_1 x + a_2 x^2 + \ldots + a_r x^r + \ldots \tag{1.27}$$

Power series are also very important in dealing with complex functions. In fact, any real function $f(x)$ which has a power series of the form in (1.27) has a corresponding complex function $f(z)$ having the same power series expansion, that is

$$f(z) = \sum_{n=0}^{\infty} a_n z^n = a_0 + a_1 z + a_2 z^2 + \ldots + a_r z^r + \ldots \tag{1.28}$$

This property enables us to extend real functions to the complex case, so that methods based on power series expansions have a key role to play in formulating the theory of complex functions. In this section we shall consider some of the properties of the power series expansion of a complex function by drawing, wherever possible, an analogy with the power series expansion of the corresponding real function.

1.4.1 Power series

A series having the form

$$\sum_{n=0}^{\infty} a_n (z - z_0)^n = a_0 + a_1(z - z_0) + a_2(z - z_0)^2 + \ldots + a_r(z - z_0)^r + \ldots \tag{1.29}$$

in which the coefficients a_r are real or complex and z_0 is a fixed point in the complex z plane is called a **power series** about z_0 or a power series centred on z_0. Where $z_0 = 0$, the series (1.29) reduces to the series (1.28), which is a power series centred at the origin. In fact, on making the change of variable $z' = z - z_0$, (1.29) takes the form (1.28), so there is no loss of generality in considering the latter below.

Tests for the convergence or divergence of complex power series are similar to those used for power series of a real variable. However, in complex series it is essential that the modulus $|a_n|$ be used. For example, the geometric series

$$\sum_{n=0}^{\infty} z^n$$

has a sum to N terms

$$S_N = \sum_{n=0}^{N-1} z^n = \frac{1 - z^N}{1 - z}$$

and converges, if $|z| < 1$, to the limit $1/(1 - z)$ as $N \to \infty$. If $|z| \geqslant 1$, the series diverges. These results appear to be identical with the requirement that $|x| < 1$ to ensure convergence of the real power series

$$\frac{1}{1-x}=\sum_{n=0}^{\infty}x^n$$

However, in the complex case the geometrical interpretation is different in that the condition $|z|<1$ implies that z lies inside the circle centred at the origin and radius 1 in the z plane. Thus the series $\sum_{n=0}^{\infty}z^n$ converges if z lies inside this circle and diverges if z lies on or outside it. The situation is illustrated in Figure 1.20.

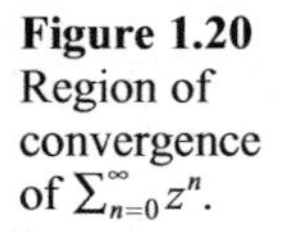

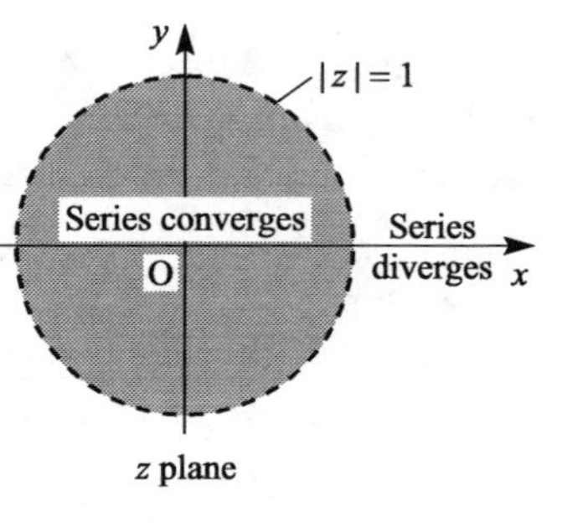

Figure 1.20 Region of convergence of $\sum_{n=0}^{\infty}z^n$.

The existence of such a circle leads to an important concept in that in general there exists a circle centred at the origin and of radius R such that the series

$$\sum_{n=0}^{\infty}a_nz^n \begin{cases}\text{converges if} & |z|<R\\ \text{diverges if} & |z|>R\end{cases}$$

The radius R is called the **radius of convergence** of the power series. What happens when $|z|=R$ is normally investigated as a special case?

We have introduced the radius of convergence based on a circle centred at the origin, while the concept obviously does not depend on the location of the centre of the circle. If the series is centred on z_0 as in (1.29) then the convergence circle would be centred on z_0. Indeed it could even be centred at infinity, when the power series becomes

$$\sum_{n=0}^{\infty}a_nz^{-n}=a_0+\frac{a_1}{z}+\frac{a_2}{z^2}+\ldots+\frac{a_r}{z^r}+\ldots$$

which we shall consider further in Section 1.4.5.

In order to determine the radius of convergence R for a given series, various tests for convergence, such as those introduced in *Modern Engineering Mathematics* for real series, may be applied. In particular, using d'Alembert's ratio test, it can be shown that the radius of convergence R of the complex series $\sum_{n=0}^{\infty}a_nz^n$ is given by

$$R=\lim_{n\to\infty}\left|\frac{a_n}{a_{n+1}}\right| \tag{1.30}$$

provided that the limit exists. Then the series is convergent within the disc $|z|<R$. In general, of course, the limit may not exist, and in such cases an alternative method must be used.

Example 1.15 Find the power series, in the form indicated, representing the function $1/(z-3)$ in the following three regions:

(a) $|z| < 3$; $\sum_{n=0}^{\infty} a_n z^n$

(b) $|z-2| < 1$; $\sum_{n=0}^{\infty} a_n (z-2)^n$

(c) $|z| > 3$; $\sum_{n=0}^{\infty} \frac{a_n}{z^n}$

and sketch these regions on an Argand diagram.

Solution We know that the binomial series expansion

$$(1+z)^n = 1 + nz + \frac{n(n-1)}{2!}z^2 + \ldots + \frac{n(n-1)(n-2)\ldots(n-r+1)}{r!}z^r + \ldots$$

is valid for $|z| < 1$. To solve the problem, we exploit this result by expanding the function $1/(z-3)$ in three different ways:

(a) $$\frac{1}{z-3} = \frac{-\frac{1}{3}}{1-\frac{1}{3}z} = -\tfrac{1}{3}(1-\tfrac{1}{3}z)^{-1} = -\tfrac{1}{3}[1+\tfrac{1}{3}z+(\tfrac{1}{3}z)^2+\ldots+(\tfrac{1}{3}z)^n+\ldots]$$

for $|\frac{1}{3}z| < 1$, that is $|z| < 3$, giving the power series

$$\frac{1}{z-3} = -\tfrac{1}{3} - \tfrac{1}{9}z - \tfrac{1}{27}z^2 - \ldots \quad (|z| < 3)$$

(b) $$\frac{1}{z-3} = \frac{1}{(z-2)-1} = [(z-2)-1]^{-1}$$

$$= -[1+(z-2)+(z-2)^2+\ldots] \quad (|z-2| < 1)$$

giving the power series

$$\frac{1}{z-3} = -1-(z-2)-(z-2)^2-\ldots \quad (|z-2| < 1)$$

(c) $$\frac{1}{z-3} = \frac{1/z}{1-3/z} = \frac{1}{z}\left[1+\frac{3}{z}+\left(\frac{3}{z}\right)^2+\ldots\right]$$

giving the power series

$$\frac{1}{z-3} = \frac{1}{z}+\frac{3}{z^2}+\frac{9}{z^3}+\ldots \quad (|z| > 3)$$

The three regions are sketched in Figure 1.21. Note that none of the regions includes the point $z = 3$, which is termed a **singularity** of the function, a concept we shall discuss in Section 1.5.1.

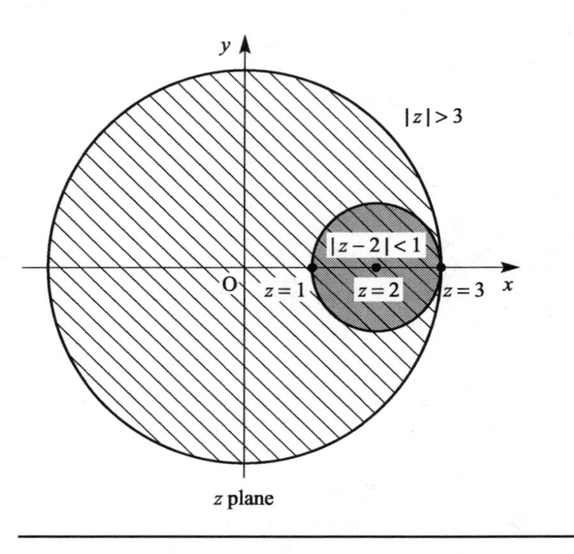

Figure 1.21 Regions of convergence for the series in Example 1.15.

In Example 1.15 the whole of the circle $|z| = 3$ was excluded from the three regions where the power series converge. In fact, it is possible to include any selected point in the z plane as a centre of the circle in which to define a power series that converges to $1/(z-3)$ everywhere inside the circle, with the exception of the point $z = 3$. For example, the point $z = 4\text{j}$ would lead to the expansion of

$$\frac{1}{z-4\text{j}+4\text{j}-3}=\frac{1}{4\text{j}-3}\,\frac{1}{\dfrac{z-4\text{j}}{4\text{j}-3}+1}$$

in a binomial series in powers of $(z-4\text{j})/(4\text{j}-3)$, which converges to $1/(z-3)$ inside the circle

$$|z-4\text{j}|=|4\text{j}-3|=\sqrt{(16+9)}=5$$

We should not expect the point $z = 3$ to be included in any of the circles, since the function $1/(z-3)$ is infinite there and hence not defined.

Example 1.16

Prove that both the power series $\sum_{n=0}^{\infty}a_nz^n$ and the corresponding series of derivatives $\sum_{n=0}^{\infty}na_nz^{n-1}$ have the same radius of convergence.

Solution

Let R be the radius of convergence of the power series $\sum_{n=0}^{\infty}a_nz^n$. Since $\lim_{n\to\infty}(a_nz_0^n)=0$ (otherwise the series has no chance of convergence), if $|z_0|<R$ for some complex number z_0 then it is always possible to choose

$$|a_n|<|z_0|^{-n}$$

for $n > N$, with N a fixed integer. We now use d'Alembert's ratio test, namely

$$\text{if}\quad\lim_{n\to\infty}\left|\frac{a_{n+1}}{a_n}\right|<1\quad\text{then}\quad\sum_{n=0}^{\infty}a_nz^n\quad\text{converges}$$

$$\text{if}\quad\lim_{n\to\infty}\left|\frac{a_{n+1}}{a_n}\right|>1\quad\text{then}\quad\sum_{n=0}^{\infty}a_nz^n\quad\text{diverges}$$

The differentiated series $\sum_{n=0}^{\infty} na_n z^{n-1}$ satisfies

$$\sum_{n=1}^{\infty} |na_n z^{n-1}| < \sum_{n=1}^{\infty} n|a_n||z|^{n-1} < \sum_{n=1}^{\infty} n\frac{|z|^{n-1}}{|z_0|^n}$$

which, by the ratio test, converges if $0 < |z_0| < R$, since $|z| < |z_0|$ and $|z_0|$ can be as close to R as we choose. If, however, $|z| > R$ then $\lim_{n\to\infty}(a_n z^n) \neq 0$ and thus $\lim_{n\to\infty}(na_n z^{n-1}) \neq 0$ too. Hence R is also the radius of convergence of the differentiated series $\sum_{n=1}^{\infty} na_n z^{n-1}$.

The result obtained in Example 1.16 is important, since if the complex function

$$f(z) = \sum_{n=0}^{\infty} a_n z^n$$

converges in $|z| < R$ then the derivative

$$f'(z) = \sum_{n=1}^{\infty} na_n z^{n-1}$$

also converges in $|z| < R$. We can go on differentiating $f(z)$ through its power series and be sure that the differentiated function and the differentiated power series are equal inside the circle of convergence.

1.4.2 Exercises

38 Find the power series representation for the function $1/(z - j)$ in the regions

(a) $|z| < 1$

(b) $|z| > 1$

(c) $|z - 1 - j| < \sqrt{2}$

Deduce that the radius of convergence of the power series representation of this function is $|z_0 - j|$, where $z = z_0$ is the centre of the circle of convergence ($z_0 \neq j$).

39 Find the power series representation of the function

$$f(z) = \frac{1}{z^2 + 1}$$

in the disc $|z| < 1$. Use Example 1.16 to deduce the power series for

(a) $\dfrac{1}{(z^2 + 1)^2}$ (b) $\dfrac{1}{(z^2 + 1)^3}$

valid in this same disc.

1.4.3 Taylor series

In *Modern Engineering Mathematics* we introduced the Taylor series expansion

$$f(x + a) = f(a) + \frac{x}{1!}f^{(1)}(a) + \frac{x^2}{2!}f^{(2)}(a) + \ldots = \sum_{n=0}^{\infty} \frac{x^n}{n!}f^{(n)}(a) \qquad \textbf{(1.31)}$$

of a function $f(x)$ of a real variable x about $x = a$ and valid within the interval of convergence of the power series. For the engineer the ability to express a function in such a power series expansion is seen to be particularly useful in the development of numerical methods and the assessment of errors. The ability to express a complex function as a Taylor series is also important to engineers in many fields of applications, such as control and communications theory. The form of the Taylor series in the complex case is identical with that of (1.31).

If $f(z)$ is a complex function analytic inside and on a simple closed curve C (usually a circle) in the z plane then it follows from Example 1.16 that the higher derivatives of $f(z)$ also exist inside C. If z_0 and $z_0 + h$ are two fixed points inside C then

$$f(z_0 + h) = f(z_0) + hf^{(1)}(z_0) + \frac{h^2}{2!}f^{(2)}(z_0) + \ldots + \frac{h^n}{n!}f^{(n)}(z_0) + \ldots$$

where $f^{(k)}(z_0)$ is the kth derivative of $f(z)$ evaluated at $z = z_0$. Normally, $z = z_0 + h$ is introduced so that $h = z - z_0$, and the series expansion then becomes

$$f(z) = f(z_0) + (z - z_0)f^{(1)}(z_0) + \frac{(z - z_0)^2}{2!}f^{(2)}(z_0) + \ldots + \frac{(z - z_0)^n}{n!}f^{(n)}(z_0) + \ldots = \sum_{n=0}^{\infty} \frac{(z - z_0)^n}{n!}f^{(n)}(z_0) \quad \textbf{(1.32)}$$

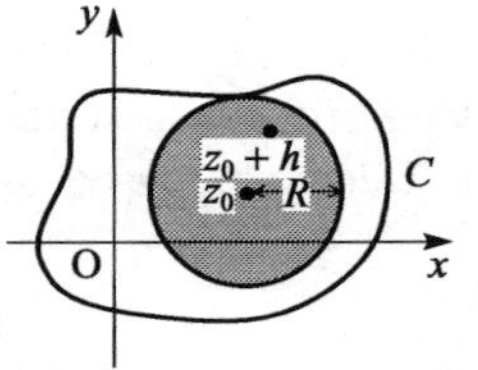

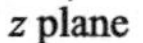

Figure 1.22 Region of convergence of the Taylor series.

The power series expansion (1.32) is called the **Taylor series expansion** of the complex function $f(z)$ about z_0. The region of convergence of this series is $|z - z_0| < R$, a disc centred on $z = z_0$ and of radius R, the radius of convergence. Figure 1.22 illustrates the region of convergence. When $z_0 = 0$, as in real variables, the series expansion about the origin is often called a **Maclaurin series expansion**.

Since the proof of the Taylor series expansion does not add to our understanding of how to apply the result to the solution of engineering problems, we omit it at this stage.

Example 1.17

Determine the Taylor series expansion of the function

$$f(z) = \frac{1}{z(z - 2\mathrm{j})}$$

about the point $z = \mathrm{j}$:

(a) directly up to the term $(z - \mathrm{j})^4$,

(b) using the binomial expansion.

Determine the radius of convergence.

Solution

(a) The disadvantage with functions other than the most straightforward is that obtaining their derivatives is prohibitively complicated in terms of algebra. It is easier in this particular case to resolve the given function into partial fractions as

$$f(z) = \frac{1}{z(z - 2\mathrm{j})} = \frac{1}{2\mathrm{j}}\left(\frac{1}{z - 2\mathrm{j}} - \frac{1}{z}\right)$$

The right-hand side is now far easier to differentiate repeatedly. Proceeding to determine $f^{(k)}(\mathrm{j})$, we have

$$f(z) = \frac{1}{2\mathrm{j}}\left(\frac{1}{z - 2\mathrm{j}} - \frac{1}{z}\right), \qquad \text{so that} \quad f(\mathrm{j}) = 1$$

$$f^{(1)}(z) = \frac{1}{2\mathrm{j}}\left[-\frac{1}{(z - 2\mathrm{j})^2} + \frac{1}{z^2}\right], \qquad \text{so that} \quad f^{(1)}(\mathrm{j}) = 0$$

$$f^{(2)}(z) = \frac{1}{2\mathrm{j}}\left[\frac{2}{(z - 2\mathrm{j})^3} - \frac{2}{z^3}\right], \qquad \text{so that} \quad f^{(2)}(\mathrm{j}) = -2$$

$$f^{(3)}(z) = \frac{1}{2\mathrm{j}}\left[-\frac{6}{(z - 2\mathrm{j})^4} + \frac{6}{z^4}\right], \qquad \text{so that} \quad f^{(3)}(\mathrm{j}) = 0$$

$$f^{(4)}(z) = \frac{1}{2\mathrm{j}}\left[\frac{24}{(z - 2\mathrm{j})^5} - \frac{24}{z^5}\right], \qquad \text{so that} \quad f^{(4)}(\mathrm{j}) = 24$$

leading from (1.32) to the Taylor series expansion

$$\frac{1}{z(z - 2\mathrm{j})} = 1 - \frac{2}{2!}(z - \mathrm{j})^2 + \frac{24}{4!}(z - \mathrm{j})^4 + \dots$$
$$= 1 - (z - \mathrm{j})^2 + (z - \mathrm{j})^4 + \dots$$

(b) To use the binomial expansion, we first express $z(z - 2\mathrm{j})$ as $(z - \mathrm{j} + \mathrm{j})(z - \mathrm{j} - \mathrm{j})$, which, being the difference of two squares $((z - \mathrm{j})^2 - \mathrm{j}^2)$, leads to

$$f(z) = \frac{1}{z(z - 2\mathrm{j})} = \frac{1}{(z - \mathrm{j})^2 + 1} = [1 + (z - \mathrm{j})^2]^{-1}$$

Use of the binomial expansion then gives

$$f(z) = 1 - (z - \mathrm{j})^2 + (z - \mathrm{j})^4 - (z - \mathrm{j})^6 + \dots$$

valid for $|z - \mathrm{j}| < 1$, so the radius of convergence is 1.

The points where $f(z)$ is infinite (its singularities) are precisely at distance 1 away from $z = \mathrm{j}$, so this value for the radius of convergence comes as no surprise.

Example 1.18 Suggest a function to represent the power series

$$1 + z + \frac{z^2}{2!} + \frac{z^3}{3!} + \dots + \frac{z^n}{n!} + \dots$$

and determine its radius of convergence.

Solution Set

$$f(z) = 1 + z + \frac{z^2}{2!} + \frac{z^3}{3!} + \dots = \sum_{n=0}^{\infty} \frac{z^n}{n!}$$

Assuming we can differentiate the series for $f(z)$ term by term, we obtain

$$f'(z) = \sum_{n=1}^{\infty} \frac{nz^{n-1}}{n!} = \sum_{n=1}^{\infty} \frac{z^{n-1}}{(n-1)!} = f(z)$$

Hence $f(z)$ is its own derivative. Since e^x is its own derivative in real variables, and is the only such function, it seems sensible to propose that

$$f(z) = \sum_{n=0}^{\infty} \frac{z^n}{n!} = e^z \tag{1.33}$$

the complex exponential function. Indeed the complex exponential e^z is defined by the power series (1.33). According to d'Alembert's ratio test the series $\sum_{n=0}^{\infty} a_n$ is convergent if $|a_{n+1}/a_n| \to L < 1$ as $n \to \infty$, where L is a real constant. If $a_n = z^n/n!$ then $|a_{n+1}/a_n| = |z|/(n+1)$ which is less than unity for sufficiently large n, no matter how big $|z|$ is. Hence $\sum_{n=0}^{\infty} z^n/n!$ is convergent for *all* z and so has an infinite radius of convergence. Note that this is confirmed from (1.30). Such functions are called **entire**.

In the same way as we define the exponential function e^z by the power series expansion (1.31), we can define the circular functions $\sin z$ and $\cos z$ by the power series expansions

$$\sin z = z - \frac{z^3}{3!} + \frac{z^5}{5!} - \frac{z^7}{7!} + \ldots + (-1)^n \frac{z^{2n+1}}{(2n+1)!} + \ldots$$

$$\cos z = 1 - \frac{z^2}{2!} + \frac{z^4}{4!} - \frac{z^6}{6!} + \ldots + (-1)^n \frac{z^{2n}}{(2n)!} + \ldots$$

both of which are valid for all z. Using these power series definitions, we can readily prove the result (1.25), namely

$$e^{jz} = \cos z + j \sin z$$

1.4.4 Exercises

40 Find the first four non-zero terms of the Taylor series expansions of the following functions about the points indicated, and determine the radius of convergence in each case:

(a) $\dfrac{1}{1+z}$ $(z = 1)$ (b) $\dfrac{1}{z(z-4j)}$ $(z = 2j)$

(c) $\dfrac{1}{z^2}$ $(z = 1 + j)$

41 Find the Maclaurin series expansion of the function

$$f(z) = \frac{1}{1 + z + z^2}$$

up to and including the term in z^3.

42 Without explicitly finding each Taylor series expansion, find the radius of convergence of the function

$$f(z) = \frac{1}{z^4 - 1}$$

about the three points $z = 0$, $z = 1 + j$ and $z = 2 + 2j$. Why is there no Taylor series expansion of this function about $z = j$?

43 Determine a Maclaurin series expansion of $f(z) = \tan z$. What is its radius of convergence?

1.4.5 Laurent series

Let us now examine more closely the solution of Example 1.15(c), where the power series obtained was

$$\frac{1}{z-3} = \frac{1}{z} + \frac{3}{z^2} + \frac{9}{z^3} + \dots$$

valid for $|z| > 3$. In the context of the definition, this is a power series about '$z = \infty$', the 'point at infinity'. Some readers, quite justifiably, may not be convinced that there is a single unique point at infinity. Figure 1.23 shows what is termed the **Riemann sphere**. A sphere lies on the complex z plane, with the contact point at the origin O. Let O′ be the top of the sphere, at the diametrically opposite point to O. Now, for any arbitrarily chosen point P in the z plane, by joining O′ and P we determine a unique point P′ where the line O′P intersects the sphere. There is thus exactly one point P′ on the sphere corresponding to each P in the z plane. The point O′ itself is the only point on the sphere that does not have a corresponding point on the (finite) z plane; we therefore say it corresponds to the **point at infinity** on the z plane.

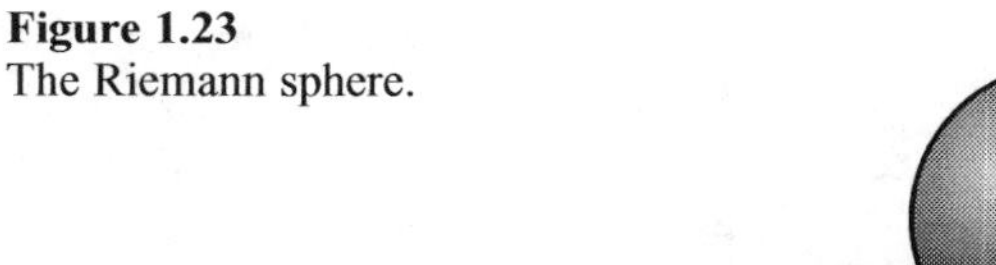

Figure 1.23
The Riemann sphere.

Returning to consider power series, we know that, inside the radius of convergence, a given function and its Taylor series expansion are identically equal. Points at which a function fails to be analytic are called **singularities**, which we shall discuss in Section 1.5.1. No Taylor series expansion is possible about a singularity. Indeed, a Taylor series expansion about a point z_0 at which a function is analytic is only valid within a circle, centre z_0, up to the nearest singularity. Thus all singularities must be excluded in any Taylor series consideration. The Laurent series representation includes (or at least takes note of) the behaviour of the function in the vicinity of a singularity.

If $f(z)$ is a complex function analytic on concentric circles C_1 and C_2 of radii r_1 and r_2 (with $r_2 < r_1$), centred at z_0, and also analytic throughout the region between the circles (that is, an annular region), then for each point z within the annulus (Figure 1.24) $f(z)$ may be represented by the **Laurent series**

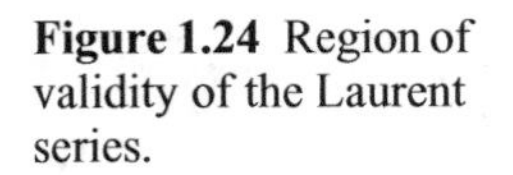

Figure 1.24 Region of validity of the Laurent series.

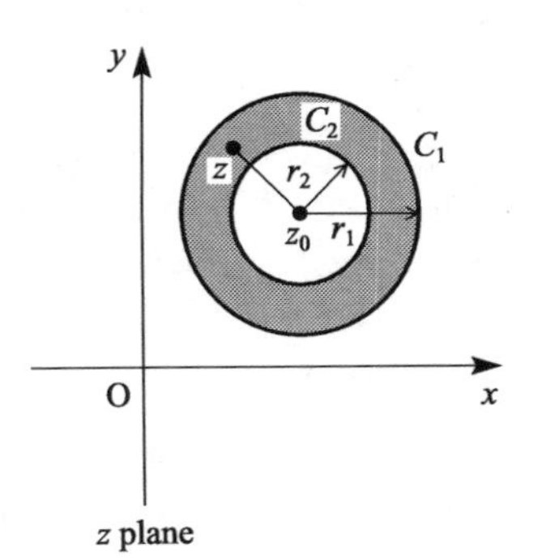

$$f(z) = \sum_{n=-\infty}^{\infty} c_n(z - z_0)^n$$
$$= \ldots + \frac{c_{-r}}{(z - z_0)^r} + \frac{c_{-r+1}}{(z - z_0)^{r-1}} + \ldots + \frac{c_{-1}}{z - z_0} + c_0$$
$$+ c_1(z - z_0) + \ldots + c_r(z - z_0)^r + \ldots \tag{1.34}$$

where in general the coefficients c_r are complex. The annular shape of the region is necessary in order to exclude the point $z = z_0$, which may be a singularity of $f(z)$, from consideration. If $f(z)$ is analytic at $z = z_0$ then $c_n = 0$ for $n = -1, -2, \ldots, -\infty$, and the Laurent series reduces to the Taylor series.

The Laurent series (1.34) for $f(z)$ may be written as

$$f(z) = \sum_{n=-\infty}^{-1} c_n(z - z_0)^n + \sum_{n=0}^{\infty} c_n(z - z_0)^n$$

and the first sum on the right-hand side, the 'non-Taylor' part, is called the **principal part** of the Laurent series.

Of course, we can seldom actually sum a series to infinity. There is therefore often more than theoretical interest in the so-called 'remainder terms', these being the difference between the first n terms of a power series and the exact value of the function. For both Taylor and Laurent series these remainder terms are expressed, as in the case of real variables, in terms of the $(n + 1)$th derivative of the function itself. For Laurent series in complex variables these derivatives can be expressed in terms of contour integrals (Section 1.6), which may be amenable to simple computation. Many of the details are outside the scope of this book, but there is some introductory material in Section 1.6.

Example 1.19

For $f(z) = 1/z^2(z + 1)$ find the Laurent series expansion about (a) $z = 0$ and (b) $z = -1$. Determine the region of validity in each case.

Solution

As with Example 1.15, problems such as this are tackled by making use of the binomial series expansion

$$(1 + z)^n = 1 + nz + \frac{n(n-1)}{2!}z^2 + \ldots + \frac{n(n-1)(n-2)\ldots(n-r+1)}{r!}z^r + \ldots$$

provided that $|z| < 1$.

(a) In this case $z_0 = 0$, so we need a series in powers of z. Thus

$$\frac{1}{z^2(1+z)} = \frac{1}{z^2}(1 + z)^{-1}$$
$$= \frac{1}{z^2}(1 - z + z^2 - z^3 + z^4 - \ldots) \quad (0 < |z| < 1)$$

Thus the required Laurent series expansion is

$$\frac{1}{z^2(z+1)} = \frac{1}{z^2} - \frac{1}{z} + 1 - z + z^2 \ldots$$

valid for $0 < |z| < 1$. The value $z = 0$ must be excluded because of the first two terms of the series. The region $0 < |z| < 1$ is an example of a **punctured disc**, a common occurrence in this branch of mathematics.

(b) In this case $z_0 = -1$, so we need a series in powers of $(z + 1)$. Thus

$$\begin{aligned}\frac{1}{z^2(z+1)} &= \frac{1}{(z+1)}(z+1-1)^{-2} \\ &= \frac{1}{(z+1)}[1-(z+1)]^{-2} \\ &= \frac{1}{(z+1)}[1+2(z+1)+3(z+1)^2+\dots] \\ &= \frac{1}{z+1}+2+3(z+1)+4(z+1)^2+\dots\end{aligned}$$

valid for $0 < |z + 1| < 1$. Note that in a meniscus-shaped region (that is, the region of overlap between the two circular regions $|z| < 1$ and $|z + 1| < 1$) both Laurent series are simultaneously valid. This is quite typical, and not a cause for concern.

Example 1.20 Determine the Laurent series expansions of

$$f(z) = \frac{1}{(z+1)(z+3)}$$

valid for

(a) $1 < |z| < 3$

(b) $|z| > 3$

(c) $0 < |z + 1| < 2$

(d) $|z| < 1$

Solution (a) Resolving into partial functions,

$$f(z) = \tfrac{1}{2}\left(\frac{1}{z+1}\right) - \tfrac{1}{2}\left(\frac{1}{z+3}\right)$$

Since $|z| > 1$ and $|z| < 3$, we express this as

$$\begin{aligned}f(z) &= \frac{1}{2z}\left(\frac{1}{1+1/z}\right) - \tfrac{1}{6}\left(\frac{1}{1+\frac{1}{3}z}\right) \\ &= \frac{1}{2z}\left(1+\frac{1}{z}\right)^{-1} - \tfrac{1}{6}(1+\tfrac{1}{3}z)^{-1} \\ &= \frac{1}{2z}\left(1-\frac{1}{z}+\frac{1}{z^2}-\frac{1}{z^3}+\dots\right) - \tfrac{1}{6}(1-\tfrac{1}{3}z+\tfrac{1}{9}z^2-\tfrac{1}{27}z^3+\dots) \\ &= \dots - \frac{1}{2z^4}+\frac{1}{2z^3}-\frac{1}{2z^2}+\frac{1}{2z}-\tfrac{1}{6}+\tfrac{1}{18}z-\tfrac{1}{54}z^2+\tfrac{1}{162}z^3-\dots\end{aligned}$$

(b) $f(z) = \frac{1}{2}\left(\frac{1}{z+1}\right) - \frac{1}{2}\left(\frac{1}{z+3}\right)$

Since $|z| > 3$, we express this as

$$\begin{aligned}
f(z) &= \frac{1}{2z}\left(\frac{1}{1+1/z}\right) - \frac{1}{2z}\left(\frac{1}{1+3/z}\right) \\
&= \frac{1}{2z}\left(1+\frac{1}{z}\right)^{-1} - \frac{1}{2z}\left(1+\frac{3}{z}\right)^{-1} \\
&= \frac{1}{2z}\left(1 - \frac{1}{z} + \frac{1}{z^2} - \frac{1}{z^3} + \dots\right) - \frac{1}{2z}\left(1 - \frac{3}{z} + \frac{9}{z^2} - \frac{27}{z^3} + \dots\right) \\
&= \frac{1}{z^2} - \frac{4}{z^3} + \frac{13}{z^4} - \frac{40}{z^5} + \dots
\end{aligned}$$

(c) We can proceed as in Example 1.18. Alternatively, we can take $z + 1 = u$; then $0 < |u| < 2$ and

$$\begin{aligned}
f(u) &= \frac{1}{u(u+2)} = \frac{1}{2u(1+\frac{1}{2}u)} \\
&= \frac{1}{2u}(1 - \tfrac{1}{2}u + \tfrac{1}{4}u^2 - \tfrac{1}{8}u^3 + \dots)
\end{aligned}$$

giving

$$f(z) = \frac{1}{2(z+1)} - \tfrac{1}{4} + \tfrac{1}{8}(z+1) - \tfrac{1}{16}(z+1)^2 + \dots$$

(d) $f(z) = \dfrac{1}{2(z+1)} - \dfrac{1}{2(z+3)}$

Since $|z| < 1$, we express this as

$$\begin{aligned}
f(z) &= \frac{1}{2(1+z)} - \frac{1}{6(1+\frac{1}{3}z)} \\
&= \tfrac{1}{2}(1+z)^{-1} - \tfrac{1}{6}(1+\tfrac{1}{3}z)^{-1} \\
&= \tfrac{1}{2}(1 - z + z^2 - z^3 + \dots) - \tfrac{1}{6}(1 - \tfrac{1}{3}z + \tfrac{1}{9}z^2 - \tfrac{1}{27}z^3 + \dots) \\
&= \tfrac{1}{3} - \tfrac{4}{9}z + \tfrac{13}{27}z^2 - \tfrac{40}{81}z^3 + \dots
\end{aligned}$$

Example 1.21 Determine the Laurent series expansion of the function $f(z) = z^3 e^{1/z}$ about

(a) $z = 0$

(b) $z = a$, a finite, non-zero complex number

(c) $z = \infty$

Solution (a) From (1.33),

$$e^z = 1 + z + \frac{z^2}{2!} + \dots \quad (0 \leqslant |z| < \infty)$$

Substituting $1/z$ for z, we obtain

$$e^{1/z} = 1 + \frac{1}{z} + \frac{1}{2!z^2} + \dots \quad (0 < |z| \leqslant \infty)$$

so that

$$z^3 e^{1/z} = z^3 + z^2 + \frac{z}{2!} + \frac{1}{3!} + \frac{1}{4!z} + \frac{1}{5!z^2} + \dots \quad (0 < |z| \leqslant \infty)$$

This series has infinitely many terms in its principal part, but stops at z^3 (it is written back to front). Series with never-ending principal parts are a problem, and fortunately are uncommon in engineering. Note also that the series is valid in an infinite punctured disc.

(b) The value of $f(a)$ must be $a^3 e^{1/a}$, which is not infinite since $a \neq 0$. Therefore $f(z)$ has a Taylor series expansion

$$f(z) = f(a) + (z - a)f^{(1)}(a) + \frac{(z-a)^2}{2!} f^{(2)}(a) + \dots$$

about $z = a$. We have

$$f^{(1)}(z) = \frac{d}{dz}(z^3 e^{1/z}) = 3z^2 e^{1/z} - z e^{1/z}$$

$$f^{(2)}(z) = \frac{d}{dz}(3z^2 e^{1/z} - z e^{1/z}) = 6z e^{1/z} - 4 e^{1/z} + \frac{1}{z^2} e^{1/z}$$

giving the series as

$$z^3 e^{1/z} = a^3 e^{1/a} + (z - a)(3a^2 e^{1/a} - a e^{1/a})$$

$$+ \frac{1}{2!}(z-a)^2\left(6a e^{1/a} - 4e^{1/a} + \frac{1}{a^2} e^{1/a}\right) + \dots$$

which is valid in the region $|z - a| < R$, where R is the distance between the origin, where $f(z)$ is not defined, and the point a; hence $R = |a|$. Thus the region of validity for this Taylor series is the disc $|z - a| < |a|$.

(c) To expand about $z = \infty$, let $w = 1/z$, so that

$$f(z) = \frac{1}{w^3} e^w$$

Expanding about $w = 0$ then gives

$$f\left(\frac{1}{w}\right) = \frac{1}{w^3}\left(1 + w + \frac{w^2}{2!} + \frac{w^3}{3!} + \dots\right)$$

$$= \frac{1}{w^3} + \frac{1}{w^2} + \frac{1}{2!w} + \frac{1}{3!} + \frac{w}{4!} + \dots \quad (0 < |w| < \infty)$$

Note that this time there are only three terms in the principal part of $f(z)(= f(1/w))$.

1.4.6 Exercises

44 Determine the Laurent series expansion of

$$f(z) = \frac{1}{z(z-1)^2}$$

about (a) $z = 0$ and (b) $z = 1$, and specify the region of validity for each.

45 Determine the Laurent series expansion of the function

$$f(z) = z^2 \sin \frac{1}{z}$$

about the points

(a) $z = 0$ (b) $z = \infty$

(c) $z = a$, a finite non-zero complex number

(For (c), do *not* calculate the coefficients explicitly.)

46 Expand

$$f(z) = \frac{z}{(z-1)(2-z)}$$

in a Laurent series expansion valid for

(a) $|z| < 1$ (b) $1 < |z| < 2$ (c) $|z| > 2$

(d) $|z-1| > 1$ (e) $0 < |z-2| < 1$

1.5 Singularities, zeros and residues

1.5.1 Singularities and zeros

As indicated in Section 1.4.5 a **singularity** of a complex function $f(z)$ is a point of the z plane where $f(z)$ ceases to be analytic. Normally, this means $f(z)$ is infinite at such a point, but it can also mean that there is a choice of values, and it is not possible to pick a particular one. In this chapter we shall be mainly concerned with singularities at which $f(z)$ has an infinite value. A **zero** of $f(z)$ is a point in the z plane at which $f(z) = 0$.

Singularities can be classified in terms of the Laurent series expansion of $f(z)$ about the point in question. If $f(z)$ has a Taylor series expansion, that is a Laurent series expansion with zero principal part, about the point $z = z_0$, then z_0 is a **regular point** of $f(z)$. If $f(z)$ has a Laurent series expansion with only a finite number of terms in its principal part, for example

$$f(z) = \frac{a_{-m}}{(z-z_0)^m} + \ldots + \frac{a_{-1}}{(z-z_0)} + a_0 + a_1(z-z_0) + \ldots + a_m(z-z_0)^m + \ldots$$

then $f(z)$ has a singularity at $z = z_0$ called a **pole**. If there are m terms in the principal part, as in this example, then the pole is said to be of **order** m. Another way of defining this is to say that z_0 is a pole of order m if

$$\lim_{z \to z_0} (z-z_0)^m f(z) = a_{-m} \tag{1.35}$$

where a_{-m} is finite and non-zero. If the principal part of the Laurent series for $f(z)$ at $z = z_0$ has infinitely many terms, which means that the above limit does not exist for any m, then $z = z_0$ is called an **essential singularity** of $f(z)$. (Note that in Example 1.20 the expansions given as representations of the function $f(z) = 1/[(z+1)(z+3)]$ in parts (a) and (b) are ***not*** valid at $z = 0$. Hence, despite appearances, they do not represent a function which possesses an essential singularity at $z = 0$. In this case $f(z)$ is ***regular*** at $z = 0$ with a value $\frac{1}{3}$.)

If $f(z)$ appears to be singular at $z = z_0$, but it turns out to be possible to define a Taylor series expansion there, then $z = z_0$ is called a **removable singularity**. The following examples illustrate these cases.

(a) $f(z) = z^{-1}$ has a pole of order one, called a **simple pole**, at $z = 0$.

(b) $f(z) = (z - 1)^{-3}$ has a pole of order three at $z = 1$.

(c) $f(z) = e^{1/(z-j)}$ has an essential singularity at $z = j$.

(d) The function

$$f(z) = \frac{z - 1}{(z + 2)(z - 3)^2}$$

has a zero at $z = 1$, a simple pole at $z = -2$ and a pole of order two at $z = 3$.

(e) The function

$$f(z) = \frac{\sin z}{z}$$

is not defined at $z = 0$, and appears to be singular there. However, defining

$$\operatorname{sinc} z = \begin{cases} (\sin z)/z & (z \neq 0) \\ 1 & (z = 0) \end{cases}$$

gives a function having a Taylor series expansion

$$\operatorname{sinc} z = 1 - \frac{z^2}{3!} + \frac{z^4}{5!} - \dots$$

that is regular at $z = 0$. Therefore the (apparent) singularity at $z = 0$ has been removed, and thus $f(z) = (\sin z)/z$ has a removable singularity at $z = 0$.

Functions whose only singularities are poles are called **meromorphic** and, by and large, in engineering applications of complex variables most functions are meromorphic. To help familiarize the reader with these definitions, the following example should prove instructive.

Example 1.22 Find the singularities and zeros of the following complex functions:

(a) $\dfrac{1}{z^4 - z^2(1 + j) + j}$ (b) $\dfrac{z - 1}{z^4 - z^2(1 + j) + j}$

(c) $\dfrac{\sin(z - 1)}{z^4 - z^2(1 + j) + j}$ (d) $\dfrac{1}{[z^4 - z^2(1 + j) + j]^3}$

Solution (a) For

$$f(z) = \frac{1}{z^4 - z^2(1 + j) + j}$$

the numerator is never zero, and the denominator is only infinite when z is infinite. Thus $f(z)$ has no zeros in the finite z plane. The denominator is zero when

$$z^4 - z^2(1 + \mathrm{j}) + \mathrm{j} = 0$$

which factorizes to give

$$(z^2 - 1)(z^2 - \mathrm{j}) = 0$$

leading to

$$z^2 = 1 \text{ or } \mathrm{j}$$

so that the singularities are at

$$z = +1, -1, (1 + \mathrm{j})/\sqrt{2}, (-1 - \mathrm{j})/\sqrt{2} \tag{1.36}$$

all of which are simple poles since none of the roots are repeated.

(b) The function

$$f(z) = \frac{z - 1}{z^4 - z^2(1 + \mathrm{j}) + \mathrm{j}}$$

is similar to $f(z)$ in (a), except that it has the additional term $z - 1$ in the numerator. Therefore, at first glance, it seems that the singularities are as in (1.36). However, a closer look indicates that $f(z)$ can be rewritten as

$$f(z) = \frac{z - 1}{(z - 1)(z + 1)[z + \sqrt{\tfrac{1}{2}}(1 + \mathrm{j})]\,[z - \sqrt{\tfrac{1}{2}}(1 + \mathrm{j})]}$$

and the factor $z - 1$ cancels, rendering $z = 1$ a removable singularity, and reducing $f(z)$ to

$$f(z) = \frac{1}{(z + 1)[z + \sqrt{\tfrac{1}{2}}(1 + \mathrm{j})]\,[z - \sqrt{\tfrac{1}{2}}(1 + \mathrm{j})]}$$

which has no (finite) zeros and $z = -1$, $\sqrt{\tfrac{1}{2}}\,(1 + \mathrm{j})$ and $\sqrt{\tfrac{1}{2}}\,(-1 - \mathrm{j})$ as simple poles.

(c) In the case of

$$f(z) = \frac{\sin(z - 1)}{z^4 - z^2(1 + \mathrm{j}) + \mathrm{j}}$$

the function may be rewritten as

$$f(z) = \frac{\sin(z - 1)}{z - 1}\,\frac{1}{(z + 1)[z + \sqrt{\tfrac{1}{2}}(1 + \mathrm{j})]\,[z - \sqrt{\tfrac{1}{2}}(1 + \mathrm{j})]}$$

Now

$$\frac{\sin(z - 1)}{z - 1} \to 1 \quad \text{as} \quad z \to 1$$

so once again $z = 1$ is a removable singularity. Also, as in (b), $z = -1$, $\sqrt{\tfrac{1}{2}}\,(1 + \mathrm{j})$ and $\sqrt{\tfrac{1}{2}}\,(-1 - \mathrm{j})$ are simple poles and the only singularities. However,

$$\sin(z - 1) = 0$$

has the general solution $z = 1 + N\pi$ $(N = 0, \pm 1, \pm 2, \dots)$. Thus, apart from $N = 0$, all of these are zeros of $f(z)$.

(d) For

$$f(z) = \frac{1}{[z^4 - z^2(1 + j) + j]^3}$$

factorizing as in (b), we have

$$f(z) = \frac{1}{(z-1)^3(z+1)^3[z + \sqrt{\tfrac{1}{2}}(1+j)]^3[z - \sqrt{\tfrac{1}{2}}(1+j)]^3}$$

so -1, $+1$, $\sqrt{\tfrac{1}{2}}(1 + j)$ and $\sqrt{\tfrac{1}{2}}(-1 - j)$ are still singularities, but this time they are triply repeated. Hence they are all poles of order three. There are no zeros.

1.5.2 Exercises

47 Determine the location of, and classify, the singularities and zeros of the following functions. Specify also any zeros that may exist.

(a) $\dfrac{\cos z}{z^2}$ (b) $\dfrac{1}{(z+j)^2(z-j)}$ (c) $\dfrac{z}{z^4 - 1}$

(d) $\coth z$ (e) $\dfrac{\sin z}{z^2 + \pi^2}$ (f) $e^{z/(1-z)}$

(g) $\dfrac{z-1}{z^2+1}$ (h) $\dfrac{z+j}{(z+2)^3(z-3)}$

(i) $\dfrac{1}{z^2(z^2 - 4z + 5)}$

48 Expand each of the following functions in a Laurent series about $z = 0$, and give the type of singularity (if any) in each case:

(a) $\dfrac{1 - \cos z}{z}$

(b) $\dfrac{e^{z^2}}{z^3}$

(c) $z^{-1} \cosh z^{-1}$

(d) $\tan^{-1}(z^2 + 2z + 2)$

49 Show that if $f(z)$ is the ratio of two polynomials then it cannot have an essential singularity.

1.5.3 Residues

If a complex function $f(z)$ has a pole at the point $z = z_0$ then the coefficient a_{-1} of the term $1/(z - z_0)$ in the Laurent series expansion of $f(z)$ about $z = z_0$ is called the **residue** of $f(z)$ at the point $z = z_0$. The importance of residues will become apparent when we discuss integration in Section 1.6. Here we shall concentrate on efficient ways of calculating them, usually without finding the Laurent series expansion explicitly. However, experience and judgement are sometimes the only help in finding the easiest way of calculating residues. First let us consider the case when $f(z)$ has a simple pole at $z = z_0$. This implies, from the definition of a simple pole, that

$$f(z) = \frac{a_{-1}}{z - z_0} + a_0 + a_1(z - z_0) + \dots$$

in an appropriate annulus $S < |z - z_0| < R$. Multiplying by $z - z_0$ gives

$$(z - z_0)f(z) = a_{-1} + a_0(z - z_0) + \dots$$

which is a Taylor series expansion of $(z - z_0)f(z)$. If we let z approach z_0, we then obtain the result

$$\text{residue at a simple pole } z_0 = \lim_{z \to z_0} [(z - z_0)f(z)] = a_{-1} \quad (1.37)$$

Hence evaluating this limit gives a way of calculating the residue at a simple pole.

Example 1.23 Determine the residues of

$$f(z) = \frac{2z}{(z^2 + 1)(2z - 1)}$$

at each of its poles in the finite z plane.

Solution Factorizing the denominator, we have

$$f(z) = \frac{2z}{(z - \mathrm{j})(z + \mathrm{j})(2z - 1)}$$

so that $f(z)$ has simple poles at $z = \mathrm{j}$, $-\mathrm{j}$ and $\frac{1}{2}$. Using (1.37) then gives

$$\text{residue at } z = \mathrm{j} = \lim_{z \to \mathrm{j}} (z - \mathrm{j}) \frac{2z}{(z - \mathrm{j})(z + \mathrm{j})(2z - 1)}$$

$$= \frac{2\mathrm{j}}{2\mathrm{j}(2\mathrm{j} - 1)} = -\frac{1 + 2\mathrm{j}}{5}$$

$$\text{residue at } z = -\mathrm{j} = \lim_{z \to -\mathrm{j}} (z + \mathrm{j}) \frac{2z}{(z - \mathrm{j})(z + \mathrm{j})(2z - 1)}$$

$$= \frac{-2\mathrm{j}}{-2\mathrm{j}(-2\mathrm{j} - 1)} = -\frac{1 - 2\mathrm{j}}{5}$$

$$\text{residue at } z = \tfrac{1}{2} = \lim_{z \to \frac{1}{2}} (z - \tfrac{1}{2}) \frac{z}{(z - \mathrm{j})(z + \mathrm{j})(z - \frac{1}{2})}$$

$$= \frac{\frac{1}{2}}{(\frac{1}{2} - \mathrm{j})(\frac{1}{2} + \mathrm{j})} = \tfrac{2}{5}$$

Note in this last case the importance of expressing $2z - 1$ as $2(z - \frac{1}{2})$.

Example 1.24 Determine the residues of the function $1/(1 + z^4)$ at each of its poles in the finite z plane.

Solution The function $1/(1 + z^4)$ has poles where

$$1 + z^4 = 0$$

that is, at the points where

$$z^4 = -1 = \mathrm{e}^{\pi\mathrm{j} + 2\pi n\mathrm{j}}$$

with n an integer. Recalling how to determine the roots of a complex number, these points are

$$z = e^{\pi j/4 + \pi j n/2} \quad (n = 0, 1, 2, 3)$$

that is

$$z = e^{\pi j/4}, e^{3\pi j/4}, e^{5\pi j/4}, e^{7\pi j/4}$$

or

$$z = (1 + j)/\sqrt{2}, (-1 + j)/\sqrt{2}, (-1 - j)/\sqrt{2}, (1 - j)/\sqrt{2}$$

To find the residue at the point z_0, we use (1.37), giving

$$\begin{matrix}\text{residue}\\ \text{at } z_0\end{matrix} = \lim_{z\to z_0}\left(\frac{z - z_0}{1 + z^4}\right)$$

where z_0 is one of the above roots of $z^4 = -1$. It pays to use L'Hôpital's rule before substituting for a particular z_0. This is justified since $(z - z_0)/(1 + z_4)$ is of the indeterminate form 0/0 at each of the four simple poles. Differentiating numerator and denominator gives

$$\lim_{z\to z_0}\left(\frac{z - z_0}{1 + z^4}\right) = \lim_{z\to z_0}\left(\frac{1}{4z^3}\right)$$

$$= \frac{1}{4z_0^3}$$

since $4z^3$ is not zero at any of the poles; $1/4z_0^3$ is thus the value of each residue at $z = z_0$. Substituting for the four values $(\pm 1 \pm j)/\sqrt{2}$ gives the following:

$$\begin{matrix}\text{residue}\\ \text{at } z = (1 + j)/\sqrt{2}\end{matrix} = \frac{1}{4(\sqrt{\frac{1}{2}})^3(1 + j)^3} = -(1 + j)/4\sqrt{2}$$

$$\begin{matrix}\text{residue}\\ \text{at } z = (1 - j)/\sqrt{2}\end{matrix} = \frac{1}{4(\sqrt{\frac{1}{2}})^3(1 - j)^3} = (-1 + j)/4\sqrt{2}$$

$$\begin{matrix}\text{residue}\\ \text{at } z = (-1 + j)/\sqrt{2}\end{matrix} = \frac{1}{4(\sqrt{\frac{1}{2}})^3(-1 + j)^3} = (1 - j)/4\sqrt{2}$$

$$\begin{matrix}\text{residue}\\ \text{at } z = (-1 - j)/\sqrt{2}\end{matrix} = \frac{1}{4(\sqrt{\frac{1}{2}})^3(-1 - j)^3} = (1 + j)/4\sqrt{2}$$

Finding each Laurent series for the four poles explicitly would involve far more difficult manipulation. However, the enthusiastic reader may like to check at least one of the above residues.

Next suppose that we have a pole of order two at $z = z_0$. The function $f(z)$ then has a Laurent series expansion of the form

$$f(z) = \frac{a_{-2}}{(z - z_0)^2} + \frac{a_{-1}}{z - z_0} + a_0 + a_1(z - z_0) + \dots$$

Again, we are only interested in isolating the residue a_{-1}. This time we cannot use (1.37). Instead, we multiply $f(z)$ by $(z - z_0)^2$ to obtain

$$(z - z_0)^2 f(z) = a_{-2} + a_{-1}(z - z_0) + a_0(z - z_0)^2 + \dots$$

and we differentiate to eliminate the unwanted a_{-2}:

$$\frac{\mathrm{d}}{\mathrm{d}z}[(z - z_0)^2 f(z)] = a_{-1} + 2a_0(z - z_0) + \dots$$

Letting z tend to z_0 then gives

$$\lim_{z \to z_0} \left[\frac{\mathrm{d}}{\mathrm{d}z}(z - z_0)^2 f(z) \right] = a_{-1}$$

the required residue.

We now have the essence of finding residues, so let us recapitulate and generalize. If $f(z)$ has a pole of order m at $z = z_0$, we first multiply $f(z)$ by $(z - z_0)^m$. If $m \geqslant 2$, we then need to differentiate as many times as it takes (that is, $m - 1$ times) to make a_{-1} the leading term, without the multiplying factor $z - z_0$. The general formula for the residue at a pole of order m is thus

$$\frac{1}{(m-1)!} \lim_{z \to z_0} \left\{ \frac{\mathrm{d}^{m-1}}{\mathrm{d}z^{m-1}} [(z - z_0)^m f(z)] \right\} \tag{1.38}$$

where the factor $(m - 1)!$ arises when the term $a_{-1}(z - z_0)^{m-1}$ is differentiated $m - 1$ times. This formula looks as difficult to apply as finding the Laurent series expansion directly. This indeed is often so; and hence experience and judgement are required. A few examples will help to decide on which way to calculate residues. A word of warning is in order here: a common source of error is confusion between the derivative in the formula for the residue, and the employment of L'Hôpital's rule to find the resulting limit.

Example 1.25 Determine the residues of

$$f(z) = \frac{z^2 - 2z}{(z + 1)^2(z^2 + 4)}$$

at each of its poles in the finite z plane.

Solution Factorizing the denominator gives

$$f(z) = \frac{z^2 - 2z}{(z + 1)^2(z - 2\mathrm{j})(z + 2\mathrm{j})}$$

so that $f(z)$ has simple poles at $z = 2\mathrm{j}$ and $z = -2\mathrm{j}$ and a pole of order two at $z = -1$. Using (1.37),

$$\begin{aligned}\text{residue at } z = 2j &= \lim_{z\to 2j} (z-2j)\frac{z^2-2z}{(z+1)^2(z-2j)(z+2j)} \\ &= \frac{-4-4j}{(2j+1)^2(4j)} = \tfrac{1}{25}(7+j)\end{aligned}$$

$$\begin{aligned}\text{residue at } z = -2j &= \lim_{z\to -2j} (z+2j)\frac{z^2-2z}{(z+1)^2(z-2j)(z+2j)} \\ &= \frac{-4+4j}{(-2j+1)^2(-4j)} = \tfrac{1}{25}(7-j)\end{aligned}$$

Using (1.38) with $m = 2$ we know that

$$\begin{aligned}\text{residue at } z = -1 &= \frac{1}{1!}\lim_{z\to -1}\frac{d}{dz}\left[(z+1)^2\frac{z^2-2z}{(z+1)^2(z^2+4)}\right] \\ &= \lim_{z\to -1}\frac{(z^2+4)(2z-2)-(z^2-2z)(2z)}{(z^2+4)^2} = \frac{(5)(-4)-(3)(-2)}{25} = -\tfrac{14}{25}\end{aligned}$$

Example 1.26 Determine the residues of the following functions at the points indicated:

(a) $\dfrac{e^z}{(1+z^2)^2}$ $(z = j)$ (b) $\left(\dfrac{\sin z}{z^2}\right)^3$ $(z = 0)$ (c) $\dfrac{z^4}{(z+1)^3}$ $(z = -1)$

Solution (a) Since

$$\frac{e^z}{(z^2+1)^2} = \frac{e^z}{(z+j)^2(z-j)^2}$$

and e^z is regular at $z = j$, it follows that $z = j$ is a pole of order two. Thus, from (1.38),

$$\begin{aligned}\text{residue} &= \lim_{z\to j}\frac{d}{dz}\left[(z-j)^2\frac{e^z}{(z+j)^2(z-j)^2}\right] \\ &= \lim_{z\to j}\left\{\frac{d}{dz}\left[\frac{e^z}{(z+j)^2}\right]\right\} = \lim_{z\to j}\frac{(z+j)^2e^z-2(z+j)e^z}{(z+j)^4} \\ &= \frac{(2j)^2e^j-2(2j)e^j}{(2j)^4} = -\tfrac{1}{4}(1+j)e^j\end{aligned}$$

Since $e^j = \cos 1 + j\sin 1$, we calculate the residue at $z = j$ as $0.075 - j0.345$.

(b) The function $[(\sin z)/z^2]^3$ has a pole at $z = 0$, and, since $(\sin z/z) \to 1$ as $z \to 0$, $(\sin^2 z)/z^2$ may also be defined as 1 at $z = 0$. Therefore, since

$$\left(\frac{\sin z}{z^2}\right)^3 = \frac{\sin^3 z}{z^3}\frac{1}{z^3}$$

the singularity at $z = 0$ must be a pole of order three. We could use (1.38) to obtain the residue, which would involve determining the second derivative, but it is easier in this case to derive the coefficient of $1/z$ from the Laurent series expansion

$$\frac{\sin z}{z} = 1 - \frac{z^2}{3!} + \frac{z^4}{5!} - \ldots$$

giving

$$\frac{\sin z}{z^2} = \frac{1}{z} - \tfrac{1}{6}z + \tfrac{1}{120}z^3 - \ldots$$

Taking the cube of this series, we have

$$\left(\frac{\sin z}{z^2}\right)^3 = \left(\frac{1}{z} - \tfrac{1}{6}z + \tfrac{1}{120}z^3 - \ldots\right)^3 = \frac{1}{z^3} - 3\frac{1}{z^2}\frac{z}{6} + \ldots = \frac{1}{z^3} - \frac{1}{2z} + \ldots$$

Hence the residue at $z = 0$ is $-\frac{1}{2}$.

(c) The function $z^4/(z + 1)^3$ has a triple pole at $z = -1$, so, using (1.38),

$$\text{residue} = \lim_{z\to-1}\left\{\tfrac{1}{2}\frac{d^2}{dz^2}\left[(z+1)^3\frac{z^4}{(z+1)^3}\right]\right\} = \lim_{z\to-1}\left[\tfrac{1}{2}\frac{d^2}{dz^2}(z^4)\right]$$

$$= \lim_{z\to-1}\tfrac{1}{2}\times 4\times 3z^2 = 6(-1)^2 = 6$$

Residues are sometimes difficult to calculate using (1.38), especially if circular functions are involved and the pole is of order three or more. In such cases direct calculation of the Laurent series expansion using the standard series for $\sin z$ and $\cos z$ together with the binomial series, as in Example 1.26(b), is the best procedure.

Exercises

50 Determine the residues of the following rational functions at each pole in the finite z plane:

(a) $\dfrac{2z+1}{z^2-z-2}$ (b) $\dfrac{1}{z^2(1-z)}$

(c) $\dfrac{3z^2+2}{(z-1)(z^2+9)}$ (d) $\dfrac{z^3-z^2+z-1}{z^3+4z}$

(e) $\dfrac{z^6+4z^4+z^3+1}{(z-1)^5}$ (f) $\left(\dfrac{z+1}{z-1}\right)^2$

(g) $\dfrac{z+1}{(z-1)^2(z+3)}$ (h) $\dfrac{3+4z}{z^3+3z^2+2z}$

51 Calculate the residues at the simple poles indicated of the following functions:

(a) $\dfrac{\cos z}{z}$ $(z = 0)$ (b) $\dfrac{\sin z}{z^4+z^2+1}$ $(z = e^{\pi j/3})$

(c) $\dfrac{z^4-1}{z^4+1}$ $(z = e^{\pi j/4})$ (d) $\dfrac{z}{\sin z}$ $(z = \pi)$

(e) $\dfrac{1}{(z^2+1)^2}$ $(z = j)$

52 The following functions have poles at the points indicated. Determine the order of the pole and the residue there.

(a) $\dfrac{\cos z}{z^3}$ $(z = 0)$

(b) $\dfrac{z^2-2z}{(z+1)^2(z^2+4)}$ $(z = -1)$

(c) $\dfrac{e^z}{\sin^2 z}$ $(z = n\pi$, n an integer)

(*Hint*: use $\lim_{u\to0}(\sin u)/u = 1$ $(u = z - n\pi)$, after differentiating, to replace $\sin u$ by u under the limit.)

1.6 Contour integration

Consider the definite integral

$$\int_{z_1}^{z_2} f(z)\,dz$$

of the function $f(z)$ of a complex variable z, in which z_1 and z_2 are a pair of complex numbers. This implies that we evaluate the integral as z takes values, in the z plane, from the point z_1 to the point z_2. Since these are two points in a plane, it follows that to evaluate the definite integral we require that some path from z_1 to z_2 be defined. It is therefore clear that a definite integral of a complex function $f(z)$ is in fact a **line integral**.

Briefly, for now, a line integral in the (x, y) plane, of the real variables x and y, is an integral of the form

$$\int_C [P(x, y)\,dx + Q(x, y)\,dy] \tag{1.39}$$

where C denotes the path of integration between two points A and B in the plane. In the particular case when

$$\frac{\partial P}{\partial y} = \frac{\partial Q}{\partial x} \tag{1.40}$$

the integrand $P(x, y)\,dx + Q(x, y)\,dy$ is a total differential, and the line integral is independent of the path C joining A and B.

In this section we introduce **contour integration**, which is the term used for evaluating line integrals in the complex plane.

1.6.1 Contour integrals

Let $f(z)$ be a complex function that is continuous at all points of a simple curve C in the z plane that is of finite length and joins two points a and b. (We have not gone into great detail regarding the question of continuity for complex variables. Suffice it to say that the intuitive concepts for real variables carry over to the case of complex variables.) Subdivide the curve into n parts by the points $z_1, z_2, \dots, z_{n-1}$, taking $z_0 = a$ and $z_n = b$ (Figure 1.25). On each arc joining z_{k-1} to z_k ($k = 1, \dots, n$) choose a point $\tilde{z}_k$. Form the sum

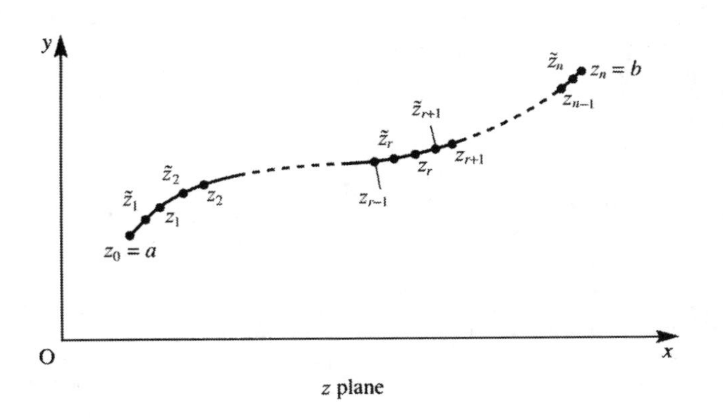

Figure 1.25 Partitioning of the curve C.

$$S_n = f(\tilde{z}_1)(z_1 - z_0) + f(\tilde{z}_2)(z_2 - z_1) + \ldots + f(\tilde{z}_n)(z_n - z_{n-1})$$

Then, writing $z_k - z_{k-1} = \Delta z_k$, S_n becomes

$$S_n = \sum_{k=1}^{n} f(\tilde{z}_k)\,\Delta z_k$$

If we let n increase in such a way that the largest of the chord lengths $|\Delta z_k|$ approaches zero then the sum S_n approaches a limit that does not depend on the mode of subdivision of the curve. We call this limit the **contour integral** of $f(z)$ along the curve C:

$$\int_C f(z)\,\mathrm{d}z = \lim_{|\Delta z_k| \to 0} \sum_{k=1}^{n} f(\tilde{z}_k)\,\Delta z_k \qquad \textbf{(1.41)}$$

If we take $z = x + \mathrm{j}y$ and express $f(z)$ as

$$f(z) = u(x, y) + \mathrm{j}v(x, y)$$

then it can be shown from (1.41) that

$$\int_C f(z)\,\mathrm{d}z = \int_C [u(x, y) + \mathrm{j}v(x, y)](\mathrm{d}x + \mathrm{j}\,\mathrm{d}y)$$

or

$$\int_C f(z)\,\mathrm{d}z = \int_C [u(x, y)\,\mathrm{d}x - v(x, y)\,\mathrm{d}y] + \mathrm{j}\int_C [v(x, y)\,\mathrm{d}x + u(x, y)\,\mathrm{d}y] \qquad \textbf{(1.42)}$$

Both of the integrals on the right-hand side of (1.42) are real line integrals of the form (1.39), and can therefore be evaluated using the methods developed for such integrals.

Example 1.27

Evaluate the contour integral $\int_C z^2 \mathrm{d}z$ along the path C from $-1 + \mathrm{j}$ to $5 + \mathrm{j}3$ and composed of two straight line segments, the first from $-1 + \mathrm{j}$ to $5 + \mathrm{j}$ and the second from $5 + \mathrm{j}$ to $5 + \mathrm{j}3$.

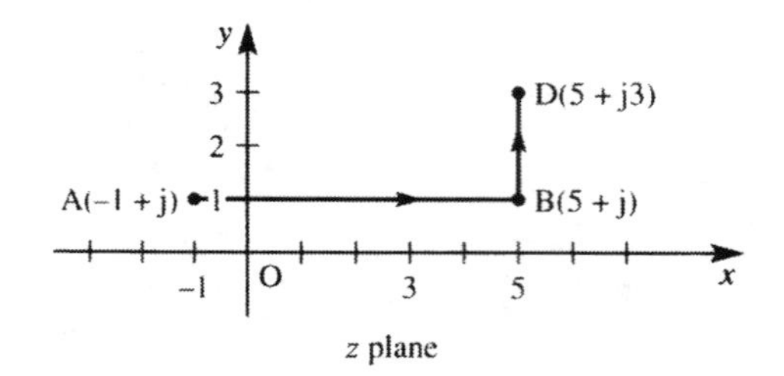

Figure 1.26 Path of integration for Example 1.27.

Solution The path of integration C is shown in Figure 1.26. Since

$$z^2 = (x + \mathrm{j}y)^2 = (x^2 - y^2) + \mathrm{j}2xy$$

it follows from (1.42) that

$$I = \int_C z^2\,dz = \int_C [(x^2 - y^2)\,dx - 2xy\,dy] + j\int_C [2xy\,dx + (x^2 - y^2)\,dy]$$

Along AB, $y = 1$ and $dy = 0$, so that

$$I_{AB} = \int_{-1}^{5} (x^2 - 1)\,dx + j\int_{-1}^{5} 2x\,dx$$

$$= [\tfrac{1}{3}x^3 - x]_{-1}^{5} + j[x^2]_{-1}^{5} = 36 + j24$$

Along BD, $x = 5$ and $dx = 0$, so that

$$I_{BD} = \int_{1}^{3} -10y\,dy + j\int_{1}^{3} (25 - y^2)\,dy$$

$$= [-5y^2]_1^3 + j[25y - \tfrac{1}{3}y^3]_1^3$$

$$= -40 + j\tfrac{124}{3}$$

Thus

$$\int_C z^2\,dz = I_{AB} + I_{BD} = (36 + j24) + (-40 + j\tfrac{124}{3}) = -4 + j\tfrac{196}{3}$$

Example 1.28

Show that $\int_C (z + 1)\,dz = 0$, where C is the boundary of the square with vertices at $z = 0$, $z = 1 + j0$, $z = 1 + j1$ and $z = 0 + j1$.

Solution

The path of integration C is shown in Figure 1.27.

Since $z + 1 = (x + 1) + jy$, it follows from (1.42) that

$$I = \int_C (z + 1)\,dz = \int_C [(x + 1)\,dx - y\,dy] + j\int_C [y\,dx + (x + 1)\,dy]$$

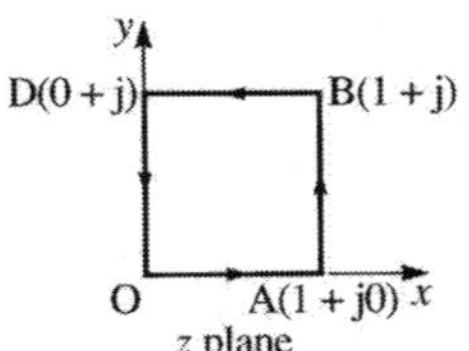

Figure 1.27 Path of integration for Example 1.28.

Along OA, $y = 0$ and $dy = 0$, so that

$$I_{OA} = \int_0^1 (x + 1)\,dx = \tfrac{3}{2}$$

Along AB, $x = 1$ and $dx = 0$, so that

$$I_{AB} = \int_0^1 -y\,dy + j\int_0^1 2\,dy = -\tfrac{1}{2} + j2$$

Along BD, $y = 1$ and $dy = 0$, so that

$$I_{BD} = \int_1^0 (x + 1)\,dx + j\int_1^0 dx = -\tfrac{3}{2} - j$$

Along DO, $x = 0$ and $dx = 0$, so that

$$I_{DO} = \int_1^0 -y\,dy + j\int_1^0 dx = \tfrac{1}{2} - j$$

Thus

$$\int_C (z+1)\,dz = I_{OA} + I_{AB} + I_{BD} + I_{DO} = 0$$

1.6.2 Cauchy's theorem

The most important result in the whole of complex variable theory is called Cauchy's theorem and it provides the foundation on which the theory of integration with respect to a complex variable is based. The theorem may be stated as follows.

Theorem 1.1 **Cauchy's theorem**

If $f(z)$ is an analytic function with derivative $f'(z)$ that is continuous at all points inside and on a simple closed curve C then

$$\oint_C f(z)\,dz = 0$$

(Note the use of the symbol $\oint_C$ to denote integration around a closed curve, with the convention being that the integral is evaluated travelling round C in the positive or anticlockwise direction.)

Proof To prove the theorem, we make use of **Green's theorem** in a plane. At this stage a statement of the theorem is sufficient.

If C is a simple closed curve enclosing a region A in a plane, and $P(x, y)$ and $Q(x, y)$ are continuous functions with continuous partial derivatives, then

$$\oint_C (P\,dx + Q\,dy) = \iint_A \left(\frac{\partial Q}{\partial x} - \frac{\partial P}{\partial y}\right) dx\,dy \tag{1.43}$$

Returning to the contour integral and taking

$$f(z) = u(x, y) + jv(x, y), \qquad z = x + jy$$

we have from (1.42)

$$\oint_C f(z)\,dz = \oint_C (u\,dx - v\,dy) + j\oint_C (v\,dx + u\,dy) \tag{1.44}$$

Since $f(z)$ is analytic, the Cauchy–Riemann equations

$$\frac{\partial u}{\partial x} = \frac{\partial v}{\partial y}, \qquad \frac{\partial v}{\partial x} = -\frac{\partial u}{\partial y}$$

are satisfied on C and within the region R enclosed by C.

Since $u(x, y)$ and $v(x, y)$ satisfy the conditions imposed on $P(x, y)$ and $Q(x, y)$ in Green's theorem, we can apply (1.43) to both integrals on the right-hand side of (1.44) to give

$$\oint_C f(z)\,dz = \iint_R \left(-\frac{\partial v}{\partial x} - \frac{\partial u}{\partial y}\right) dx\,dy + j\iint_R \left(\frac{\partial u}{\partial x} - \frac{\partial v}{\partial y}\right) dx\,dy = 0 + j0$$

by the Cauchy–Riemann equations. Thus

$$\oint_C f(z)\,dz = 0$$

as required.

end of theorem

In fact, the restriction in Cauchy's theorem that $f'(z)$ has to be continuous on C can be removed and so make the theorem applicable to a wider class of functions. A revised form of Theorem 1.1, with the restriction removed, is referred to as the **fundamental theorem of complex integration**. Since the proof that $f'(z)$ need not be continuous on C was first proposed by Goursat, the fundamental theorem is also sometimes referred to as the **Cauchy–Goursat theorem**. We shall not pursue the consequences of relaxation of this restriction any further in this book.

In practice, we frequently need to evaluate contour integrals involving functions such as

$$f_1(z) = \frac{1}{z-2}, \qquad f_2(z) = \frac{z}{(z-3)^2(z+2)}$$

that have singularities associated with them. Since the function ceases to be analytic at such points, how do we accommodate for a singularity if it is inside the contour of integration? To resolve the problem the singularity is removed by **deforming the contour**.

First let us consider the case when the complex function $f(z)$ has a single isolated singularity at $z = z_0$ inside a closed curve C. To remove the singularity, we surround it by a circle γ, of radius ρ, and then cut the region between the circle and the outer contour C by a straight line AB. This leads to the deformed contour indicated by the arrows in Figure 1.28. In the figure the line linking the circle γ to the contour C is shown as a narrow channel in order to enable us to distinguish between the path A to B and the path B to A. The region inside this deformed contour is shown shaded in the figure (recall that the region inside a closed contour is the region on the left as we travel round it). Since this contains no singularities, we can apply Cauchy's theorem and write

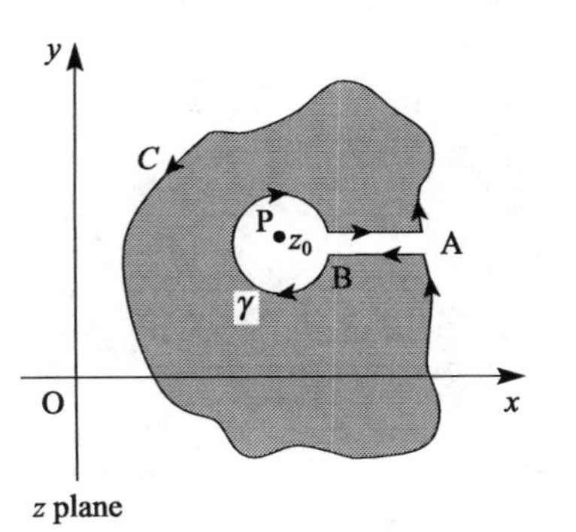

Figure 1.28 Deformed contour for an isolated singularity.

$$\oint_C f(z)\,dz + \int_{AB} f(z)\,dz + \oint_\gamma f(z)\,dz + \oint_{BA} f(z)\,dz = 0$$

Since

$$\oint_{BA} = -\oint_{AB}, \quad \text{and} \quad \oint_\gamma = -\oint_\gamma$$

this reduces to

$$\oint_C f(z)\,dz = \oint_{\gamma^+} f(z)\,dz \tag{1.45}$$

with the + indicating the change of sense from clockwise to anticlockwise around the circle γ.

Example 1.29

Evaluate the integral $\oint_C dz/z$ around

(a) any contour containing the origin;

(b) any contour not containing the origin.

Solution

(a) $f(z) = 1/z$ has a singularity (a simple pole) at $z = 0$. Hence, using (1.45), the integral around any contour enclosing the origin is the same as the integral around a circle γ, centred at the origin and of radius ρ_0. We thus need to evaluate

$$\oint_\gamma \frac{1}{z}\,dz$$

As can be seen from Figure 1.29, on the circle γ

$$z = \rho_0\,e^{j\theta} \ (0 \leqslant \theta < 2\pi)$$

so

$$dz = j\rho_0\,e^{j\theta}\,d\theta$$

leading to

$$\oint_\gamma \frac{1}{z}\,dz = \int_0^{2\pi} \frac{j\rho_0\,e^{j\theta}}{\rho_0\,e^{j\theta}}\,d\theta = \int_0^{2\pi} j\,d\theta = 2\pi j$$

Hence if C encloses the origin then

$$\oint_C \frac{dz}{z} = 2\pi j$$

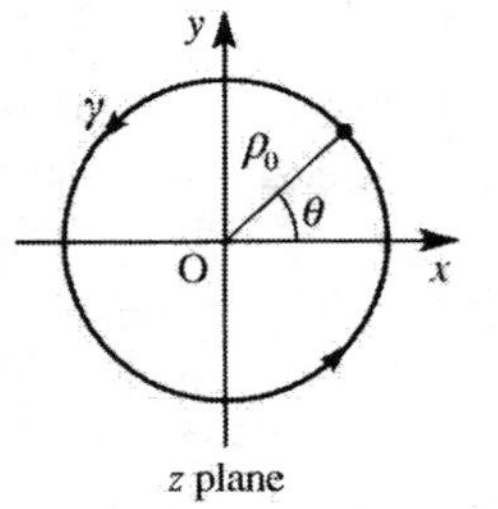

Figure 1.29 A circle of radius ρ_0 centred at the origin.

(b) If C does not enclose the origin then, by Cauchy's theorem,

$$\oint_C \frac{dz}{z} = 0$$

since $1/z$ is analytic inside and on any curve that does not enclose the origin.

Example 1.30 Generalize the result of Example 1.29 by evaluating

$$\oint_C \frac{dz}{z^n}$$

where n is an integer, around any contour containing the origin.

Solution If $n \leqslant 0$, we can apply Cauchy's theorem straight away (or evaluate the integral directly) to show the integral is zero. If $n > 1$, we proceed as in Example 1.29 and evaluate the integral around a circle, centred at the origin. Taking $z = \rho_0 e^{j\theta}$ as in Example 1.29, we have

$$\oint_C \frac{dz}{z^n} = \int_0^{2\pi} \frac{j\rho_0 e^{j\theta}}{\rho_0^n e^{nj\theta}} d\theta$$

where ρ_0 is once more the radius of the circle. If $n \neq 1$,

$$\oint_C \frac{dz}{z^n} = j\int_0^{2\pi} \frac{d\theta}{\rho_0^{n-1} e^{(n-1)j\theta}} = j\rho_0^{1-n}\left[\frac{e^{(1-n)j\theta}}{(1-n)j}\right]_0^{2\pi} = \frac{\rho_0^{1-n}}{1-n}(e^{(1-n)2\pi j} - 1) = 0$$

since $e^{2\pi jN} = 1$ for any integer N. Hence

$$\oint_C \frac{dz}{z^n} = 0 \quad (n \neq 1)$$

In Examples 1.29 and 1.30 we have thus established the perhaps surprising result that if C is a contour containing the origin then

$$\oint_C \frac{dz}{z^n} = \begin{cases} 2\pi j & (n = 1) \\ 0 & (n \text{ any other integer}) \end{cases}$$

If C does not contain the origin, the integral is of course zero by Cauchy's theorem.

Example 1.31 Evaluate the integral

$$\oint_C \frac{dz}{z - 2 - j}$$

around any contour C containing the point $z = 2 + j$.

Solution The function

$$f(z) = \frac{1}{z - 2 - j}$$

has a singularity (simple pole) at $z = 2 + j$. Hence, using (1.45), the integral around any contour C enclosing the point $z = 2 + j$ is the same as the integral around a circle γ centred at $z = 2 + j$ and of radius ρ. Thus we need to evaluate

$$\oint_\gamma \frac{dz}{z - 2 - j}$$

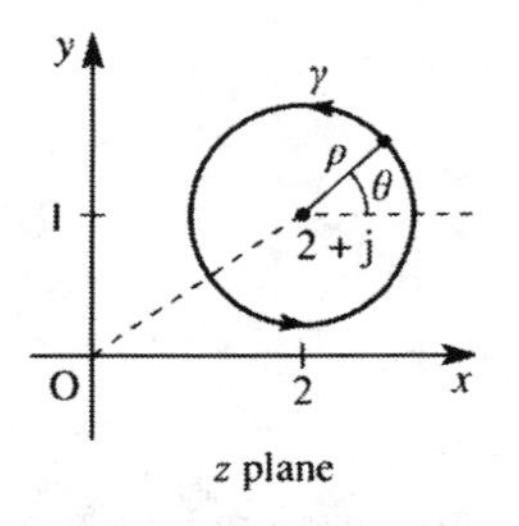

Figure 1.30 A circle of radius ρ centred at $2 + \mathrm{j}$.

As can be seen from Figure 1.30, on the circle γ

$$z = (2 + \mathrm{j}) + \rho\mathrm{e}^{\mathrm{j}\theta} \quad (0 \leqslant \theta < 2\pi)$$

$$\mathrm{d}z = \mathrm{j}\rho\mathrm{e}^{\mathrm{j}\theta}\,\mathrm{d}\theta$$

leading to

$$\oint_{\gamma} \frac{\mathrm{d}z}{z - 2 - \mathrm{j}} = \int_{0}^{2\pi} \frac{\mathrm{j}\rho\,\mathrm{e}^{\mathrm{j}\theta}}{\rho\,\mathrm{e}^{\mathrm{j}\theta}}\,\mathrm{d}\theta = \int_{0}^{2\pi} \mathrm{j}\,\mathrm{d}\theta = 2\pi\mathrm{j}$$

Hence if C encloses the point $z = 2 + \mathrm{j}$ then

$$\oint_{C} \frac{\mathrm{d}z}{z - 2 - \mathrm{j}} = 2\pi\mathrm{j}$$

Compare this with the answer to Example 1.29.

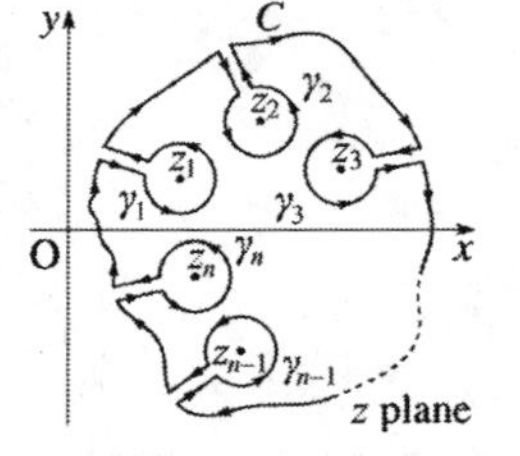

Figure 1.31 Deformed contour for n singularities.

So far we have only considered functions having a single singularity inside the closed contour C. The method can be extended to accommodate any finite number of singularities. If the function $f(z)$ has a finite number of singularities at $z = z_1, z_2, \ldots, z_n$, inside a closed contour C, then we can deform the latter by introducing n circles $\gamma_1, \gamma_2, \ldots, \gamma_n$ to surround each of the singularities as shown in Figure 1.31. It is then readily shown that

$$\oint_{C} f(z)\,\mathrm{d}z = \oint_{\gamma_1} f(z)\,\mathrm{d}z + \oint_{\gamma_2} f(z)\,\mathrm{d}z + \ldots + \oint_{\gamma_n} f(z)\,\mathrm{d}z \tag{1.46}$$

Example 1.32

Evaluate the contour integral

$$\oint_{C} \frac{z\,\mathrm{d}z}{(z - 1)(z + 2\mathrm{j})}$$

where C is

(a) any contour enclosing both the points $z = 1$ and $z = -2\mathrm{j}$;

(b) any contour enclosing $z = -2\mathrm{j}$ but excluding the point $z = 1$.

Solution The function

$$f(z) = \frac{z}{(z - 1)(z + 2\mathrm{j})}$$

has singularities at both $z = 1$ and $z = -2\mathrm{j}$.

(a) Since the contour encloses both singularities, we need to evaluate the integrals around circles γ_1 and γ_2 of radii ρ_1 and ρ_2 surrounding the points $z = 1$ and $z = -2\mathrm{j}$ respectively. Alternatively, we can resolve $f(z)$ into partial fractions as

$$f(z) = \frac{\frac{1}{5}(1 - \mathrm{j}2)}{z - 1} + \frac{\frac{1}{5}(4 + 2\mathrm{j})}{z + 2\mathrm{j}}$$

and consider

$$I = \oint_C \frac{z\,dz}{(z-1)(2-2j)} = \tfrac{1}{3}(1-2j)\oint_C \frac{dz}{z-1} + \tfrac{1}{5}(4+2j)\oint_C \frac{dz}{z+2j} = I_1 + I_2$$

The integrand of I_1 has a single singularity at $z = 1$, and we simply need to evaluate it around the circle γ_1 of radius ρ_1 about $z = 1$ to give

$$I_1 = 2\pi j$$

Similarly, I_2 has a single singularity at $z = -2j$, and we evaluate it around the circle γ_2 to give

$$I_2 = 2\pi j$$

Then

$$I = \tfrac{1}{3}(1 - j2)2\pi j + \tfrac{1}{5}(4 + j2)2\pi j = 2\pi j(\tfrac{17}{15} - j\tfrac{4}{15})$$

Thus if the contour C contains both the singularities then

$$\oint_C \frac{z\,dz}{(z-1)(z+j2)} = 2\pi j(\tfrac{17}{15} - j\tfrac{4}{15})$$

(b) If the contour C only contains the singularity $z = -2j$ then

$$\oint_C \frac{z\,dz}{(z-1)(z+2j)} = I_2 = 2\pi j(\tfrac{4}{5} + j\tfrac{2}{5})$$

In Examples 1.29–1.32 we can note some similarity in the answers, with the common occurrence of the term $2\pi j$. It therefore appears that it may be possible to obtain some general results to assist in the evaluation of contour integrals. Indeed, this is the case, and such general results are contained in the **Cauchy integral theorem**.

Theorem 1.2 **Cauchy integral theorem**

Let $f(z)$ be an analytic function within and on a simple closed contour C. If z_0 is any point in C then

$$\oint_C \frac{f(z)}{z-z_0}\,dz = 2\pi j\,f(z_0) \tag{1.47}$$

If we differentiate repeatedly n times with respect to z under the integral sign then it also follows that

$$\oint_C \frac{f(z)}{(z-z_0)^{n+1}}\,dz = \frac{2\pi j}{n!}\,f^{(n)}(z_0) \tag{1.48}$$

end of theorem

Note that (1.48) implies that if $f'(z)$ exists at $z = z_0$ so does $f^{(n)}(z)$ for all n, as predicted earlier in the observations following Example 1.16.

Example 1.33 Evalute the contour integral

$$\oint_C \frac{2z}{(z-1)(z+2)(z+\mathrm{j})}\,\mathrm{d}z$$

where C is a contour that includes the three points $z = 1$, $z = -2$ and $z = -\mathrm{j}$.

Solution Since

$$f(z) = \frac{2z}{(z-1)(z+2)(z+\mathrm{j})}$$

has singularities at the points $z = 1$, $z = -2$ and $z = -\mathrm{j}$ inside the contour, it follows from (1.46) that

$$\oint_C f(z)\,\mathrm{d}z = \oint_{\gamma_1} f(z)\,\mathrm{d}z + \oint_{\gamma_2} f(z)\,\mathrm{d}z + \oint_{\gamma_3} f(z)\,\mathrm{d}z \tag{1.49}$$

where γ_1, γ_2 and γ_3 are circles centred at the singularities $z = 1$, $z = -2$ and $z = -\mathrm{j}$ respectively. In order to make use of the Cauchy integral theorem, (1.49) is written as

$$\oint_C f(z)\,\mathrm{d}z = \oint_{\gamma_1} \frac{\{2z/[(z+2)(z+\mathrm{j})]\}}{z-1}\,\mathrm{d}z + \oint_{\gamma_2} \frac{\{2z/[(z-1)(z+\mathrm{j})]\}}{z+2}\,\mathrm{d}z$$

$$+ \oint_{\gamma_3} \frac{\{2z/[(z-1)(z+2)]\}}{z+\mathrm{j}}\,\mathrm{d}z$$

$$= \oint_{\gamma_1} \frac{f_1(z)}{z-1}\,\mathrm{d}z + \oint_{\gamma_2} \frac{f_2(z)}{z+2}\,\mathrm{d}z + \oint_{\gamma_3} \frac{f_3(z)}{z+\mathrm{j}}\,\mathrm{d}z$$

Since $f_1(z)$, $f_2(z)$ and $f_3(z)$ are analytic within and on the circles γ_1, γ_2 and γ_3 respectively, it follows from (1.47) that

$$\oint_C f(z)\,\mathrm{d}z = 2\pi\mathrm{j}[f_1(1) + f_2(-2) + f_3(-\mathrm{j})]$$

$$= 2\pi\mathrm{j}\left[\frac{3}{2(1+\mathrm{j})} + \frac{-4}{(-3)(-2+\mathrm{j})} + \frac{-2\mathrm{j}}{(-\mathrm{j}-1)(-\mathrm{j}+2)}\right]$$

so that

$$\oint_C \frac{2z\,\mathrm{d}z}{(z-1)(z+2)(z+\mathrm{j})} = 0$$

Example 1.34 Evaluate the contour integral

$$\oint_C \frac{z^4}{(z-1)^3}\,\mathrm{d}z$$

where the contour C encloses the point $z = 1$.

Solution Since $f(z) = z^4/(z-1)^3$ has a pole of order three at $z = 1$, it follows that

$$\oint_C f(z)\,\mathrm{d}z = \oint_{\gamma} \frac{z^4}{(z-1)^3}\,\mathrm{d}z$$

where γ is a circle centred at $z = 1$. Writing $f_1(z) = z^4$, then

$$\oint_C f(z)\,dz = \oint_\gamma \frac{f_1(z)}{(z-1)^3}\,dz$$

and, since $f_1(z)$ is analytic within and on the circle γ, it follows from (1.48) that

$$\oint_C f(z)\,dz = 2\pi j \frac{1}{2!}\left[\frac{d^2}{dz^2} f_1(z)\right]_{z=1} = \pi j(12z^2)_{z=1}$$

so that

$$\oint_C \frac{z^4}{(z-1)^3}\,dz = 12\pi j$$

1.6.3 Exercises

53 Evaluate $\int_C (z^2 + 3z)\,dz$ along the following contours C in the complex z plane:

(a) the straight line joining $2 + j0$ to $0 + j2$;
(b) the straight lines from $2 + j0$ to $2 + j2$ and then to $0 + j2$;
(c) the circle $|z| = 2$ from $2 + j0$ to $0 + j2$ in an anticlockwise direction.

54 Evaluate $\oint_C (5z^4 - z^3 + 2)\,dz$ around the following closed contours C in the z plane:

(a) the circle $|z| = 1$;
(b) the square with vertices at $0 + j0$, $1 + j0$, $1 + j1$ and $0 + j1$;
(c) the curve consisting of the parabolas $y = x^2$ from $0 + j0$ to $1 + j1$ and $y^2 = x$ from $1 + j$ to $0 + j0$.

55 Generalize the result of Example 1.30, and show that

$$\oint_C \frac{dz}{(z-z_0)^n} = \begin{cases} j2\pi & (n = 1) \\ 0 & (n \neq 1) \end{cases}$$

where C is a simple closed contour surrounding the point $z = z_0$.

56 Evaluate the contour integral

$$\oint_C \frac{dz}{z-4}$$

where C is any simple closed curve and $z = 4$ is

(a) outside C (b) inside C

57 Using the Cauchy integral theorem, evaluate the contour integral

$$\oint_C \frac{2z\,dz}{(2z-1)(z+2)}$$

where C is

(a) the circle $|z| = 1$
(b) the circle $|z| = 3$

58 Using the Cauchy integral theorem, evaluate the contour integral

$$\oint_C \frac{5z\,dz}{(z+1)(z-2)(z+4j)}$$

where C is

(a) the circle $|z| = 3$
(b) the circle $|z| = 5$

59 Using the Cauchy integral theorem, evaluate the following contour integrals:

(a) $$\oint_C \frac{z^3+z}{(2z+1)^3}\,dz$$

where C is the unit circle $|z| = 1$;

(b) $$\oint_C \frac{4z}{(z-1)(z+2)^2}\,dz$$

where C is the circle $|z| = 3$.

1.6.4 The residue theorem

This theorem draws together the theories of differentiation and integration of a complex function. It is concerned with the evaluation of the contour integral

$$I = \oint_C f(z)\,dz$$

where the complex function $f(z)$ has a finite number n of isolated singularities at z_1, $z_2, \dots, z_n$ inside the closed contour C. Defining the contour C as in Figure 1.31, we have as in (1.46) that

$$I = \oint_C f(z)\,dz = \oint_{\gamma_1} f(z)\,dz + \oint_{\gamma_2} f(z)\,dz + \dots + \oint_{\gamma_n} f(z)\,dz \qquad \textbf{(1.46)}$$

If we assume that $f(z)$ has a pole of order m at $z = z_i$ then it can be represented by the Laurent series expansion

$$f(z) = \frac{a_{-m}^{(i)}}{(z - z_i)^m} + \dots + \frac{a_{-1}^{(i)}}{z - z_i} + a_0^{(i)} + a_1^{(i)}(z - z_i) + \dots + a_m^{(i)}(z - z_i)^m + \dots$$

valid in the annulus $r_i < |z - z_i| < R_i$. If the curve C lies entirely within this annulus then, by Cauchy's theorem, (1.46) becomes

$$I = \oint_C f(z)\,dz = \oint_{\gamma_i} f(z)\,dz$$

Substituting the Laurent series expansion of $f(z)$, which we can certainly do since we are within the annulus of convergence, we obtain

$$\begin{aligned}\oint_{\gamma_i} f(z)\,dz &= \oint_{\gamma_i} \left[\frac{a_{-m}^{(i)}}{(z - z_i)^m} + \dots + \frac{a_{-1}^{(i)}}{z - z_i} + a_0^{(i)} + a_1^{(i)}(z - z_i) + \dots \right.\\ &\qquad \left. + a_m^{(i)}(z - z_i)^m + \dots \right] dz\\ &= a_{-m}^{(i)} \oint_{\gamma_i} \frac{dz}{(z - z_i)^m} + \dots + a_{-1}^{(i)} \oint_{\gamma_i} \frac{dz}{z - z_i} + a_0^{(i)} \oint_{\gamma_i} dz\\ &\qquad + a_1^{(i)} \oint (z - z_i)\,dz + \dots\end{aligned}$$

Using the result from Exercise 55, all of these integrals are zero, except the one multiplying $a_{-1}^{(i)}$, the residue, which has the value $2\pi j$. We have therefore shown that

$$\oint_{\gamma_i} f(z)\,dz = 2\pi j a_{-1}^{(i)} = 2\pi j \times \text{residue at } z = z_i$$

This clearly generalizes, so that (1.46) becomes

$$\begin{aligned}I = \oint_C f(z)\,dz &= 2\pi j \sum_{i=1}^{n} (\text{residue at } z = z_i)\\ &= 2\pi j \times (\text{sum of residues inside } C)\end{aligned}$$

Thus we have the following general result.

Theorem 1.3 **The residue theorem**

If $f(z)$ is an analytic function within and on a simple closed curve C, apart from a finite number of poles, then

$$\oint_C f(z)\,\mathrm{d}z = 2\pi\mathrm{j} \times [\text{sum of residues of } f(z) \text{ at the poles inside } C]$$

end of theorem

This is quite a remarkable result in that it enables us to evaluate the contour integral $\oint_C f(z)\,\mathrm{d}z$ by simply evaluating one coefficient of the Laurent series expansion of $f(z)$ at each of its singularities inside C.

Example 1.35

Evaluate the contour integral $\oint_C \mathrm{d}z/[z(1+z)]$ if C is

(a) the circle $|z| = \frac{1}{2}$; (b) the circle $|z| = 2$.

Solution

The singularities of $1/[z(1+z)]$ are at $z = 0$ and -1. Evaluating the residues using (1.37), we have

$$\begin{array}{l}\text{residue} \\ \text{at } z = 0\end{array} = \lim_{z \to 0} z \frac{1}{z(1+z)} = 1$$

$$\begin{array}{l}\text{residue} \\ \text{at } z = -1\end{array} = \lim_{z \to -1} (z+1) \frac{1}{z(1+z)} = -1$$

(a) If C is $|z| = \frac{1}{2}$ then it contains the pole at $z = 0$, but *not* the pole at $z = -1$. Hence, by the residue theorem,

$$\oint_C \frac{\mathrm{d}z}{z(z+1)} = 2\pi\mathrm{j} \times (\text{residue at } z = 0) = 2\pi\mathrm{j}$$

(b) If C is $|z| = 2$ then both poles are inside C. Hence, by the residue theorem,

$$\oint_C \frac{\mathrm{d}z}{z(z+1)} = 2\pi\mathrm{j}(1 - 1) = 0$$

Example 1.36

Evaluate the contour integral $\displaystyle\oint_C \frac{z^3 - z^2 + z - 1}{z^3 + 4z}\,\mathrm{d}z$ where C is

(a) $|z| = 1$ (b) $|z| = 3$

Solution

The rational function

$$\frac{z^3 - z^2 + z - 1}{z^3 + 4z}$$

has poles at $z = 0$ and $\pm 2j$. Evaluating the residues using (1.37) gives

$$\text{residue at } z = 0 = \lim_{z\to 0} \frac{z(z^3 - z^2 + z - 1)}{z(z^2 + 4)} = -\tfrac{1}{4}$$

$$\text{residue at } z = 2j = \lim_{z\to 2j} \frac{(z - 2j)(z^3 - z^2 + z - 1)}{z(z - 2j)(z + 2j)} = -\tfrac{3}{8} + \tfrac{3}{4}j$$

$$\text{residue at } z = -2j = \lim_{z\to -2j} \frac{(z + 2j)(z^3 - z^2 + z - 1)}{z(z - 2j)(z + 2j)} = -\tfrac{3}{8} - \tfrac{3}{4}j$$

(Note that these have been evaluated in Exercise 50(d).)

(a) If C is $|z| = 1$ then only the pole at $z = 0$ is inside the contour, so only the residue there is taken into account in the residue theorem, and

$$\oint_C \frac{z^3 - z^2 + z - 1}{z^3 + 4z}\,dz = 2\pi j(-\tfrac{1}{4}) = -\tfrac{1}{2}\pi j$$

(b) If C is $|z| = 3$ then all the poles are inside the contour. Hence, by the residue theorem,

$$\oint_C \frac{z^3 - z^2 + z - 1}{z^3 + 4z}\,dz = 2\pi j(-\tfrac{1}{4} - \tfrac{3}{8} + \tfrac{3}{4}j - \tfrac{3}{8} - \tfrac{3}{4}j) = -2\pi j$$

Example 1.37 Evaluate the contour integral

$$\oint_C \frac{dz}{z^3(z^2 + 2z + 2)}$$

where C is the circle $|z| = 3$.

Solution The poles of $1/z^3(z^2 + 2z + 2)$ are as follows: a pole of order three at $z = 0$, and two simple poles where $z^2 + 2z + 2 = 0$, that is at $z = -1 \pm j$. All of these poles lie inside the contour C.

From (1.38), the residue at $z = 0$ is given by

$$\lim_{z\to 0} \frac{1}{2!}\frac{d^2}{dz^2}\left[\frac{1}{z^2 + 2z + 2}\right] = \lim_{z\to 0} \tfrac{1}{2}\frac{d}{dz}\left[\frac{-(2z + 2)}{(z^2 + 2z + 2)^2}\right] = \lim_{z\to 0} \frac{d}{dz}\left[\frac{-(z + 1)}{(z^2 + 2z + 2)^2}\right]$$

$$= \lim_{z\to 0} \frac{-(z^2 + 2z + 2)^2 + (z + 1)2(z^2 + 2z + 2)(2z + 2)}{(z^2 + 2z + 2)^4} = \tfrac{1}{4}$$

From (1.37), the residue at $z = -1 - j$ is

$$\lim_{z\to -1-j} (z + 1 + j)\frac{1}{z^3(z + 1 + j)(z + 1 - j)} = \lim_{z\to -1-j} \frac{1}{z^3(z + 1 - j)}$$

$$= \frac{1}{(-1 - j)^3(-2j)} = \frac{1}{(1 + j)^3 2j} = \frac{1}{(-2 + 2j)2j}$$

using $(1+j)^3 = 1 + 3j + 3j^2 + j^3 = -2 + 2j$. Hence

$$\begin{matrix}\text{residue} \\ \text{at } z = -1 - j\end{matrix} = \tfrac{1}{4}\frac{1}{-1-j} = -\tfrac{1}{4}\frac{1-j}{2} = \tfrac{1}{8}(-1+j)$$

Also, using (1.37),

$$\begin{matrix}\text{residue} \\ \text{at } z = -1 + j\end{matrix} = \lim_{z\to -1+j}(z+1-j)\frac{1}{z^3(z+1+j)(z+1-j)}$$

which is precisely the complex conjugate of the residue at $z = -1 - j$. Hence we can take a short cut with the algebra and state the residue as $\frac{1}{8}(-1 - j)$.

The sum of the residues is

$$\tfrac{1}{4} + \tfrac{1}{8}(-1+j) + \tfrac{1}{8}(-1-j) = 0$$

so, by the residue theorem,

$$\oint_C \frac{dz}{z^3(z^2 + 2z + 2)} = 2\pi j(0) = 0$$

1.6.5 Evaluation of definite real integrals

The evaluation of definite integrals is often achieved by using the residue theorem together with a suitable complex function $f(z)$ and a suitable closed contour C. In this section we shall briefly consider two of the most common types of real integrals that can be evaluated in this way.

Type 1: Infinite real integrals of the form $\int_{-\infty}^{\infty} f(x)\,dx$ where $f(x)$ is a rational function of the real variable x

To evaluate such integrals we consider the contour integral

$$\oint_C f(z)\,dz$$

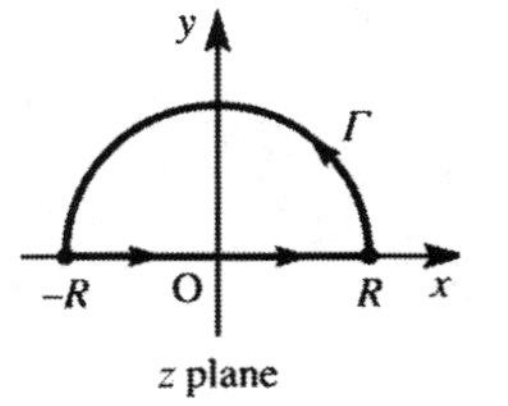

Figure 1.32
The closed contour for evaluating $\int_{-\infty}^{\infty} f(x)\,dx$.

where C is the closed contour illustrated in Figure 1.32, consisting of the real axis from $-R$ to $+R$ and the semicircle Γ, of radius R, in the upper half z plane. Since $z = x$ on the real axis,

$$\oint_C f(z)\,dz = \int_{-R}^{R} f(x)\,dx + \int_\Gamma f(z)\,dz$$

Then, provided that $\lim_{R\to\infty}\int_\Gamma f(z)\,dz = 0$, taking $R \to \infty$ gives

$$\oint_C f(z)\,dz = \int_{-\infty}^{\infty} f(x)\,dx$$

On the semicircular path Γ, $z = R\,e^{j\theta}$ $(0 \leqslant \theta \leqslant \frac{1}{2}\pi)$, giving

$$dz = jR\,e^{j\theta}\,d\theta$$

and

$$\int_{\Gamma} f(z)\,\mathrm{d}z = \int_{0}^{\pi/2} f(R\,\mathrm{e}^{\mathrm{j}\theta})\,\mathrm{j}R\,\mathrm{e}^{\mathrm{j}\theta}\,\mathrm{d}\theta$$

For this to tend to zero as $R \to \infty$, $|f(R\,\mathrm{e}^{\mathrm{j}\theta})|$ must decrease at least as rapidly as R^{-2}, implying that the degree of the denominator of the rational function $f(x)$ must be at least two more than the degree of the numerator. Thus, provided that this condition is satisfied, this approach may be used to calculate the infinite real integral $\int_{-\infty}^{\infty} f(x)\,\mathrm{d}x$. Note that if $f(x)$ is an even function of x then the same approach can also be used to evaluate $\int_{0}^{\infty} f(x)\,\mathrm{d}x$, since if $f(x)$ is even, it follows that

$$\int_{-\infty}^{\infty} f(x)\,\mathrm{d}x = 2\int_{0}^{\infty} f(x)\,\mathrm{d}x$$

Example 1.38 Using contour integration, show that

$$\int_{-\infty}^{\infty} \frac{\mathrm{d}x}{(x^2+4)^2} = \tfrac{1}{16}\pi$$

Solution Consider the contour integral

$$I = \oint_C \frac{\mathrm{d}z}{(z^2+4)^2}$$

where C is the closed semicircular contour shown in Figure 1.32. The integrand $1/(z^2+4)^2$ has poles of order two at $z = \pm 2\mathrm{j}$. However, the only singularity inside the contour C is the double pole at $z = 2\mathrm{j}$. From (1.38),

$$\begin{aligned}\text{residue at } z = 2\mathrm{j} &= \lim_{z\to 2\mathrm{j}} \frac{1}{1!}\frac{\mathrm{d}}{\mathrm{d}z}(z-2\mathrm{j})^2\frac{1}{(z-2\mathrm{j})^2(z+2\mathrm{j})^2}\\ &= \lim_{z\to 2\mathrm{j}} \frac{-2}{(z+2\mathrm{j})^3} = \frac{-2}{(4\mathrm{j})^3} = -\tfrac{1}{32}\mathrm{j}\end{aligned}$$

so, by the residue theorem,

$$\oint_C \frac{\mathrm{d}z}{(z^2+4)^2} = 2\pi\mathrm{j}(-\tfrac{1}{32}\mathrm{j}) = \tfrac{1}{16}\pi$$

Since

$$\oint_C \frac{\mathrm{d}z}{(z^2+4)^2} = \int_{-R}^{R} \frac{\mathrm{d}x}{(x^2+4)^2} + \int_{\Gamma} \frac{\mathrm{d}z}{(z^2+4)^2}$$

letting $R \to \infty$, and noting that the second integral becomes zero, gives

$$\oint_C \frac{\mathrm{d}z}{(z^2+4)^2} = \int_{-\infty}^{\infty} \frac{\mathrm{d}x}{(x^2+4)^2} = \tfrac{1}{16}\pi$$

Note that in this particular case we could have evaluated the integral without using contour integration. Making the substitution $x = 2\tan\theta$, $dx = 2\sec^2\theta\, d\theta$ gives

$$\int_{-\infty}^{\infty} \frac{dx}{(x^2+4)^2} = \int_{-\pi/2}^{\pi/2} \frac{2\sec^2\theta\, d\theta}{(4\sec^2\theta)^2} = \tfrac{1}{8}\int_{-\pi/2}^{\pi/2} \cos^2\theta\, d\theta = \tfrac{1}{16}\left[\tfrac{1}{2}\sin 2\theta + \theta\right]_{-\pi/2}^{\pi/2} = \tfrac{1}{16}\pi$$

Type 2: Real integrals of the form $I = \int_0^{2\pi} G(\sin\theta, \cos\theta)\, d\theta$ where G is a rational function of $\sin\theta$ and $\cos\theta$

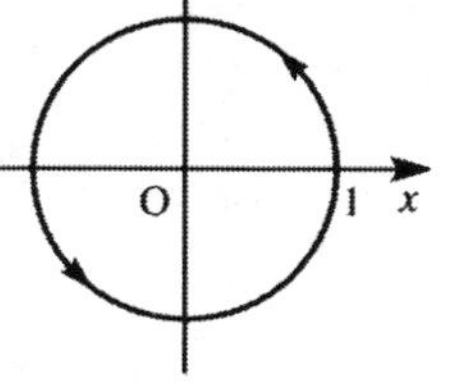

Figure 1.33 The unit-circle contour for evaluating $\int_0^{2\pi} G(\sin\theta, \cos\theta)\, d\theta$.

We take $z = e^{j\theta}$, so that

$$\sin\theta = \frac{1}{2j}\left(z - \frac{1}{z}\right), \qquad \cos\theta = \tfrac{1}{2}\left(z + \frac{1}{z}\right)$$

and

$$dz = j\, e^{j\theta}\, d\theta, \quad \text{or} \quad d\theta = \frac{dz}{jz}$$

On substituting back, the integral I becomes

$$I = \oint_C f(z)\, dz$$

where C is the unit circle $|z| = 1$ shown in Figure 1.33.

Example 1.39

Using contour integration, evaluate

$$I = \int_0^{2\pi} \frac{d\theta}{2 + \cos\theta}$$

Solution

Take $z = e^{j\theta}$, so that

$$\cos\theta = \tfrac{1}{2}\left(z + \frac{1}{z}\right), \qquad d\theta = \frac{dz}{jz}$$

On substituting, the integral becomes

$$I = \oint_C \frac{dz}{jz\,[2 + \frac{1}{2}(z + 1/z)]} = \frac{2}{j}\oint_C \frac{dz}{z^2 + 4z + 1}$$

where C is the unit circle $|z| = 1$ shown in Figure 1.33. The integrand has singularities at

$$z^2 + 4z + 1 = 0$$

that is, at $z = -2 \pm \sqrt{3}$. The only singularity inside the contour C is the simple pole at $z = -2 + \sqrt{3}$. From (1.37),

residue at $z = -2 + \sqrt{3}$

$$= \lim_{z \to -2+\sqrt{3}} \left[\frac{2}{j}(z + 2 - \sqrt{3})\frac{1}{(z + 2 - \sqrt{3})(z + 2 + \sqrt{3})}\right] = \frac{2}{j}\frac{1}{2\sqrt{3}} = \frac{1}{j\sqrt{3}}$$

so, by the residue theorem,

$$I = 2\pi j\left(\frac{1}{j\sqrt{3}}\right) = \frac{2\pi}{\sqrt{3}}$$

Thus

$$\int_0^{2\pi} \frac{d\theta}{2 + \cos\theta} = \frac{2\pi}{\sqrt{3}}$$

1.6.6 Exercises

60 Evaluate the integral

$$\oint_C \frac{z\,dz}{z^2 + 1}$$

where C is

(a) the circle $|z| = \frac{1}{2}$ (b) the circle $|z| = 2$

61 Evaluate the integral

$$\oint_C \frac{z^2 + 3jz - 2}{z^3 + 9z}\,dz$$

where C is

(a) the circle $|z| = 1$ (b) the circle $|z| = 4$

62 Calculate the residues at all the poles of the function

$$f(z) = \frac{(z^2 + 2)(z^2 + 4)}{(z^2 + 1)(z^2 + 6)}$$

Hence calculate the integral

$$\oint_C f(z)\,dz$$

where C is

(a) the circle $|z| = 2$ (b) the circle $|z - j| = 1$
(c) the circle $|z| = 4$

63 Evaluate the integral

$$\oint_C \frac{dz}{z^2(1 + z^2)^2}$$

where C is

(a) the circle $|z| = \frac{1}{2}$ (b) the circle $|z| = 2$

64 Using the residue theorem, evaluate the following contour integrals:

(a) $\displaystyle\oint_C \frac{(3z^2 + 2)\,dz}{(z - 1)(z^2 + 4)}$,

where C is
(i) the circle $|z - 2| = 2$
(ii) the circle $|z| = 4$

(b) $\displaystyle\oint_C \frac{(z^2 - 2z)\,dz}{(z + 1)^2(z^2 + 4)}$,

where C is
(i) the circle $|z| = 3$
(ii) the circle $|z + j| = 2$

(c) $\displaystyle\oint_C \frac{dz}{(z + 1)^3(z - 1)(z - 2)}$,

where C is
(i) the circle $|z| = \frac{1}{2}$
(ii) the circle $|z + 1| = 1$
(iii) the rectangle with vertices at $\pm j$, $3 \pm j$

(d) $\displaystyle\oint_C \frac{(z - 1)\,dz}{(z^2 - 4)(z + 1)^4}$,

where C is
(i) the circle $|z| = \frac{1}{2}$
(ii) the circle $\left|z + \frac{3}{2}\right| = 2$
(iii) the triangle with vertices at $-\frac{3}{2} + j$, $-\frac{3}{2} - j$, $3 + j0$

65 Using a suitable contour integral, evaluate the following real integrals:

(a) $\displaystyle\int_{-\infty}^{\infty} \frac{\mathrm{d}x}{x^2+x+1}$ (b) $\displaystyle\int_{-\infty}^{\infty} \frac{\mathrm{d}x}{(x^2+1)^2}$

(c) $\displaystyle\int_{0}^{\infty} \frac{\mathrm{d}x}{(x^2+1)(x^2+4)^2}$

(d) $\displaystyle\int_{0}^{2\pi} \frac{\cos 3\theta}{5-4\cos\theta}\,\mathrm{d}\theta$ (e) $\displaystyle\int_{0}^{2\pi} \frac{4\,\mathrm{d}\theta}{5+4\sin\theta}$

(f) $\displaystyle\int_{-\infty}^{\infty} \frac{x^2\,\mathrm{d}x}{(x^2+1)^2(x^2+2x+2)}$

(g) $\displaystyle\int_{0}^{2\pi} \frac{\mathrm{d}\theta}{3-2\cos\theta+\sin\theta}$ (h) $\displaystyle\int_{0}^{\infty} \frac{\mathrm{d}x}{x^4+1}$

(i) $\displaystyle\int_{-\infty}^{\infty} \frac{\mathrm{d}x}{(x^2+4x+5)^2}$

(j) $\displaystyle\int_{0}^{2\pi} \frac{\cos\theta}{3+2\cos\theta}\,\mathrm{d}\theta$

1.7 Engineering application: analysing AC circuits

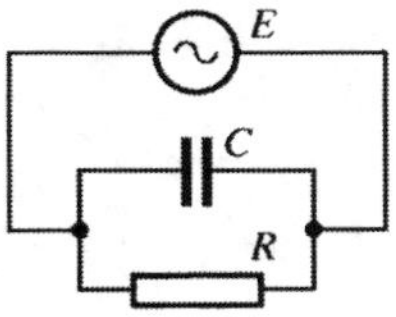

In the circuit shown in Figure 1.34 we wish to find the variation in impedance Z and admittance Y as the capacitance C of the capacitor varies from 0 to ∞. Here

$$\frac{1}{Z}=\frac{1}{R}+\mathrm{j}\omega C, \qquad Y=\frac{1}{Z}$$

Figure 1.34 AC circuit of Section 1.7.

Writing

$$\frac{1}{Z}=\frac{1+\mathrm{j}\omega CR}{R}$$

we clearly have

$$Z=\frac{R}{1+\mathrm{j}\omega CR} \tag{1.50}$$

Equation (1.50) can be interpreted as a bilinear mapping with Z and C as the two variables. We examine what happens to the real axis in the C plane (C varies from 0 to ∞ and, of course, is real) under the inverse of the mapping given by (1.50). Rearranging (1.50), we have

$$C=\frac{R-Z}{\mathrm{j}\omega RZ} \tag{1.51}$$

Taking $Z=x+\mathrm{j}y$

$$C=\frac{R-x-\mathrm{j}y}{\mathrm{j}\omega R(x+\mathrm{j}y)}=\frac{x+\mathrm{j}y-R}{\omega R(y-\mathrm{j}x)}=\frac{(x+\mathrm{j}y-R)(y+\mathrm{j}x)}{\omega R(x^2+y^2)} \tag{1.52}$$

Equating imaginary parts, and remembering that C is real, gives

$$0=x^2+y^2-Rx \tag{1.53}$$

which represents a circle, with centre at $(\frac{1}{2}R, 0)$ and of radius $\frac{1}{2}R$. Thus the real axis in the C plane is mapped onto the circle given by (1.53) in the Z plane. Of course, C is positive. If $C=0$, (1.53) indicates that $Z=R$. The circuit of Figure 1.34 confirms

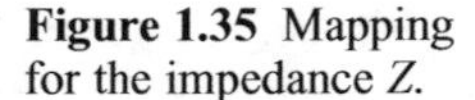

Figure 1.35 Mapping for the impedance Z.

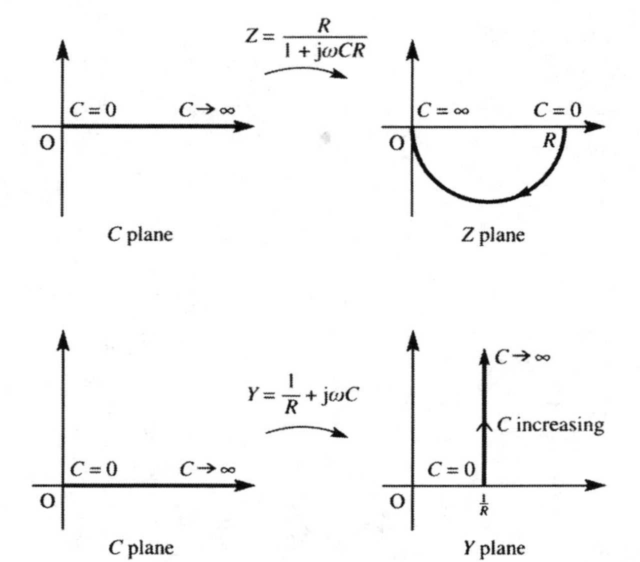

Figure 1.36 Mapping for the admittance Y.

that the impedance is R in this case. If $C \to \infty$ then $Z \to 0$, so the positive real axis in the plane is mapped onto either the upper or lower half of the circle. Equating real parts in (1.52) gives

$$C = \frac{-y}{\omega(x^2 + y^2)}$$

so $C > 0$ gives $y < 0$, implying that the lower half of the circle is the image in the Z plane of the positive real axis in the C plane, as indicated in Figure 1.35. A diagram such as Figure 1.35 gives an immediate visual impression of how the impedance Z varies as C varies.

The admittance $Y = 1/Z$ is given by

$$Y = \frac{1}{R} + j\omega C$$

which represents a linear mapping as shown in Figure 1.36.

1.8 Engineering application: use of harmonic functions

In this section we discuss two engineering applications where use is made of the properties of harmonic functions.

1.8.1 A heat transfer problem

We saw in Section 1.3.2 that every analytic function generates a pair of harmonic functions. The problem of finding a function that is harmonic in a specified region and satisfies prescribed boundary conditions is one of the oldest and most important problems in science-based engineering. Sometimes the solution can be found by means of a conformal mapping defined by an analytic function. This, essentially, is a consequence of the 'function of a function' rule of calculus, which implies that every harmonic function of x and y transforms into a harmonic function of u and v under the mapping

$$w = u + jv = f(x + jy) = f(z)$$

where $f(z)$ is analytic. Furthermore, the level curves of the harmonic function in the z plane are mapped onto corresponding level curves in the w plane, so that a harmonic function that has a constant value along part of the boundary of a region or has a zero normal derivative along part of the boundary is mapped onto a harmonic function with the same property in the w plane.

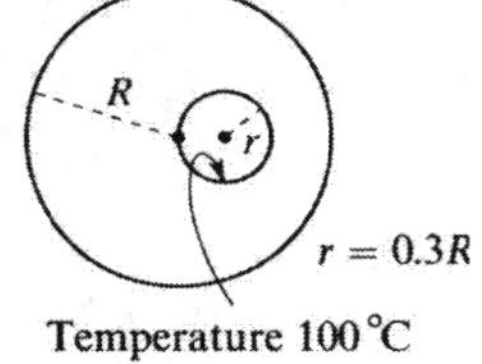

Figure 1.37 Schematic diagram of heat transfer problem.

For heat transfer problems the level curves of the harmonic function correspond to isotherms, and a zero normal derivative corresponds to thermal insulation. To illustrate these ideas, consider the simple steady-state heat transfer problem shown schematically in Figure 1.37. There is a cylindrical pipe with an offset cylindrical cavity through which steam passes at 100 °C. The outer temperature of the pipe is 0 °C. The radius of the inner circle is $\frac{3}{10}$ of that of the outer circle, so by choosing the outer radius as the unit of length the problem can be stated as that of finding a harmonic function $T(x, y)$ such that

$$\frac{\partial^2 T}{\partial x^2} + \frac{\partial^2 T}{\partial y^2} = 0$$

in the region between the circles $|z| = 1$ and $|z - 0.3| = 0.3$, and $T = 0$ on $|z| = 1$ and $T = 100$ on $|z - 0.3| = 0.3$.

The mapping

$$w = \frac{z - 3}{3z - 1}$$

transforms the circle $|z| = 1$ onto the circle $|w| = 1$ and the circle $|z - 0.3| = 0.3$ onto the circle $|w| = 3$ as shown in Figure 1.38. Thus the problem is transformed into the axially symmetric problem in the w plane of finding a harmonic function $T(u, v)$ such that $T(u, v) = 100$ on $|w| = 1$ and $T(u, v) = 0$ on $|w| = 3$. Harmonic functions with such axial symmetry have the general form

$$T(u, v) = A \ln (u^2 + v^2) + B$$

where A and B are constants.

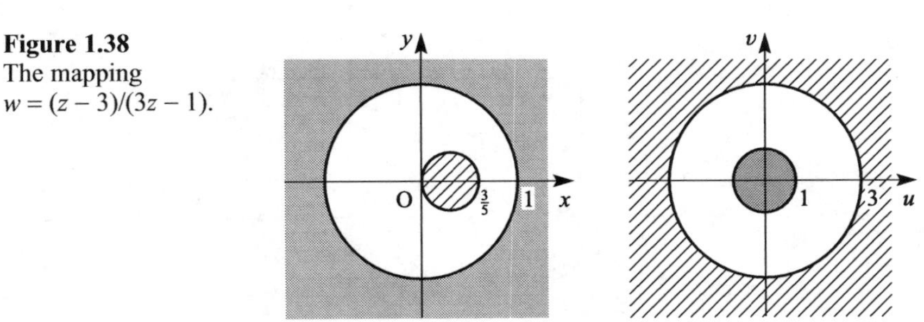

Figure 1.38 The mapping $w = (z - 3)/(3z - 1)$.

Here we require, in addition to the axial symmetry, that $T(u, v) = 100$ on $u^2 + v^2 = 1$ and $T(u, v) = 0$ on $u^2 + v^2 = 9$. Thus $B = 100$ and $A = -100 \ln 9$, and the solution on the w plane is

$$T(u, v) = \frac{100[1 - \ln(u^2 + v^2)]}{\ln 9}$$

We need the solution on the z plane, which means in general we have to obtain u and v in terms of x and y. Here, however, it is a little easier, since $u^2 + v^2 = |w|^2$ and

$$|w|^2 = \left|\frac{z-3}{3z-1}\right|^2 = \frac{|z-3|^2}{|3z-1|^2} = \frac{(x-3)^2 + y^2}{(3x-1)^2 + 9y^2}$$

Thus

$$T(x, y) = \frac{100}{\ln 9}\{1 - \ln[(x-3)^2 + y^2] - \ln[(3x-1)^2 + 9y^2]\}$$

1.8.2 Current in a field-effect transistor

The fields (E_x, E_y) in an insulated-gate field-effect transistor are harmonic conjugates that satisfy a non-linear boundary condition. For the transistor shown schematically in Figure 1.39 we have

$$\frac{\partial E_y}{\partial x} = \frac{\partial E_x}{\partial y}, \qquad \frac{\partial E_y}{\partial y} = \frac{-\partial E_x}{\partial x}$$

with conditions

$$E_x = 0 \quad \text{on the electrodes}$$

$$E_x\left(E_y + \frac{V_0}{h}\right) = -\frac{I}{2\mu\varepsilon_0\varepsilon_r} \quad \text{on the channel}$$

$$E_y \to -\frac{V_g}{h} \quad \text{as} \quad x \to -\infty \quad (0 < y < h)$$

$$E_y \to \frac{V_d - V_g}{h} \quad \text{as} \quad x \to \infty \quad (0 < y < h)$$

where V_0 is a constant with dimensions of potential, h is the insulator thickness, I is the current in the channel, which is to be found, μ, ε_0 and ε_r have their usual meanings, and the gate potential V_g and the drain potential V_d are taken with respect to the source potential.

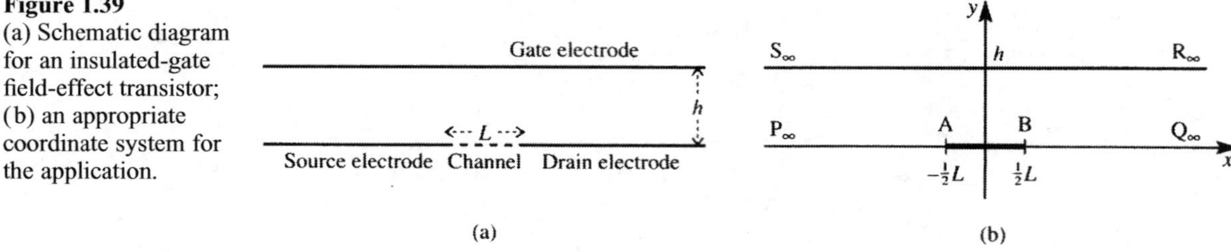

Figure 1.39
(a) Schematic diagram for an insulated-gate field-effect transistor; (b) an appropriate coordinate system for the application.

The key to the solution of this problem is the observation that the non-linear boundary condition

$$2E_x\left(E_y + \frac{V_0}{h}\right) = -\frac{I}{\mu\varepsilon_0\varepsilon_r}$$

contains the harmonic function (now of E_x and E_y)

$$H(E_x, E_y) = 2E_x\left(E_y + \frac{V_0}{h}\right)$$

A harmonic conjugate of H is the function

$$G(E_x, E_y) = \left(E_y + \frac{V_0}{h}\right)^2 - E_x^2$$

Since E_x and E_y are harmonic conjugates with respect to x and y, so are G and H. Thus the problem may be restated as that of finding harmonic conjugates G and H such that

$$H = 0 \quad \text{on the electrodes}$$

$$H = -\frac{I}{\mu\varepsilon_0\varepsilon_r} \quad \text{on the channel}$$

$$G \to \left(\frac{V_0 - V_g}{h}\right)^2 \quad \text{as} \quad x \to \infty \quad (0 < y < h)$$

$$G \to \left(\frac{V_0 + V_d - V_g}{h}\right)^2 \quad \text{as} \quad x \to -\infty \quad (0 < y < h)$$

Using the sequence of mappings shown in Figure 1.40, which may be composed into the single formula

$$w = \frac{a\,\mathrm{e}^{bz} - a^2}{a\,\mathrm{e}^{bz} - 1}$$

where $a = \mathrm{e}^{bL/2}$ and $b = \pi/h$, the problem is transformed into finding harmonic-conjugate functions G and H (on the w plane) such that

$$H = 0 \quad \text{on} \quad v = 0 \quad (u > 0) \tag{1.54}$$

$$H = -\frac{I}{\mu\varepsilon_0\varepsilon_r} \quad \text{on} \quad v = 0 \quad (u < 0) \tag{1.55}$$

$$G = \left(\frac{V_0 - V_g}{h}\right)^2 \quad \text{at} \quad w = \mathrm{e}^{bL} \tag{1.56}$$

$$G = \left(\frac{V_0 + V_d - V_g}{h}\right)^2 \quad \text{at} \quad w = 1 \tag{1.57}$$

The conditions (1.54), (1.55) and (1.57) are sufficient to determine H and G completely

$$H = -\frac{I\arg(w)}{\pi\mu\varepsilon_0\varepsilon_r}$$

$$G = \frac{I\ln|w|}{\pi\mu\varepsilon_0\varepsilon_r} + \left(\frac{V_0 + V_d - V_g}{h}\right)^2$$

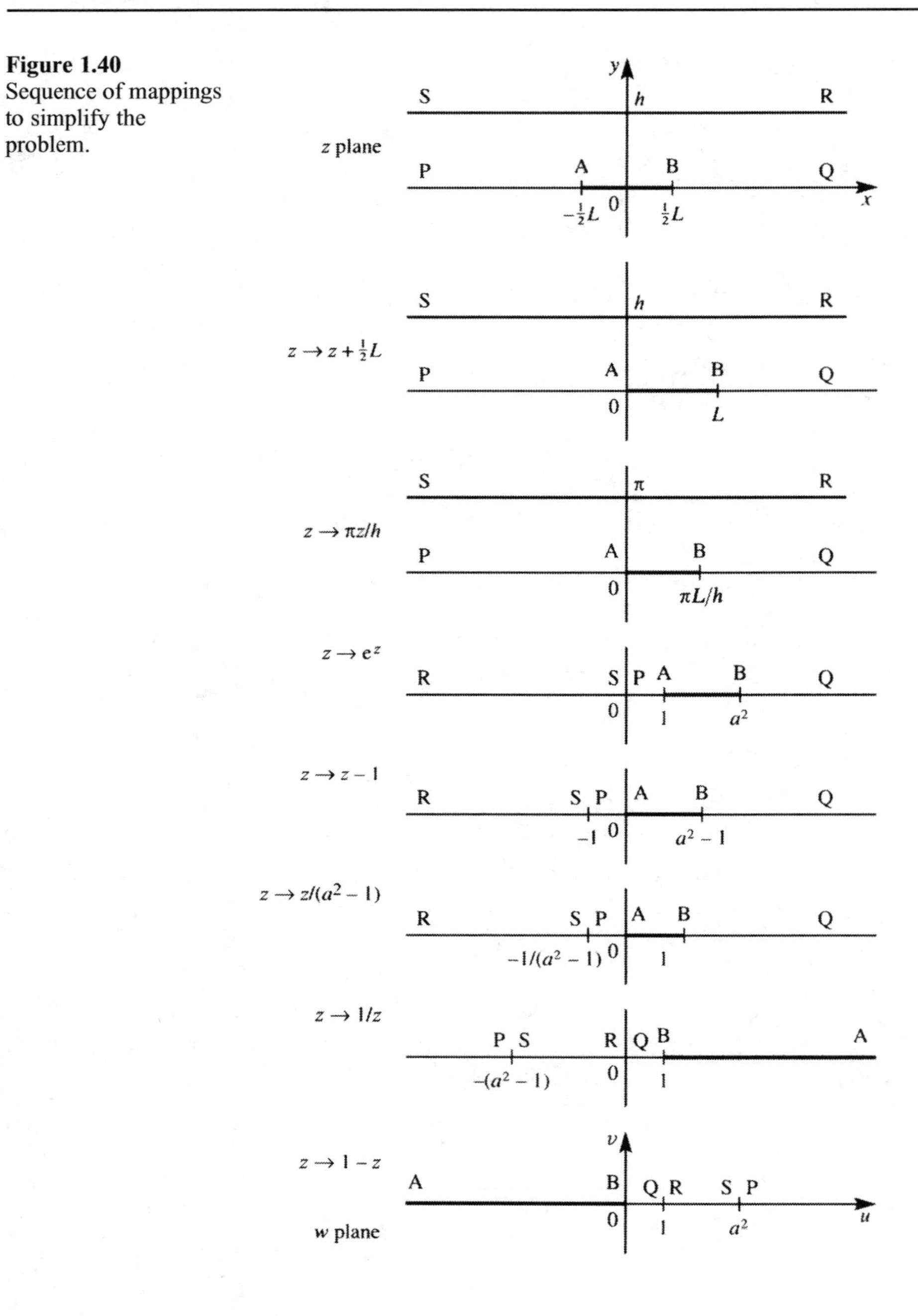

Figure 1.40 Sequence of mappings to simplify the problem.

while the condition (1.56) determines the values of I

$$I = \frac{\mu \varepsilon_0 \varepsilon_r}{Lh}(2V_0 - 2V_g + V_d)V_d$$

This example shows the power of complex variable methods for solving difficult problems arising in engineering mathematics. The following exercises give some simpler examples for the reader to investigate.

1.8.3 Exercises

66 Show that the transformation $w = 1/z$, $w = u + jv$, $z = x + jy$, transforms the circle $x^2 + y^2 = 2ax$ in the z plane into the straight line $u = 1/2a$ in the w plane. Two long conducting wires of radius a are placed adjacent and parallel to each other, so that their cross-section appears as in Figure 1.41. The wires are separated at O by an insulating gap of negligible dimensions, and carry potentials $\pm V_0$ as indicated. Find an expression for the potential at a general point (x, y) in the plane of the cross-section and sketch the equipotentials.

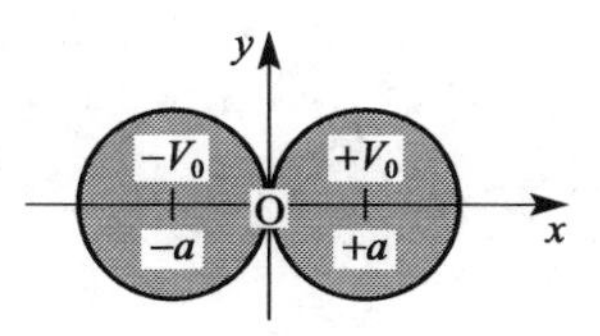

Figure 1.41 Conducting wires of Exercise 66.

67 Find the images under the mapping

$$w = \frac{z+1}{1-z}$$

$z = x + jy$, of

(a) the points A(−1, 0), B(0, 1), C$(\frac{24}{25}, \frac{7}{25})$ and D$(\frac{3}{4}, 0)$ in the z plane,
(b) the straight line $y = 0$,
(c) the circle $x^2 + y^2 = 1$.

Illustrate your answer with a diagram showing the z and w planes and shade on the w plane the region corresponding to $x^2 + y^2 < 1$.

A semicircular disc of unit radius, $[(x, y): x^2 + y^2 \leqslant 1, y \geqslant 0]$, has its straight boundary at temperature 0 °C and its curved boundary at 100 °C. Prove that the temperature at the point (x, y) is

$$T = \frac{200}{\pi}\tan^{-1}\left(\frac{2y}{1 - x^2 - y^2}\right)$$

68 (a) Show that the function

$$G(x, y) = 2x(1 - y)$$

satisfies the Laplace equation and construct its harmonic conjugate $H(x, y)$ that satisfies $H(0, 0) = 0$. Hence obtain, in terms of z, where $z = x + jy$, the function F such that $W = F(z)$ where $W = G + jH$.

(b) Show that under the mapping $w = \ln z$, the harmonic function $G(x, y)$ defined in (a) is mapped into the function

$$G(u, v) = 2e^u \cos v - e^{2u} \sin 2v$$

Verify that $G(u, v)$ is harmonic.

(c) Generalize the result (b) to prove that under the mapping $w = f(z)$, where $f'(z)$ exists, a harmonic function of (x, y) is transformed into a harmonic function of (u, v).

69 Show that if $w = (z + 3)/(z - 3)$, $w = u + jv$, $z = x + jy$, the circle $u^2 + v^2 = k^2$ in the w plane is the image of the circle

$$x^2 + y^2 + 6\frac{1+k^2}{1-k^2}x + 9 = 0 \quad (k^2 \neq 1)$$

in the z plane.

Two long cylindrical wires, each of radius 4 mm, are placed parallel to each other with their axes 10 mm apart, so that their cross-section appears as in Figure 1.42. The wires carry potentials $\pm V_0$ as shown. Show that the potential $V(x, y)$ at the point (x, y) is given by

$$V = \frac{V_0}{\ln 4}\{\ln[(x+3)^2 + y^2] - \ln[(x-3)^2 + y^2]\}$$

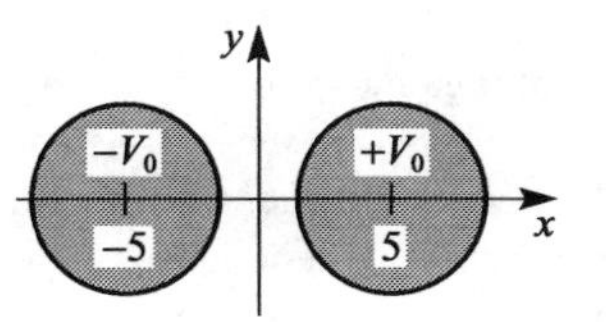

Figure 1.42 Cylindrical wires of Exercise 69.

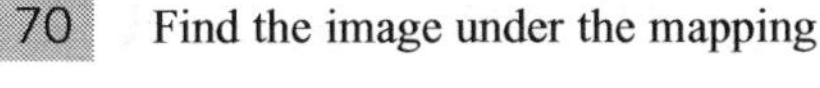

70 Find the image under the mapping

$$w = \frac{j(1-z)}{1+z}$$

$z = x + jy$, $w = u + jv$, of

(a) the points A(1, 0), B(0, 1), C(0, −1) in the z plane,
(b) the straight line $y = 0$,
(c) the circle $x^2 + y^2 = 1$.

A circular plate of unit radius, $[(x, y): x^2 + y^2 \leqslant 1]$, has one half (with $y > 0$) of its rim, $x^2 + y^2 = 1$, at temperature 0 °C and the other half (with $y < 0$) at temperature 100 °C. Using the above mapping, prove that the steady-state temperature at the point (x, y) is

$$T = \frac{100}{\pi}\tan^{-1}\left(\frac{1 - x^2 - y^2}{2y}\right)$$

71 The problem shown schematically in Figure 1.43 arose during a steady-state heat transfer investigation. T is the temperature. By applying the successive mappings

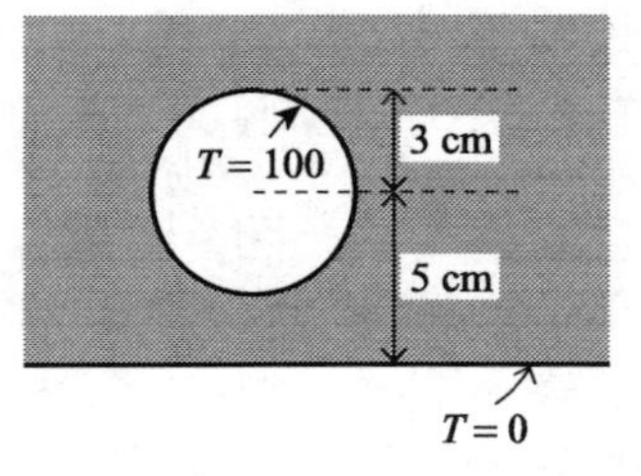

Figure 1.43 Schematic representation of Exercise 71.

$$z_1 = \frac{z + \mathrm{j}4}{z - \mathrm{j}4}, \qquad w = \ln z_1$$

show that the temperature at the point (x, y) in the shaded region in the figure is given by

$$T(x, y) = \frac{50}{\ln 3} \ln\left[\frac{x^2 + (4 + y)^2}{x^2 + (4 - y)^2}\right]$$

72 The functions

$$w = z + \frac{1}{z}, \quad w = \frac{z + 1}{z - 1}$$

perform the mappings shown in Figure 1.44. A long bar of semicircular cross-section has the temperature of the part of its curved surface corresponding to the arc PQ in Figure 1.45 kept at 100 °C while the rest of the surface is kept at 0 °C. Show that the temperature T at the point (x, y) is given by

$$T = \frac{100}{\pi}[\arg(z^2 + z + 1) - \arg(z^2 - z + 1)]$$

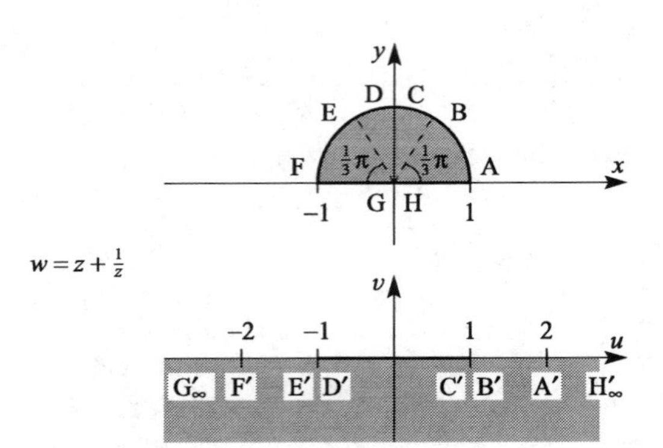

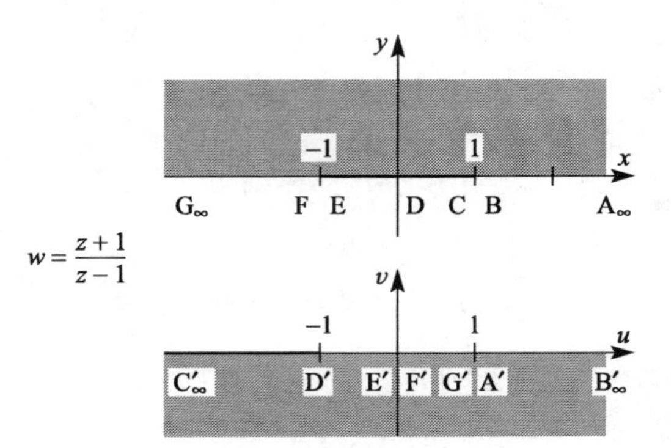

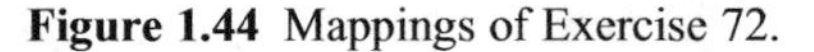

Figure 1.44 Mappings of Exercise 72.

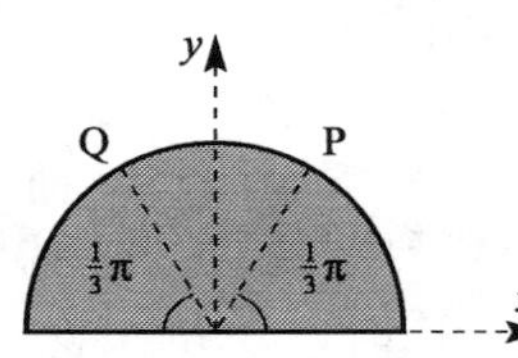

Figure 1.45 Cross-section of bar of Exercise 72.

1.9 Review exercises (1–24)

1 Find the images of the following points under the mappings given:

(a) $z = 1 + \mathrm{j}$ under $w = (1 + \mathrm{j})z + \mathrm{j}$

(b) $z = 1 - \mathrm{j}2$ under $w = \mathrm{j}3z + \mathrm{j} + 1$

(c) $z = 1$ under $w = \frac{1}{2}(1 - \mathrm{j})z + \frac{1}{2}(1 + \mathrm{j})$

(d) $z = \mathrm{j}2$ under $w = \frac{1}{2}(1 - \mathrm{j})z + \frac{1}{2}(1 + \mathrm{j})$

2 Under each of the mappings given in Review exercise 1, find the images in the w plane of the two straight lines

(a) $y = 2x$

(b) $x + y = 1$

in the z plane, $z = x + \mathrm{j}y$.

3 The linear mapping $w = \alpha z + \beta$, where α and β are complex constants, maps the point $z = 2 - \mathrm{j}$ in the z plane to the point $w = 1$ in the w plane, and the point $z = 0$ to the point $w = 3 + \mathrm{j}$.

(a) Determine α and β.
(b) Find the region in the w plane corresponding to the left half-plane $\mathrm{Re}(z) \leqslant 0$ in the z plane.
(c) Find the region in the w plane corresponding to the circular region $5|z| \leqslant 1$ in the z plane.
(d) Find the fixed point of the mapping.

4 Map the following straight lines from the z plane, $z = x + \mathrm{j}y$, to the w plane under the inverse mapping $w = \mathrm{j}/z$:

(a) $x = y + 1$
(b) $y = 3x$
(c) the line joining A$(1 + \mathrm{j})$ to B$(2 + \mathrm{j}3)$ in the z plane
(d) $y = 4$

In each case sketch the image curve.

5 Two complex variables w and z are related by the mapping

$$w = \frac{z+1}{z-1}$$

Sketch this mapping by finding the images in the w plane of the lines $\mathrm{Re}(z) =$ constant and $\mathrm{Im}(z) =$ constant. Find the fixed points of the mapping.

6 The mapping

$$w = \frac{1-z^2}{z}$$

takes points from the z plane to the w plane. Find the fixed points of the mapping, and show that the circle of radius r with centre at the origin in the z plane is transformed to the ellipse

$$\left(\frac{ur^2}{r^2-1}\right)^2 + \left(\frac{vr^2}{r^2+1}\right)^2 = r^2$$

in the w plane, where $w = u + \mathrm{j}v$. Investigate what happens when $r = 1$.

7 Find the real and imaginary parts of the complex function $w = z^3$, and verify the Cauchy–Riemann equations.

8 Find a function $v(x, y)$ such that, given

$$u(x, y) = x \sin x \cosh y - y \cos x \sinh y$$

$f(z) = u + \mathrm{j}v$ is an analytic function of z, $f(0) = 0$.

9 Find the bilinear transformation that maps the three points $z = 0$, j and $\frac{1}{2}(1 + \mathrm{j})$ in the z plane to the three points $w = \infty$, $-\mathrm{j}$ and $1 - \mathrm{j}$ respectively in the w plane. Check that the transformation will map

(a) the lower half of the z plane onto the upper half of the w plane
(b) the interior of the circle with centre $z = \mathrm{j}\frac{1}{2}$ and radius $\frac{1}{2}$ in the z plane onto the half-plane $\mathrm{Im}(w) < -1$ in the w plane.

10 Show that the mapping

$$z = \zeta + \frac{a^2}{4\zeta}$$

where $z = x + \mathrm{j}y$ and $\zeta = R\,\mathrm{e}^{\mathrm{j}\theta}$ maps the circle $R =$ constant in the ζ plane onto an ellipse in the z plane. Suggest a possible use for this mapping.

11 Find the power series representation of the function

$$\frac{1}{1+z^3}$$

in the disc $|z| < 1$. Deduce the power series for

$$\frac{1}{(1+z^3)^2}$$

valid in the same disc.

12 Find the first four non-zero terms of the Taylor series expansion of the following functions about the point indicated, and determine the radius of convergence of each:

(a) $\dfrac{1-z}{1+z}$ $\quad(z = 0)$ $\qquad$ (b) $\dfrac{1}{z^2+1}$ $\quad(z = 1)$

(c) $\dfrac{z}{z+1}$ $\quad(z = \mathrm{j})$

13 Find the radius of convergence of each Taylor series expansion of the following function about the points indicated, *without* finding the series itself:

$$f(z) = \frac{1}{z(z^2+1)}$$

at the points $z = 1, -1, 1 + \mathrm{j}, 1 + \mathrm{j}\frac{1}{2}$ and $2 + \mathrm{j}3$.

14 Determine the Laurent series expansion of the function

$$f(z) = \frac{1}{(z^2+1)z}$$

about the points (a) $z = 0$ and (b) $z = 1$, and determine the region of validity of each.

15 Find the Laurent series expansion of the function

$$f(z) = e^z \sin\left(\frac{1}{1-z}\right)$$

about (a) $z = 0$, (b) $z = 1$ and (c) $z = \infty$, indicating the range of validity in each case. (Do *not* find terms explicitly; indicate only the form of the principal part.)

16 Find the real and imaginary parts of the functions

(a) $e^z \sinh z$ (b) $\cos 2z$

(c) $\dfrac{\sin z}{z}$ (d) $\tan z$

17 Determine whether the following mappings are conformal, and, if not, find the non-conformal points:

(a) $w = \dfrac{1}{z^2}$

(b) $w = 2z^3 + 3z^2 + 6(1 - j)z + 1$

(c) $w = 64z + \dfrac{1}{z^3}$

18 Consider the mapping $w = \cos z$. Determine the points where the mapping is not conformal. By finding the images in the w plane of the lines x = constant and y = constant in the z plane ($z = x + jy$), draw the mapping similarly to Figures 1.14 and 1.18.

19 Determine the location of and classify the singularities of the following functions:

(a) $\dfrac{\sin z}{z^2}$ (b) $\dfrac{1}{(z^3-8)^2}$

(c) $\dfrac{z+1}{z^4-1}$ (d) $\operatorname{sech} z$

(e) $\sinh z$ (f) $\sin\left(\dfrac{1}{z}\right)$ (g) z^z

20 Find the residues of the following functions at the points indicated:

(a) $\dfrac{e^{2z}}{(1+z)^2}$ $(z = -1)$ (b) $\dfrac{\cos z}{2z - \pi}$ $(z = \frac{1}{2}\pi)$

(c) $\dfrac{\tan z}{2z - \pi}$ $(z = \frac{1}{2}\pi)$ (d) $\dfrac{z}{(z+8)^3}$ $(z = -8)$

21 Find the poles and zeros, and determine all the residues, of the rational function

$$f(z) = \frac{(z^2-1)(z^2+3z+5)}{z(z^4+1)}$$

22 Determine the residue of the rational function

$$\frac{z^7 + 6z^5 - 30z^4}{(z-1-j)^3}$$

23 Evaluate the following contour integrals along the circular paths indicated:

(a) $\displaystyle\oint_C \frac{z\,dz}{z^2+7z+6}$, where C is $|z| = 2$

(b) $\displaystyle\oint_C \frac{(z^2+1)(z^2+3)}{(z^2+9)(z^2+4)}\,dz$, where C is $|z| = 4$

(c) $\displaystyle\oint_C \frac{dz}{z^2(1-z^2)^2}$, where $\begin{cases}\text{(i) } C \text{ is } |z| = \frac{1}{2}\\ \text{(ii) } C \text{ is } |z| = 2\end{cases}$

(d) $\displaystyle\oint_C \frac{dz}{(2z-3j)(z+j)}$, where $\begin{cases}\text{(i) } C \text{ is } |z| = 2\\ \text{(ii) } C \text{ is } |z-1| = 1\end{cases}$

(e) $\displaystyle\oint_C \frac{z^3\,dz}{(z^2+1)(z^2+z+1)}$, where C is $|z - j| = \frac{1}{2}$

(f) $\displaystyle\oint_C \frac{(z-1)\,dz}{z(z-2)^2(z-3)}$, where $\begin{cases}\text{(i) } C \text{ is } |z| = 1\\ \text{(ii) } C \text{ is } |z| = \frac{5}{2}\end{cases}$

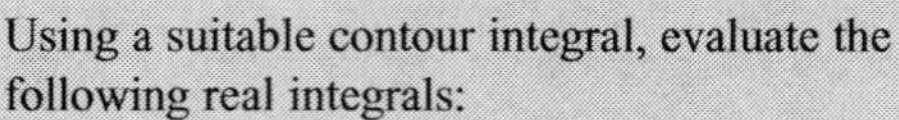

24 Using a suitable contour integral, evaluate the following real integrals:

(a) $\displaystyle\int_{-\infty}^{\infty} \frac{x^2\,dx}{(x^2+1)^2(x^2+2x+2)}$

(b) $\displaystyle\int_0^{\infty} \frac{x^2\,dx}{x^4+16}$ (c) $\displaystyle\int_0^{2\pi} \frac{\sin^2\theta\,d\theta}{5+4\cos\theta}$

(d) $\displaystyle\int_0^{2\pi} \frac{\cos 2\theta\,d\theta}{5-4\cos\theta}$

2 Laplace Transforms

Chapter 2 Contents

2.1 Introduction

Laplace transform methods have a key role to play in the modern approach to the analysis and design of engineering systems. The stimulus for developing these methods was the pioneering work of the English electrical engineer Oliver Heaviside (1850–1925) in developing a method for the systematic solution of ordinary differential equations with constant coefficients. Heaviside was concerned with solving practical problems, and his method was based mainly on intuition, lacking mathematical rigour: consequently it was frowned upon by theoreticians at the time. However, Heaviside himself was not concerned with rigorous proofs, and was satisfied that his method gave the correct results. Using his ideas, he was able to solve important practical problems that could not be dealt with using classical methods. This led to many new results in fields such as the propagation of currents and voltages along transmission lines.

Because it worked in practice, Heaviside's method was widely accepted by engineers. As its power for problem-solving became more and more apparent, the method attracted the attention of mathematicians, who set out to justify it. This provided the stimulus for rapid developments in many branches of mathematics including improper integrals, asymptotic series and transform theory. Research on the problem continued for many years before it was eventually recognized that an integral transform developed by the French mathematician Pierre Simon de Laplace (1749–1827) almost a century before provided a theoretical foundation for Heaviside's work. It was also recognized that the use of this integral transform provided a more systematic alternative for investigating differential equations than the method proposed by Heaviside. It is this alternative approach that is the basis of the **Laplace transform method**.

We have already come across instances where a mathematical transformation has been used to simplify the solution of a problem. For example, the logarithm is used to simplify multiplication and division problems. To multiply or divide two numbers, we transform them into their logarithms, add or subtract these, and then perform the inverse transformation (that is, the antilogarithm) to obtain the product or quotient of the original numbers. The purpose of using a transformation is to create a new domain in which it is easier to handle the problem being investigated. Once results have been obtained in the new domain, they can be inverse-transformed to give the desired results in the original domain.

The Laplace transform is an example of a class called **integral transforms**, and it takes a function $f(t)$ of one variable t (which we shall refer to as **time**) into a function $F(s)$ of another variable s (the **complex frequency**). Another integral transform widely used by engineers is the **Fourier transform**, which is dealt with in Chapter 5. The attraction of the Laplace transform is that it transforms *differential* equations in the t (time) domain into *algebraic* equations in the s (frequency) domain. Solving differential equations in the t domain therefore reduces to solving algebraic equations in the s domain. Having done the latter for the desired unknowns, their values as functions of time may be found by taking inverse transforms. Another advantage of using the Laplace transform for solving differential equations is that initial conditions play an essential role in the transformation process, so they are automatically incorporated into the solution.

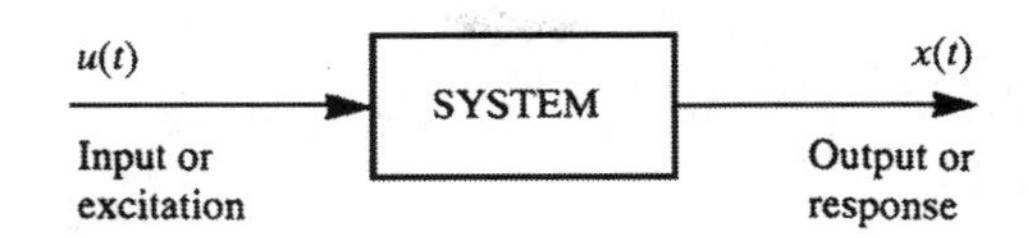

Figure 2.1 Schematic representation of a system.

The initial conditions are only introduced when the unknown constants of integration are determined. The Laplace transform is therefore an ideal tool for solving initial-value problems such as those occurring in the investigation of electrical circuits and mechanical vibrations.

The Laplace transform finds particular application in the field of signals and linear systems analysis. A distinguishing feature of a system is that when it is subjected to an excitation (input), it produces a response (output). When the input $u(t)$ and output $x(t)$ are functions of a single variable t, representing time, it is normal to refer to them as **signals**. Schematically, a system may be represented as in Figure 2.1. The problem facing the engineer is that of determining the system output $x(t)$ when it is subjected to an input $u(t)$ applied at some instant of time, which we can take to be $t = 0$. The relationship between output and input is determined by the laws governing the behaviour of the system. If the system is linear and time-invariant then the output is related to the input by a linear differential equation with constant coefficients, and we have a standard initial-value problem, which is amenable to solution using the Laplace transform.

While many of the problems considered in this chapter can be solved by the classical approach, the Laplace transform leads to a more unified approach and provides the engineer with greater insight into system behaviour. In practice, the input signal $u(t)$ may be a discontinuous or periodic function, or even a pulse, and in such cases the use of the Laplace transform has distinct advantages over the classical approach. Also, more often than not, an engineer is interested not only in system analysis but also in system synthesis or design. Consequently, an engineer's objective in studying a system's response to specific inputs is frequently to learn more about the system with a view to improving or controlling it so that it satisfies certain specifications. It is in this area that the use of the Laplace transform is attractive, since by considering the system response to particular inputs, such as a sinusoid, it provides the engineer with powerful graphical methods for system design that are relatively easy to apply and widely used in practice.

In modelling the system by a differential equation, it has been assumed that both the input and output signals can vary at any instant of time; that is, they are functions of a continuous time variable (note that this does not mean that the signals themselves have to be continuous functions of time). Such systems are called **continuous-time systems**, and it is for investigating these that the Laplace transform is best suited. With the introduction of computer control into system design, signals associated with a system may only change at discrete instants of time. In such cases the system is said to be a **discrete-time system**, and is modelled by a difference equation rather than a differential equation. Such systems are dealt with using the z transform considered in Chapter 3.

Throughout the chapter operations that can be carried out in MATLAB, incorporating both the Symbolic Math and Control Toolboxes, are highlighted and basic commands introduced. Where appropriate users are encouraged to use these facilities to check their solutions to the exercises.

2.2 The Laplace transform

2.2.1 Definition and notation

We define the Laplace transform of a function $f(t)$ by the expression

$$\mathscr{L}\{f(t)\} = \int_0^\infty e^{-st} f(t)\,dt \tag{2.1}$$

where s is a complex variable and e^{-st} is called the **kernel** of the transformation.

It is usual to represent the Laplace transform of a function by the corresponding capital letter, so that we write

$$\mathscr{L}\{f(t)\} = F(s) = \int_0^\infty e^{-st} f(t)\,dt \tag{2.2}$$

An alternative notation in common use is to denote $\mathscr{L}\{f(t)\}$ by $\bar{f}(s)$ or simply $\bar{f}$.

Before proceeding, there are a few observations relating to the definition (2.2) worthy of comment.

(a) The symbol $\mathscr{L}$ denotes the **Laplace transform operator**; when it operates on a function $f(t)$, it transforms it into a function $F(s)$ of the complex variable s. We say the operator transforms the function $f(t)$ in the t domain (usually called the **time domain**) into the function $F(s)$ in the s domain (usually called the **complex frequency domain**, or simply the **frequency domain**). This relationship is depicted graphically in Figure 2.2, and it is usual to refer to $f(t)$ and $F(s)$ as a **Laplace transform pair**, written as $\{f(t), F(s)\}$.

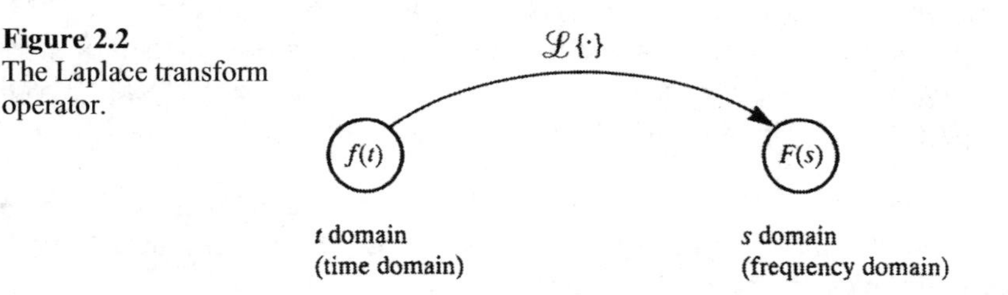

Figure 2.2
The Laplace transform operator.

(b) Because the upper limit in the integral is infinite, the domain of integration is infinite. Thus the integral is an example of an **improper integral**; that is,

$$\int_0^\infty e^{-st} f(t)\,dt = \lim_{T\to\infty} \int_0^T e^{-st} f(t)\,dt$$

This immediately raises the question of whether or not the integral converges, an issue we shall consider in Section 2.2.3.

(c) Because the lower limit in the integral is zero, it follows that when taking the Laplace transform, the behaviour of $f(t)$ for negative values of t is ignored or suppressed. This means that $F(s)$ contains information on the behaviour of $f(t)$ only for $t \geqslant 0$, so that the Laplace transform is not a suitable tool for investigating problems in which values of $f(t)$ for $t < 0$ are relevant. In most engineering applications this does not cause any problems, since we are then concerned with physical systems for which the functions we are dealing with vary with time t. An attribute of physical realizable systems is that they are **non-anticipatory** in the sense that there is no output (or response) until an input (or excitation) is applied. Because of this causal relationship between the input and output, we define a function $f(t)$ to be **causal** if $f(t) = 0$ $(t < 0)$. In general, however, unless the domain is clearly specified, a function $f(t)$ is normally intepreted as being defined for all real values, both positive and negative, of t. Making use of the Heaviside unit step function $H(t)$ (see also Section 2.5.1), where

$$H(t) = \begin{cases} 0 & (t < 0) \\ 1 & (t \geqslant 0) \end{cases}$$

we have

$$f(t)H(t) = \begin{cases} 0 & (t < 0) \\ f(t) & (t \geqslant 0) \end{cases}$$

Thus the effect of multiplying $f(t)$ by $H(t)$ is to convert it into a causal function. Graphically, the relationship between $f(t)$ and $f(t)H(t)$ is as shown in Figure 2.3.

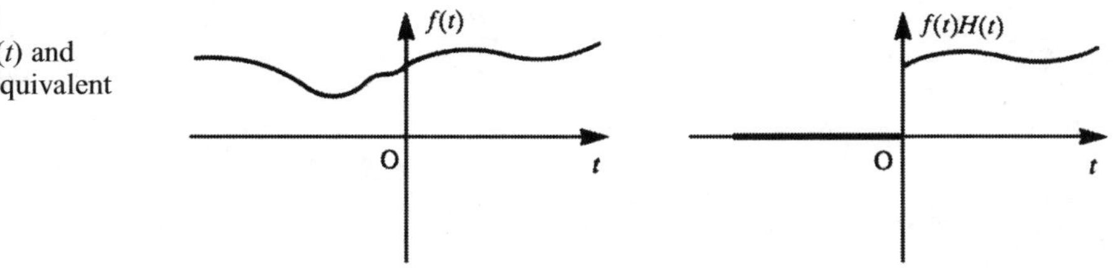

Figure 2.3 Graph of $f(t)$ and its causal equivalent function.

It follows that the corresponding Laplace transform $F(s)$ contains full information on the behaviour of $f(t)H(t)$. Consequently, strictly speaking one should refer to $\{f(t)H(t), F(s)\}$ rather than $\{f(t), F(s)\}$ as being a Laplace transform pair. However, it is common practice to drop the $H(t)$ and assume that we are dealing with causal functions.

(d) If the behaviour of $f(t)$ for $t < 0$ is of interest then we need to use the alternative **two-sided** or **bilateral Laplace transform** of the function $f(t)$, defined by

$$\mathscr{L}_B\{f(t)\} = \int_{-\infty}^{\infty} e^{-st} f(t)\,dt \tag{2.3}$$

The Laplace transform defined by (2.2), with lower limit zero, is sometimes referred to as the **one-sided** or **unilateral Laplace transform** of the function $f(t)$. In this chapter we shall concern ourselves only with the latter transform, and refer to it simply as the Laplace transform of the function $f(t)$. Note that when $f(t)$ is a causal function,

$$\mathscr{L}_B\{f(t)\} = \mathscr{L}\{f(t)\}$$

(e) Another issue concerning the lower limit of zero is the interpretation of $f(0)$ when $f(t)$ has a peculiarity at the origin. The question then arises as to whether or not we should include the peculiarity and take the lower limit as 0^- or exclude it and take the lower limit as 0^+ (as conventional 0^- and 0^+ denote values of t just to the left and right of the origin respectively). Provided we are consistent, we can take either, both interpretations being adopted in practice. In order to accommodate any peculiarities that may occur at $t = 0$, such as an impulse applied at $t = 0$, we take 0^- as the lower limit and interpret (2.2) as

$$\mathscr{L}\{f(t)\} = F(s) = \int_{0^-}^{\infty} e^{-st} f(t)\,dt \tag{2.4}$$

We shall return to this issue when considering the impulse response in Section 2.5.8.

2.2.2 Transforms of simple functions

In this section we obtain the Laplace transformations of some simple functions.

Example 2.1 Determine the Laplace transform of the function

$$f(t) = c$$

where c is a constant.

Solution Using the definition (2.2),

$$\mathscr{L}(c) = \int_0^{\infty} e^{-st} c\,dt = \lim_{T\to\infty} \int_0^{T} e^{-st} c\,dt$$

$$= \lim_{T\to\infty} \left[-\frac{c}{s} e^{-st} \right]_0^T = \frac{c}{s}\left(1 - \lim_{T\to\infty} e^{-sT}\right)$$

Taking $s = \sigma + j\omega$, where σ and ω are real,

$$\lim_{T\to\infty} e^{-sT} = \lim_{T\to\infty} (e^{-(\sigma+j\omega)T}) = \lim_{T\to\infty} e^{-\sigma T}(\cos \omega T + j \sin \omega T)$$

A finite limit exists provided that $\sigma = \text{Re}(s) > 0$, when the limit is zero. Thus, provided that $\text{Re}(s) > 0$, the Laplace transform is

$$\mathscr{L}(c) = \frac{c}{s}, \quad \text{Re}(s) > 0$$

so that

$$\left.\begin{aligned} f(t) &= c \\ F(s) &= \frac{c}{s} \end{aligned}\right\} \quad \text{Re}(s) > 0 \tag{2.5}$$

constitute an example of a Laplace transform pair.

Example 2.2 Determine the Laplace transform of the ramp function

$$f(t) = t$$

Solution From the definition (2.2),

$$\mathscr{L}\{t\} = \int_0^\infty e^{-st} t \,dt = \lim_{T\to\infty} \int_0^T e^{-st} t \,dt$$

$$= \lim_{T\to\infty} \left[-\frac{t}{s} e^{-st} - \frac{e^{-st}}{s^2} \right]_0^T = \frac{1}{s^2} - \lim_{T\to\infty} \frac{Te^{-sT}}{s} - \lim_{T\to\infty} \frac{e^{-sT}}{s^2}$$

Following the same procedure as in Example 2.1, limits exist provided that $\mathrm{Re}(s) > 0$, when

$$\lim_{T\to\infty} \frac{Te^{-sT}}{s} = \lim_{T\to\infty} \frac{e^{-sT}}{s^2} = 0$$

Thus, provided that $\mathrm{Re}(s) > 0$,

$$\mathscr{L}\{t\} = \frac{1}{s^2}$$

giving us the Laplace transform pair

$$\left. \begin{aligned} f(t) &= t \\ F(s) &= \frac{1}{s^2} \end{aligned} \right\} \quad \mathrm{Re}(s) > 0 \tag{2.6}$$

Example 2.3 Determine the Laplace transform of the one-sided exponential function

$$f(t) = e^{kt}$$

Solution The definition (2.2) gives

$$\mathscr{L}\{e^{kt}\} = \int_0^\infty e^{-st} e^{kt} \,dt = \lim_{T\to\infty} \int_0^T e^{-(s-k)t} \,dt$$

$$= \lim_{T\to\infty} \frac{-1}{s-k} [e^{-(s-k)t}]_0^T = \frac{1}{s-k} \left(1 - \lim_{T\to\infty} e^{-(s-k)T} \right)$$

Writing $s = \sigma + j\omega$, where σ and ω are real, we have

$$\lim_{T\to\infty} e^{-(s-k)T} = \lim_{T\to\infty} e^{-(\sigma-k)T} e^{j\omega T}$$

If k is real, then, provided that $\sigma = \mathrm{Re}(s) > k$, the limit exists, and is zero. If k is complex, say $k = a + jb$, then the limit will also exist, and be zero, provided that $\sigma > a$ (that is, $\mathrm{Re}(s) > \mathrm{Re}(k)$). Under these conditions, we then have

$$\mathscr{L}\{e^{kt}\} = \frac{1}{s-k}$$

giving us the Laplace transform pair

$$\left.\begin{aligned} f(t) &= \mathrm{e}^{kt} \\ F(s) &= \frac{1}{s-k} \end{aligned}\right\} \quad \mathrm{Re}(s) > \mathrm{Re}(k) \tag{2.7}$$

Example 2.4 Determine the Laplace transforms of the sine and cosine functions

$$f(t) = \sin at, \qquad g(t) = \cos at$$

where a is a real constant.

Solution Since

$$\mathrm{e}^{\mathrm{j}at} = \cos at + \mathrm{j} \sin at$$

we may write

$$f(t) = \sin at = \mathrm{Im}\, \mathrm{e}^{\mathrm{j}at}$$

$$g(t) = \cos at = \mathrm{Re}\, \mathrm{e}^{\mathrm{j}at}$$

Using this formulation, the required transforms may be obtained from the result

$$\mathscr{L}\{\mathrm{e}^{kt}\} = \frac{1}{s-k}, \quad \mathrm{Re}(s) > \mathrm{Re}(k)$$

of Example 2.3.

Taking $k = \mathrm{j}a$ in this result gives

$$\mathscr{L}\{\mathrm{e}^{\mathrm{j}at}\} = \frac{1}{s-\mathrm{j}a}, \quad \mathrm{Re}(s) > 0$$

or

$$\mathscr{L}\{\mathrm{e}^{\mathrm{j}at}\} = \frac{s+\mathrm{j}a}{s^2+a^2}, \quad \mathrm{Re}(s) > 0$$

Thus, equating real and imaginary parts and assuming s is real,

$$\mathscr{L}\{\sin at\} = \mathrm{Im}\, \mathscr{L}\{\mathrm{e}^{\mathrm{j}at}\} = \frac{a}{s^2+a^2}$$

$$\mathscr{L}\{\cos at\} = \mathrm{Re}\, \mathscr{L}\{\mathrm{e}^{\mathrm{j}at}\} = \frac{s}{s^2+a^2}$$

These results also hold when s is complex, giving us the Laplace transform pairs

$$\mathscr{L}\{\sin at\} = \frac{a}{s^2+a^2}, \quad \mathrm{Re}(s) > 0 \tag{2.8}$$

$$\mathscr{L}\{\cos at\} = \frac{s}{s^2+a^2}, \quad \mathrm{Re}(s) > 0 \tag{2.9}$$

In MATLAB, using the Symbolic Toolbox, the Laplace transform of a function $f(t)$ is obtained by entering the commands

```
syms s t
laplace(f(t))
```

with the purpose of the first command being that of setting up s and t as symbolic variables.

To search for a simpler form of the symbolic answer enter the command `simple(ans)`. Sometimes repeated use of this command may be necessary. To display the answer in a format that resembles typeset mathematics, use is made of the `pretty` command. Use of such commands will be illustrated later in some of the examples.

If the function $f(t)$ includes a parameter then this must be declared as a symbolic term at the outset. For example, the sequence of commands

```
syms s t a
laplace(sin(a*t))
```

gives, as required,

```
ans=a/(s^2+a^2)
```

as the Laplace transform of $\sin(at)$.

2.2.3 Existence of the Laplace transform

Clearly, from the definition (2.2), the Laplace transform of a function $f(t)$ exists if and only if the improper integral in the definition converges for at least some values of s. The examples of Section 2.2.2 suggest that this relates to the boundedness of the function, with the factor e^{-st} in the transform integral acting like a convergence factor in that the allowed values of Re(s) are those for which the integral converges. In order to be able to state sufficient conditions on $f(t)$ for the existence of $\mathcal{L}\{f(t)\}$, we first introduce the definition of a function of exponential order.

DEFINITION 2.1

A function $f(t)$ is said to be of **exponential order** as $t \to \infty$ if there exists a real number σ and positive constants M and T such that

$$|f(t)| < M e^{\sigma t}$$

for all $t > T$.

What this definition tells us is that a function $f(t)$ is of exponential order if it does not grow faster than some exponential function of the form $M e^{\sigma t}$. Fortunately most functions of practical significance satisfy this requirement, and are therefore of exponential order. There are, however, functions that are not of exponential order, an example being e^{t^2}, since this grows more rapidly than $M e^{\sigma t}$ as $t \to \infty$ whatever the values of M and σ.

Example 2.5 The function $f(t) = e^{3t}$ is of exponential order, with $\sigma \geqslant 3$.

Example 2.6 Show that the function $f(t) = t^3$ $(t \geqslant 0)$ is of exponential order.

Solution Since

$$e^{\alpha t} = 1 + \alpha t + \tfrac{1}{2}\alpha^2 t^2 + \tfrac{1}{6}\alpha^3 t^3 + \dots$$

it follows that for any $\alpha > 0$

$$t^3 < \frac{6}{\alpha^3} e^{\alpha t}$$

so that t^3 is of exponential order, with $\sigma > 0$.

It follows from Examples 2.5 and 2.6 that the choice of σ in Definition 2.1 is not unique for a particular function. For this reason, we define the greatest lower bound σ_c of the set of possible values of σ to be the **abscissa of convergence** of $f(t)$. Thus, in the case of the function $f(t) = e^{3t}$, $\sigma_c = 3$, while in the case of the function $f(t) = t^3$, $\sigma_c = 0$.

Returning to the definition of the Laplace transform given by (2.2), it follows that if $f(t)$ is a continuous function and is also of exponential order with abscissa of convergence σ_c, so that

$$|f(t)| < M e^{\sigma t}, \quad \sigma > \sigma_c$$

then, taking $T = 0$ in Definition 2.1,

$$|F(s)| = \left| \int_0^\infty e^{-st} f(t)\,dt \right| \leqslant \int_0^\infty |e^{-st}|\,|f(t)|\,dt$$

Writing $s = \sigma + j\omega$, where σ and ω are real, since $|e^{-j\omega t}| = 1$, we have

$$|e^{-st}| = |e^{-\sigma t}||e^{-j\omega t}| = |e^{-\sigma t}| = e^{-\sigma t}$$

so that

$$|F(s)| \leqslant \int_0^\infty e^{-\sigma t}\,|f(t)|\,dt \leqslant M \int_0^\infty e^{-\sigma t} e^{\sigma_d t}\,dt, \quad \sigma_d > \sigma_c$$

$$= M \int_0^\infty e^{-(\sigma - \sigma_d)t}\,dt$$

This last integral is finite whenever $\sigma = \text{Re}(s) > \sigma_d$. Since σ_d can be chosen arbitrarily such that $\sigma_d > \sigma_c$ we conclude that $F(s)$ exists for $\sigma > \sigma_c$. Thus a continuous function $f(t)$ of exponential order, with abscissa of convergence σ_c, has a Laplace transform

$$\mathscr{L}\{f(t)\} = F(s), \quad \text{Re}(s) > \sigma_c$$

where the region of convergence is as shown in Figure 2.4.

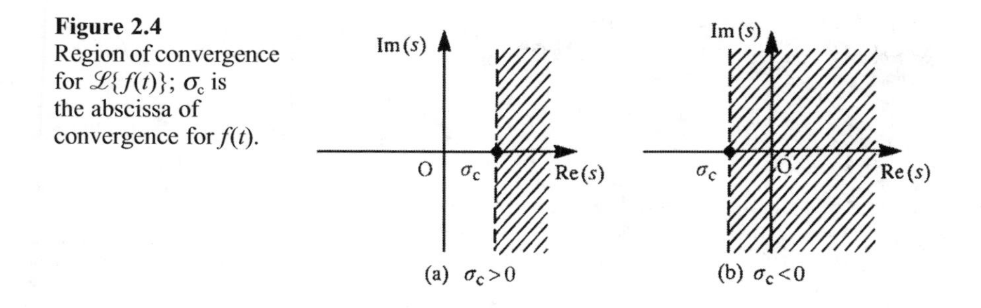

Figure 2.4 Region of convergence for $\mathcal{L}\{f(t)\}$; σ_c is the abscissa of convergence for $f(t)$.

In fact, the requirement that $f(t)$ be continuous is not essential, and may be relaxed to $f(t)$ being piecewise-continuous; that is, $f(t)$ must have only a finite number of finite discontinuities, being elsewhere continuous and bounded.

We conclude this section by stating a theorem that ensures the existence of a Laplace transform.

Theorem 2.1 **Existence of Laplace transform**

If the causal function $f(t)$ is piecewise-continuous on $[0, \infty]$ and is of exponential order, with abscissa of convergence σ_c, then its Laplace transform exists, with region of convergence $\text{Re}(s) > \sigma_c$ in the s domain; that is,

$$\mathcal{L}\{f(t)\} = F(s) = \int_0^\infty e^{-st} f(t)\,dt, \quad \text{Re}(s) > \sigma_c$$

end of theorem

The conditions of this theorem are *sufficient* for ensuring the existence of the Laplace transform of a function. They do not, however, constitute *necessary* conditions for the existence of such a transform, and it does not follow that if the conditions are violated then a transform does not exist. In fact, the conditions are more restrictive than necessary, since there exist functions with infinite discontinuities that possess Laplace transforms.

2.2.4 Properties of the Laplace transform

In this section we consider some of the properties of the Laplace transform that will enable us to find further transform pairs $\{f(t), F(s)\}$ without having to compute them directly using the definition. Further properties will be developed in later sections when the need arises.

Property 2.1: The linearity property

A fundamental property of the Laplace transform is its linearity, which may be stated as follows:

If $f(t)$ and $g(t)$ are functions having Laplace transforms and if α and β are any constants then

$$\mathscr{L}\{\alpha f(t) + \beta g(t)\} = \alpha\mathscr{L}\{f(t)\} + \beta\mathscr{L}\{g(t)\}$$

As a consequence of this property, we say that the Laplace transform operator $\mathscr{L}$ is a **linear operator**. A proof of the property follows readily from the definition (2.2), since

$$\begin{aligned}\mathscr{L}\{\alpha f(t) + \beta g(t)\} &= \int_0^\infty [\alpha f(t) + \beta g(t)]\,\mathrm{e}^{-st}\,\mathrm{d}t \\ &= \int_0^\infty \alpha f(t)\,\mathrm{e}^{-st}\,\mathrm{d}t + \int_0^\infty \beta g(t)\,\mathrm{e}^{-st}\,\mathrm{d}t \\ &= \alpha\int_0^\infty f(t)\,\mathrm{e}^{-st}\,\mathrm{d}t + \beta\int_0^\infty g(t)\,\mathrm{e}^{-st}\,\mathrm{d}t \\ &= \alpha\mathscr{L}\{f(t)\} + \beta\mathscr{L}\{g(t)\}\end{aligned}$$

Regarding the region of convergence, if $f(t)$ and $g(t)$ have abscissae of convergence σ_f and σ_g respectively, and $\sigma_1 > \sigma_f$, $\sigma_2 > \sigma_g$, then

$$|f(t)| < M_1\mathrm{e}^{\sigma_1 t}, \qquad |g(t)| < M_2\mathrm{e}^{\sigma_2 t}$$

It follows that

$$\begin{aligned}|\alpha f(t) + \beta g(t)| &\leqslant |\alpha|\,|f(t)| + |\beta|\,|g(t)| \leqslant |\alpha|M_1\,\mathrm{e}^{\sigma_1 t} + |\beta|M_2\,\mathrm{e}^{\sigma_2 t} \\ &\leqslant (|\alpha|M_1 + |\beta|M_2)\,\mathrm{e}^{\sigma t}\end{aligned}$$

where $\sigma = \max(\sigma_1, \sigma_2)$, so that the abscissa of convergence of the linear sum $\alpha f(t) + \beta g(t)$ is less than or equal to the maximum of those for $f(t)$ and $g(t)$.

This linearity property may clearly be extended to a linear combination of any finite number of functions.

Example 2.7 Determine $\mathscr{L}\{3t + 2\mathrm{e}^{3t}\}$.

Solution Using the results given in (2.6) and (2.7),

$$\mathscr{L}\{t\} = \frac{1}{s^2}, \quad \mathrm{Re}(s) > 0$$

$$\mathscr{L}\{\mathrm{e}^{3t}\} = \frac{1}{s-3}, \quad \mathrm{Re}(s) > 3$$

so, by the linearity property,

$$\begin{aligned}\mathscr{L}\{3t + 2\mathrm{e}^{3t}\} &= 3\mathscr{L}\{t\} + 2\mathscr{L}\{\mathrm{e}^{3t}\} \\ &= \frac{3}{s^2} + \frac{2}{s-3}, \quad \mathrm{Re}(s) > \max\{0, 3\} \\ &= \frac{3}{s^2} + \frac{2}{s-3}, \quad \mathrm{Re}(s) > 3\end{aligned}$$

Assuming that s and t have been set up as symbolic variables the command

```
laplace(3*t+2*exp(3*t))
```

returns

```
ans=3/s^2+2/(s-3)
```

Example 2.8 Determine $\mathcal{L}\{5 - 3t + 4\sin 2t - 6e^{4t}\}$.

Solution Using the results given in (2.5)–(2.8),

$$\mathcal{L}\{5\} = \frac{5}{s}, \quad \text{Re}(s) > 0 \qquad \mathcal{L}\{t\} = \frac{1}{s^2}, \quad \text{Re}(s) > 0$$

$$\mathcal{L}\{\sin 2t\} = \frac{2}{s^2+4}, \quad \text{Re}(s) > 0 \qquad \mathcal{L}\{e^{4t}\} = \frac{1}{s-4}, \quad \text{Re}(s) > 4$$

so, by the linearity property,

$$\begin{aligned}\mathcal{L}\{5 - 3t + 4\sin 2t - 6e^{4t}\} &= \mathcal{L}\{5\} - 3\mathcal{L}\{t\} + 4\mathcal{L}\{\sin 2t\} - 6\mathcal{L}\{e^{4t}\} \\ &= \frac{5}{s} - \frac{3}{s^2} + \frac{8}{s^2+4} - \frac{6}{s-4}, \quad \text{Re}(s) > \max\{0, 4\} \\ &= \frac{5}{s} - \frac{3}{s^2} + \frac{8}{s^2+4} - \frac{6}{s-4}, \quad \text{Re}(s) > 4\end{aligned}$$

Again, this answer can be confirmed using the command

```
laplace(5-3*t+4*sin(2*t)-6*exp(4*t))
```

The first shift property is another property that enables us to add more combinations to our repertoire of Laplace transform pairs. As with the linearity property, it will prove to be of considerable importance in our later discussions particularly when considering the inversion of Laplace transforms.

Property 2.2: The first shift property

The property is contained in the following theorem, commonly referred to as the **first shift theorem** or sometimes as the **exponential modulation theorem**.

Theorem 2.2 **The first shift theorem**

If $f(t)$ is a function having Laplace transform $F(s)$, with $\text{Re}(s) > \sigma_c$, then the function $e^{at}f(t)$ also has a Laplace transform, given by

$$\mathcal{L}\{e^{at}f(t)\} = F(s-a), \quad \text{Re}(s) > \sigma_c + \text{Re}(a)$$

Proof A proof of the theorem follows directly from the definition of the Laplace transform, since

$$\mathscr{L}\{e^{at}f(t)\} = \int_0^\infty e^{at}f(t)\,e^{-st}\,dt = \int_0^\infty f(t)\,e^{-(s-a)t}\,dt$$

Then, since

$$\mathscr{L}\{f(t)\} = F(s) = \int_0^\infty f(t)\,e^{-st}\,dt, \quad \text{Re}(s) > \sigma_c$$

we see that the last integral above is in structure exactly the Laplace transform of $f(t)$ itself, except that $s - a$ takes the place of s, so that

$$\mathscr{L}\{e^{at}f(t)\} = F(s-a), \quad \text{Re}(s-a) > \sigma_c$$

or

$$\mathscr{L}\{e^{at}f(t)\} = F(s-a), \quad \text{Re}(s) > \sigma_c + \text{Re}(a)$$

end of theorem

An alternative way of expressing the result of Theorem 2.2, which may be found more convenient in application, is

$$\mathscr{L}\{e^{at}f(t)\} = [\mathscr{L}\{f(t)\}]_{s\to s-a} = [F(s)]_{s\to s-a}$$

In other words, the theorem says that the Laplace transform of e^{at} times a function $f(t)$ is equal to the Laplace transform of $f(t)$ itself, with s replaced by $s - a$.

Example 2.9 Determine $\mathscr{L}\{t\,e^{-2t}\}$.

Solution From the result given in (2.6),

$$\mathscr{L}\{t\} = F(s) = \frac{1}{s^2}, \quad \text{Re}(s) > 0$$

so, by the first shift theorem,

$$\mathscr{L}\{t\,e^{-2t}\} = F(s+2) = [F(s)]_{s\to s+2}, \quad \text{Re}(s) > 0 - 2$$

that is,

$$\mathscr{L}\{t\,e^{-2t}\} = \frac{1}{(s+2)^2}, \quad \text{Re}(s) > -2$$

This is readily dealt with in MATLAB, for using the command

```
laplace(t*exp(-2*t))
```

returns

```
ans=1/(s+2)^2
```

as required.

Example 2.10 Determine $\mathscr{L}\{e^{-3t}\sin 2t\}$.

Solution From the result (2.8),

$$\mathscr{L}\{\sin 2t\} = F(s) = \frac{2}{s^2+4}, \quad \text{Re}(s) > 0$$

so, by the first shift theorem,

$$\mathscr{L}\{e^{-3t}\sin 2t\} = F(s+3) = [F(s)]_{s \to s+3}, \quad \text{Re}(s) > 0 - 3$$

that is,

$$\mathscr{L}\{e^{-3t}\sin 2t\} = \frac{2}{(s+3)^2+4} = \frac{2}{s^2+6s+13}, \quad \text{Re}(s) > -3$$

Using the command

```
laplace(exp(-3*t)*sin(2*t))
```

returns

```
ans=2/((s+3)^2+4)
```

Entering the command

```
simple(ans)
```

returns

```
ans=2/(s^2+6*s+13)
```

as an alternative form of the answer.

The function $e^{-3t}\sin 2t$ in Example 2.10 is a member of a general class of functions called **damped sinusoids**. These play an important role in the study of engineering systems, particularly in the analysis of vibrations. For this reason, we add the following two general members of the class to our standard library of Laplace transform pairs:

$$\mathscr{L}\{e^{-kt}\sin at\} = \frac{a}{(s+k)^2+a^2}, \quad \text{Re}(s) > -k \tag{2.10}$$

$$\mathscr{L}\{e^{-kt}\cos at\} = \frac{s+k}{(s+k)^2+a^2}, \quad \text{Re}(s) > -k \tag{2.11}$$

where in both cases k and a are real constants.

Property 2.3: Derivative-of-transform property

This property relates operations in the time domain to those in the transformed s domain, but initially we shall simply look upon it as a method of increasing our repertoire of Laplace transform pairs. The property is also sometimes referred to as the **multiplication-by-*t*** property. A statement of the property is contained in the following theorem.

Theorem 2.3 **Derivative of transform**

If $f(t)$ is a function having Laplace transform

$$F(s) = \mathscr{L}\{f(t)\}, \quad \text{Re}(s) > \sigma_c$$

then the functions $t^n f(t)$ $(n = 1, 2, \dots)$ also have Laplace transforms, given by

$$\mathscr{L}\{t^n f(t)\} = (-1)^n \frac{\mathrm{d}^n F(s)}{\mathrm{d}s^n}, \quad \text{Re}(s) > \sigma_c$$

Proof By definition,

$$\mathscr{L}\{f(t)\} = F(s) = \int_0^\infty \mathrm{e}^{-st} f(t)\,\mathrm{d}t$$

so that

$$\frac{\mathrm{d}^n F(s)}{\mathrm{d}s^n} = \frac{\mathrm{d}^n}{\mathrm{d}s^n} \int_0^\infty \mathrm{e}^{-st} f(t)\,\mathrm{d}t$$

Owing to the convergence properties of the improper integral involved, we can interchange the operations of differentiation and integration and differentiate with respect to s under the integral sign. Thus

$$\frac{\mathrm{d}^n F(s)}{\mathrm{d}s^n} = \int_0^\infty \frac{\partial^n}{\partial s^n} [\mathrm{e}^{-st} f(t)]\,\mathrm{d}t$$

which, on carrying out the repeated differentiation, gives

$$\frac{\mathrm{d}^n F(s)}{\mathrm{d}s^n} = (-1)^n \int_0^\infty \mathrm{e}^{-st} t^n f(t)\,\mathrm{d}t = (-1)^n \mathscr{L}\{t^n f(t)\}, \quad \text{Re}(s) > \sigma_c$$

the region of convergence remaining unchanged.

end of theorem

In other words, Theorem 2.3 says that differentiating the transform of a function with respect to s is equivalent to multiplying the function itself by $-t$. As with the previous properties, we can now use this result to add to our list of Laplace transform pairs.

Example 2.11 Determine $\mathscr{L}\{t \sin 3t\}$.

Solution Using the result (2.8),

$$\mathscr{L}\{\sin 3t\} = F(s) = \frac{3}{s^2 + 9}, \quad \text{Re}(s) > 0$$

so, by the derivative theorem,

$$\mathscr{L}\{t \sin 3t\} = -\frac{\mathrm{d}F(s)}{\mathrm{d}s} = \frac{6s}{(s^2 + 9)^2}, \quad \text{Re}(s) > 0$$

In MATLAB the command

```
laplace(t*sin(3*t))
```

gives the transform as

```
ans=1/(s^2+9)*sin(2*atan(3/s))
```

Applying the command

```
simple(ans)
```

reduces this to

```
ans=6/(s^2+9)/s/(1+9/s^2)
```

Repeating the simple command

```
simple(ans)
```

reduces the answer to the more desirable form

```
ans=6*s/(s^2+9)^2
```

Example 2.12 Determine $\mathscr{L}\{t^2\,\mathrm{e}^t\}$.

Solution From the result (2.7),

$$\mathscr{L}\{\mathrm{e}^t\} = F(s) = \frac{1}{s-1}, \quad \mathrm{Re}(s) > 1$$

so, by the derivative theorem,

$$\begin{aligned}\mathscr{L}\{t^2\mathrm{e}^t\} &= (-1)^2\frac{\mathrm{d}^2F(s)}{\mathrm{d}s^2}\\ &= (-1)^2\frac{\mathrm{d}^2}{\mathrm{d}s^2}\left(\frac{1}{s-1}\right)\\ &= (-1)\frac{\mathrm{d}}{\mathrm{d}s}\left(\frac{1}{(s-1)^2}\right)\\ &= \frac{2}{(s-1)^3}, \quad \mathrm{Re}(s) > 1\end{aligned}$$

Note that the result is easier to deduce using the first shift theorem.

Check that the MATLAB command `laplace(t^2*exp(t))` confirms the answer.

Example 2.13 Determine $\mathcal{L}\{t^n\}$, where n is a positive integer.

Solution Using the result (2.5),

$$\mathcal{L}\{1\} = \frac{1}{s}, \quad \text{Re}(s) > 0$$

so, by the derivative theorem,

$$\mathcal{L}\{t^n\} = (-1)^n \frac{\mathrm{d}^n}{\mathrm{d}s^n}\left(\frac{1}{s}\right) = \frac{n!}{s^{n+1}}, \quad \text{Re}(s) > 0$$

2.2.5 Table of Laplace transforms

It is appropriate at this stage to draw together the results proved to date for easy access. This is done in the form of two short tables. Figure 2.5(a) lists some Laplace transform pairs and Figure 2.5(b) lists the properties already considered.

Figure 2.5
(a) Table of Laplace transform pairs;
(b) some properties of the Laplace transform.

(a)

$f(t)$	$\mathcal{L}\{f(t)\} = F(s)$	Region of convergence
c, c a constant	$\dfrac{c}{s}$	$\text{Re}(s) > 0$
t	$\dfrac{1}{s^2}$	$\text{Re}(s) > 0$
t^n, n a positive integer	$\dfrac{n!}{s^{n+1}}$	$\text{Re}(s) > 0$
e^{kt}, k a constant	$\dfrac{1}{s-k}$	$\text{Re}(s) > \text{Re}(k)$
$\sin at$, a a real constant	$\dfrac{a}{s^2+a^2}$	$\text{Re}(s) > 0$
$\cos at$, a a real constant	$\dfrac{s}{s^2+a^2}$	$\text{Re}(s) > 0$
$e^{-kt}\sin at$, k and a real constants	$\dfrac{a}{(s+k)^2+a^2}$	$\text{Re}(s) > -k$
$e^{-kt}\cos at$, k and a real constants	$\dfrac{s+k}{(s+k)^2+a^2}$	$\text{Re}(s) > -k$

(b)

$$\mathcal{L}\{f(t)\} = F(s), \quad \text{Re}(s) > \sigma_1 \quad \text{and} \quad \mathcal{L}\{g(t)\} = G(s), \quad \text{Re}(s) > \sigma_2$$

Linearity: $\mathcal{L}\{\alpha f(t) + \beta g(t)\} = \alpha F(s) + \beta G(s), \quad \text{Re}(s) > \max(\sigma_1, \sigma_2)$

First shift theorem: $\mathcal{L}\{e^{at}f(t)\} = F(s-a), \quad \text{Re}(s) > \sigma_1 + \text{Re}(a)$

Derivative of transform:

$$\mathcal{L}\{t^n f(t)\} = (-1)^n \frac{\mathrm{d}^n F(s)}{\mathrm{d}s^n}, \quad (n = 1, 2, \dots), \ \text{Re}(s) > \sigma_1$$

2.2.6 Exercises

1. Use the definition of the Laplace transform to obtain the transforms of $f(t)$ when $f(t)$ is given by

   (a) $\cosh 2t$ (b) t^2 (c) $3 + t$ (d) $t\,e^{-t}$

   stating the region of convergence in each case.

2. What are the abscissae of convergence for the following functions?

   (a) e^{5t} (b) e^{-3t}
   (c) $\sin 2t$ (d) $\sinh 3t$
   (e) $\cosh 2t$ (f) t^4
   (g) $e^{-5t} + t^2$ (h) $3\cos 2t - t^3$
   (i) $3\,e^{2t} - 2\,e^{-2t} + \sin 2t$ (j) $\sinh 3t + \sin 3t$

3. Using the results shown in Figure 2.5, obtain the Laplace transforms of the following functions, stating the region of convergence:

   (a) $5 - 3t$ (b) $7t^3 - 2\sin 3t$
   (c) $3 - 2t + 4\cos 2t$ (d) $\cosh 3t$
   (e) $\sinh 2t$ (f) $5e^{-2t} + 3 - 2\cos 2t$
   (g) $4t\,e^{-2t}$ (h) $2e^{-3t}\sin 2t$
   (i) $t^2 e^{-4t}$ (j) $6t^3 - 3t^2 + 4t - 2$
   (k) $2\cos 3t + 5\sin 3t$ (l) $t\cos 2t$
   (m) $t^2\sin 3t$ (n) $t^2 - 3\cos 4t$
   (o) $t^2 e^{-2t} + e^{-t}\cos 2t + 3$

   Confirm your answers using MATLAB.

2.2.7 The inverse transform

The symbol $\mathscr{L}^{-1}\{F(s)\}$ denotes a causal function $f(t)$ whose Laplace transform is $F(s)$; that is,

$$\text{if} \quad \mathscr{L}\{f(t)\} = F(s) \quad \text{then} \quad f(t) = \mathscr{L}^{-1}\{F(s)\}$$

This correspondence between the functions $F(s)$ and $f(t)$ is called the **inverse Laplace transformation**, $f(t)$ being the **inverse transform** of $F(s)$, and $\mathscr{L}^{-1}$ being referred to as the **inverse Laplace transform operator**. These relationships are depicted in Figure 2.6.

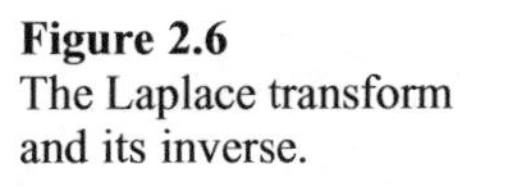

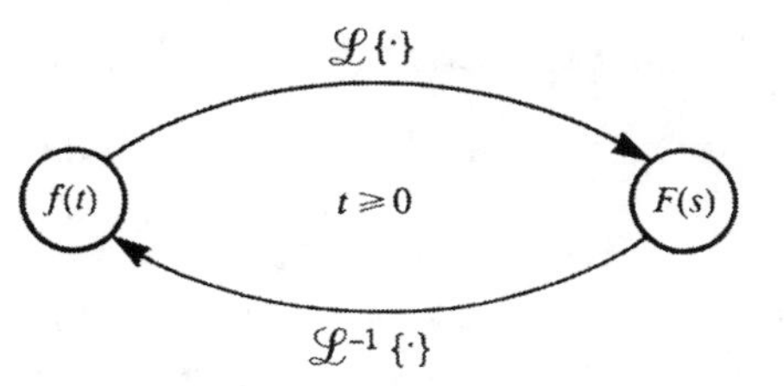

Figure 2.6 The Laplace transform and its inverse.

As was pointed out in observation (c) of Section 2.2.1, the Laplace transform $F(s)$ only determines the behaviour of $f(t)$ for $t \geqslant 0$. Thus $\mathscr{L}^{-1}\{F(s)\} = f(t)$ only for $t \geqslant 0$. When writing $\mathscr{L}^{-1}\{F(s)\} = f(t)$, it is assumed that $t \geqslant 0$ so strictly speaking, we should write

$$\mathscr{L}^{-1}\{F(s)\} = f(t)H(t) \tag{2.12}$$

Example 2.14 Since

$$\mathscr{L}\{e^{at}\} = \frac{1}{s-a}$$

if follows that

$$\mathscr{L}^{-1}\left\{\frac{1}{s-a}\right\} = e^{at}$$

Example 2.15 Since

$$\mathscr{L}\{\sin \omega t\} = \frac{\omega}{s^2+\omega^2}$$

it follows that

$$\mathscr{L}^{-1}\left\{\frac{\omega}{s^2+\omega^2}\right\} = \sin \omega t$$

The linearity property for the Laplace transform (Property 2.1) states that if α and β are any constants then

$$\begin{aligned}\mathscr{L}\{\alpha f(t) + \beta g(t)\} &= \alpha\mathscr{L}\{f(t)\} + \beta\mathscr{L}\{g(t)\}\\ &= \alpha F(s) + \beta G(s)\end{aligned}$$

It then follows from the above definition that

$$\begin{aligned}\mathscr{L}^{-1}\{\alpha F(s) + \beta G(s)\} &= \alpha f(t) + \beta g(t)\\ &= \alpha\mathscr{L}^{-1}\{F(s)\} + \beta\mathscr{L}^{-1}\{G(s)\}\end{aligned}$$

so that the inverse Laplace transform operator $\mathscr{L}^{-1}$ is also a linear operator.

2.2.8 Evaluation of inverse transforms

The most obvious way of finding the inverse transform of the function $F(s)$ is to make use of a table of transforms such as that given in Figure 2.5. Sometimes it is possible to write down the inverse transform directly from the table, but more often than not it is first necessary to carry out some algebraic manipulation on $F(s)$. In particular, we frequently need to determine the inverse transform of a rational function of the form $p(s)/q(s)$, where $p(s)$ and $q(s)$ are polynomials in s. In such cases the procedure is first to resolve the function into partial fractions and then to use the table of transforms.

Assuming that s and t are set up as symbolic variables, the MATLAB command

```
ilaplace (F(s))
```

will return the inverse Laplace transform of $F(s)$.

Example 2.16 Find

$$\mathscr{L}^{-1}\left\{\frac{1}{(s+3)(s-2)}\right\}$$

Solution First $1/(s+3)(s-2)$ is resolved into partial fractions, giving

$$\frac{1}{(s+3)(s-2)} = \frac{-\frac{1}{5}}{s+3} + \frac{\frac{1}{5}}{s-2}$$

Then, using the result $\mathscr{L}^{-1}\{1/(s+a)\} = e^{-at}$ together with the linearity property, we have

$$\mathscr{L}^{-1}\left\{\frac{1}{(s+3)(s-2)}\right\} = -\tfrac{1}{5}\mathscr{L}^{-1}\left\{\frac{1}{s+3}\right\} + \tfrac{1}{5}\mathscr{L}^{-1}\left\{\frac{1}{s-2}\right\} = -\tfrac{1}{5}e^{-3t} + \tfrac{1}{5}e^{2t}$$

The MATLAB command

```
ilaplace(1/((s+3)*(s-2)))
```

returns

```
ans=-1/5*exp(-3*t)+1/5*exp(2*t)
```

thus confirming the calculated answer.

Using the `pretty` command

```
pretty(ans)
```

returns the more readable display

```
ans=-1/5exp(-3t)+1/5exp(2t)
```

Example 2.17 Find

$$\mathscr{L}^{-1}\left\{\frac{s+1}{s^2(s^2+9)}\right\}$$

Solution Resolving $(s+1)/s^2(s^2+9)$ into partial fractions gives

$$\frac{s+1}{s^2(s^2+9)} = \frac{\frac{1}{9}}{s} + \frac{\frac{1}{9}}{s^2} - \frac{1}{9}\frac{s+1}{s^2+9} = \frac{\frac{1}{9}}{s} + \frac{\frac{1}{9}}{s^2} - \frac{1}{9}\frac{s}{s^2+3^2} - \frac{1}{27}\frac{3}{s^2+3^2}$$

Using the results in Figure 2.5, together with the linearity property, we have

$$\mathscr{L}^{-1}\left\{\frac{s+1}{s^2(s^2+9)}\right\} = \tfrac{1}{9} + \tfrac{1}{9}t - \tfrac{1}{9}\cos 3t - \tfrac{1}{27}\sin 3t$$

Check that the MATLAB sequence of commands

```
ilaplace((s+1)/(s^2*(s^2+9)))
pretty(ans)
```

confirms the answer.

2.2.9 Inversion using the first shift theorem

In Theorem 2.2 we saw that if $F(s)$ is the Laplace transform of $f(t)$ then, for a scalar a, $F(s-a)$ is the Laplace transform of $e^{at}f(t)$. This theorem normally causes little difficulty when used to obtain the Laplace transforms of functions, but it does frequently lead to problems when used to obtain inverse transforms. Expressed in the inverse form, the theorem becomes

$$\mathscr{L}^{-1}\{F(s-a)\} = e^{at}f(t)$$

The notation

$$\mathscr{L}^{-1}\{[F(s)]_{s\to s-a}\} = e^{at}[f(t)]$$

where $F(s) = \mathscr{L}\{f(t)\}$ and $[F(s)]_{s\to s-a}$ denotes that s in $F(s)$ is replaced by $s-a$, may make the relation clearer.

Example 2.18 Find

$$\mathscr{L}^{-1}\left\{\frac{1}{(s+2)^2}\right\}$$

Solution

$$\frac{1}{(s+2)^2} = \left[\frac{1}{s^2}\right]_{s\to s+2}$$

and, since $1/s^2 = \mathscr{L}\{t\}$, the shift theorem gives

$$\mathscr{L}^{-1}\left\{\frac{1}{(s+2)^2}\right\} = t\,e^{-2t}$$

Check that the MATLAB command

```
ilaplace(1/(s+2)^2)
```

confirms the answer.

Example 2.19 Find

$$\mathscr{L}^{-1}\left\{\frac{2}{s^2+6s+13}\right\}$$

Solution

$$\frac{2}{s^2+6s+13} = \frac{2}{(s+3)^2+4} = \left[\frac{2}{s^2+2^2}\right]_{s\to s+3}$$

and, since $2/(s^2+2^2) = \mathscr{L}\{\sin 2t\}$, the shift theorem gives

$$\mathscr{L}^{-1}\left\{\frac{2}{s^2+6s+13}\right\} = e^{-3t}\sin 2t$$

The MATLAB commands

```
ilaplace(2/(s^2+6*s+13))
simple(ans)
pretty(simple(ans))
```

return

```
ans=-1/2i(exp((-3+2i)t)-exp((-3-2i)t))
```

To obtain the same format as calculated, further manipulation is required as follows:

$$\begin{aligned} \text{ans} &= 1/2i[-e^{-3t}e^{2it} + e^{-3t}e^{-2it}] \\ &= e^{-3t}((e^{2it} - e^{-2it})/(2i)) \\ &= e^{-3t}\sin 2t \end{aligned}$$

Example 2.20

Find

$$\mathscr{L}^{-1}\left\{\frac{s+7}{s^2+2s+5}\right\}$$

Solution

$$\begin{aligned} \frac{s+7}{s^2+2s+5} &= \frac{s+7}{(s+1)^2+4} \\ &= \frac{(s+1)}{(s+1)^2+4} + 3\,\frac{2}{(s+1)^2+4} \\ &= \left[\frac{s}{s^2+2^2}\right]_{s\to s+1} + 3\left[\frac{2}{s^2+2^2}\right]_{s\to s+1} \end{aligned}$$

Since $s/(s^2+2^2) = \mathscr{L}\{\cos 2t\}$ and $2/(s^2+2^2) = \mathscr{L}\{\sin 2t\}$, the shift theorem gives

$$\mathscr{L}^{-1}\left\{\frac{s+7}{s^2+2s+5}\right\} = e^{-t}\cos 2t + 3e^{-t}\sin 2t$$

Check that the MATLAB commands

```
ilaplace((s+7)/(s^2+2*s+5))
pretty(ans)
```

return the calculated answer.

Example 2.21 Find

$$\mathscr{L}^{-1}\left\{\frac{1}{(s+1)^2(s^2+4)}\right\}$$

Solution Resolving $1/(s+1)^2(s^2+4)$ into partial fractions gives

$$\frac{1}{(s+1)^2(s^2+4)} = \frac{\frac{2}{25}}{s+1} + \frac{\frac{1}{5}}{(s+1)^2} - \frac{1}{25}\frac{2s+3}{s^2+4}$$

$$= \frac{\frac{2}{25}}{s+1} + \frac{1}{5}\left[\frac{1}{s^2}\right]_{s \to s+1} - \frac{2}{25}\frac{s}{s^2+2^2} - \frac{3}{50}\frac{2}{s^2+2^2}$$

Since $1/s^2 = \mathscr{L}\{t\}$, the shift theorem, together with the results in Figure 2.5, gives

$$\mathscr{L}^{-1}\left\{\frac{1}{(s+1)^2(s^2+4)}\right\} = \frac{2}{25}\mathrm{e}^{-t} + \frac{1}{5}\mathrm{e}^{-t}t - \frac{2}{25}\cos 2t - \frac{3}{50}\sin 2t$$

Check that the MATLAB commands

```
ilaplace(1/((s+1)^2*(s^2+4)))
pretty(ans)
```

return the calculated answer.

2.2.10 Exercise

4 Find $\mathscr{L}^{-1}\{F(s)\}$ when $F(s)$ is given by

(a) $\dfrac{1}{(s+3)(s+7)}$

(b) $\dfrac{s+5}{(s+1)(s-3)}$

(c) $\dfrac{s-1}{s^2(s+3)}$

(d) $\dfrac{2s+6}{s^2+4}$

(e) $\dfrac{1}{s^2(s^2+16)}$

(f) $\dfrac{s+8}{s^2+4s+5}$

(g) $\dfrac{s+1}{s^2(s^2+4s+8)}$

(h) $\dfrac{4s}{(s-1)(s+1)^2}$

(i) $\dfrac{s+7}{s^2+2s+5}$

(j) $\dfrac{3s^2-7s+5}{(s-1)(s-2)(s-3)}$

(k) $\dfrac{5s-7}{(s+3)(s^2+2)}$

(l) $\dfrac{s}{(s-1)(s^2+2s+2)}$

(m) $\dfrac{s-1}{s^2+2s+5}$

(n) $\dfrac{s-1}{(s-2)(s-3)(s-4)}$

(o) $\dfrac{3s}{(s-1)(s^2-4)}$

(p) $\dfrac{36}{s(s^2+1)(s^2+9)}$

(q) $\dfrac{2s^2+4s+9}{(s+2)(s^2+3s+3)}$

(r) $\dfrac{1}{(s+1)(s+2)(s^2+2s+10)}$

Confirm your answers using MATLAB.

2.3 Solution of differential equations

We first consider the Laplace transforms of derivatives and integrals, and then apply these to the solution of differential equations.

2.3.1 Transforms of derivatives

If we are to use Laplace transform methods to solve differential equations, we need to find convenient expressions for the Laplace transforms of derivatives such as $\mathrm{d}f/\mathrm{d}t$, $\mathrm{d}^2f/\mathrm{d}t^2$ or, in general, $\mathrm{d}^nf/\mathrm{d}t^n$. By definition,

$$\mathscr{L}\left\{\frac{\mathrm{d}f}{\mathrm{d}t}\right\}=\int_0^\infty \mathrm{e}^{-st}\frac{\mathrm{d}f}{\mathrm{d}t}\,\mathrm{d}t$$

Integrating by parts, we have

$$\mathscr{L}\left\{\frac{\mathrm{d}f}{\mathrm{d}t}\right\}=[\mathrm{e}^{-st}f(t)]_0^\infty+s\int_0^\infty \mathrm{e}^{-st}f(t)\,\mathrm{d}t=-f(0)+sF(s)$$

that is,

$$\mathscr{L}\left\{\frac{\mathrm{d}f}{\mathrm{d}t}\right\}=sF(s)-f(0) \tag{2.13}$$

In taking the Laplace transform of a derivative we have assumed that $f(t)$ is continuous at $t = 0$, so that $f(0^-) = f(0) = f(0^+)$. In Section 2.5.8, when considering the impulse function, $f(0^-) \neq f(0^+)$ and we have to revert to a more generalized calculus to resolve the problem.

The advantage of using the Laplace transform when dealing with differential equations can readily be seen, since it enables us to replace the operation of differentiation in the time domain by a simple algebraic operation in the s domain.

Note that to deduce the result (2.13), we have assumed that $f(t)$ is continuous, with a piecewise-continuous derivative $\mathrm{d}f/\mathrm{d}t$, for $t \geqslant 0$ and that it is also of exponential order as $t \to \infty$.

Likewise, if both $f(t)$ and $\mathrm{d}f/\mathrm{d}t$ are continuous on $t \geqslant 0$ and are of exponential order as $t \to \infty$, and $\mathrm{d}^2f/\mathrm{d}t^2$ is piecewise-continuous for $t \geqslant 0$, then

$$\mathscr{L}\left\{\frac{\mathrm{d}^2f}{\mathrm{d}t^2}\right\}=\int_0^\infty \mathrm{e}^{-st}\frac{\mathrm{d}^2f}{\mathrm{d}t^2}\,\mathrm{d}t=\left[\mathrm{e}^{-st}\frac{\mathrm{d}f}{\mathrm{d}t}\right]_0^\infty+s\int_0^\infty \mathrm{e}^{-st}\frac{\mathrm{d}f}{\mathrm{d}t}\,\mathrm{d}t=-\left[\frac{\mathrm{d}f}{\mathrm{d}t}\right]_{t=0}+s\mathscr{L}\left\{\frac{\mathrm{d}f}{\mathrm{d}t}\right\}$$

which, on using (2.12), gives

$$\mathscr{L}\left\{\frac{\mathrm{d}^2f}{\mathrm{d}t^2}\right\}=-\left[\frac{\mathrm{d}f}{\mathrm{d}t}\right]_{t=0}+s[sF(s)-f(0)]$$

leading to the result

$$\mathscr{L}\left\{\frac{\mathrm{d}^2f}{\mathrm{d}t^2}\right\}=s^2F(s)-sf(0)-\left[\frac{\mathrm{d}f}{\mathrm{d}t}\right]_{t=0}=s^2F(s)-sf(0)-f^{(1)}(0) \tag{2.14}$$

Clearly, provided that $f(t)$ and its derivatives satisfy the required conditions, this procedure may be extended to obtain the Laplace transform of $f^{(n)}(t) = \mathrm{d}^n f/\mathrm{d}t^n$ in the form

$$\begin{aligned}\mathscr{L}\{f^{(n)}(t)\} &= s^n F(s) - s^{n-1}f(0) - s^{n-2}f^{(1)}(0) - \ldots - f^{(n-1)}(0) \\ &= s^n F(s) - \sum_{i=1}^{n} s^{n-i} f^{(i-1)}(0)\end{aligned} \tag{2.15}$$

a result that may be readily proved by induction.

Again it is noted that in determining the Laplace transform of $f^{(n)}(t)$ we have assumed that $f^{(n-1)}(t)$ is continuous.

2.3.2 Transforms of integrals

In some applications the behaviour of a system may be represented by an **integro-differential equation**, which is an equation containing both derivatives and integrals of the unknown variable. For example, the current i in a series electrical circuit consisting of a resistance R, an inductance L and capacitance C, and subject to an applied voltage E, is given by

$$L\frac{\mathrm{d}i}{\mathrm{d}t} + iR + \frac{1}{C}\int_0^t i(\tau)\,\mathrm{d}\tau = E$$

To solve such equations directly, it is convenient to be able to obtain the Laplace transform of integrals such as $\int_0^t f(\tau)\,\mathrm{d}\tau$.

Writing

$$g(t) = \int_0^t f(\tau)\,\mathrm{d}\tau$$

we have

$$\frac{\mathrm{d}g}{\mathrm{d}t} = f(t), \quad g(0) = 0$$

Taking Laplace transforms,

$$\mathscr{L}\left\{\frac{\mathrm{d}g}{\mathrm{d}t}\right\} = \mathscr{L}\{f(t)\}$$

which, on using (2.13), gives

$$sG(s) = F(s)$$

or

$$\mathscr{L}\{g(t)\} = G(s) = \frac{1}{s}F(s) = \frac{1}{s}\mathscr{L}\{f(t)\}$$

leading to the result

$$\mathscr{L}\left\{\int_0^t f(\tau)\,\mathrm{d}\tau\right\} = \frac{1}{s}\mathscr{L}\{f(t)\} = \frac{1}{s}F(s) \tag{2.16}$$

Example 2.22 Obtain

$$\mathscr{L}\left\{\int_0^t (\tau^3 + \sin 2\tau)\,\mathrm{d}\tau\right\}$$

In this case $f(t) = t^3 + \sin 2t$, giving

$$F(s) = \mathscr{L}\{f(t)\} = \mathscr{L}\{t^3\} + \mathscr{L}\{\sin 2t\}$$

$$= \frac{6}{s^4} + \frac{2}{s^2 + 4}$$

so, by (2.16),

$$\mathscr{L}\left\{\int_0^t (\tau^3 + \sin 2\tau)\,\mathrm{d}\tau\right\} = \frac{1}{s}F(s) = \frac{6}{s^5} + \frac{2}{s(s^2 + 4)}$$

2.3.3 Ordinary differential equations

Having obtained expressions for the Laplace transforms of derivatives, we are now in a position to use Laplace transform methods to solve ordinary linear differential equations with constant coefficients. To illustrate this, consider the general second-order linear differential equation

$$a\frac{\mathrm{d}^2x}{\mathrm{d}t^2} + b\frac{\mathrm{d}x}{\mathrm{d}t} + cx = u(t) \quad (t \geqslant 0) \tag{2.17}$$

subject to the initial conditions $x(0) = x_0$, $\dot{x}(0) = v_0$ where as usual a dot denotes differentiaton with respect to time, t. Such a differential equation may model the dynamics of some system for which the variable $x(t)$ determines the **response** of the system to the **forcing** or **excitation** term $u(t)$. The terms **system input** and **system output** are also frequently used for $u(t)$ and $x(t)$ respectively. Since the differential equation is linear and has constant coefficients, a system characterized by such a model is said to be a **linear time-invariant system**.

Taking Laplace transforms of each term in (2.17) gives

$$a\mathscr{L}\left\{\frac{\mathrm{d}^2x}{\mathrm{d}t^2}\right\} + b\mathscr{L}\left\{\frac{\mathrm{d}x}{\mathrm{d}t}\right\} + c\mathscr{L}\{x\} = \mathscr{L}\{u(t)\}$$

which on using (2.13) and (2.14) leads to

$$a[s^2X(s) - sx(0) - \dot{x}(0)] + b[sX(s) - x(0)] + cX(s) = U(s)$$

Rearranging, and incorporating the given initial conditions, gives

$$(as^2 + bs + c)X(s) = U(s) + (as + b)x_0 + av_0$$

so that

$$X(s) = \frac{U(s) + (as + b)x_0 + av_0}{as^2 + bs + c} \tag{2.18}$$

Equation (2.18) determines the Laplace transform $X(s)$ of the response, from which, by taking the inverse transform, the desired time response $x(t)$ may be obtained.

Before considering specific examples, there are a few observations worth noting at this stage.

(a) As we have already noted in Section 2.3.1, a distinct advantage of using the Laplace transform is that it enables us to replace the operation of differentiation by an algebraic operation. Consequently, by taking the Laplace transform of each term in a differential equation, it is converted into an algebraic equation in the variable s. This may then be rearranged using algebraic rules to obtain an expression for the Laplace transform of the response; the desired time response is then obtained by taking the inverse transform.

(b) The Laplace transform method yields the complete solution to the linear differential equation, with the initial conditions automatically included. This contrasts with the classical approach, in which the general solution consists of two components, the **complementary function** and the **particular integral**, with the initial conditions determining the undetermined constants associated with the complementary function. When the solution is expressed in the general form (2.18), upon inversion the term involving $U(s)$ leads to a particular integral while that involving x_0 and v_0 gives a complementary function. A useful side issue is that an explicit solution for the transient is obtained that reflects the initial conditions.

(c) The Laplace transform method is ideally suited for solving initial-value problems; that is, linear differential equations in which all the initial conditions $x(0)$, $\dot{x}(0)$, and so on, at time $t = 0$ are specified. The method is less attractive for boundary-value problems, when the conditions on $x(t)$ and its derivatives are not all specified at $t = 0$, but some are specified at other values of the independent variable. It is still possible, however, to use the Laplace transform method by assigning arbitrary constants to one or more of the initial conditions and then determining their values using the given boundary conditions.

(d) It should be noted that the denominator of the right-hand side of (2.18) is the left-hand side of (2.17) with the operator $\mathrm{d}/\mathrm{d}t$ replaced by s. The denominator equated to zero also corresponds to the auxiliary equation or characteristic equation used in the classical approach. Given a specific initial-value problem, the process of obtaining a solution using Laplace transform methods is fairly straightforward, and is illustrated by Example 2.23.

Example 2.23 Solve the differential equation

$$\frac{\mathrm{d}^2x}{\mathrm{d}t^2} + 5\frac{\mathrm{d}x}{\mathrm{d}t} + 6x = 2\,\mathrm{e}^{-t} \quad (t \geqslant 0)$$

subject to the initial conditions $x = 1$ and $\mathrm{d}x/\mathrm{d}t = 0$ at $t = 0$.

Solution Taking Laplace transforms

$$\mathscr{L}\left\{\frac{\mathrm{d}^2x}{\mathrm{d}t^2}\right\} + 5\mathscr{L}\left\{\frac{\mathrm{d}x}{\mathrm{d}t}\right\} + 6\mathscr{L}\{x\} = 2\mathscr{L}\{\mathrm{e}^{-t}\}$$

leads to the transformed equation

$$[s^2X(s) - sx(0) - \dot{x}(0)] + 5[sX(s) - x(0)] + 6X(s) = \frac{2}{s+1}$$

which on rearrangement gives

$$(s^2 + 5s + 6)X(s) = \frac{2}{s+1} + (s + 5)x(0) + \dot{x}(0)$$

Incorporating the given initial conditions $x(0) = 1$ and $\dot{x}(0) = 0$ leads to

$$(s^2 + 5s + 6)X(s) = \frac{2}{s+1} + s + 5$$

That is,

$$X(s) = \frac{2}{(s+1)(s+2)(s+3)} + \frac{s+5}{(s+3)(s+2)}$$

Resolving the rational terms into partial fractions gives

$$X(s) = \frac{1}{s+1} - \frac{2}{s+2} + \frac{1}{s+3} + \frac{3}{s+2} - \frac{2}{s+3}$$

$$= \frac{1}{s+1} + \frac{1}{s+2} - \frac{1}{s+3}$$

Taking inverse transforms gives the desired solution

$$x(t) = e^{-t} + e^{-2t} - e^{-3t} \quad (t \geqslant 0)$$

In principle the procedure adopted in Example 2.23 for solving a second-order linear differential equation with constant coefficients is readily carried over to higher-order differential equations. A general nth-order linear differential equation may be written as

$$a_n \frac{d^n x}{dt^n} + a_{n-1} \frac{d^{n-1} x}{dt^{n-1}} + \ldots + a_0 x = u(t) \quad (t \geqslant 0) \tag{2.19}$$

where $a_n, a_{n-1}, \ldots, a_0$ are constants, with $a_n \neq 0$. This may be written in the more concise form

$$q(D)x(t) = u(t) \tag{2.20}$$

where D denotes the operator d/dt and $q(D)$ is the polynomial

$$q(D) = \sum_{r=0}^{n} a_r D^r$$

The objective is then to determine the response $x(t)$ for a given forcing function $u(t)$ subject to the given set of initial conditions

$$D^r x(0) = \left[\frac{d^r x}{dt^r}\right]_{t=0} = c_r \quad (r = 0, 1, \ldots, n-1)$$

Taking Laplace transforms in (2.20) and proceeding as before leads to

$$X(s) = \frac{p(s)}{q(s)}$$

where

$$p(s) = U(s) + \sum_{r=0}^{n-1} c_r \sum_{i=r+1}^{n} a_i s^{i-r-1}$$

Then, in principle, by taking the inverse transform, the desired response $x(t)$ may be obtained as

$$x(t) = \mathscr{L}^{-1}\left\{\frac{p(s)}{q(s)}\right\}$$

For high-order differential equations the process of performing this inversion may prove to be rather tedious, and matrix methods may be used.

To conclude this section, further worked examples are developed in order to help consolidate understanding of this method for solving linear differential equations.

Example 2.24 Solve the differential equation

$$\frac{d^2x}{dt^2} + 6\frac{dx}{dt} + 9x = \sin t \quad (t \geqslant 0)$$

subject to the initial conditions $x = 0$ and $dx/dt = 0$ at $t = 0$.

Solution Taking the Laplace transforms

$$\mathscr{L}\left\{\frac{d^2x}{dt^2}\right\} + 6\mathscr{L}\left\{\frac{dx}{dt}\right\} + 9\mathscr{L}\{x\} = \mathscr{L}\{\sin t\}$$

leads to the equation

$$[s^2X(s) - sx(0) - \dot{x}(0)] + 6[sX(s) - x(0)] + 9X(s) = \frac{1}{s^2 + 1}$$

which on rearrangement gives

$$(s^2 + 6s + 9)X(s) = \frac{1}{s^2 + 1} + (s + 6)x(0) + \dot{x}(0)$$

Incorporating the given initial conditions $x(0) = \dot{x}(0) = 0$ leads to

$$X(s) = \frac{1}{(s^2 + 1)(s + 3)^2}$$

Resolving into partial fractions gives

$$X(s) = \tfrac{3}{50}\frac{1}{s + 3} + \tfrac{1}{10}\frac{1}{(s + 3)^2} + \tfrac{2}{25}\frac{1}{s^2 + 1} - \tfrac{3}{50}\frac{s}{s^2 + 1}$$

that is,

$$X(s) = \tfrac{3}{50}\frac{1}{s + 3} + \tfrac{1}{10}\left[\frac{1}{s^2}\right]_{s\to s+3} + \tfrac{2}{25}\frac{1}{s^2 + 1} - \tfrac{3}{50}\frac{s}{s^2 + 1}$$

Taking inverse transforms, using the shift theorem, leads to the desired solution

$$x(t) = \tfrac{3}{50}e^{-3t} + \tfrac{1}{10}te^{-3t} + \tfrac{2}{25}\sin t - \tfrac{3}{50}\cos t \quad (t \geqslant 0)$$

In MATLAB the command `dsolve` computes symbolic solutions to differential equations. The letter D denotes differentiation whilst the symbols `D2`, `D3`, . . . , `DN` denote the 2nd, 3rd, . . . , Nth derivatives respectively. The dependent variable is that preceded by `D` whilst the default independent variable is `t`. The independent variable can be changed from `t` to another symbolic variable by including that variable as the last input variable. The initial conditions are specified by additional equations, such as `Dx(0)=6`. If the initial conditions are not specified the solution will contain constants of integration such as `C1` and `C2`.

To solve the differential equation of Example 2.24 we use the following MATLAB commands

```
x=dsolve('D2x+6*Dx+9*x=sin(t)','x(0)=0,Dx(0)=0');
pretty(simple(x))
```

which provide the solution

```
x=-3/50cos(t)+2/25sin(t)+3/50(1/exp(t)^3)+1/10(t/exp(t)^3)
```

It is left as an exercise to express $1/\exp(t)^3$ as e^{-3t}.

[*Note*: Inserting a semicolon (;) at the end of the `dsolve` command suppresses display of the output on entering the command.]

Example 2.25 Solve the differential equation

$$\frac{d^3x}{dt^3} + 5\frac{d^2x}{dt^2} + 17\frac{dx}{dt} + 13x = 1 \quad (t \geqslant 0)$$

subject to the initial conditions $x = dx/dt = 1$ and $d^2x/dt^2 = 0$ at $t = 0$.

Solution Taking Laplace transforms

$$\mathscr{L}\left\{\frac{d^3x}{dt^3}\right\} + 5\mathscr{L}\left\{\frac{d^2x}{dt^2}\right\} + 17\mathscr{L}\left\{\frac{dx}{dt}\right\} + 13\mathscr{L}\{x\} = \mathscr{L}\{1\}$$

leads to the equation

$$s^3X(s) - s^2x(0) - s\dot{x}(0) - \ddot{x}(0) + 5[s^2X(s) - sx(0) - \dot{x}(0)]$$
$$+ 17[sX(s) - x(0)] + 13X(s) = \frac{1}{s}$$

which on rearrangement gives

$$(s^3 + 5s^2 + 17s + 13)X(s) = \frac{1}{s} + (s^2 + 5s + 17)x(0) + (s + 5)\dot{x}(0) + \ddot{x}(0)$$

Incorporating the given initial conditions $x(0) = \dot{x}(0) = 1$ and $\ddot{x}(0) = 0$ leads to

$$X(s) = \frac{s^3 + 6s^2 + 22s + 1}{s(s^3 + 5s^2 + 17s + 13)}$$

Clearly $s + 1$ is a factor of $s^3 + 5s^2 + 17s + 13$, and by algebraic division we have

$$X(s) = \frac{s^3 + 6s^2 + 22s + 1}{s(s + 1)(s^2 + 4s + 13)}$$

Resolving into partial fractions,

$$X(s) = \frac{\frac{1}{13}}{s} + \frac{\frac{8}{5}}{s+1} - \frac{1}{65}\frac{44s + 7}{s^2 + 4s + 13} = \frac{\frac{1}{13}}{s} + \frac{\frac{8}{5}}{s+1} - \frac{1}{65}\frac{44(s+2) - 27(3)}{(s+2)^2 + 3^2}$$

Taking inverse transforms, using the shift theorem, leads to the solution

$$x(t) = \tfrac{1}{13} + \tfrac{8}{5}e^{-t} - \tfrac{1}{65}e^{-2t}(44 \cos 3t - 27 \sin 3t) \quad (t \geq 0)$$

Check that the MATLAB commands

```
x=dsolve('D3x+5*D2x+17*Dx+13*x=1','x(0)=1,Dx(0)=1,D2x(0)=0');
pretty(simple(x))
```

output the correct solution.

2.3.4 Simultaneous differential equations

In engineering we frequently encounter systems whose characteristics are modelled by a set of simultaneous linear differential equations with constant coefficients. The method of solution is essentially the same as that adopted in Section 2.3.3 for solving a single differential equation in one unknown. Taking Laplace transforms throughout, the system of simultaneous differential equations is transformed into a system of simultaneous algebraic equations, which are then solved for the transformed variables; inverse transforms then give the desired solutions.

Example 2.26 Solve for $t \geq 0$ the simultaneous first-order differential equations

$$\frac{dx}{dt} + \frac{dy}{dt} + 5x + 3y = e^{-t} \tag{2.21}$$

$$2\frac{dx}{dt} + \frac{dy}{dt} + x + y = 3 \tag{2.22}$$

subject to the initial conditions $x = 2$ and $y = 1$ at $t = 0$.

Solution Taking Laplace transforms in (2.21) and (2.22) gives

$$sX(s) - x(0) + sY(s) - y(0) + 5X(s) + 3Y(s) = \frac{1}{s+1}$$

$$2[sX(s) - x(0)] + sY(s) - y(0) + X(s) + Y(s) = \frac{3}{s}$$

Rearranging and incorporating the given initial conditions $x(0) = 2$ and $y(0) = 1$ leads to

$$(s + 5)X(s) + (s + 3)Y(s) = 3 + \frac{1}{s+1} = \frac{3s+4}{s+1} \quad \textbf{(2.23)}$$

$$(2s + 1)X(s) + (s + 1)Y(s) = 5 + \frac{3}{s} = \frac{5s+3}{s} \quad \textbf{(2.24)}$$

Hence, by taking Laplace transforms, the pair of simultaneous differential equations (2.21) and (2.22) in $x(t)$ and $y(t)$ has been transformed into a pair of simultaneous algebraic equations (2.23) and (2.24) in the transformed variables $X(s)$ and $Y(s)$. These algebraic equations may now be solved simultaneously for $X(s)$ and $Y(s)$ using standard algebraic techniques.

Solving first for $X(s)$ gives

$$X(s) = \frac{2s^2 + 14s + 9}{s(s+2)(s-1)}$$

Resolving into partial fractions,

$$X(s) = \frac{-\frac{9}{2}}{s} - \frac{\frac{11}{6}}{s+2} + \frac{\frac{25}{3}}{s-1}$$

which on inversion gives

$$x(t) = -\tfrac{9}{2} - \tfrac{11}{6}e^{-2t} + \tfrac{25}{3}e^{t} \quad (t \geqslant 0) \quad \textbf{(2.25)}$$

Likewise, solving for $Y(s)$ gives

$$Y(s) = \frac{s^3 - 22s^2 - 39s - 15}{s(s+1)(s+2)(s-1)}$$

Resolving into partial fractions,

$$Y(s) = \frac{\frac{15}{2}}{s} + \frac{\frac{1}{2}}{s+1} + \frac{\frac{11}{2}}{s+2} - \frac{\frac{25}{2}}{s-1}$$

which on inversion gives

$$y(t) = \tfrac{15}{2} + \tfrac{1}{2}e^{-t} + \tfrac{11}{2}e^{-2t} - \tfrac{25}{2}e^{t} \quad (t \geqslant 0)$$

Thus the solution to the given pair of simultaneous differential equations is

$$\left.\begin{aligned} x(t) &= -\tfrac{9}{2} - \tfrac{11}{6}e^{-2t} + \tfrac{25}{3}e^{t} \\ y(t) &= \tfrac{15}{2} + \tfrac{1}{2}e^{-t} + \tfrac{11}{2}e^{-2t} - \tfrac{25}{2}e^{t} \end{aligned}\right\} \quad (t \geqslant 0)$$

Note: When solving a pair of first-order simultaneous differential equations such as (2.21) and (2.22), an alternative approach to obtaining the value of $y(t)$ having obtained $x(t)$ is to use (2.21) and (2.22) directly.

Eliminating dy/dt from (2.21) and (2.22) gives

$$2y = \frac{dx}{dt} - 4x - 3 + e^{-t}$$

Substituting the solution obtained in (2.25) for $x(t)$ gives

$$2y = (\tfrac{11}{3}\,e^{-2t} + \tfrac{25}{3}\,e^{t}) - 4(-\tfrac{9}{2} - \tfrac{11}{6}\,e^{-2t} + \tfrac{25}{3})\,e^{t} - 3 + e^{-t}$$

leading as before to the solution

$$y = \tfrac{15}{2} + \tfrac{1}{2}\,e^{-t} + \tfrac{11}{2}\,e^{-2t} - \tfrac{25}{2}\,e^{t}$$

A further alternative is to express (2.23) and (2.24) in matrix form and solve for $X(s)$ and $Y(s)$ using Gaussian elimination.

In MATLAB the solution to the pair of simultaneous equations of Example 2.26 is obtained using the command

```
[x,y]=dsolve('Dx+Dy+5*x+3*y=exp(-t)','2*Dx+Dy+x+y=3',
'x(0)=2,y(0)=1')
```

which returns

```
x= -11/6*exp(-2*t)+25/3*exp(t)-9/2
y= -25/2*exp(t)+11/2*exp(-2*t)+15/2+1/2*exp(-t)
```

These may be simplified using the commands

```
pretty(simple(x))
pretty(simple(y))
```

In principle, the same procedure as used in Example 2.26 can be employed to solve a pair of higher-order simultaneous differential equations or a larger system of differential equations involving more unknowns. However, the algebra involved can become quite complicated, and matrix methods are usually preferred.

2.3.5 Exercises

To increase proficiency in the use of MATLAB use it to confirm your answers to Exercises 5 and 6.

5 Using Laplace transform methods, solve for $t \geqslant 0$ the following differential equations, subject to the specified initial conditions:

(a) $\dfrac{dx}{dt} + 3x = e^{-2t}$

subject to $x = 2$ at $t = 0$

(b) $3\dfrac{dx}{dt} - 4x = \sin 2t$

subject to $x = \tfrac{1}{3}$ at $t = 0$

(c) $\dfrac{d^2x}{dt^2} + 2\dfrac{dx}{dt} + 5x = 1$

subject to $x = 0$ and $\dfrac{dx}{dt} = 0$ at $t = 0$

(d) $\dfrac{d^2y}{dt^2} + 2\dfrac{dy}{dt} + y = 4\cos 2t$

subject to $y = 0$ and $\dfrac{dy}{dt} = 2$ at $t = 0$

(e) $\dfrac{d^2x}{dt^2} - 3\dfrac{dx}{dt} + 2x = 2\,e^{-4t}$

subject to $x = 0$ and $\dfrac{dx}{dt} = 1$ at $t = 0$

(f) $\dfrac{d^2x}{dt^2} + 4\dfrac{dx}{dt} + 5x = 3\,e^{-2t}$

subject to $x = 4$ and $\dfrac{dx}{dt} = -7$ at $t = 0$

(g) $\dfrac{d^2x}{dt^2} + \dfrac{dx}{dt} - 2x = 5\,e^{-t}\sin t$

subject to $x = 1$ and $\dfrac{dx}{dt} = 0$ at $t = 0$

(h) $\dfrac{d^2y}{dt^2} + 2\dfrac{dy}{dt} + 3y = 3t$

subject to $y = 0$ and $\dfrac{dy}{dt} = 1$ at $t = 0$

(i) $\dfrac{d^2x}{dt^2} + 4\dfrac{dx}{dt} + 4x = t^2 + e^{-2t}$

subject to $x = \frac{1}{2}$ and $\dfrac{dx}{dt} = 0$ at $t = 0$

(j) $9\dfrac{d^2x}{dt^2} + 12\dfrac{dx}{dt} + 5x = 1$

subject to $x = 0$ and $\dfrac{dx}{dt} = 0$ at $t = 0$

(k) $\dfrac{d^2x}{dt^2} + 8\dfrac{dx}{dt} + 16x = 16 \sin 4t$

subject to $x = -\frac{1}{2}$ and $\dfrac{dx}{dt} = 1$ at $t = 0$

(l) $9\dfrac{d^2y}{dt^2} + 12\dfrac{dy}{dt} + 4y = e^{-t}$

subject to $y = 1$ and $\dfrac{dy}{dt} = 1$ at $t = 0$

(m) $\dfrac{d^3x}{dt^3} - 2\dfrac{d^2x}{dt^2} - \dfrac{dx}{dt} + 2x = 2 + t$

subject to $x = 0$, $\dfrac{dx}{dt} = 1$ and $\dfrac{d^2x}{dt^2} = 0$ at $t = 0$

(n) $\dfrac{d^3x}{dt^3} + \dfrac{d^2x}{dt^2} + \dfrac{dx}{dt} + x = \cos 3t$

subject to $x = 0$, $\dfrac{dx}{dt} = 1$ and $\dfrac{d^2x}{dt^2} = 1$ at $t = 0$

6 Using Laplace transform methods, solve for $t \geqslant 0$ the following simultaneous differential equations subject to the given initial conditions:

(a) $2\dfrac{dx}{dt} - 2\dfrac{dy}{dt} - 9y = e^{-2t}$

$2\dfrac{dx}{dt} + 4\dfrac{dy}{dt} + 4x - 37y = 0$

subject to $x = 0$ and $y = \frac{1}{4}$ at $t = 0$

(b) $\dfrac{dx}{dt} + 2\dfrac{dy}{dt} + x - y = 5 \sin t$

$2\dfrac{dx}{dt} + 3\dfrac{dy}{dt} + x - y = e^{t}$

subject to $x = 0$ and $y = 0$ at $t = 0$

(c) $\dfrac{dx}{dt} + \dfrac{dy}{dt} + 2x + y = e^{-3t}$

$\dfrac{dy}{dt} + 5x + 3y = 5e^{-2t}$

subject to $x = -1$ and $y = 4$ at $t = 0$

(d) $3\dfrac{dx}{dt} + 3\dfrac{dy}{dt} - 2x = e^{t}$

$\dfrac{dx}{dt} + 2\dfrac{dy}{dt} - y = 1$

subject to $x = 1$ and $y = 1$ at $t = 0$

(e) $3\dfrac{dx}{dt} + \dfrac{dy}{dt} - 2x = 3 \sin t + 5 \cos t$

$2\dfrac{dx}{dt} + \dfrac{dy}{dt} + y = \sin t + \cos t$

subject to $x = 0$ and $y = -1$ at $t = 0$

(f) $\dfrac{dx}{dt} + \dfrac{dy}{dt} + y = t$

$\dfrac{dx}{dt} + 4\dfrac{dy}{dt} + x = 1$

subject to $x = 1$ and $y = 0$ at $t = 0$

(g) $2\dfrac{dx}{dt} + 3\dfrac{dy}{dt} + 7x = 14t + 7$

$5\dfrac{dx}{dt} - 3\dfrac{dy}{dt} + 4x + 6y = 14t - 14$

subject to $x = y = 0$ at $t = 0$

(h) $\dfrac{d^2x}{dt^2} = y - 2x \qquad \dfrac{d^2y}{dt^2} = x - 2y$

subject to $x = 4$, $y = 2$, $dx/dt = 0$ and $dy/dt = 0$ at $t = 0$

(i) $5\dfrac{d^2x}{dt^2} + 12\dfrac{d^2y}{dt^2} + 6x = 0$

$5\dfrac{d^2x}{dt^2} + 16\dfrac{d^2y}{dt^2} + 6y = 0$

subject to $x = \frac{7}{4}$, $y = 1$, $dx/dt = 0$ and $dy/dt = 0$ at $t = 0$

(j) $2\dfrac{d^2x}{dt^2} - \dfrac{d^2y}{dt^2} - \dfrac{dx}{dt} - \dfrac{dy}{dt} = 3y - 9x$

$2\dfrac{d^2x}{dt^2} - \dfrac{d^2y}{dt^2} + \dfrac{dx}{dt} + \dfrac{dy}{dt} = 5y - 7x$

subject to $x = dx/dt = 1$ and $y = dy/dt = 0$ at $t = 0$

2.4 Engineering applications: electrical circuits and mechanical vibrations

To illustrate the use of Laplace transforms, we consider here their application to the analysis of electrical circuits and vibrating mechanical systems. Since initial conditions are automatically taken into account in the transformation process, the Laplace transform is particularly attractive for examining the transient behaviour of such systems.

Using the commands adopted in Sections 2.3.3 and 2.3.4 MATLAB can be used throughout this section to confirm answers obtained.

2.4.1 Electrical circuits

Passive electrical circuits are constructed of three basic elements: **resistors** (having resistance R, measured in ohms Ω), **capacitors** (having capacitance C, measured in farads F) and **inductors** (having inductance L, measured in henries H), with the associated variables being **current** $i(t)$ (measured in amperes A) and **voltage** $v(t)$ (measured in volts V). The current flow in the circuit is related to the charge $q(t)$ (measured in coulombs C) by the relationship

$$i = \frac{\mathrm{d}q}{\mathrm{d}t}$$

Conventionally, the basic elements are represented symbolically as in Figure 2.7.

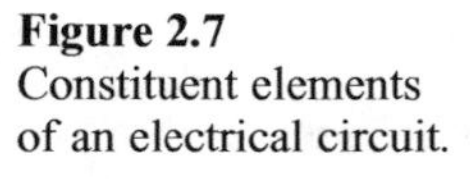
Figure 2.7 Constituent elements of an electrical circuit.

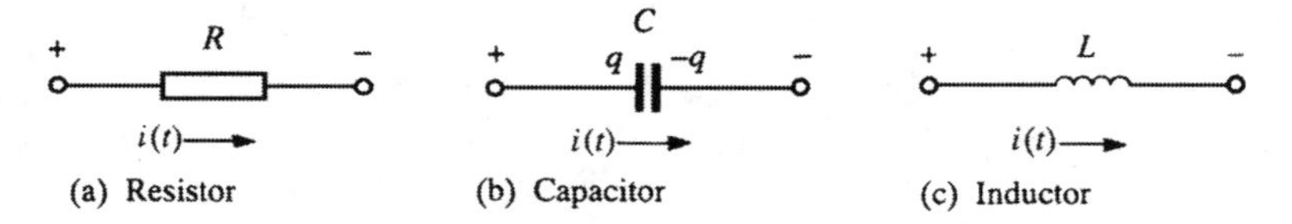

The relationship between the flow of current $i(t)$ and the voltage drops $v(t)$ across these elements at time t are

$$\text{voltage drop across resistor} = Ri \text{ (Ohm's law)}$$

$$\text{voltage drop across capacitor} = \frac{1}{C}\int i\,\mathrm{d}t = \frac{q}{C}$$

The interaction between the individual elements making up an electrical circuit is determined by **Kirchhoff's laws**:

Law 1

The algebraic sum of all the currents entering any junction (or node) of a circuit is zero.

Law 2

The algebraic sum of the voltage drops around any closed loop (or path) in a circuit is zero.

Use of these laws leads to circuit equations, which may then be analysed using Laplace transform techniques.

Example 2.27

The *LCR* circuit of Figure 2.8 consists of a resistor R, a capacitor C and an inductor L connected in series together with a voltage source $e(t)$. Prior to closing the switch at time $t = 0$, both the charge on the capacitor and the resulting current in the circuit are zero. Determine the charge $q(t)$ on the capacitor and the resulting current $i(t)$ in the circuit at time t given that $R = 160\ \Omega$, $L = 1$ H, $C = 10^{-4}$ F and $e(t) = 20$ V.

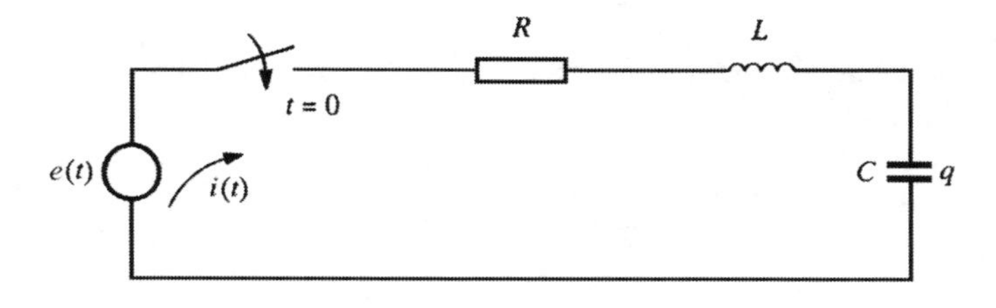

Figure 2.8 *LCR* circuit of Example 2.27.

Solution Applying Kirchhoff's second law to the circuit of Figure 2.8 gives

$$Ri + L\frac{\mathrm{d}i}{\mathrm{d}t} + \frac{1}{C}\int i\,\mathrm{d}t = e(t) \tag{2.26}$$

or, using $i = \mathrm{d}q/\mathrm{d}t$,

$$L\frac{\mathrm{d}^2q}{\mathrm{d}t^2} + R\frac{\mathrm{d}q}{\mathrm{d}t} + \frac{1}{C}q = e(t)$$

Substituting the given values for L, R, C and $e(t)$ gives

$$\frac{\mathrm{d}^2q}{\mathrm{d}t^2} + 160\frac{\mathrm{d}q}{\mathrm{d}t} + 10^4q = 20$$

Taking Laplace transforms throughout leads to the equation

$$(s^2 + 160s + 10^4)Q(s) = [sq(0) + \dot{q}(0)] + 160q(0) + \frac{20}{s}$$

where $Q(s)$ is the transform of $q(t)$. We are given that $q(0) = 0$ and $\dot{q}(0) = i(0) = 0$, so that this reduces to

$$(s^2 + 160s + 10^4)Q(s) = \frac{20}{s}$$

that is,

$$Q(s) = \frac{20}{s(s^2 + 160s + 10^4)}$$

Resolving into partial fractions gives

$$\begin{aligned}
Q(s) &= \frac{\frac{1}{500}}{s} - \frac{1}{500}\frac{s + 160}{s^2 + 160s + 10^4} \\
&= \frac{1}{500}\left[\frac{1}{s} - \frac{(s+80) + \frac{4}{3}(60)}{(s+80)^2 + (60)^2}\right] \\
&= \frac{1}{500}\left[\frac{1}{s} - \left[\frac{s + \frac{4}{3}\times 60}{s^2 + 60^2}\right]_{s \to s+80}\right]
\end{aligned}$$

Taking inverse transforms, making use of the shift theorem (Theorem 2.2), gives

$$q(t) = \tfrac{1}{500}(1 - e^{-80t}\cos 60t - \tfrac{4}{3}e^{-80t}\sin 60t)$$

The resulting current $i(t)$ in the circuit is then given by

$$i(t) = \frac{dq}{dt} = \tfrac{1}{3}e^{-80t}\sin 60t$$

Note that we could have determined the current by taking Laplace transforms in (2.26). Substituting the given values for L, R, C and $e(t)$ and using (2.26) leads to the transformed equation

$$160I(s) + sI(s) + \frac{10^4}{s}I(s) = \frac{20}{s}$$

that is,

$$I(s) = \frac{20}{(s^2 + 80)^2 + 60^2} \qquad (= sQ(s) \quad \text{since} \quad q(0) = 0)$$

which, on taking inverse transforms, gives as before

$$i(t) = \tfrac{1}{3}e^{-80t}\sin 60t$$

Example 2.28

In the parallel network of Figure 2.9 there is no current flowing in either loop prior to closing the switch at time $t = 0$. Deduce the currents $i_1(t)$ and $i_2(t)$ flowing in the loops at time t.

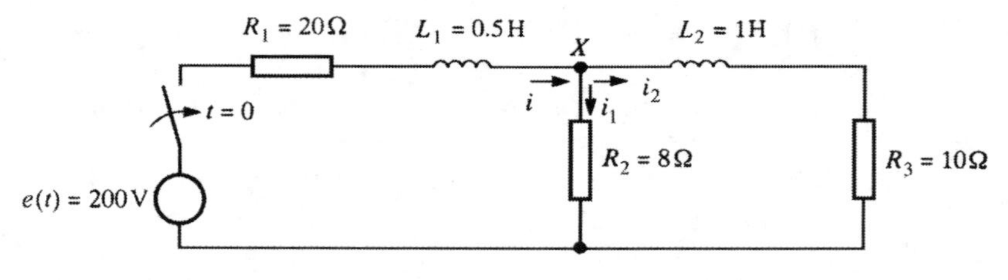

Figure 2.9 Parallel circuit of Example 2.28.

Solution

Applying Kirchhoff's first law to node X gives

$$i = i_1 + i_2$$

Applying Kirchhoff's second law to each of the two loops in turn gives

$$R_1(i_1 + i_2) + L_1\frac{d}{dt}(i_1 + i_2) + R_2 i_1 = 200$$

$$L_2\frac{di_2}{dt} + R_3 i_2 - R_2 i_1 = 0$$

Substituting the given values for the resistances and inductances gives

$$\left.\begin{aligned} &\frac{di_1}{dt} + \frac{di_2}{dt} + 56i_1 + 40i_2 = 400 \\ &\frac{di_2}{dt} - 8i_1 + 10i_2 = 0 \end{aligned}\right\} \qquad \textbf{(2.27)}$$

Taking Laplace transforms and incorporating the initial conditions $i_1(0) = i_2(0) = 0$ leads to the transformed equations

$$(s + 56)I_1(s) + (s + 40)I_2(s) = \frac{400}{s} \qquad \textbf{(2.28)}$$

$$-8I_1(s) + (s + 10)I_2(s) = 0 \qquad \textbf{(2.29)}$$

Hence

$$I_2(s) = \frac{3200}{s(s^2 + 74s + 880)}$$

$$= \frac{3200}{s(s + 59.1)(s + 14.9)}$$

Resolving into partial fractions gives

$$I_2(s) = \frac{3.64}{s} + \frac{1.22}{s + 59.1} - \frac{4.86}{s + 14.9}$$

which, on taking inverse transforms, leads to

$$i_2(t) = 3.64 + 1.22\,\mathrm{e}^{-59.1t} - 4.86\,\mathrm{e}^{-14.9t}$$

From (2.27),

$$i_1(t) = \tfrac{1}{8}\left(10i_2 + \frac{\mathrm{d}i_2}{\mathrm{d}t}\right)$$

that is,

$$i_1(t) = 4.55 - 7.49\,\mathrm{e}^{-59.1t} + 2.98\,\mathrm{e}^{-14.9t}$$

Note that as $t \to \infty$, the currents $i_1(t)$ and $i_2(t)$ approach the constant values 4.55 and 3.64 A respectively. (Note that $i(0) = i_1(0) + i_2(0) \neq 0$ due to rounding errors in the calculation.)

Example 2.29

A voltage $e(t)$ is applied to the primary circuit at time $t = 0$, and mutual induction M drives the current $i_2(t)$ in the secondary circuit of Figure 2.10. If, prior to closing the switch, the currents in both circuits are zero, determine the induced current $i_2(t)$ in the secondary circuit at time t when $R_1 = 4\ \Omega$, $R_2 = 10\ \Omega$, $L_1 = 2$ H, $L_2 = 8$ H, $M = 2$ H and $e(t) = 28 \sin 2t$ V.

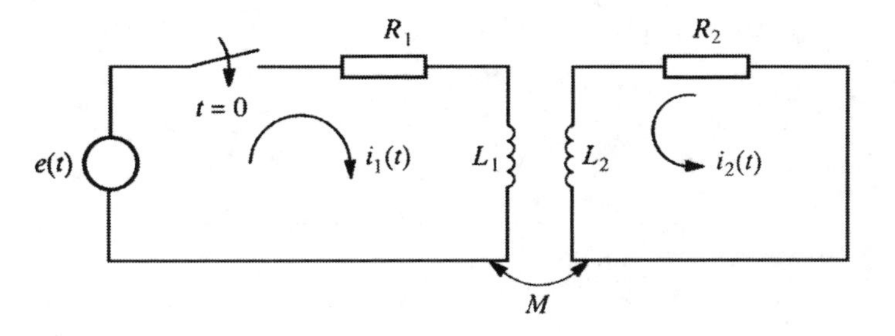

Figure 2.10 Circuit of Example 2.29.

Solution Applying Kirchhoff's second law to the primary and secondary circuits respectively gives

$$R_1 i_1 + L_1 \frac{\mathrm{d}i_1}{\mathrm{d}t} + M\frac{\mathrm{d}i_2}{\mathrm{d}t} = e(t)$$

$$R_2 i_2 + L_2 \frac{\mathrm{d}i_2}{\mathrm{d}t} + M\frac{\mathrm{d}i_1}{\mathrm{d}t} = 0$$

Substituting the given values for the resistances, inductances and applied voltage leads to

$$2\frac{\mathrm{d}i_1}{\mathrm{d}t} + 4i_1 + 2\frac{\mathrm{d}i_2}{\mathrm{d}t} = 28 \sin 2t$$

$$2\frac{\mathrm{d}i_1}{\mathrm{d}t} + 8\frac{\mathrm{d}i_2}{\mathrm{d}t} + 10i_2 = 0$$

Taking Laplace transforms and noting that $i_1(0) = i_2(0) = 0$ leads to the equations

$$(s + 2)I_1(s) + sI_2(s) = \frac{28}{s^2 + 4} \qquad \textbf{(2.30)}$$

$$sI_1(s) + (4s + 5)I_2(s) = 0 \qquad \textbf{(2.31)}$$

Solving for $I_2(s)$ yields

$$I_2(s) = -\frac{28s}{(3s + 10)(s + 1)(s^2 + 4)}$$

Resolving into partial fractions gives

$$I_2(s) = -\frac{\frac{45}{17}}{3s + 10} + \frac{\frac{4}{5}}{s + 1} + \frac{7}{85}\frac{s - 26}{s^2 + 4}$$

Taking inverse Laplace transforms gives the current in the secondary circuit as

$$i_2(t) = \tfrac{4}{5}\mathrm{e}^{-t} - \tfrac{15}{17}\mathrm{e}^{-10t/3} + \tfrac{7}{85}\cos 2t - \tfrac{91}{85}\sin 2t$$

As $t \to \infty$, the current will approach the sinusoidal response

$$i_2(t) = \tfrac{7}{85}\cos 2t - \tfrac{91}{85}\sin 2t$$

2.4.2 Mechanical vibrations

Mechanical translational systems may be used to model many situations, and involve three basic elements: **masses** (having mass M, measured in kg), **springs** (having spring stiffness K, measured in $\mathrm{N\,m^{-1}}$) and **dampers** (having damping coefficient B, measured in $\mathrm{N\,s\,m^{-1}}$). The associated variables are **displacement** $x(t)$ (measured in m) and **force** $F(t)$ (measured in N). Conventionally, the basic elements are represented symbolically as in Figure 2.11.

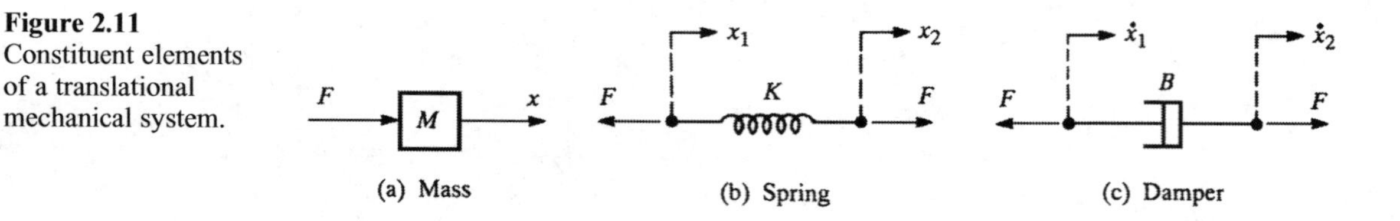

Figure 2.11 Constituent elements of a translational mechanical system.

Assuming we are dealing with ideal springs and dampers (that is, assuming that they behave linearly), the relationships between the forces and displacements at time t are:

mass: $F = M\dfrac{d^2x}{dt^2} = M\ddot{x}$ (Newton's law)

spring: $F = K(x_2 - x_1)$ (Hooke's law)

damper: $F = B\left(\dfrac{dx_2}{dt} - \dfrac{dx_1}{dt}\right) = B(\dot{x}_2 - \dot{x}_1)$

Using these relationships leads to the system equations, which may then be analysed using Laplace transform techniques.

Example 2.30

The mass of the mass–spring–damper system of Figure 2.12(a) is subjected to an externally applied periodic force $F(t) = 4 \sin \omega t$ at time $t = 0$. Determine the resulting displacement $x(t)$ of the mass at time t, given that $x(0) = \dot{x}(0) = 0$, for the two cases

(a) $\omega = 2$ (b) $\omega = 5$

In the case $\omega = 5$, what would happen to the response if the damper were missing?

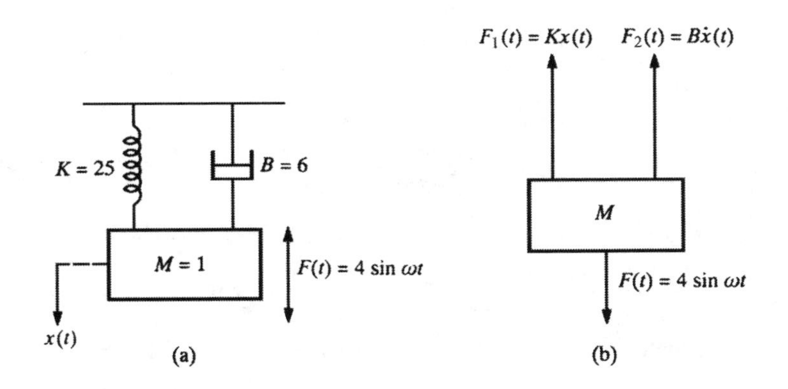

Figure 2.12 Mass–spring–damper system of Example 2.30.

Solution As indicated in Figure 1.12(b), the forces acting on the mass M are the applied force $F(t)$ and the restoring forces F_1 and F_2 due to the spring and damper respectively. Thus, by Newton's law,

$$M\ddot{x}(t) = F(t) - F_1(t) - F_2(t)$$

Since $M = 1$, $F(t) = 4 \sin \omega t$, $F_1(t) = Kx(t) = 25x(t)$ and $F_2(t) = B\dot{x}(t) = 6\dot{x}(t)$, this gives

$$\ddot{x}(t) + 6\dot{x}(t) + 25x(t) = 4 \sin \omega t \qquad \textbf{(2.32)}$$

as the differential equation representing the motion of the system.

Taking Laplace transforms throughout in (2.32) gives

$$(s^2 + 6s + 25)X(s) = [sx(0) + \dot{x}(0)] + 6x(0) + \frac{4\omega}{s^2 + \omega^2}$$

where $X(s)$ is the transform of $x(t)$. Incorporating the given initial conditions $x(0) = \dot{x}(0) = 0$ leads to

$$X(s) = \frac{4\omega}{(s^2 + \omega^2)(s^2 + 6s + 25)} \tag{2.33}$$

In case (a), with $\omega = 2$, (2.33) gives

$$X(s) = \frac{8}{(s^2 + 4)(s^2 + 6s + 25)}$$

which, on resolving into partial fractions, leads to

$$X(s) = \tfrac{4}{195}\frac{-4s + 14}{s^2 + 4} + \tfrac{2}{195}\frac{8s + 20}{s^2 + 6s + 25}$$

$$= \tfrac{4}{195}\frac{-4s + 14}{s^2 + 4} + \tfrac{2}{195}\frac{8(s + 3) - 4}{(s + 3)^2 + 16}$$

Taking inverse Laplace transforms gives the required response

$$x(t) = \tfrac{4}{195}(7 \sin 2t - 4 \cos 2t) + \tfrac{2}{195}\mathrm{e}^{-3t}(8 \cos 4t - \sin 4t) \tag{2.34}$$

In case (b), with $\omega = 5$, (2.33) gives

$$X(s) = \frac{20}{(s^2 + 25)(s^2 + 6s + 25)} \tag{2.35}$$

that is,

$$X(s) = \frac{-\tfrac{2}{15}s}{s^2 + 25} + \tfrac{1}{15}\frac{2(s + 3) + 6}{(s + 3)^2 + 16}$$

which, on taking inverse Laplace transforms, gives the required response

$$x(t) = -\tfrac{2}{15}\cos 5t + \tfrac{1}{15}\mathrm{e}^{-3t}(2 \cos 4t + \tfrac{3}{2}\sin 4t) \tag{2.36}$$

If the damping term were missing then (2.35) would become

$$X(s) = \frac{20}{(s^2 + 25)^2} \tag{2.37}$$

By Theorem 2.3,

$$\mathscr{L}\{t \cos 5t\} = -\frac{\mathrm{d}}{\mathrm{d}s}\mathscr{L}\{\cos 5t\} = -\frac{\mathrm{d}}{\mathrm{d}s}\left(\frac{s}{s^2 + 25}\right)$$

that is,

$$\mathscr{L}\{t \cos 5t\} = -\frac{1}{s^2 + 25} + \frac{2s^2}{(s^2 + 25)^2}$$

$$= \frac{1}{s^2 + 25} - \frac{50}{(s^2 + 25)^2}$$

$$= \tfrac{1}{5}\mathscr{L}\{\sin 5t\} - \frac{50}{(s^2 + 25)^2}$$

Thus, by the linearity property (2.11),

$$\mathscr{L}\{\tfrac{1}{5}\sin 5t - t\cos 5t\} = \frac{50}{(s^2+25)^2}$$

so that taking inverse Laplace transforms in (2.37) gives the response as

$$x(t) = \tfrac{2}{25}(\sin 5t - 5t\cos 5t)$$

Because of the term $t\cos 5t$, the response $x(t)$ is unbounded as $t \to \infty$. This arises because in this case the applied force $F(t) = 4\sin 5t$ is in **resonance** with the system (that is, the vibrating mass), whose natural oscillating frequency is $5/2\pi$ Hz, equal to that of the applied force. Even in the presence of damping, the amplitude of the system response is maximized when the applied force is approaching resonance with the system. (This is left as an exercise for the reader.) In the absence of damping we have the limiting case of **pure resonance**, leading to an unbounded response. Resonance is of practical importance, since, for example, it can lead to large and strong structures collapsing under what appears to be a relatively small force.

Example 2.31

Consider the mechanical system of Figure 2.13(a), which consists of two masses $M_1 = 1$ and $M_2 = 2$, each attached to a fixed base by a spring, having constants $K_1 = 1$ and $K_3 = 2$ respectively, and attached to each other by a third spring having constant $K_2 = 2$. The system is released from rest at time $t = 0$ in a position in which M_1 is displaced 1 unit to the left of its equilibrium position and M_2 is displaced 2 units to the right of its equilibrium position. Neglecting all frictional effects, determine the positions of the masses at time t.

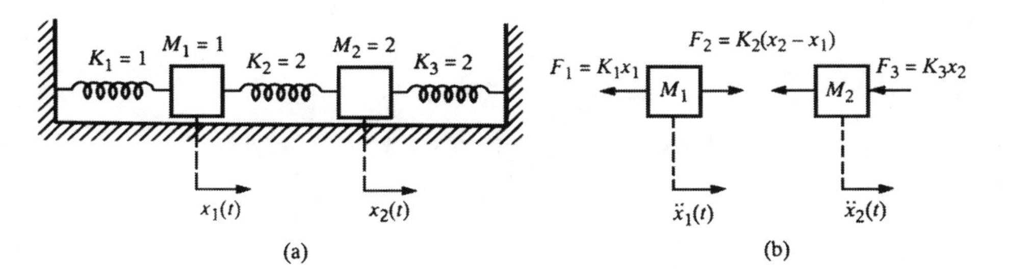

Figure 2.13 Two-mass system of Example 2.31.

Solution Let $x_1(t)$ and $x_2(t)$ denote the displacements of the masses M_1 and M_2 respectively from their equilibrium positions. Since frictional effects are neglected, the only forces acting on the masses are the restoring forces due to the springs, as shown in Figure 2.13(b). Applying Newton's law to the motions of M_1 and M_2 respectively gives

$$M_1\ddot{x}_1 = F_2 - F_1 = K_2(x_2 - x_1) - K_1x_1$$

$$M_2\ddot{x}_2 = -F_3 - F_2 = -K_3x_2 - K_2(x_2 - x_1)$$

which, on substituting the given values for M_1, M_2, K_1, K_2 and K_3, gives

$$\ddot{x}_1 + 3x_1 - 2x_2 = 0 \qquad \textbf{(2.38)}$$

$$2\ddot{x}_2 + 4x_2 - 2x_1 = 0 \qquad \textbf{(2.39)}$$

Taking Laplace transforms leads to the equations

$$(s^2 + 3)X_1(s) - 2X_2(s) = sx_1(0) + \dot{x}_1(0)$$

$$-X_1(s) + (s^2 + 2)X_2(s) = sx_2(0) + \dot{x}_2(0)$$

Since $x_1(t)$ and $x_2(t)$ denote displacements to the right of the equilibrium positions, we have $x_1(0) = -1$ and $x_2(0) = 2$. Also, the system is released from rest, so that $\dot{x}_1(0) = \dot{x}_2(0) = 0$. Incorporating these initial conditions, the transformed equations become

$$(s^2 + 3)X_1(s) - 2X_2(s) = -s \tag{2.40}$$

$$-X_1(s) + (s^2 + 2)X_2(s) = 2s \tag{2.41}$$

Hence

$$X_2(s) = \frac{2s^3 + 5s}{(s^2 + 4)(s^2 + 1)}$$

Resolving into partial fractions gives

$$X_2(s) = \frac{s}{s^2 + 1} + \frac{s}{s^2 + 4}$$

which, on taking inverse Laplace transforms, leads to the response

$$x_2(t) = \cos t + \cos 2t$$

Substituting for $x_2(t)$ in (2.39) gives

$$x_1(t) = 2x_2(t) + \ddot{x}_2(t)$$

$$= 2\cos t + 2\cos 2t - \cos t - 4\cos 2t$$

that is,

$$x_1(t) = \cos t - 2\cos 2t$$

Thus the positions of the masses at time t are

$$x_1(t) = \cos t - 2\cos 2t$$

$$x_2(t) = \cos t + \cos 2t$$

2.4.3 Exercises

7. Use the Laplace transform technique to find the transforms $I_1(s)$ and $I_2(s)$ of the respective currents flowing in the circuit of Figure 2.14, where $i_1(t)$ is that through the capacitor and $i_2(t)$ that through the resistance. Hence, determine $i_2(t)$. (Initially, $i_1(0) = i_2(0) = q_1(0) = 0$.) Sketch $i_2(t)$ for large values of t.

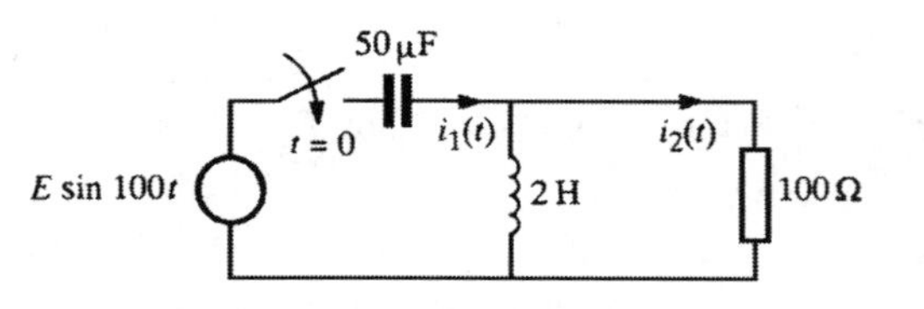

Figure 2.14 Circuit of Exercise 7.

8. At time $t = 0$, with no currents flowing, a voltage $v(t) = 10 \sin t$ is applied to the primary circuit of a transformer that has a mutual inductance of 1 H, as shown in Figure 2.15. Denoting the current flowing at time t in the secondary circuit by $i_2(t)$, show that

$$\mathscr{L}\{i_2(t)\} = \frac{10s}{(s^2 + 7s + 6)(s^2 + 1)}$$

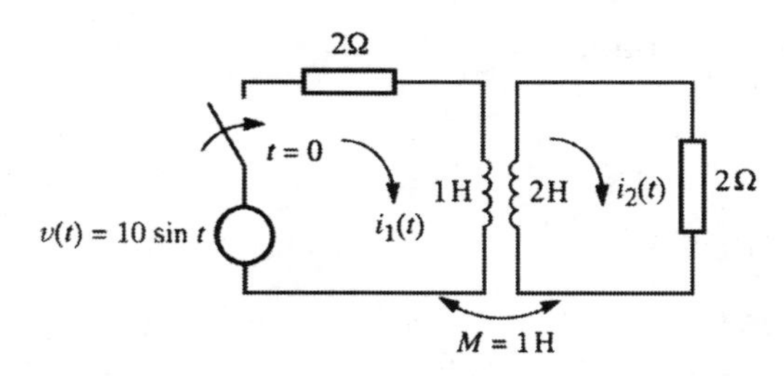

Figure 2.15 Circuit of Exercise 8.

and deduce that

$$i_2(t) = -e^{-t} + \tfrac{12}{37}e^{-6t} + \tfrac{25}{37}\cos t + \tfrac{35}{37}\sin t$$

9 In the circuit of Figure 2.16 there is no energy stored (that is, there is no charge on the capacitors and no current flowing in the inductances) prior to the closure of the switch at time $t = 0$. Determine $i_1(t)$ for $t > 0$ for a constant applied voltage $E_0 = 10$ V.

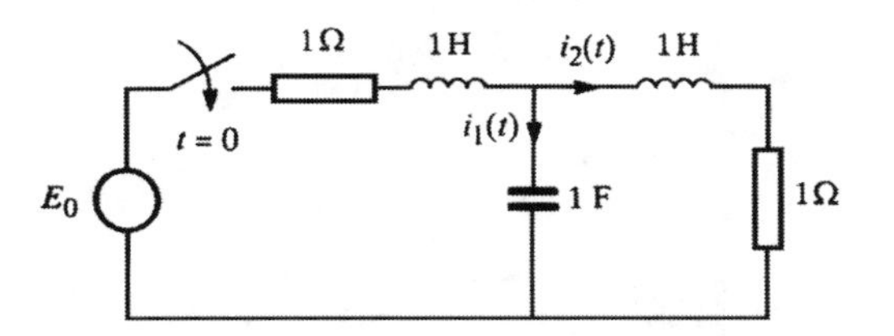

Figure 2.16 Circuit of Exercise 9.

10 Determine the displacements of the masses M_1 and M_2 in Figure 2.13 at time $t > 0$ when

$$M_1 = M_2 = 1$$

$$K_1 = 1, K_2 = 3 \quad \text{and} \quad K_3 = 9$$

What are the natural frequencies of the system?

11 When testing the landing-gear unit of a space vehicle, drop tests are carried out. Figure 2.17 is a schematic model of the unit at the instant when it first touches the ground. At this instant the spring is fully extended and the velocity of the mass is $\surd(2gh)$, where h is the height from which the unit has been dropped. Obtain the equation representing the displacement of the mass at time $t > 0$ when $M = 50$ kg, $B = 180$ N s m^{-1} and

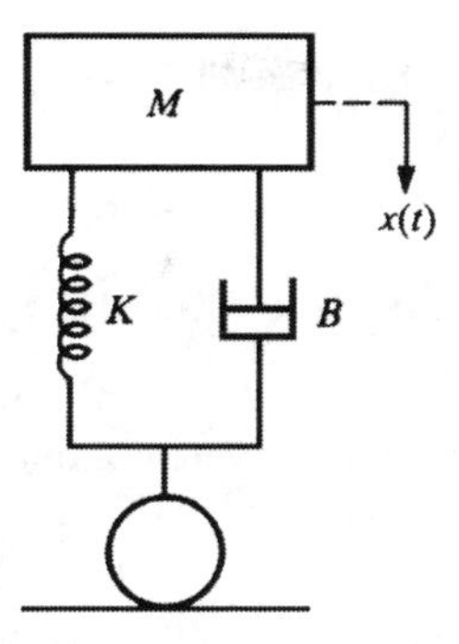

Figure 2.17 Landing-gear of Exercise 11.

$K = 474.5$ N m^{-1}, and investigate the effects of different dropping heights h. (g is the acceleration due to gravity, and may be taken as 9.8 m s^{-2}.)

12 Consider the mass–spring–damper system of Figure 2.18, which may be subject to two input forces $u_1(t)$ and $u_2(t)$. Show that the displacements $x_1(t)$ and $x_2(t)$ of the two masses are given by

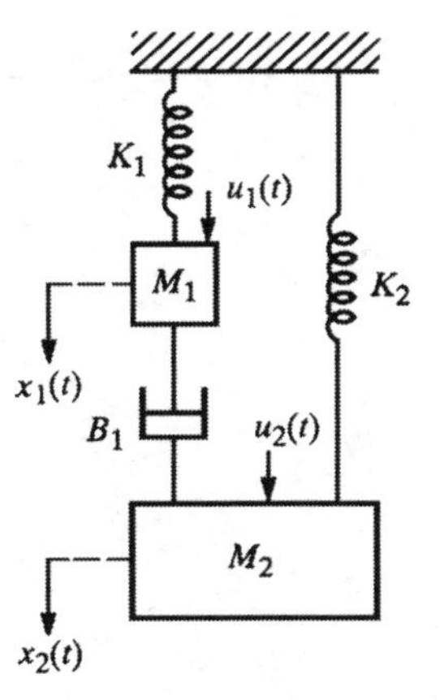

Figure 2.18 Mechanical system of Exercise 12.

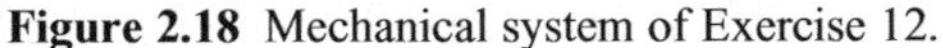

$$x_1(t) = \mathscr{L}^{-1}\left\{\frac{M_2s^2 + B_1s + K_2}{\Delta}U_1(s) + \frac{B_1s}{\Delta}U_2(s)\right\}$$

$$x_2(t) = \mathscr{L}^{-1}\left\{\frac{B_1s}{\Delta}U_1(s) + \frac{M_1s^2 + B_1s + K_1}{\Delta}U_2(s)\right\}$$

where

$$\Delta = (M_1s^2 + B_1s + K_1)(M_2s^2 + B_1s + K_2) - B_1^2s^2$$

2.5 Step and impulse functions

2.5.1 The Heaviside step function

In Sections 2.3 and 2.4 we considered linear differential equations in which the forcing functions were continuous. In many engineering applications the forcing function may frequently be discontinuous, for example a square wave resulting from an on/off switch. In order to accommodate such discontinuous functions, we use the Heaviside unit step function $H(t)$, which, as we saw in Section 2.2.1, is defined by

$$H(t) = \begin{cases} 0 & (t < 0) \\ 1 & (t \geqslant 0) \end{cases}$$

and is illustrated graphically in Figure 2.19(a). The Heaviside function is also frequently referred to simply as the **unit step function**. A function representing a unit step at $t = a$ may be obtained by a horizontal translation of duration a. This is depicted graphically in Figure 2.19(b), and defined by

$$H(t-a) = \begin{cases} 0 & (t < a) \\ 1 & (t \geqslant a) \end{cases}$$

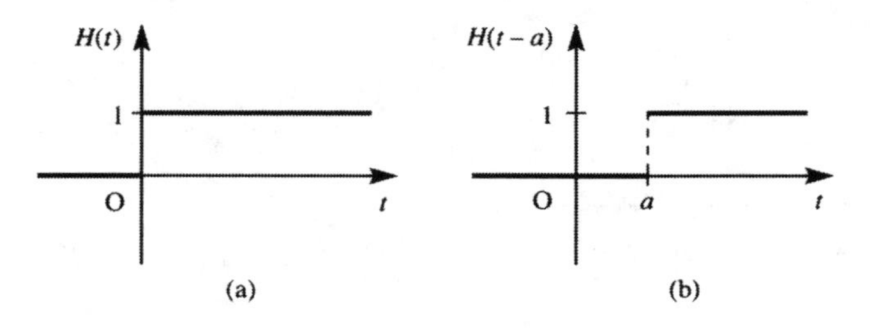

Figure 2.19 Heaviside unit step function.

The product function $f(t)H(t - a)$ takes values

$$f(t)H(t-a) = \begin{cases} 0 & (t < a) \\ f(t) & (t \geqslant a) \end{cases}$$

so the function $H(t - a)$ may be interpreted as a device for 'switching on' the function $f(t)$ at $t = a$. In this way the unit step function may be used to write a concise formulation of piecewise-continuous functions. To illustrate this, consider the piecewise-continuous function $f(t)$ illustrated in Figure 2.20 and defined by

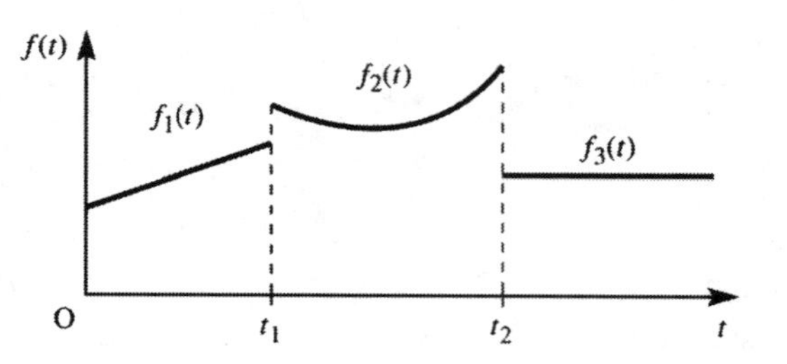

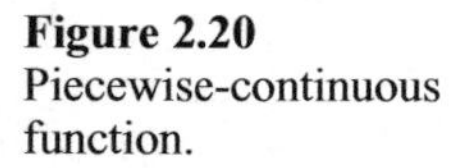

Figure 2.20 Piecewise-continuous function.

$$f(t) = \begin{cases} f_1(t) & (0 \leqslant t < t_1) \\ f_2(t) & (t_1 \leqslant t < t_2) \\ f_3(t) & (t \geqslant t_2) \end{cases}$$

To construct this function $f(t)$, we could use the following 'switching' operations:

(a) switch on the function $f_1(t)$ at $t = 0$;
(b) switch on the function $f_2(t)$ at $t = t_1$ and at the same time switch off the function $f_1(t)$;
(c) switch on the function $f_3(t)$ at $t = t_2$ and at the same time switch off the function $f_2(t)$.

In terms of the unit step function, the function $f(t)$ may thus be expressed as

$$f(t) = f_1(t)H(t) + [f_2(t) - f_1(t)]H(t - t_1) + [f_3(t) - f_2(t)]H(t - t_2)$$

Alternatively, $f(t)$ may be constructed using the **top hat function** $H(t - a) - H(t - b)$. Clearly,

$$H(t-a) - H(t-b) = \begin{cases} 1 & (a \leqslant t < b) \\ 0 & \text{otherwise} \end{cases} \tag{2.42}$$

which, as illustrated in Figure 2.21, gives

$$f(t)[H(t-a) - H(t-b)] = \begin{cases} f(t) & (a \leqslant t < b) \\ 0 & \text{otherwise} \end{cases}$$

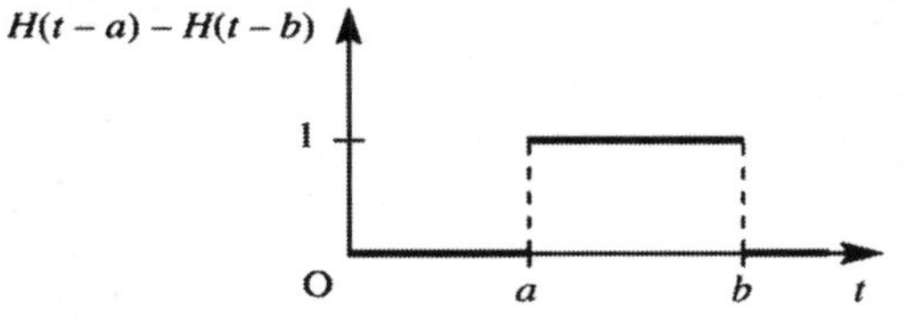

Figure 2.21
Top hat function.

Using this approach, the function $f(t)$ of Figure 2.20 may be expressed as

$$f(t) = f_1(t)[H(t) - H(t - t_1)] + f_2(t)[H(t - t_1) - H(t - t_2)] + f_3(t)H(t - t_2)$$

giving, as before,

$$f(t) = f_1(t)H(t) + [f_2(t) - f_1(t)]H(t - t_1) + [f_3(t) - f_2(t)]H(t - t_2)$$

It is easily checked that this corresponds to the given formulation, since for $0 \leqslant t < t_1$

$$H(t) = 1, \qquad H(t - t_1) = H(t - t_2) = 0$$

giving

$$f(t) = f_1(t) \quad (0 \leqslant t < t_1)$$

while for $t_1 \leqslant t < t_2$

$$H(t) = H(t - t_1) = 1, \qquad H(t - t_2) = 0$$

giving

$$f(t) = f_1(t) + [f_2(t) - f_1(t)] = f_2(t) \quad (t_1 \leqslant t \leqslant t_2)$$

and finally for $t \geqslant t_2$

$$H(t) = H(t - t_1) = H(t - t_2) = 1$$

giving

$$f(t) = f_1(t) + [f_2(t) - f_1(t)] + [f_3(t) - f_2(t)] = f_3(t) \quad (t \geqslant t_2)$$

Example 2.32

Express in terms of unit step functions the piecewise-continuous causal function

$$f(t) = \begin{cases} 2t^2 & (0 \leqslant t < 3) \\ t+4 & (3 \leqslant t < 5) \\ 9 & (t \geqslant 5) \end{cases}$$

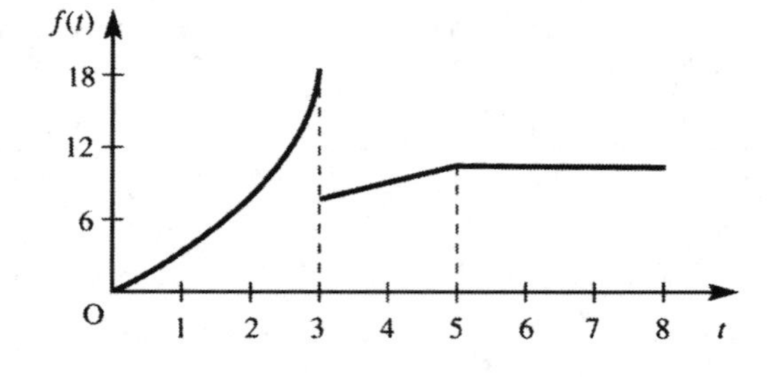

Figure 2.22 Piecewise-continuous function of Example 2.32.

Solution $f(t)$ is depicted graphically in Figure 2.22, and in terms of unit step functions it may be expressed as

$$f(t) = 2t^2H(t) + (t + 4 - 2t^2)H(t - 3) + (9 - t - 4)H(t - 5)$$

That is,

$$f(t) = 2t^2H(t) + (4 + t - 2t^2)H(t - 3) + (5 - t)H(t - 5)$$

Example 2.33

Express in terms of unit step functions the piecewise-continuous causal function

$$f(t) = \begin{cases} 0 & (t < 1) \\ 1 & (1 \leqslant t < 3) \\ 3 & (3 \leqslant t < 5) \\ 2 & (5 \leqslant t < 6) \\ 0 & (t \geqslant 6) \end{cases}$$

Solution $f(t)$ is depicted graphically in Figure 2.23, and in terms of unit step functions it may be expressed as

$$f(t) = 1H(t - 1) + (3 - 1)H(t - 3) + (2 - 3)H(t - 5) + (0 - 2)H(t - 6)$$

That is,

$$f(t) = 1H(t - 1) + 2H(t - 3) - 1H(t - 5) - 2H(t - 6)$$

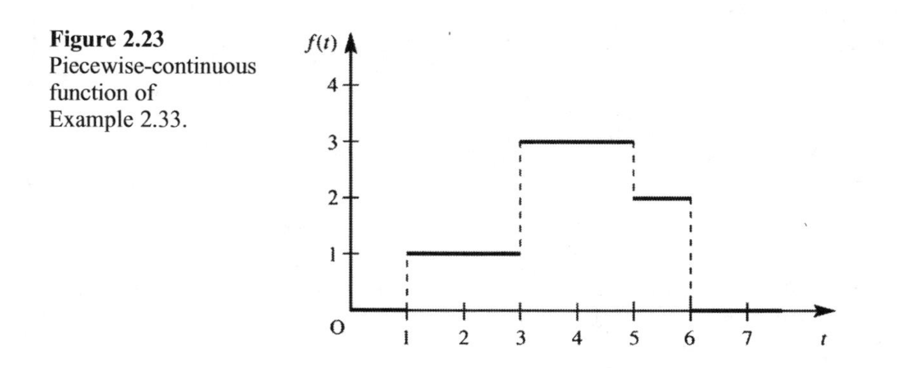

Figure 2.23 Piecewise-continuous function of Example 2.33.

2.5.2 Laplace transform of unit step function

By definition of the Laplace transform, the transform of $H(t-a)$, $a \geqslant 0$, is given by

$$\mathscr{L}\{H(t-a)\} = \int_0^\infty H(t-a)\,e^{-st}\,dt = \int_0^a 0\,e^{-st}\,dt + \int_a^\infty 1\,e^{-st}\,dt$$

$$= \left[\frac{e^{-st}}{-s}\right]_a^\infty = \frac{e^{-as}}{s}$$

That is,

$$\mathscr{L}\{H(t-a)\} = \frac{e^{-as}}{s} \quad (a \geqslant 0) \tag{2.43}$$

and in the particular case of $a = 0$

$$\mathscr{L}\{H(t)\} = \frac{1}{s} \tag{2.44}$$

This may be implemented in MATLAB using the commands

```
syms s t
H=sym('Heaviside(t)')
laplace(H)
```

which return

```
ans=1/s
```

It may also be obtained directly using the command

```
laplace(sym('Heaviside(t)'))
```

Likewise to obtain the Laplace transform of `H(t-2)` we use the commands

```
H2=sym('Heaviside(t-2)')
laplace(H2)
```

which return

```
ans=exp(-3*s)/s
```

Example 2.34

Determine the Laplace transform of the rectangular pulse

$$f(t) = \begin{cases} 0 & (t < a) \\ K & (a \leqslant t < b) \quad K \text{ constant}, \quad b > a > 0 \\ 0 & (t \geqslant b) \end{cases}$$

Solution

The pulse is depicted graphically in Figure 2.24. In terms of unit step functions, it may be expressed, using the top hat function, as

$$f(t) = K[H(t-a) - H(t-b)]$$

Then, taking Laplace transforms,

$$\mathscr{L}\{f(t)\} = K\mathscr{L}\{H(t-a)\} - K\mathscr{L}\{H(t-b)\}$$

Figure 2.24
Rectangular pulse.

which, on using the result (2.24), gives

$$\mathscr{L}\{f(t)\} = K\frac{e^{-as}}{s} - K\frac{e^{-bs}}{s}$$

That is,

$$\mathscr{L}\{f(t)\} = \frac{K}{s}(e^{-as} - e^{-bs})$$

Example 2.35

Determine the Laplace transform of the piecewise-constant function $f(t)$ shown in Figure 2.23.

Solution

From Example 2.33 $f(t)$ may be expressed as

$$f(t) = 1H(t-1) + 2H(t-3) - 1H(t-5) - 2H(t-6)$$

Taking Laplace transforms,

$$\mathscr{L}\{f(t)\} = 1\mathscr{L}\{H(t-1)\} + 2\mathscr{L}\{H(t-3)\} - 1\mathscr{L}\{H(t-5)\} - 2\mathscr{L}\{H(t-6)\}$$

which, on using the result (2.43), gives

$$\mathscr{L}\{f(t)\} = \frac{e^{-s}}{s} + 2\frac{e^{-3s}}{s} - \frac{e^{-5s}}{s} - 2\frac{e^{-6s}}{s}$$

That is,

$$\mathscr{L}\{f(t)\} = \frac{1}{s}(e^{-s} + 2e^{-3s} - e^{-5s} - 2e^{-6s})$$

Check that the same answer is obtained using the MATLAB sequence of commands

```
syms s t
H1=sym('Heaviside(t-1)');
H2=sym('Heaviside(t-3)');
H5=sym('Heaviside(t-5)');
H6=sym('Heaviside(t-6)');
laplace(H1-2*H3-H5-2*H6)
```

2.5.3 The second shift theorem

This theorem is dual to the first shift theorem given as Theorem 2.2, and is sometimes referred to as the **Heaviside** or **delay theorem**.

Theorem 2.4

If $\mathscr{L}\{f(t)\} = F(s)$ then for a positive constant a

$$\mathscr{L}\{f(t-a)H(t-a)\} = \text{e}^{-as}F(s)$$

Proof By definition,

$$\mathscr{L}\{f(t-a)H(t-a)\} = \int_0^\infty f(t-a)H(t-a)\,\text{e}^{-st}\,\text{d}t$$

$$= \int_a^\infty f(t-a)\,\text{e}^{-st}\,\text{d}t$$

Making the substitution $T = t - a$,

$$\mathscr{L}\{f(t-a)H(t-a)\} = \int_0^\infty f(T)\,\text{e}^{-s(T+a)}\,\text{d}T$$

$$= \text{e}^{-sa}\int_0^\infty f(T)\,\text{e}^{-sT}\,\text{d}T$$

Since $F(s) = \mathscr{L}\{f(t)\} = \int_0^\infty f(T)\,\text{e}^{-sT}$, it follows that

$$\mathscr{L}\{f(t-a)H(t-a)\} = \text{e}^{-as}F(s)$$

end of theorem

It is important to distinguish between the two functions $f(t)H(t-a)$ and $f(t-a)H(t-a)$. As we saw earlier, $f(t)H(t-a)$ simply indicates that the function $f(t)$ is 'switched on' at time $t = a$, so that

$$f(t)H(t-a) = \begin{cases} 0 & (t < a) \\ f(t) & (t \geqslant a) \end{cases}$$

On the other hand, $f(t-a)H(t-a)$ represents a translation of the function $f(t)$ by a units to the right (to the right, since $a > 0$), so that

$$f(t-a)H(t-a) = \begin{cases} 0 & (t < a) \\ f(t-a) & (t \geqslant a) \end{cases}$$

The difference between the two is illustrated graphically in Figure 2.25. $f(t-a)H(t-a)$ may be interpreted as representing the function $f(t)$ delayed in time by a units. Thus, when considering its Laplace transform $\text{e}^{-as}F(s)$, where $F(s)$ denotes the Laplace transform of $f(t)$, the component e^{-as} may be interpreted as a delay operator on the transform $F(s)$, indicating that the response of the system characterized by $F(s)$ will be delayed in time by a units. Since many practically important systems have some form of delay inherent in their behaviour, it is clear that the result of this theorem is very useful.

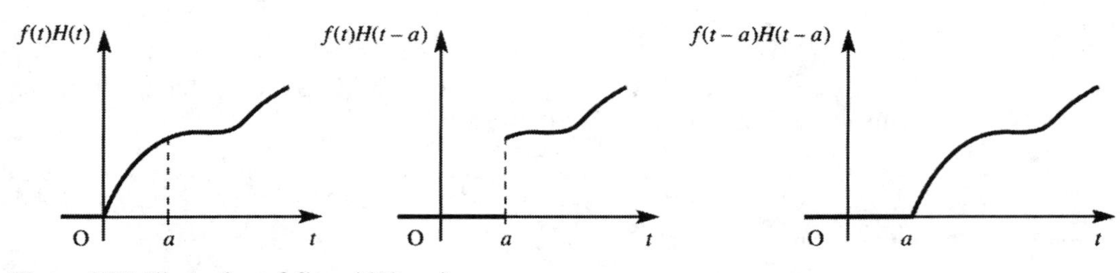

Figure 2.25 Illustration of $f(t-a)H(t-a)$.

Example 2.36 Determine the Laplace transform of the causal function $f(t)$ defined by

$$f(t)=\begin{cases} t & (0 \leqslant t < b) \\ 0 & (t \geqslant b) \end{cases}$$

Solution $f(t)$ is illustrated graphically in Figure 2.26, and is seen to characterize a sawtooth pulse of duration b. In terms of unit step functions,

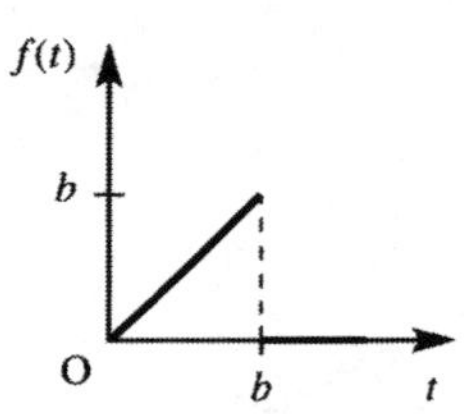

Figure 2.26 Sawtooth pulse.

$$f(t)=tH(t)-tH(t-b)$$

In order to apply the second shift theorem, each term must be rearranged to be of the form $f(t-a)H(t-a)$; that is, the time argument $t-a$ of the function must be the same as that of the associated step function. In this particular example this gives

$$f(t)=tH(t)-(t-b)H(t-b)-bH(t-b)$$

Taking Laplace transforms,

$$\mathscr{L}\{f(t)\}=\mathscr{L}\{tH(t)\}-\mathscr{L}\{(t-b)H(t-b)\}-b\mathscr{L}\{H(t-b)\}$$

which, on using Theorem 2.4, leads to

$$\mathscr{L}\{f(t)\}=\frac{1}{s^2}-\mathrm{e}^{-bs}\mathscr{L}(t)-b\frac{\mathrm{e}^{-bs}}{s}=\frac{1}{s^2}-\frac{\mathrm{e}^{-bs}}{s^2}-b\frac{\mathrm{e}^{-bs}}{s}$$

giving

$$\mathscr{L}\{f(t)\}=\frac{1}{s^2}(1-\mathrm{e}^{-bs})-\frac{b}{s}\mathrm{e}^{-bs}$$

It should be noted that this result could have been obtained without the use of the second shift theorem, since, directly from the definition of the Laplace transform,

$$\mathscr{L}\{f(t)\}=\int_0^\infty f(t)\,\mathrm{e}^{-st}\,\mathrm{d}t=\int_0^b t\,\mathrm{e}^{-st}\,\mathrm{d}t+\int_b^\infty 0\,\mathrm{e}^{-st}\,\mathrm{d}t$$

$$=\left[-\frac{t\,\mathrm{e}^{-st}}{s}\right]_0^b+\int_0^b\frac{\mathrm{e}^{-st}}{s}\,\mathrm{d}t=\left[-\frac{t\,\mathrm{e}^{-st}}{s}-\frac{\mathrm{e}^{-st}}{s^2}\right]_0^b$$

$$=\left(-\frac{b\,\mathrm{e}^{-sb}}{s}-\frac{\mathrm{e}^{-sb}}{s^2}\right)-\left(-\frac{1}{s^2}\right)=\frac{1}{s^2}(1-\mathrm{e}^{-bs})-\frac{b}{s}\mathrm{e}^{-bs}$$

as before.

Example 2.37 Obtain the Laplace transform of the piecewise-continuous causal function

$$f(t) = \begin{cases} 2t^2 & (0 \leqslant t < 3) \\ t+4 & (3 \leqslant t < 5) \\ 9 & (t \geqslant 5) \end{cases}$$

considered in Example 2.32.

Solution In Example 2.32 we saw that $f(t)$ may be expressed in terms of unit step functions as

$$f(t) = 2t^2H(t) - (2t^2 - t - 4)H(t-3) - (t-5)H(t-5)$$

Before we can find $\mathscr{L}\{f(t)\}$, the function $2t^2 - t - 4$ must be expressed as a function of $t - 3$. This may be readily achieved as follows. Let $z = t - 3$. Then

$$\begin{aligned} 2t^2 - t - 4 &= 2(z+3)^2 - (z+3) - 4 \\ &= 2z^2 + 11z + 11 \\ &= 2(t-3)^2 + 11(t-3) + 11 \end{aligned}$$

Hence

$$f(t) = 2t^2H(t) - [2(t-3)^2 + 11(t-3) + 11]H(t-3) - (t-5)H(t-5)$$

Taking Laplace transforms,

$$\begin{aligned} \mathscr{L}\{f(t)\} = 2\mathscr{L}\{t^2H(t)\} &- \mathscr{L}\{[2(t-3)^2 + 11(t-3) + 11]H(t-3)\} \\ &- \mathscr{L}\{(t-5)H(t-5)\} \end{aligned}$$

which, on using Theorem 2.4, leads to

$$\begin{aligned} \mathscr{L}\{f(t)\} &= 2\frac{2}{s^3} - e^{-3s}\mathscr{L}\{2t^2 + 11t + 11\} - e^{-5s}\mathscr{L}\{t\} \\ &= \frac{4}{s^3} - e^{-3s}\left(\frac{4}{s^3} + \frac{11}{s^2} + \frac{11}{s}\right) - \frac{e^{-5s}}{s^2} \end{aligned}$$

Again this result could have been obtained directly from the definition of the Laplace transform, but in this case the required integration by parts is a little more tedious.

Having set up s and t as symbolic variables and specified `H`, `H1` and `H5` then the MATLAB commands

```
laplace(2*t^2*H-(2*t^2-t-4)*H3-(t-5)*H5);
pretty(ans)
```

generate

```
ans= 4/s^3-11exp(-3s)/s-11exp(-3s)/s^2-4exp(-3s)/s^3-exp(-5s)/s^2
```

2.5.4 Inversion using the second shift theorem

We have seen in Examples 2.34 and 2.35 that, to obtain the Laplace transforms of piecewise-continuous functions, use of the second shift theorem could be avoided, since it is possible to obtain such transforms directly from the definition of the Laplace transform.

In practice, the importance of the theorem lies in determining *inverse* transforms, since, as indicated earlier, delays are inherent in most practical systems and engineers are interested in knowing how these influence the system response. Consequently, by far the most useful form of the second shift theorem is

$$\mathscr{L}^{-1}\{e^{-as}F(s)\} = f(t-a)H(t-a) \tag{2.45}$$

Comparing (2.45) with the result (2.12), namely

$$\mathscr{L}^{-1}\{F(s)\} = f(t)H(t)$$

we see that

$$\mathscr{L}^{-1}\{e^{-as}F(s)\} = [f(t)H(t)] \quad \text{with } t \text{ replaced by } t-a$$

indicating that the response $f(t)$ has been delayed in time by a units. This is why the theorem is sometimes called the delay theorem.

This is readily implemented in MATLAB using the command `ilaplace`.

Example 2.38

Determine $\mathscr{L}^{-1}\left\{\dfrac{4\,e^{-4s}}{s(s+2)}\right\}$.

Solution

This may be written as $\mathscr{L}^{-1}\{e^{-4s}F(s)\}$, where

$$F(s) = \frac{4}{s(s+2)}$$

First we obtain the inverse transform $f(t)$ of $F(s)$. Resolving into partial fractions,

$$F(s) = \frac{2}{s} - \frac{2}{s+2}$$

which, on inversion, gives

$$f(t) = 2 - 2\,e^{-2t}$$

a graph of which is shown in Figure 2.27(a). Then, using (2.45), we have

$$\begin{aligned}\mathscr{L}^{-1}\left\{e^{-4s}\frac{4}{s(s+2)}\right\} &= \mathscr{L}^{-1}\{e^{-4s}F(s)\} = f(t-4)H(t-4)\\ &= (2-2e^{-2(t-4)})H(t-4)\end{aligned}$$

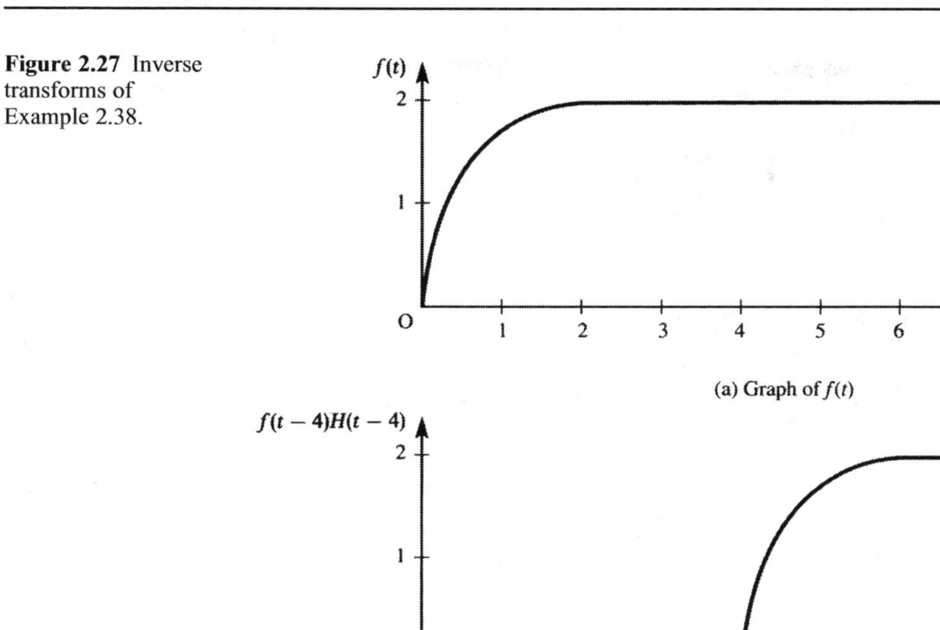

Figure 2.27 Inverse transforms of Example 2.38.

giving

$$\mathcal{L}^{-1}\left\{\frac{4\,\mathrm{e}^{-4s}}{s(s+2)}\right\} = \begin{cases} 0 & (t < 4) \\ 2(1-\mathrm{e}^{-2(t-4)}) & (t \geqslant 4) \end{cases}$$

which is plotted in Figure 2.27(b).

Using MATLAB confirm that the commands

```
ilaplace(4*exp(-4*s)/(s*(s+2)));
pretty(ans)
```

generate the answer

```
2H(t-4)(1-exp(-2t+8))
```

Example 2.39 Determine $\mathcal{L}^{-1}\left\{\frac{\mathrm{e}^{-s\pi}(s+3)}{s(s^2+1)}\right\}$.

Solution This may be written as $\mathcal{L}^{-1}\{\mathrm{e}^{-s\pi}F(s)\}$, where

$$F(s) = \frac{s+3}{s(s^2+1)}$$

Resolving into partial fractions,

$$F(s) = \frac{3}{s} - \frac{3s}{s^2+1} + \frac{1}{s^2+1}$$

which, on inversion, gives

$$f(t) = 3 - 3\cos t + \sin t$$

a graph of which is shown in Figure 2.28(a). Then, using (2.45), we have

$$\mathscr{L}^{-1}\left\{\frac{e^{-s\pi}(s+3)}{s(s^2+1)}\right\} = \mathscr{L}^{-1}\{e^{-s\pi}F(s)\} = f(t-\pi)H(t-\pi)$$

$$= [3 - 3\cos(t-\pi) + \sin(t-\pi)]H(t-\pi)$$

$$= (3 + 3\cos t - \sin t)H(t-\pi)$$

giving

$$\mathscr{L}^{-1}\left\{\frac{e^{-s\pi}(s+3)}{s(s^2+1)}\right\} = \begin{cases} 0 & (t < \pi) \\ 3 + 3\cos t - \sin t & (t \geq \pi) \end{cases}$$

which is plotted in Figure 2.28(b).

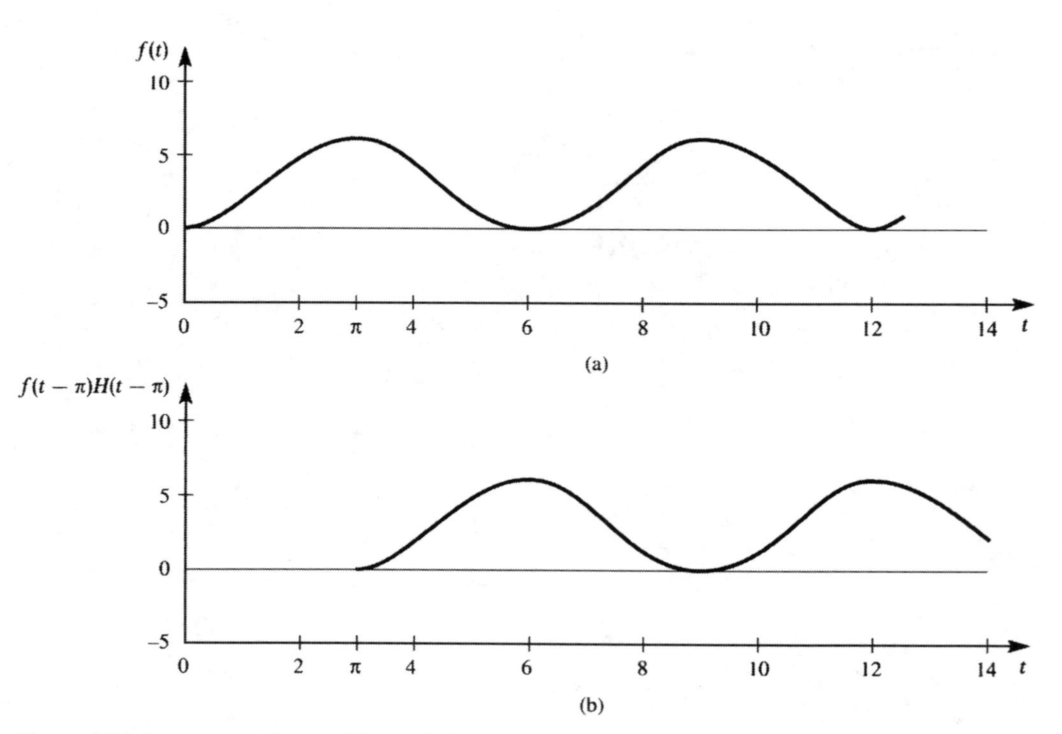

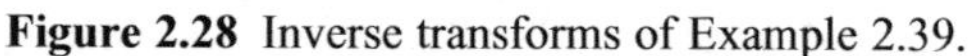
Figure 2.28 Inverse transforms of Example 2.39.

2.5.5 Differential equations

We now return to the solution of linear differential equations for which the forcing function $f(t)$ is piecewise-continuous, like that illustrated in Figure 2.20. One approach to solving a differential equation having such a forcing function is to solve it separately for each of the continuous components $f_1(t), f_2(t)$, and so on, comprising $f(t)$, using the fact that in this equation all the derivatives, except the highest, must remain continuous so that values at the point of discontinuity provide the initial conditions for the next section. This approach is obviously rather tedious, and a much more direct one is to make use of Heaviside step functions to specify $f(t)$. Then the method of solution follows that used in Section 2.3, and we shall simply illustrate it by examples.

Example 2.40

Obtain the solution $x(t)$, $t \geqslant 0$, of the differential equation

$$\frac{d^2x}{dt^2} + 5\frac{dx}{dt} + 6x = f(t) \tag{2.46}$$

where $f(t)$ is the pulse function

$$f(t) = \begin{cases} 3 & (0 \leqslant t < 6) \\ 0 & (t \geqslant 6) \end{cases}$$

and subject to the initial conditions $x(0) = 0$ and $\dot{x}(0) = 2$.

Solution To illustrate the advantage of using a step function formulation of the forcing function $f(t)$, we shall first solve separately for each of the time ranges.

Method 1 For $0 \leqslant t < 6$, (2.46) becomes

$$\frac{d^2x}{dt^2} + 5\frac{dx}{dt} + 6x = 3$$

with $x(0) = 0$ and $\dot{x}(0) = 2$.

Taking Laplace transforms gives

$$(s^2 + 5s + 6)X(s) = sx(0) + \dot{x}(0) + 5x(0) + \frac{3}{s} = 2 + \frac{3}{s}$$

That is,

$$X(s) = \frac{2s+3}{s(s+2)(s+3)} = \frac{\frac{1}{2}}{s} + \frac{\frac{1}{2}}{s+2} - \frac{1}{s+3}$$

which, on inversion, gives

$$x(t) = \tfrac{1}{2} + \tfrac{1}{2}e^{-2t} - e^{-3t} \quad (0 \leqslant t < 6)$$

We now determine the values of $x(6)$ and $\dot{x}(6)$ in order to provide the initial conditions for the next stage:

$$x(6) = \tfrac{1}{2} + \tfrac{1}{2}e^{-12} - e^{-18} = \alpha, \quad \dot{x}(6) = -e^{-12} + 3e^{-18} = \beta$$

For $t \geqslant 6$ we make the change of independent variable $T = t - 6$, whence (2.46) becomes

$$\frac{d^2x}{dT^2} + 5\frac{dx}{dT} + 6x = 0$$

subject to $x(T = 0) = \alpha$ and $\dot{x}(T = 0) = \beta$.

Taking Laplace transforms gives

$$(s^2 + 5s + 6)X(s) = sx(T = 0) + \dot{x}(T = 0) + 5x(T = 0) = \alpha s + 5\alpha + \beta$$

That is,

$$X(s) = \frac{\alpha s + 5\alpha + \beta}{(s+2)(s+3)} = \frac{\beta + 3\alpha}{s+2} - \frac{\beta + 2\alpha}{s+3}$$

which, on taking inverse transforms, gives

$$x(T) = (\beta + 3\alpha)e^{-2T} - (\beta + 2\alpha)e^{-3T}$$

Substituting the values of α and β and reverting to the independent variable t gives

$$x(t) = (\tfrac{3}{2} + \tfrac{1}{2}e^{-12})e^{-2(t-6)} - (1 + e^{-18})e^{-3(t-6)} \quad (t \geq 6)$$

That is,

$$x(t) = (\tfrac{1}{2}e^{-2t} - e^{-3t}) + (\tfrac{3}{2}e^{-2(t-6)} - e^{-3(t-6)}) \quad (t \geq 6)$$

Thus the solution of the differential equation is

$$x(t) = \begin{cases} \tfrac{1}{2} + \tfrac{1}{2}e^{-2t} - e^{-3t} & (0 \leq t < 6) \\ (\tfrac{1}{2}e^{-2t} - e^{-3t}) + (\tfrac{3}{2}e^{-2(t-6)} - e^{-3(t-6)}) & (t \geq 6) \end{cases}$$

The forcing function $f(t)$ and response $x(t)$ are shown in Figures 2.29(a) and (b) respectively.

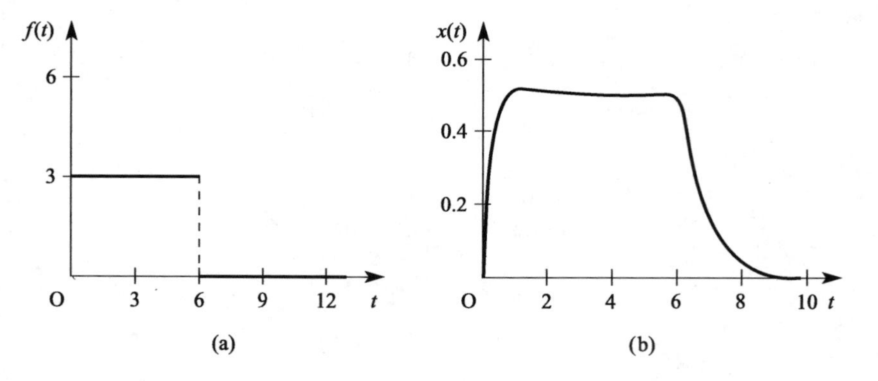

Figure 2.29 Forcing function and response of Example 2.40.

Method 2 In terms of Heaviside step functions,

$$f(t) = 3H(t) - 3H(t - 6)$$

so that, using (2.43),

$$\mathscr{L}\{f(t)\} = \frac{3}{s} - \frac{3}{s}e^{-6s}$$

Taking Laplace transforms in (2.46) then gives

$$(s^2 + 5s + 6)X(s) = sx(0) + \dot{x}(0) + 5x(0) + \mathscr{L}\{f(t)\} = 2 + \frac{3}{s} - \frac{3}{s}e^{-6s}$$

That is,

$$X(s) = \frac{2s+3}{s(s+2)(s+3)} - e^{-6s}\frac{3}{s(s+2)(s+3)}$$

$$= \left(\frac{\frac{1}{2}}{s} + \frac{\frac{1}{2}}{s+2} - \frac{1}{s+3}\right) - e^{-6s}\left(\frac{\frac{1}{2}}{s} - \frac{\frac{3}{2}}{s+2} + \frac{1}{s+3}\right)$$

Taking inverse Laplace transforms and using the result (2.45) gives

$$x(t) = (\tfrac{1}{2} + \tfrac{1}{2}e^{-2t} - e^{-3t}) - (\tfrac{1}{2} - \tfrac{3}{2}e^{-2(t-6)} + e^{-3(t-6)})H(t-6)$$

which is the required solution. This corresponds to that obtained in Method 1, since, using the definition of $H(t-6)$, it may be written as

$$x(t) = \begin{cases} \frac{1}{2} + \frac{1}{2}e^{-2t} - e^{-3t} & (0 \leqslant t < 6) \\ (\frac{1}{2}e^{-2t} - e^{-3t}) + (\frac{3}{2}e^{-2(t-6)} - e^{-3(t-6)}) & (t \geqslant 6) \end{cases}$$

This approach is clearly less tedious, since the initial conditions at the discontinuities are automatically taken account of in the solution.

It seems that the standard `dsolve` comand is unable to deal with differential equations having such Heaviside functions as their forcing function. To resolve this problem use can be made of the `maple` command in MATLAB, which lets us access MAPLE commands directly. Confirm that the following commands produce the correct solution:

```
maple('de:=diff(x(t),t$2)+5*diff(x(t),t)+6*x(t)=
3*Heaviside-3*Heaviside(t-6);')
ans=
de := diff(x(t),'$'(t,2))+5*diff(x(t),t)+6*x(t)=
3*Heaviside-3*Heaviside(t-6)
maple('dsolve({de,x(0)=0,D(x)(0)=2},x(t)),method=laplace;')
```

Example 2.41 Determine the solution $x(t)$, $t \geqslant 0$, of the differential equation

$$\frac{d^2x}{dt^2} + 2\frac{dx}{dt} + 5x = f(t) \tag{2.47}$$

where

$$f(t) = \begin{cases} t & (0 \leqslant t \leqslant \pi) \\ 0 & (t \geqslant \pi) \end{cases}$$

and subject to the initial conditions $x(0) = 0$ and $\dot{x}(0) = 3$.

Solution Following the procedures of Example 2.36, we have

$$f(t) = tH(t) - tH(t-\pi)$$
$$= tH(t) - (t-\pi)H(t-\pi) - \pi H(t-\pi)$$

so that, using Theorem 2.4,

$$\mathscr{L}\{f(t)\} = \frac{1}{s^2} - \frac{e^{-\pi s}}{s^2} - \frac{\pi e^{-\pi s}}{s} = \frac{1}{s^2} - e^{-\pi s}\left(\frac{1}{s^2} + \frac{\pi}{s}\right)$$

Taking Laplace transforms in (2.47) then gives

$$\begin{aligned}(s^2 + 2s + 5)X(s) &= sx(0) + \dot{x}(0) + 2x(0) + \mathscr{L}\{f(t)\} \\ &= 3 + \frac{1}{s^2} - e^{-\pi s}\left(\frac{1}{s^2} + \frac{\pi}{s}\right)\end{aligned}$$

using the given initial conditions.

Thus

$$X(s) = \frac{3s^2 + 1}{s^2(s^2 + 2s + 5)} - e^{-\pi s}\frac{1 + s\pi}{s^2(s^2 + 2s + 5)}$$

which, on resolving into partial fractions, leads to

$$\begin{aligned}X(s) &= \tfrac{1}{25}\left[-\frac{2}{s} + \frac{5}{s^2} + \frac{2s + 74}{(s + 1)^2 + 4}\right] - \frac{e^{-\pi s}}{25}\left[\frac{5\pi - 2}{s} + \frac{5}{s^2} - \frac{(5\pi - 2)s + (10\pi + 1)}{(s + 1)^2 + 4}\right] \\ &= \tfrac{1}{25}\left[-\frac{2}{s} + \frac{5}{s^2} + \frac{2(s + 1) + 72}{(s + 1)^2 + 4}\right] \\ &\quad - \frac{e^{-\pi s}}{25}\left[\frac{5\pi - 2}{s} + \frac{5}{s^2} - \frac{(5\pi - 2)(s + 1) + (5\pi + 3)}{(s + 1)^2 + 4}\right]\end{aligned}$$

Taking inverse Laplace transforms and using (2.45) gives the desired solution:

$$\begin{aligned}x(t) &= \tfrac{1}{25}(-2 + 5t + 2\,e^{-t}\cos 2t + 36\,e^{-t}\sin 2t) \\ &\quad - \tfrac{1}{25}[(5\pi - 2) + 5(t - \pi) - (5\pi - 2)\,e^{-(t-\pi)}\cos 2(t - \pi) \\ &\quad - \tfrac{1}{2}(5\pi + 3)\,e^{-(t-\pi)}\sin 2(t - \pi)]H(t - \pi)\end{aligned}$$

That is,

$$\begin{aligned}x(t) &= \tfrac{1}{25}[5t - 2 + 2\,e^{-t}(\cos 2t + 18\sin 2t)] \\ &\quad - \tfrac{1}{25}\{5t - 2 - e^{\pi}e^{-t}[(5\pi - 2)\cos 2t + \tfrac{1}{2}(5\pi + 3)\sin 2t]\}H(t - \pi)\end{aligned}$$

or, in alternative form,

$$x(t) = \begin{cases}\tfrac{1}{25}[5t - 2 + 2\,e^{-t}(\cos 2t + 18\sin 2t)] & (0 \leqslant t < \pi) \\ \tfrac{1}{25}\,e^{-t}\{(2 + (5\pi - 2)\,e^{\pi})\cos 2t + [36 + \tfrac{1}{2}(5\pi + 3)\,e^{\pi}]\sin 2t\} & (t \geqslant \pi)\end{cases}$$

2.5.6 Periodic functions

We have already determined the Laplace transforms of periodic functions, such as $\sin \omega t$ and $\cos \omega t$, which are smooth (differentiable) continuous functions. In many engineering applications, however, one frequently encounters periodic functions that

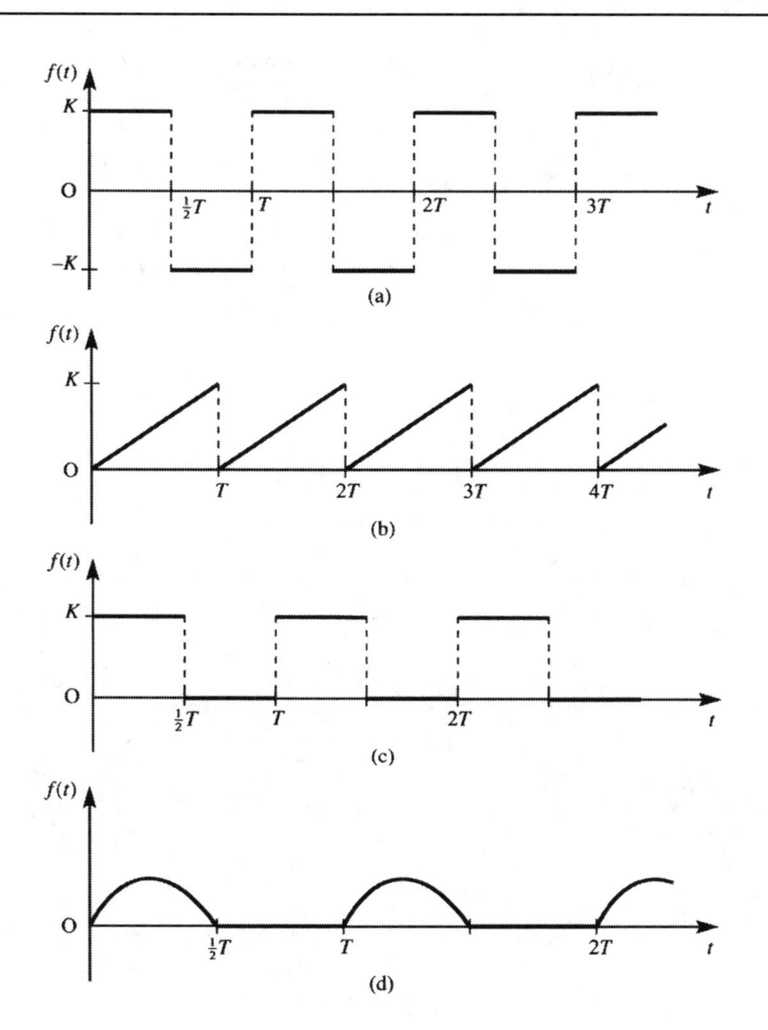

Figure 2.30 Typical practically important periodic functions: (a) square wave; (b) sawtooth wave; (c) repeated pulse wave; (d) half-wave rectifier.

exhibit discontinuous behaviour. Examples of typical periodic functions of practical importance are shown in Figure 2.30.

Such periodic functions may be represented as infinite series of terms involving step functions; once expressed in such a form, the result (2.43) may then be used to obtain their Laplace transforms.

Example 2.42 Obtain the Laplace transform of the square wave illustrated in Figure 2.30(a).

Solution In terms of step functions, the square wave may be expressed in the form

$$\begin{aligned} f(t) &= KH(t) - 2KH(t - \tfrac{1}{2}T) + 2KH(t - T) - 2KH(t - \tfrac{3}{2}T) + 2KH(t - 2T) + \dots \\ &= K[H(t) - 2H(t - \tfrac{1}{2}T) + 2H(t - T) - 2H(t - \tfrac{3}{2}T) + 2H(t - 2T) + \dots] \end{aligned}$$

Taking Laplace transforms and using the result (2.43) gives

$$\mathscr{L}\{f(t)\} = F(s) = K\left(\frac{1}{s} - \frac{2}{s}e^{-sT/2} + \frac{2}{s}e^{-sT} - \frac{2}{s}e^{-3sT/2} + \frac{2}{s}e^{-2sT} + \ldots\right)$$

$$= \frac{2K}{s}[1 - e^{-sT/2} + (e^{-sT/2})^2 - (e^{-sT/2})^3 + (e^{-sT/2})^4 - \ldots] - \frac{K}{s}$$

The series inside the square brackets is an infinite geometric progression with first term 1 and common ratio $-e^{-sT/2}$, and therefore has sum $(1 + e^{-sT/2})^{-1}$. Thus,

$$F(s) = \frac{2K}{s}\frac{1}{1+e^{-sT/2}} - \frac{K}{s} = \frac{K}{s}\frac{1-e^{-sT/2}}{1+e^{-sT/2}}$$

That is,

$$\mathscr{L}\{f(t)\} = F(s) = \frac{K}{s}\tanh\tfrac{1}{4}sT$$

The approach used in Example 2.42 may be used to prove the following theorem, which provides an explicit expression for the Laplace transform of a periodic function.

Theorem 2.5

If $f(t)$, defined for all positive t, is a periodic function with period T, that is $f(t + nT) = f(t)$ for all integers n, then

$$\mathscr{L}\{f(t)\} = \frac{1}{1-e^{-sT}}\int_0^T e^{-st}f(t)\,dt$$

Proof If, as illustrated in Figure 2.31, the periodic function $f(t)$ is piecewise-continuous over an interval of length T, then its Laplace transform exists and can be expressed as a series of integrals over successive periods; that is,

$$\mathscr{L}\{f(t)\} = \int_0^\infty f(t)\,e^{-st}\,dt$$

$$= \int_0^T f(t)\,e^{-st}\,dt + \int_T^{2T} f(t)\,e^{-st}\,dt + \int_{2T}^{3T} f(t)\,e^{-st}\,dt + \ldots$$

$$+ \int_{(n-1)T}^{nT} f(t)\,e^{-st}\,dt + \ldots$$

If in successive integrals we make the substitutions

$$t = \tau + nT \quad (n = 0, 1, 2, 3, \ldots)$$

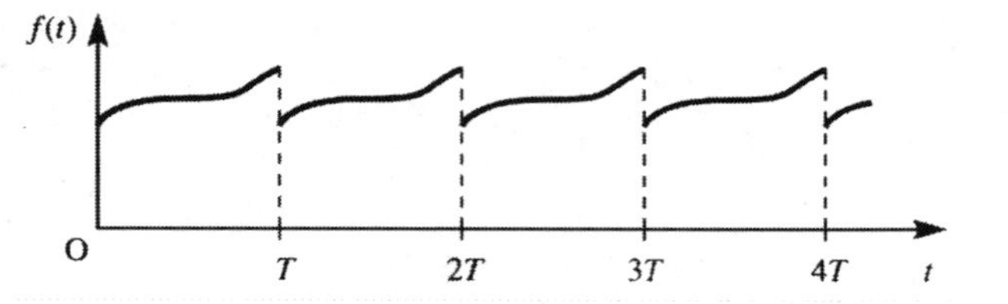

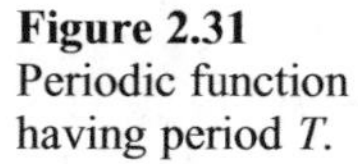
Figure 2.31 Periodic function having period T.

then

$$\mathscr{L}\{f(t)\} = \sum_{n=0}^{\infty} \int_0^T f(\tau + nT)\, e^{-s(\tau+nT)}\, d\tau$$

Since $f(t)$ is periodic with period T,

$$f(\tau + nT) = f(t) \quad (n = 0, 1, 2, 3, \dots)$$

so that

$$\mathscr{L}\{f(t)\} = \sum_{n=0}^{\infty} \int_0^T f(\tau)\, e^{-s\tau}\, e^{-snT}\, d\tau = \left(\sum_{n=0}^{\infty} e^{-snT}\right) \int_0^T f(\tau)\, e^{-s\tau}\, d\tau$$

The series $\sum_{n=0}^{\infty} e^{-snT} = 1 + e^{-sT} + e^{-2sT} + e^{-3sT} + \dots$ is an infinite geometric progression with first term 1 and common ratio e^{-sT}. Its sum is given by $(1 - e^{-sT})^{-1}$, so that

$$\mathscr{L}\{f(t)\} = \frac{1}{1 - e^{-sT}} \int_0^T f(\tau)\, e^{-s\tau}\, d\tau$$

Since, within the integral, τ is a 'dummy' variable, it may be replaced by t to give the desired result.

end of theorem

We note that, in terms of the Heaviside step function, Theorem 2.5 may be stated as follows:

> If $f(t)$, defined for all positive t, is a periodic function with period T and
>
> $$f_1(t) = f(t)(H(t) - H(t - T))$$
>
> then
>
> $$\mathscr{L}\{f(t)\} = (1 - e^{-sT})^{-1} \mathscr{L}\{f_1(t)\}$$

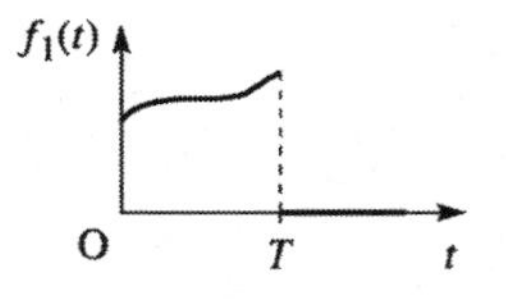

Figure 2.32 Plot of periodic function within one period.

This formulation follows since $f(t)$ is periodic and $f_1(t) = 0$ for $t > T$. For the periodic function $f(t)$ shown in Figure 2.31 the corresponding function $f_1(t)$ is shown in Figure 2.32. We shall see from the following examples that this formulation simplifies the process of obtaining Laplace transforms of periodic functions.

Example 2.43 Confirm the result obtained in Example 2.42 using Theorem 2.5.

Solution For the square wave $f(t)$ illustrated in Figure 2.30(a), $f(t)$ is defined over the period $0 < t < T$ by

$$f(t) = \begin{cases} K & (0 < t < \frac{1}{2}T) \\ -K & (\frac{1}{2}T < t < T) \end{cases}$$

Hence we can write $f_1(t) = K[H(t) - 2H(t - \frac{1}{2}T) + H(t - T)]$, and thus

$$\mathscr{L}\{f_1(t)\} = K\left(\frac{1}{s} - \frac{2}{s} e^{-sT/2} + \frac{1}{s} e^{-sT}\right) = \frac{K}{s}(1 - e^{-sT/2})^2$$

Using the result of Theorem 2.5,

$$\mathscr{L}\{f(t)\} = \frac{K(1 - e^{-sT/2})^2}{s(1 - e^{-sT})} = \frac{K(1 - e^{-sT/2})^2}{s(1 - e^{-sT/2})(1 + e^{-sT/2})}$$

$$= \frac{K}{s}\frac{1 - e^{-sT/2}}{1 + e^{-sT/2}} = \frac{K}{s}\tanh \tfrac{1}{4}sT$$

confirming the result obtained in Example 2.42.

Example 2.44 Determine the Laplace transform of the rectified half-wave defined by

$$f(t) = \begin{cases} \sin \omega t & (0 < t < \pi/\omega) \\ 0 & (\pi/\omega < t < 2\pi/\omega) \end{cases}$$

$$f(t + 2n\pi/\omega) = f(t) \quad \text{for all integers } n$$

Solution $f(t)$ is illustrated in Figure 2.30(d), with $T = 2\pi/\omega$. We can express $f_1(t)$ as

$$f_1(t) = \sin \omega t[H(t) - H(t - \pi/\omega)]$$
$$= \sin \omega t H(t) + \sin \omega(t - \pi/\omega)H(t - \pi/\omega)$$

So

$$\mathscr{L}\{f_1(t)\} = \frac{\omega}{s^2 + \omega^2} + e^{-s\pi/\omega}\frac{\omega}{s^2 + \omega^2} = \frac{\omega}{s^2 + \omega^2}(1 + e^{-s\pi/\omega})$$

Then, by the result of Theorem 2.5,

$$\mathscr{L}\{f(t)\} = \frac{\omega}{s^2 + \omega^2}\frac{1 + e^{-s\pi/\omega}}{1 - e^{-2s\pi/\omega}} = \frac{\omega}{(s^2 + \omega^2)(1 - e^{-s\pi/\omega})}$$

2.5.7 Exercises

Throughout this set of exercises, when appropriate, MATLAB may be used to check your answers.

13 A function $f(t)$ is defined by

$$f(t) = \begin{cases} t & (0 \leqslant t \leqslant 1) \\ 0 & (t > 1) \end{cases}$$

Express $f(t)$ in terms of Heaviside unit step functions and show that

$$\mathscr{L}\{f(t)\} = \frac{1}{s^2}(1 - e^{-s}) - \frac{1}{s}e^{-s}$$

14 Express in terms of Heaviside unit step functions the following piecewise-continuous causal functions. In each case obtain the Laplace transform of the function.

(a) $f(t) = \begin{cases} 3t^2 & (0 < t \leqslant 4) \\ 2t - 3 & (4 < t < 6) \\ 5 & (t > 6) \end{cases}$

(b) $g(t) = \begin{cases} t & (0 \leqslant t < 1) \\ 2 - t & (1 < t < 2) \\ 0 & (t > 2) \end{cases}$

15 Obtain the inverse Laplace transforms of the following:

(a) $\dfrac{e^{-5s}}{(s - 2)^4}$

(b) $\dfrac{3\,e^{-2s}}{(s + 3)(s + 1)}$

(c) $\dfrac{s + 1}{s^2(s^2 + 1)}e^{-s}$

(d) $\dfrac{s + 1}{s^2 + s + 1}e^{-\pi s}$

(e) $\dfrac{s}{s^2+25}\mathrm{e}^{-4\pi s/5}$ (f) $\dfrac{\mathrm{e}^{-s}(1-\mathrm{e}^{-s})}{s^2(s^2+1)}$

16 Given that $x = 0$ when $t = 0$, obtain the solution of the differential equation

$$\frac{\mathrm{d}x}{\mathrm{d}t} + x = f(t) \quad (t \geq 0)$$

where $f(t)$ is the function defined in Exercise 13. Sketch a graph of the solution.

17 Given that $x = 1$ and $\mathrm{d}x/\mathrm{d}t = 0$, obtain the solution of the differential equation

$$\frac{\mathrm{d}^2x}{\mathrm{d}t^2} + \frac{\mathrm{d}x}{\mathrm{d}t} + x = g(t) \quad (t \geq 0)$$

where $g(t)$ is the piecewise-continuous function defined in Exercise 14(b).

18 Show that the function

$$f(t) = \begin{cases} 0 & (0 \leq t < \frac{1}{2}\pi) \\ \sin t & (t \geq \frac{1}{2}\pi) \end{cases}$$

may be expressed in the form $f(t) = \cos(t - \frac{1}{2}\pi)$ $H(t - \frac{1}{2}\pi)$, where $H(t)$ is the Heaviside unit step function. Hence solve the differential equation

$$\frac{\mathrm{d}^2x}{\mathrm{d}t^2} + 3\frac{\mathrm{d}x}{\mathrm{d}t} + 2x = f(t)$$

where $f(t)$ is given above, and $x = 1$ and $\mathrm{d}x/\mathrm{d}t = -1$ when $t = 0$.

19 Express the function

$$f(t) = \begin{cases} 3 & (0 \leq t < 4) \\ 2t - 5 & (t \geq 4) \end{cases}$$

in terms of Heaviside unit step functions and obtain its Laplace transform. Obtain the response of the harmonic oscillator

$$\ddot{x} + x = f(t)$$

to such a forcing function, given that $x = 1$ and $\mathrm{d}x/\mathrm{d}t = 0$ when $t = 0$.

20 The response $\theta_o(t)$ of a system to a forcing function $\theta_i(t)$ is determined by the second-order differential equation

$$\ddot{\theta}_o + 6\dot{\theta}_o + 10\theta_o = \theta_i \quad (t \geq 0)$$

Suppose that $\theta_i(t)$ is a constant stimulus applied for a limited period and characterized by

$$\theta_i(t) = \begin{cases} 3 & (0 \leq t < a) \\ 0 & (t \geq a) \end{cases}$$

Determine the response of the system at time t given that the system was initially in a quiescent state. Show that the transient response at time $T(> a)$ is

$$-\tfrac{3}{10}\mathrm{e}^{-3T}\{\cos T + 3\sin T - \mathrm{e}^{3a}[\cos(T-a) + 3\sin(T-a)]\}$$

21 The input $\theta_i(t)$ and output $\theta_o(t)$ of a servomechanism are related by the differential equation

$$\ddot{\theta}_o + 8\dot{\theta}_o + 16\theta_o = \theta_i \quad (t \geq 0)$$

and initially $\theta_o(0) = \dot{\theta}_o(0) = 0$. For $\theta_i = f(t)$, where

$$f(t) = \begin{cases} 1 - t & (0 < t < 1) \\ 0 & (t > 1) \end{cases}$$

Show that

$$\mathscr{L}\{\theta_i(t)\} = \frac{s-1}{s^2} + \frac{1}{s^2}\mathrm{e}^{-s}$$

and hence obtain an expression for the response of the system at time t.

22 During the time interval t_1 to t_2, a constant electromotive force e_0 acts on the series RC circuit shown in Figure 2.33. Assuming that the circuit is initially in a quiescent state, show that the current in the circuit at time t is

$$i(t) = \frac{e_0}{R}[\mathrm{e}^{-(t-t_1)/RC}H(t-t_1) - \mathrm{e}^{-(t-t_2)/RC}H(t-t_2)]$$

Sketch this as a function of time.

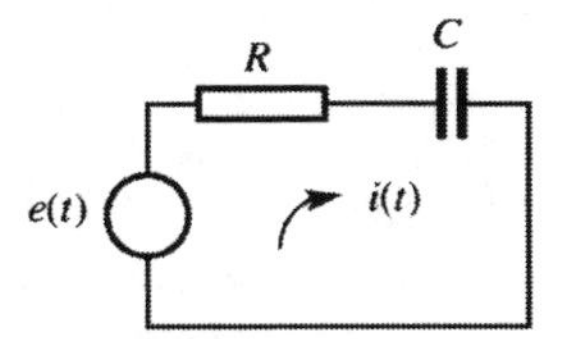

Figure 2.33 Circuit of Exercise 22.

23 A periodic function $f(t)$, with period 4 units, is defined within the interval $0 \leq t < 4$ by

$$f(t) = \begin{cases} 3t & (0 \leq t < 2) \\ 6 & (2 \leq t < 4) \end{cases}$$

Sketch a graph of the function for $0 \leq t < 12$ and obtain its Laplace transform.

24 Obtain the Laplace transform of the periodic sawtooth wave with period T, illustrated in Figure 2.30(b).

2.5.8 The impulse function

In many engineering applications we are interested in seeking the responses of systems to forcing functions that are applied suddenly but only for a very short time. These functions are known as **impulsive forces**. Mathematically, such forcing functions are idealized by the **impulse function**, which is a function whose total value is concentrated at one point. To develop a mathematical formulation of the impulse function and obtain some insight into its physical interpretation, consider the pulse function $\phi(t)$ defined by

$$\phi(t) = \begin{cases} 0 & (0 < t < a - \frac{1}{2}T) \\ A/T & (a - \frac{1}{2}T \leqslant t < a + \frac{1}{2}T) \\ 0 & (t \geqslant a + \frac{1}{2}T) \end{cases}$$

and illustrated in Figure 2.34(a). Since the height of the pulse is A/T and its duration (or width) is T, the area under the pulse is A; that is,

$$\int_{-\infty}^{\infty} \phi(t)\,\mathrm{d}t = \int_{a-T/2}^{a+T/2} \frac{A}{T}\,\mathrm{d}t = A$$

If we now consider the limiting process in which the duration of the pulse approaches zero, in such a way that the area under the pulse remains A, then we obtain a formulation of the impulse function of magnitude A occurring at time $t = a$. It is important to appreciate that the magnitude of the impulse function is measured by its area.

The impulse function whose magnitude is unity is called the **unit impulse function** or **Dirac delta function** (or simply **delta function**). The unit impulse occurring at $t = a$ is the limiting case of the pulse $\phi(t)$ of Figure 2.34(a) with A having the value unity. It is denoted by $\delta(t - a)$ and has the properties

$$\delta(t - a) = 0 \quad (t \neq a)$$

$$\int_{-\infty}^{\infty} \delta(t - a)\,\mathrm{d}t = 1$$

Likewise, an impulse function of magnitude A occurring at $t = a$ is denoted by $A\delta(t - a)$ and may be represented diagrammatically as in Figure 2.34(b).

An impulse function is not a function in the usual sense, but is an example of a class of what are called **generalized functions**, which may be analysed using the theory of **generalized calculus**. (It may also be regarded mathematically as a **distribution** and investigated using the **theory of distributions**.) However, its properties are such that, used with care, it can lead to results that have physical or practical significance and

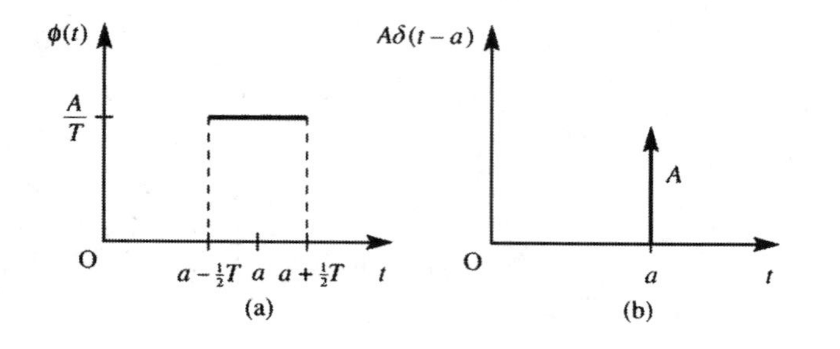

Figure 2.34 Impulse function.

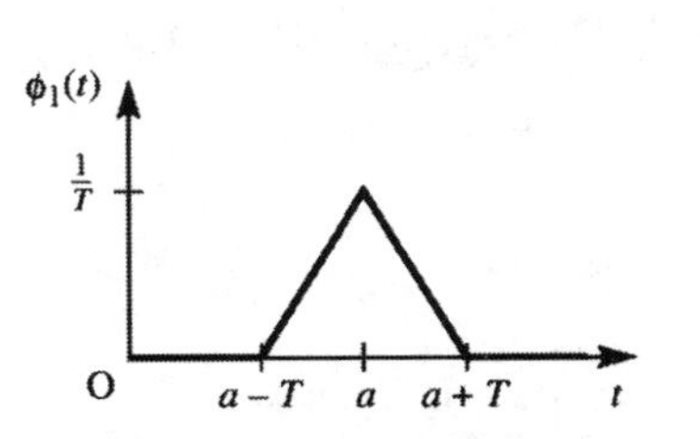

Figure 2.35 Approximation to a unit pulse.

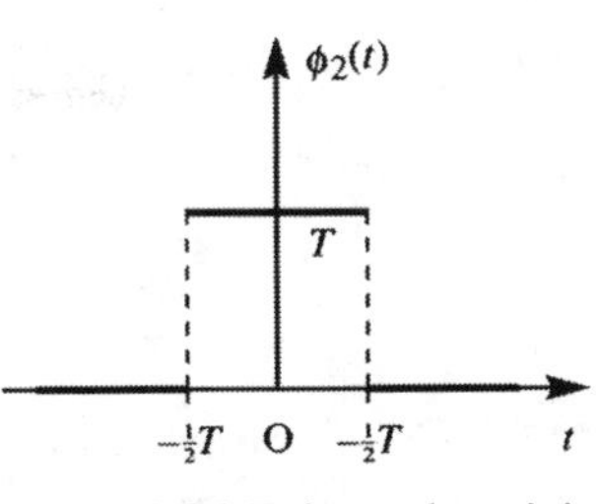

Figure 2.36 Pulse at the origin.

which in many cases cannot be obtained by any other method. In this context it provides engineers with an important mathematical tool. Although, clearly, an impulse function is not physically realizable, it follows from the above formulation that physical signals can be produced that closely approximate it.

We noted that the magnitude of the impulse function is determined by the area under the limiting pulse. The actual shape of the limiting pulse is not really important, provided that the area contained within it remains constant as its duration approaches zero. Physically, therefore, the unit impulse function at $t = a$ may equally well be regarded as the pulse $\phi_1(t)$ of Figure 2.35 in the limiting case as T approaches zero.

In some applications we need to consider a unit impulse function at time $t = 0$. This is denoted by $\delta(t)$ and is defined as the limiting case of the pulse $\phi_2(t)$ illustrated in Figure 2.36 as T approaches zero. It has the properties

$$\delta(t) = 0 \quad (t \neq 0)$$

$$\int_{-\infty}^{\infty} \delta(t)\,\mathrm{d}t = 1$$

2.5.9 The sifting property

An important property of the unit impulse function that is of practical significance is the so-called **sifting property**, which states that if $f(t)$ is continuous at $t = a$ then

$$\int_{-\infty}^{\infty} f(t)\delta(t-a)\,\mathrm{d}t = f(a) \tag{2.48}$$

This is referred to as the sifting property because it provides a method of isolating, or sifting out, the value of a function at any particular point.

For theoretical reasons it is convenient to use infinite limits in (2.48), while in reality finite limits can be substituted. This follows since for $\alpha < a < \beta$, where α and β are constants,

$$\int_{\alpha}^{\beta} f(t)\delta(t-a)\,\mathrm{d}t = f(a) \tag{2.49}$$

For example,

$$\int_{0}^{2\pi} \cos t\,\delta(t - \tfrac{1}{3}\pi)\,\mathrm{d}t = \cos\tfrac{1}{3}\pi = \tfrac{1}{2}$$

2.5.10 Laplace transforms of impulse functions

By the definition of the Laplace transform, we have for any $a > 0$

$$\mathscr{L}\{\delta(t-a)\} = \int_0^\infty \delta(t-a)\,\mathrm{e}^{-st}\,\mathrm{d}t$$

which, using the sifting property, gives the important result

$$\mathscr{L}\{\delta(t-a)\} = \mathrm{e}^{-as} \tag{2.50}$$

or, in terms of the inverse transform,

$$\mathscr{L}^{-1}\{\mathrm{e}^{-as}\} = \delta(t-a) \tag{2.51}$$

As mentioned earlier, in many applications we may have an impulse function $\delta(t)$ at $t = 0$, and it is in order to handle such a function that we must carefully specify whether the lower limit in the Laplace integral defined in Section 2.2.1 is 0^- or 0^+. Adopting the notation

$$\mathscr{L}_+\{f(t)\} = \int_{0^+}^\infty f(t)\,\mathrm{e}^{-st}\,\mathrm{d}t$$

$$\mathscr{L}_-\{f(t)\} = \int_{0^-}^\infty f(t)\,\mathrm{e}^{-st}\,\mathrm{d}t$$

we have

$$\mathscr{L}_-\{f(t)\} = \int_{0^-}^{0^+} f(t)\,\mathrm{e}^{-st}\,\mathrm{d}t + \int_{0^+}^\infty f(t)\,\mathrm{e}^{-st}\,\mathrm{d}t$$

If $f(t)$ does not involve an impulse function at $t = 0$ then clearly $\mathscr{L}_+\{f(t)\} = \mathscr{L}_-\{f(t)\}$. However, if $f(t)$ does involve an impulse function at $t = 0$ then

$$\int_{0^-}^{0^+} f(t)\,\mathrm{d}t \neq 0$$

and it follows that

$$\mathscr{L}_+\{f(t)\} \neq \mathscr{L}_-\{f(t)\}$$

In Section 2.2.1 we adopted the definition

$$\mathscr{L}\{f(t)\} = \mathscr{L}_-\{f(t)\}$$

so that (2.50) and (2.51) hold for $a = 0$, giving

$$\mathscr{L}\{\delta(t)\} = \int_{0^-}^\infty \delta(t)\,\mathrm{e}^{-st}\,\mathrm{d}t = \mathrm{e}^{-s0} = 1$$

so that

$$\mathscr{L}\{\delta(t)\} = 1 \tag{2.52}$$

or, in inverse form,

$$\mathscr{L}^{-1}\{1\} = \delta(t) \tag{2.53}$$

This transform can be implemented in MATLAB using the sequence of commands

```
syms s t
del=sym('Dirac(t)');
laplace(del)
```

Likewise for (2.50); for example, if $a = 2$ then the Laplace transform of $\delta(t - 2)$ is generated by the commands

```
del2=sym('Dirac(t-2)');
laplace(del2)
```

or directly using the command

```
laplace(sym('Dirac(t-2)'))
```

giving the answer `exp(-2*s)` in each case.

Example 2.45 Determine $\mathscr{L}^{-1}\left\{\dfrac{s^2}{s^2+4}\right\}$.

Solution Since

$$\frac{s^2}{s^2+4} = \frac{s^2+4-4}{s^2+4} = 1 - \frac{4}{s^2+4}$$

we have

$$\mathscr{L}^{-1}\left\{\frac{s^2}{s^2+4}\right\} = \mathscr{L}^{-1}\{1\} - \mathscr{L}^{-1}\left\{\frac{4}{s^2+4}\right\}$$

giving

$$\mathscr{L}^{-1}\left\{\frac{s^2}{s^2+4}\right\} = \delta(t) - 2\sin 2t$$

In MATLAB this is obtained directly, with the commands

```
ilaplace(s^2/(s^2+4));
pretty(ans)
```

generating the answer

```
Dirac(t)-2sin2t
```

Example 2.46 Determine the solution of the differential equation

$$\frac{d^2x}{dt^2} + 3\frac{dx}{dt} + 2x = 1 + \delta(t-4) \tag{2.54}$$

subject to the initial conditions $x(0) = \dot{x}(0) = 0$.

Solution Taking Laplace transforms in (2.54) gives

$$[s^2X(s) - sx(0) - \dot{x}(0)] + 3[sX(s) - x(0)] + 2X(s) = \mathscr{L}\{1\} + \mathscr{L}\{\delta(t-4)\}$$

which, on incorporating the given initial conditions and using (2.50), leads to

$$(s^2 + 3s + 2)X(s) = \frac{1}{s} + e^{-4s}$$

giving

$$X(s) = \frac{1}{s(s+2)(s+1)} + e^{-4s}\frac{1}{(s+2)(s+1)}$$

Resolving into partial fractions, we have

$$X(s) = \tfrac{1}{2}\left(\frac{1}{s} + \frac{1}{s+2} - \frac{2}{s+1}\right) + e^{-4s}\left(\frac{1}{s+1} - \frac{1}{s+2}\right)$$

which, on taking inverse transforms and using the result (2.45), gives the required response:

$$x(t) = \tfrac{1}{2}(1 + e^{-2t} - 2\,e^{-t}) + (e^{-(t-4)} - e^{-2(t-4)})H(t-4)$$

or, in an alternative form,

$$x(t) = \begin{cases} \tfrac{1}{2}(1 + e^{-2t} - 2\,e^{-t}) & (0 \leqslant t < 4) \\ \tfrac{1}{2} + (e^4 - 1)\,e^{-t} - (e^8 - \tfrac{1}{2})\,e^{-2t} & (t \geqslant 4) \end{cases}$$

We note that, although the response $x(t)$ is continuous at $t = 4$, the consequence of the impulsive input at $t = 4$ is a step change in the derivative $\dot{x}(t)$.

As was the case in Example 2.40, when considering Heaviside functions as forcing terms, it seems that the `dsolve` command in MATLAB cannot be used directly in this case. Using the `maple` command the following commands:

```
maple('de:=diff(x(t),t$2)+3*diff(x(t),t)+2*x(t)
= 1+Dirac(t-4);')
ans=
de := diff(x(t),'$'(t,2))+3*diff(x(t),t)+2*x(t)
= 1+Dirac(t-4)
maple('dsolve({de,x(0)=0,D(x)(0)=0},x(t)),
method=laplace;')
```

output the required answer:

```
x(t)=1/2-exp(-t)+1/2*exp(-2*t)-Heaviside(t-4)*
exp(-2*t+8)+Heaviside(t-4)*exp(-t+4)
```

2.5.11 Relationship between Heaviside step and impulse functions

From the definitions of $H(t)$ and $\delta(t)$, it can be argued that

$$H(t) = \int_{-\infty}^{t} \delta(\tau)\,\mathrm{d}\tau \tag{2.55}$$

since the interval of integration contains zero if $t > 0$ but not if $t < 0$. Conversely, (2.55) may be written as

$$\delta(t) = \frac{\mathrm{d}}{\mathrm{d}t} H(t) = H'(t) \tag{2.56}$$

which expresses the fact that $H'(t)$ is zero everywhere except at $t = 0$, when the jump in $H(t)$ occurs.

While this argument may suffice in practice, since we are dealing with generalized functions a more formal proof requires the development of some properties of generalized functions. In particular, we need to define what is meant by saying that two generalized functions are equivalent.

One method of approach is to use the concept of a **test function** $\theta(t)$, which is a continuous function that has continuous derivatives of all orders and that is zero outside a finite interval. One class of testing function, adopted by R. R. Gabel and R. A. Roberts (*Signals and Linear Systems*, Wiley, New York, 1973), is

$$\theta(t) = \begin{cases} \mathrm{e}^{-d^2/(d^2-t^2)} & (|t| < d), \quad \text{where } d = \text{constant} \\ 0 & \text{otherwise} \end{cases}$$

For a generalized function $g(t)$ the integral

$$G(\theta) = \int_{-\infty}^{\infty} \theta(t) g(t)\,\mathrm{d}t$$

is evaluated. This integral assigns the number $G(\theta)$ to each function $\theta(t)$, so that $G(\theta)$ is a generalization of the concept of a function: it is a **linear functional** on the space of test functions $\theta(t)$. For example, if $g(t) = \delta(t)$ then

$$G(\theta) = \int_{-\infty}^{\infty} \theta(t)\,\delta(t)\,\mathrm{d}t = \theta(0)$$

so that in this particular case, for each weighting function $\theta(t)$, the value $\theta(0)$ is assigned to $G(\theta)$.

We can now use the concept of a test function to define what is meant by saying that two generalized functions are equivalent or 'equal'.

DEFINITION 2.2: The equivalence property

If $g_1(t)$ and $g_2(t)$ are two generalized functions then $g_1(t) = g_2(t)$ if and only if

$$\int_{-\infty}^{\infty} \theta(t) g_1(t)\,\mathrm{d}t = \int_{-\infty}^{\infty} \theta(t) g_2(t)\,\mathrm{d}t$$

for all test functions $\theta(t)$ for which the integrals exist.

The test function may be regarded as a 'device' for examining the generalized function. Gabel and Roberts draw a rough parallel with the role of using the output of a measuring instrument to deduce properties about what is being measured. In such an analogy $g_1(t) = g_2(t)$ if the measuring instrument can detect no differences between them.

Using the concept of a test function $\theta(t)$, the Dirac delta function $\delta(t)$ may be defined in the generalized form

$$\int_{-\infty}^{\infty} \theta(t)\delta(t)\,\mathrm{d}t = \theta(0)$$

Interpreted as an ordinary integral, this has no meaning. The integral and the function $\delta(t)$ are merely defined by the number $\theta(0)$. In this sense we can handle $\delta(t)$ as if it were an ordinary function, except that we never talk about the value of $\delta(t)$; rather we talk about the value of integrals involving $\delta(t)$.

Using the equivalence property, we can now confirm the result (2.56), namely that

$$\delta(t) = \frac{\mathrm{d}}{\mathrm{d}t}H(t) = H'(t)$$

To prove this, we must show that

$$\int_{-\infty}^{\infty} \theta(t)\delta(t)\,\mathrm{d}t = \int_{-\infty}^{\infty} \theta(t)H'(t)\,\mathrm{d}t \tag{2.57}$$

Integrating the right-hand side of (2.57) by parts, we have

$$\int_{-\infty}^{\infty} \theta(t)H'(t)\,\mathrm{d}t = [H(t)\theta(t)]_{-\infty}^{\infty} - \int_{-\infty}^{\infty} H(t)\theta'(t)\,\mathrm{d}t$$

$$= 0 - \int_{-\infty}^{\infty} \theta'(t)\mathrm{d}t \quad \text{(by the definitions of } \theta(t) \text{ and } H(t)\text{)}$$

$$= -[\theta(t)]_0^{\infty} = \theta(0)$$

Since the left-hand side of (2.57) is also $\theta(0)$, the equivalence of $\delta(t)$ and $H'(t)$ is proved.

Likewise, it can be shown that

$$\delta(t-a) = \frac{\mathrm{d}}{\mathrm{d}t}H(t-a) = H'(t-a) \tag{2.58}$$

The results (2.56) and (2.58) may be used to obtain the **generalized derivatives** of piecewise-continuous functions having jump discontinuities $d_1, d_2, \ldots, d_n$ at times $t_1, t_2, \ldots, t_n$ respectively, as illustrated in Figure 2.37. On expressing $f(t)$ in terms of Heaviside step functions as in Section 2.5.1, and differentiating using the product rule, use of (2.56) and (2.58) leads to the result

$$f'(t) = g'(t) + \sum_{i=1}^{n} d_i\delta(t-t_i) \tag{2.59}$$

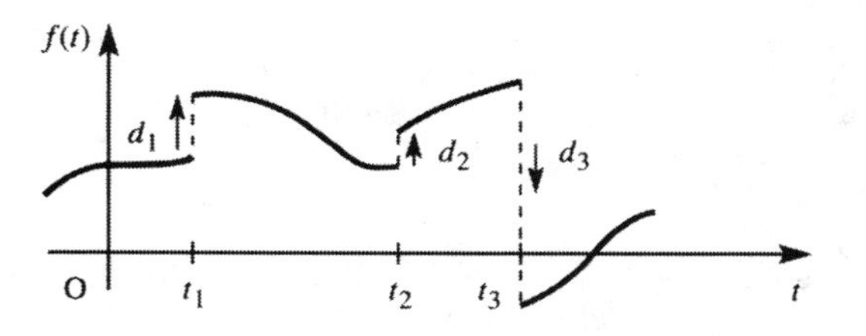

Figure 2.37 Piecewise-continuous function with jump discontinuities.

where $g'(t)$ denotes the ordinary derivative of $f(t)$ where it exists. The result (2.59) tells us that the derivative of a piecewise-continuous function with jump discontinuities is the ordinary derivative where it exists plus the sum of delta functions at the discontinuities multiplied by the magnitudes of the respective jumps.

By the magnitude d_i of a jump in a function $f(t)$ at a point t_i, we mean the difference between the right-hand and left-hand limits of $f(t)$ at t_i; that is,

$$d_i = f(t_i + 0) - f(t_i - 0)$$

If follows that an upward jump, such as d_1 and d_2 in Figure 2.37, is positive, while a downward jump, such as d_3 in Figure 2.37, is negative.

The result (2.59) gives an indication as to why the use of differentiators in practical systems is not encouraged, since the introduction of impulses means that derivatives increase noise levels in signal reception. In contrast, integrators have a smoothing effect on signals, and are widely used.

Example 2.47

Obtain the generalized derivative of the piecewise-continuous function

$$f(t) = \begin{cases} 2t^2 + 1 & (0 \leqslant t < 3) \\ t + 4 & (3 \leqslant t < 5) \\ 4 & (t \geqslant 5) \end{cases}$$

Solution $f(t)$ is depicted graphically in Figure 2.38, and it has jump discontinuities of magnitudes 1, −12 and −5 at times $t = 0$, 3 and 5 respectively. Using (2.59), the generalized derivative is

$$f'(t) = g'(t) + 1\delta(t) - 12\delta(t - 3) - 5\delta(t - 5)$$

where

$$g'(t) = \begin{cases} 4t & (0 \leqslant t < 3) \\ 1 & (3 \leqslant t < 5) \\ 0 & (t \geqslant 5) \end{cases}$$

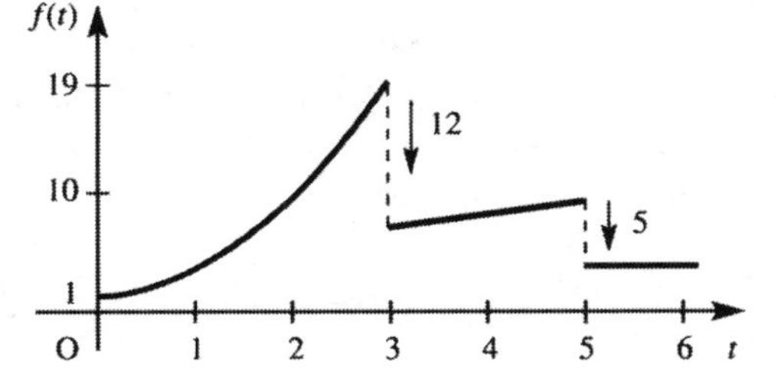

Figure 2.38 Piecewise-continuous function of Example 2.47.

Example 2.48 A system is characterized by the differential equation model

$$\frac{d^2x}{dt^2} + 5\frac{dx}{dt} + 6x = u + 3\frac{du}{dt} \tag{2.60}$$

Determine the response of the system to a forcing function $u(t) = e^{-t}$ applied at time $t = 0$, given that it was initially in a quiescent state.

Solution Since the system is initially in a quiescent state, the transformed equation corresponding to (2.60) is

$$(s^2 + 5s + 6)X(s) = (3s + 1)U(s)$$

giving

$$X(s) = \frac{3s + 1}{s^2 + 5s + 6}U(s)$$

In the particular case when $u(t) = e^{-t}$, $U(s) = 1/(s + 1)$, so that

$$X(s) = \frac{(3s + 1)}{(s + 1)(s + 2)(s + 3)} = \frac{-1}{s + 1} + \frac{5}{s + 2} - \frac{4}{s + 3}$$

which, on taking inverse transforms, gives the desired response as

$$x(t) = -e^{-t} + 5\,e^{-2t} - 4\,e^{-3t} \quad (t \geqslant 0)$$

One might have been tempted to adopt a different approach and substitute for $u(t)$ directly in (2.60) before taking Laplace transforms. This leads to

$$\frac{d^2x}{dt^2} + 5\frac{dx}{dt} + 6x = e^{-t} - 3\,e^{-t} = -2\,e^{-t}$$

which, on taking Laplace transforms, leads to

$$(s^2 + 5s + 6)X(s) = -\frac{2}{s + 1}$$

giving

$$X(s) = \frac{-2}{(s + 1)(s + 2)(s + 3)} = \frac{-1}{s + 1} + \frac{2}{s + 2} - \frac{1}{s + 3}$$

which, on inversion, gives

$$x(t) = -e^{-t} + 2\,e^{-2t} - e^{-3t} \quad (t \geqslant 0)$$

Clearly this approach results in a different solution, and therefore appears to lead to a paradox. However, this apparent paradox can be resolved by noting that the second approach is erroneous in that it ignores the important fact that we are dealing with causal functions. Strictly speaking,

$$u(t) = e^{-t}H(t)$$

and, when determining du/dt, the product rule of differential calculus should be employed, giving

$$\begin{aligned}\frac{\mathrm{d}u}{\mathrm{d}t} &= -\mathrm{e}^{-t}H(t) + \mathrm{e}^{-t}\frac{\mathrm{d}}{\mathrm{d}t}H(t)\\ &= -\mathrm{e}^{-t}H(t) + \mathrm{e}^{-t}\delta(t)\end{aligned}$$

Substituting this into (2.60) and taking Laplace transforms gives

$$\begin{aligned}(s^2 + 5s + 6)X(s) &= \frac{1}{s+1} + 3\left(-\frac{1}{s+1} + 1\right)\\ &= \frac{3s+1}{s+1}\end{aligned}$$

That is,

$$X(s) = \frac{3s+1}{(s+1)(s^2+5s+6)}$$

leading to the same response

$$x(t) = -\mathrm{e}^{-t} + 5\,\mathrm{e}^{-2t} - 4\,\mathrm{e}^{-3t} \quad (t \geqslant 0)$$

as in the first approach above.

The differential equation used in Example 2.48 is of a form that occurs frequently in practice, so it is important that the causal nature of the forcing term be recognized.

The derivative $\delta'(t)$ of the impulse function is also a generalized function, and, using the equivalence property, it is readily shown that

$$\int_{-\infty}^{\infty} f(t)\delta'(t)\,\mathrm{d}t = -f'(0)$$

or, more generally,

$$\int_{-\infty}^{\infty} f(t)\delta'(t-a)\,\mathrm{d}t = -f'(a)$$

provided that $f'(t)$ is continuous at $t = a$.

Likewise, the nth derivative satisfies

$$\int_{-\infty}^{\infty} f(t)\delta^n(t-a)\,\mathrm{d}t = (-1)^n f^{(n)}(a)$$

provided that $f^{(n)}(t)$ is continuous at $t = a$.

Using the definition of the Laplace transform, it follows that

$$\mathscr{L}\{\delta^{(n)}(t-a)\} = s^n\mathrm{e}^{-as}$$

and, in particular,

$$\mathscr{L}\{\delta^{(n)}(t)\} = s^n \tag{2.61}$$

2.5.12 Exercises

25 Obtain the inverse Laplace transforms of the following:

(a) $\dfrac{2s^2+1}{(s+2)(s+3)}$

(b) $\dfrac{s^2-1}{s^2+4}$ (c) $\dfrac{s^2+2}{s^2+2s+5}$

26 Solve for $t \geqslant 0$ the following differential equations, subject to the specified initial conditions:

(a) $\dfrac{d^2x}{dt^2}+7\dfrac{dx}{dt}+12x=2+\delta(t-2)$

subject to $x=0$ and $\dfrac{dx}{dt}=0$ at $t=0$

(b) $\dfrac{d^2x}{dt^2}+6\dfrac{dx}{dt}+13x=\delta(t-2\pi)$

subject to $x=0$ and $\dfrac{dx}{dt}=0$ at $t=0$

(c) $\dfrac{d^2x}{dt^2}+7\dfrac{dx}{dt}+12x=\delta(t-3)$

subject to $x=1$ and $\dfrac{dx}{dt}=1$ at $t=0$

27 Obtain the generalized derivatives of the following piecewise-continuous functions:

(a) $f(t)=\begin{cases}3t^2 & (0 \leqslant t < 4)\\ 2t-3 & (4 \leqslant t < 6)\\ 5 & (t \geqslant 6)\end{cases}$

(b) $g(t)=\begin{cases}t & (0 \leqslant t < 1)\\ 2-t & (1 \leqslant t < 2)\\ 0 & (t \geqslant 2)\end{cases}$

(c) $f(t)=\begin{cases}2t+5 & (0 \leqslant t < 2)\\ 9-3t & (2 \leqslant t < 4)\\ t^2-t & (t \geqslant 4)\end{cases}$

28 Solve for $t \geqslant 0$ the differential equation

$$\frac{d^2x}{dt^2}+7\frac{dx}{dt}+10x=2u+3\frac{du}{dt}$$

subject to $x=0$ and $dx/dt=2$ at $t=0$ and where $u(t)=e^{-2t}H(t)$.

29 A periodic function $f(t)$ is an infinite train of unit impulses at $t=0$ and repeated at intervals of $t=T$. Show that

$$\mathscr{L}\{f(t)\}=\frac{1}{1-e^{-sT}}$$

The response of a harmonic oscillator to such a periodic stimulus is determined by the differential equation

$$\frac{d^2x}{dt^2}+\omega^2x=f(t) \quad (t \geqslant 0)$$

Show that

$$x(t)=\frac{1}{\omega}\sum_{n=0}^{\infty}H(t-nT)\sin\omega(t-nT) \quad (t \geqslant 0)$$

and sketch the responses from $t=0$ to $t=6\pi/\omega$ for the two cases (a) $T=\pi/\omega$ and (b) $T=2\pi/\omega$.

30 An impulse voltage $E\delta(t)$ is applied at time $t=0$ to a circuit consisting of a resistor R, a capacitor C and an inductor L connected in series. Prior to application of this voltage, both the charge on the capacitor and the resulting current in the circuit are zero. Determine the charge $q(t)$ on the capacitor and the resulting current $i(t)$ in the circuit at time t.

2.5.13 Bending of beams

So far, we have considered examples in which Laplace transform methods have been used to solve initial-value-type problems. These methods may also be used to solve boundary-value problems, and, to illustrate, we consider in this section the application of Laplace transform methods to determine the transverse deflection of a uniform thin beam due to loading.

Consider a thin uniform beam of length l and let $y(x)$ be its transverse displacement, at distance x measured from one end, from the original position due to loading. The

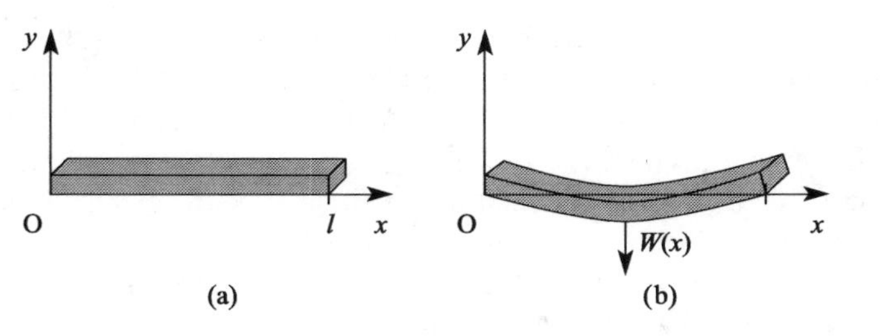

Figure 2.39 Transverse deflection of a beam: (a) initial position; (b) displaced position.

situation is illustrated in Figure 2.39, with the displacement measured upwards. Then, from the elementary theory of beams, we have

$$EI\frac{d^4y}{dx^4} = -W(x) \tag{2.62}$$

where $W(x)$ is the transverse force per unit length, with a downwards force taken to be positive, and EI is the flexural rigidity of the beam (E is Young's modulus of elasticity and I is the moment of inertia of the beam about its central axis). It is assumed that the beam has uniform elastic properties and a uniform cross-section over its length, so that both E and I are taken to be constants.

Equation (2.62) is sometimes written as

$$EI\frac{d^4y}{dx^4} = W(x)$$

where $y(x)$ is the transverse displacement measured downwards and not upwards as in (2.62).

In cases when the loading is uniform along the full length of the beam, that is $W(x)$ = constant, (2.62) may be readily solved by the normal techniques of integral calculus. However, when the loading is non-uniform, the use of Laplace transform methods has a distinct advantage, since by making use of Heaviside unit functions and impulse functions, the problem of solving (2.62) independently for various sections of the beam may be avoided.

Taking Laplace transforms throughout in (2.62) gives

$$EI[s^4Y(s) - s^3y(0) - s^2y_1(0) - sy_2(0) - y_3(0)] = -W(s) \tag{2.63}$$

where

$$y_1(0) = \left(\frac{dy}{dx}\right)_{x=0}, \quad y_2(0) = \left(\frac{d^2y}{dx^2}\right)_{x=0}, \quad y_3(0) = \left(\frac{d^3y}{dx^3}\right)_{x=0}$$

and may be interpreted physically as follows:

$EIy_3(0)$ is the shear at $x = 0$

$EIy_2(0)$ is the bending moment at $x = 0$

$y_1(0)$ is the slope at $x = 0$

$y(0)$ is the deflection at $x = 0$

Solving (2.63) for $y(s)$ leads to

$$Y(s) = -\frac{W(s)}{EIs^4} + \frac{y(0)}{s} + \frac{y_1(0)}{s^2} + \frac{y_2(0)}{s^3} + \frac{y_3(0)}{s^4} \tag{2.64}$$

Thus four boundary conditions need to be found, and ideally they should be the shear, bending moment, slope and deflection at $x = 0$. However, in practice these boundary conditions are not often available. While some of them are known, other boundary conditions are specified at points along the beam other than at $x = 0$, for example conditions at the far end, $x = l$, or conditions at possible points of support along the beam. That is, we are faced with a boundary-value problem rather than an initial-value problem.

To proceed, known conditions at $x = 0$ are inserted, while the other conditions among $y(0)$, $y_1(0)$, $y_2(0)$ and $y_3(0)$ that are not specified are carried forward as undetermined constants. Inverse transforms are taken throughout in (2.45) to obtain the deflection $y(x)$, and the outstanding undetermined constants are obtained using the boundary conditions specified at points along the beam other than at $x = 0$.

The boundary conditions are usually embodied in physical conditions such as the following:

(a) The beam is freely, or simply, supported at both ends, indicating that both the bending moments and deflection are zero at both ends, so that $y = \mathrm{d}^2y/\mathrm{d}x^2 = 0$ at both $x = 0$ and $x = l$.

(b) At both ends the beam is clamped, or built into a wall. Thus the beam is horizontal at both ends, so that $y = \mathrm{d}y/\mathrm{d}x = 0$ at both $x = 0$ and $x = l$.

(c) The beam is a cantilever with one end free (that is, fixed horizontally at one end, with the other end free). At the fixed end (say $x = 0$)

$$y = \frac{\mathrm{d}y}{\mathrm{d}x} = 0 \quad \text{at } x = 0$$

and at the free end ($x = l$), since both the shearing force and bending moment are zero,

$$\frac{\mathrm{d}^2y}{\mathrm{d}x^2} = \frac{\mathrm{d}^3y}{\mathrm{d}x^3} = 0 \quad \text{at } x = l$$

If the load is not uniform along the full length of the beam, use is made of Heaviside step functions and impulse functions in specifying $W(x)$ in (2.62). For example, a uniform load w per unit length over the portion of the beam $x = x_1$ to $x = x_2$ is specified as $wH(x - x_1) - wH(x - x_2)$, and a point load w at $x = x_1$ is specified as $w\delta(x - x_1)$.

Example 2.49

Figure 2.40 illustrates a uniform beam of length l, freely supported at both ends, bending under uniformly distributed self-weight W and a concentrated point load P at $x = \frac{1}{3}l$. Determine the transverse deflection $y(x)$ of the beam.

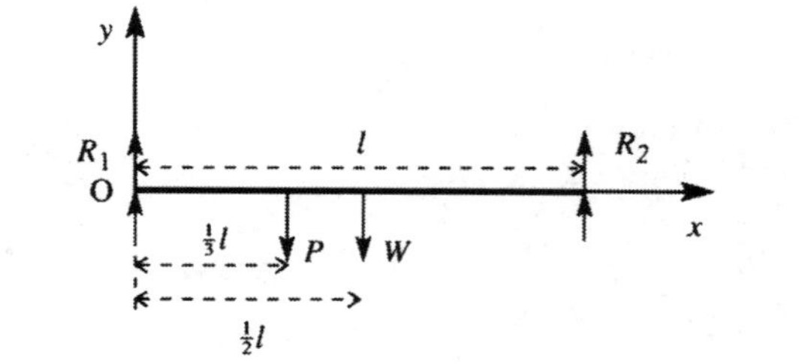

Figure 2.40 Loaded beam of Example 2.49.

Solution As in Figure 2.39, the origin is taken at the left-hand end of the beam, and the deflection $y(x)$ measured upwards from the horizontal at the level of the supports. The deflection

$y(x)$ is then given by (2.62), with the force function $W(x)$ having contributions from the weight W, the concentrated load P and the support reactions R_1 and R_2. However, since we are interested in solving (2.62) for $0 \leqslant x \leqslant l$, point loads or reactions at the end $x = l$ may be omitted from the force function.

As a preliminary, we need to determine R_1. This is done by taking static moments about the end $x = l$, assuming the weight W to be concentrated at the centroid $x = \frac{1}{2}l$, giving

$$R_1 l = \tfrac{1}{2}Wl + P\tfrac{2}{3}l$$

or

$$R_1 = \tfrac{1}{2}W + \tfrac{2}{3}P$$

The force function $W(x)$ may then be expressed as

$$W(x) = \frac{W}{l}H(x) + P\delta(x - \tfrac{1}{3}l) - (\tfrac{1}{2}W + \tfrac{2}{3}P)\delta(x)$$

with a Laplace transform

$$W(s) = \frac{W}{ls} + P\,\mathrm{e}^{-ls/3} - (\tfrac{1}{2}W + \tfrac{2}{3}P)$$

Since the beam is freely supported at both ends, the deflection and bending moments are zero at both ends, so we take the boundary conditions as

$$y = 0 \quad \text{at } x = 0 \text{ and } x = l$$

$$\frac{\mathrm{d}^2 y}{\mathrm{d}x^2} = 0 \quad \text{at } x = 0 \text{ and } x = l$$

The transformed equation (2.64) becomes

$$Y(s) = -\frac{1}{EI}\left[\frac{W}{ls^5} + \frac{P}{s^4}\mathrm{e}^{-ls/3} - (\tfrac{1}{2}W + \tfrac{2}{3}P)\frac{1}{s^4}\right] + \frac{y_1(0)}{s^2} + \frac{y_3(0)}{s^4}$$

Taking inverse transforms, making use of the second shift theorem (Theorem 2.4), gives the deflection $y(x)$ as

$$y(x) = -\frac{1}{EI}\left[\tfrac{1}{24}\frac{W}{l}x^4 + \tfrac{1}{6}P(x - \tfrac{1}{3}l)^3 H(x - \tfrac{1}{3}l) - \tfrac{1}{6}(\tfrac{1}{2}W + \tfrac{2}{3}P)x^3\right]$$
$$+ y_1(0)x + \tfrac{1}{6}y_3(0)x^3$$

To obtain the value of the undetermined constants $y_1(0)$ and $y_3(0)$, we employ the unused boundary conditions at $x = l$, namely $y(l) = 0$ and $y_2(l) = 0$. For $x > \frac{1}{3}l$

$$y(x) = -\frac{1}{EI}\left[\tfrac{1}{24}\frac{W}{l}x^4 + \tfrac{1}{6}P(x - \tfrac{1}{3}l)^3 - \tfrac{1}{6}(\tfrac{1}{2}W + \tfrac{2}{3}P)x^3\right] + y_1(0)x + \tfrac{1}{6}y_3(0)x^3$$

$$\frac{\mathrm{d}^2 y}{\mathrm{d}x^2} = y_2(x) = -\frac{1}{EI}\left[\frac{Wx^2}{2l} + P(x - \tfrac{1}{3}l) - \left(\tfrac{1}{3}W + \frac{2P}{3}\right)x\right] + y_3(0)x$$

Thus taking $y_2(l) = 0$ gives $y_3(0) = 0$, and taking $y(l) = 0$ gives

$$-\frac{1}{EI}(\tfrac{1}{24}Wl^3 + \tfrac{4}{81}Pl^3 - \tfrac{1}{12}Wl^3 - \tfrac{1}{9}Pl^3) + y_1(0)l = 0$$

so that

$$y_1(0) = -\frac{l^2}{EI}\left(\tfrac{1}{24}W + \tfrac{5}{81}P\right)$$

Substituting back, we find that the deflection $y(x)$ is given by

$$y(x) = -\frac{W}{EI}\left(\frac{x^4}{24l} - \tfrac{1}{12}x^3 + \tfrac{1}{24}l^2x\right) - \frac{P}{EI}\left(\tfrac{5}{81}l^2x - \tfrac{1}{9}x^3\right) - \frac{P}{6EI}\left(x - \tfrac{1}{3}l\right)^3 H\left(x - \tfrac{1}{3}l\right)$$

or, for the two sections of the beam,

$$y(x) = \begin{cases} -\dfrac{W}{EI}\left(\dfrac{x}{24l} - \tfrac{1}{12}x^3 + \tfrac{1}{24}l^2x\right) - \dfrac{P}{EI}\left(\tfrac{5}{81}l^2x - \tfrac{1}{9}x^3\right) & (0 < x < \tfrac{1}{3}l) \\ -\dfrac{W}{EI}\left(\dfrac{x^4}{24l} - \tfrac{1}{12}x^3 + \tfrac{1}{24}l^2x\right) - \dfrac{P}{EI}\left(\tfrac{19}{162}l^2x + \tfrac{1}{18}x^3 - \tfrac{1}{6}x^2l - \tfrac{1}{162}l^3\right) & (\tfrac{1}{3}l < x < l) \end{cases}$$

2.5.14 Exercises

31 Find the deflection of a beam simply supported at its ends $x = 0$ and $x = l$, bending under a uniformly distributed self-weight M and a concentrated load W at $x = \frac{1}{2}l$.

32 A cantilever beam of negligible weight and of length l is clamped at the end $x = 0$. Determine the deflection of the beam when it is subjected to a load per unit length, w, over the section $x = x_1$ to $x = x_2$. What is the maximum deflection if $x_1 = 0$ and $x_2 = l$?

33 A uniform cantilever beam of length l is subjected to a concentrated load W at a point distance b from the fixed end. Determine the deflection of the beam, distinguishing between the sections $0 < x \leqslant b$ and $b < x \leqslant l$.

2.6 Transfer functions

2.6.1 Definitions

The **transfer function** of a linear time-invariant system is defined to be the ratio of the Laplace transform of the system output (or response function) to the Laplace transform of the system input (or forcing function), *under the assumption that all the initial conditions are zero* (that is, the system is initially in a **quiescent state**).

Transfer functions are frequently used in engineering to characterize the input–output relationships of linear time-invariant systems, and play an important role in the analysis and design of such systems.

Consider a linear time-invariant system characterized by the differential equation

$$a_n\frac{d^nx}{dt^n} + a_{n-1}\frac{d^{n-1}x}{dt^{n-1}} + \ldots + a_0x = b_m\frac{d^mu}{dt^m} + \ldots + b_0u \tag{2.65}$$

where $n \geqslant m$, the as and bs are constant coefficients, and $x(t)$ is the system response or output to the input or forcing term $u(t)$ applied at time $t = 0$. Taking Laplace transforms throughout in (2.65) will lead to the transformed equation. Since all the initial conditions are assumed to be zero, we see from (2.15) that, in order to obtain the transformed equation, we simply replace d/dt by s, giving

$$(a_n s^n + a_{n-1} s^{n-1} + \ldots + a_0)X(s) = (b_m s^m + \ldots + b_0)U(s)$$

where $X(s)$ and $U(s)$ denote the Laplace transforms of $x(t)$ and $u(t)$ respectively.

The system transfer function $G(s)$ is then defined to be

$$G(s) = \frac{X(s)}{U(s)} = \frac{b_m s^m + \ldots + b_0}{a_n s^n + \ldots + a_0} \tag{2.66}$$

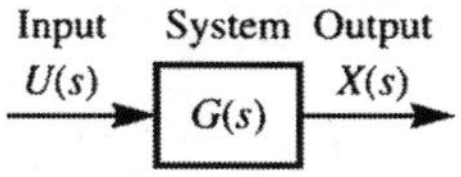

Figure 2.41 Transfer function block diagram.

and the system may be represented diagrammatically by the operation box of Figure 2.41. This representation is referred to as the **input–output block diagram** representation of the system.

Writing

$$P(s) = b_m s^m + \ldots + b_0$$

$$Q(s) = a_n s^n + \ldots + a_0$$

the transfer function may be expressed as

$$G(s) = \frac{P(s)}{Q(s)}$$

where, in order to make the system physically realizable, the degrees m and n of the polynomials $P(s)$ and $Q(s)$ must be such that $n \geqslant m$. This is because it follows from (2.61) that if $m > n$ then the system response $x(t)$ to a realistic input $u(t)$ will involve impulses.

The equation $Q(s) = 0$ is called the **characteristic equation** of the system; its order determines the **order of the system**, and its roots are referred to as the **poles** of the transfer function. Likewise, the roots of $P(s) = 0$ are referred to as the **zeros** of the transfer function.

It is important to realize that, in general, a transfer function is only used to characterize a linear time-invariant system. It is a property of the system itself, and is independent of both system input and output.

Although the transfer function characterizes the dynamics of the system, it provides no information concerning the actual physical structure of the system, and in fact systems that are physically different may have identical transfer functions; for example, the mass–spring–damper system of Figure 2.12 and the *LCR* circuit of Figure 2.8 both have the transfer function

$$G(s) = \frac{X(s)}{U(s)} = \frac{1}{\alpha s^2 + \beta s + \gamma}$$

In the mass–spring–damper system $X(s)$ determines the displacement $x(t)$ of the mass and $U(s)$ represents the applied force $F(t)$, while α denotes the mass, β the damping coefficient and γ the spring constant. On the other hand, in the *LCR* circuit $X(s)$ determines the charge $q(t)$ on the condenser and $U(s)$ represents the applied emf $e(t)$, while α denotes the inductance, β the resistance and γ the reciprocal of the capacitance.

In practice, an overall system may be made up of a number of components each characterized by its own transfer function and related operation box. The overall system input–output transfer function is then obtained by the rules of **block diagram algebra**.

Since $G(s)$ may be written as

$$G(s) = \frac{b_m}{a_m} \frac{(s - z_1)(s - z_2) \ldots (s - z_m)}{(s - p_1)(s - p_2) \ldots (s - p_n)}$$

where the z_is and p_is are the transfer function zeros and poles respectively, we observe that $G(s)$ is known, apart from a constant factor, if the positions of all the poles and zeros are known. Consequently, a plot of the poles and zeros of $G(s)$ is often used as an aid in the graphical analysis of the transfer function (a common convention is to mark the position of a zero by a circle ○ and that of a pole by a cross ×). Since the coefficients of the polynomials $P(s)$ and $Q(s)$ are real, all complex roots always occur in complex conjugate pairs, so that the **pole–zero plot** is symmetrical about the real axis.

Example 2.50

The response $x(t)$ of a system to a forcing function $u(t)$ is determined by the differential equation

$$9\frac{d^2x}{dt^2} + 12\frac{dx}{dt} + 13x = 2\frac{du}{dt} + 3u$$

(a) Determine the transfer function characterizing the system.

(b) Write down the characteristic equation of the system. What is the order of the system?

(c) Determine the transfer function poles and zeros, and illustrate them diagrammatically in the s plane.

Solution

(a) Assuming all the initial conditions to be zero, taking Laplace transforms throughout in the differential equation

$$9\frac{d^2x}{dt^2} + 12\frac{dx}{dt} + 13x = 2\frac{du}{dt} + 3u$$

leads to

$$(9s^2 + 12s + 13)X(s) = (2s + 3)U(s)$$

so that the system transfer function is given by

$$G(s) = \frac{X(s)}{U(s)} = \frac{2s + 3}{9s^2 + 12s + 13}$$

(b) The characteristic equation of the system is

$$9s^2 + 12s + 13 = 0$$

and the system is of order 2.

(c) The transfer function poles are the roots of the characteristic equation

$$9s^2 + 12s + 13 = 0$$

which are

$$s = \frac{-12 \pm \sqrt{(144 - 468)}}{18} = \frac{-2 \pm j3}{3}$$

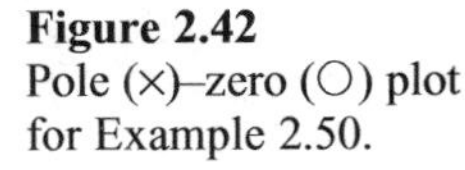

Figure 2.42
Pole (×)–zero (O) plot for Example 2.50.

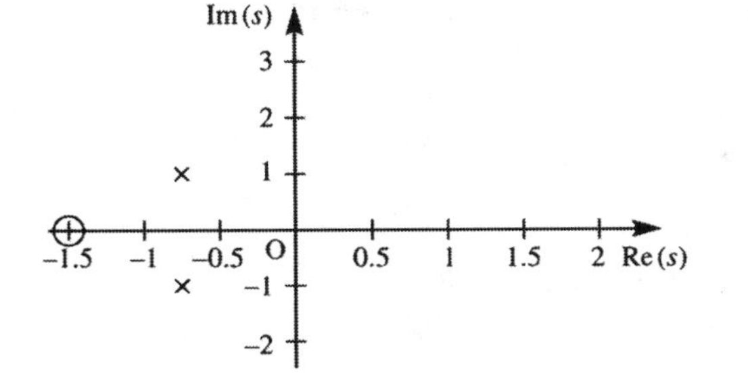

That is, the transfer function has simple poles at

$$s = -\tfrac{2}{3} + \mathrm{j} \quad \text{and} \quad s = -\tfrac{2}{3} - \mathrm{j}$$

The transfer function zeros are determined by equating the numerator polynomial $2s + 3$ to zero, giving a single zero at

$$s = -\tfrac{3}{2}$$

The corresponding pole–zero plot in the s plane is shown in Figure 2.42.

A transfer function (tf) is implemented within MATLAB using the commands

```
s = tf('s')
G = G(s)
```

Thus, entering `G=(2*s+3)/(9*s^2+12*s+13)` generates

```
                        2s + 3
transfer function = ---------------
                     9s^2 + 12s + 13
```

The command `poly(G)` generates the characteristic polynomial, whilst the commands `pole(G)` and `zero(G)` generate the poles and zeros respectively. The command `pzmap(G)` draws the pole–zero map.

2.6.2 Stability

The stability of a system is a property of vital importance to engineers. Intuitively, we may regard a stable system as one that will remain at rest unless it is excited by an external source, and will return to rest if all such external influences are removed. Thus a stable system is one whose response, in the absence of an input, will approach zero as time approaches infinity. This then ensures that any bounded input produces a bounded output; this property is frequently taken to be the definition of a **stable linear system**.

Clearly, stability is a property of the system itself, and does not depend on the system input or forcing function. Since a system may be characterized in the s domain by its transfer function $G(s)$, it should be possible to use the transfer function to specify conditions for the system to be stable.

In considering the time response of

$$X(s) = G(s)U(s), \qquad G(s) = \frac{P(s)}{Q(s)}$$

to any given input $u(t)$, it is necessary to factorize the denominator polynomial

$$Q(s) = a_n s^n + a_{n-1} s^{n-1} + \ldots + a_0$$

and various forms of factors can be involved.

Simple factor of the form $s + \alpha$, with α real

This corresponds to a simple pole at $s = -\alpha$, and will in the partial-fractions expansion of $G(s)$ lead to a term of the form $c/(s + \alpha)$ having corresponding time response $c\,\mathrm{e}^{-\alpha t}H(t)$, using the strict form of the inverse given in (2.12). If $\alpha > 0$, so that the pole is in the left half of the s plane, the time response will tend to zero as $t \to \infty$. If $\alpha < 0$, so that the pole is in the right half of the s plane, the time response will increase without bound as $t \to \infty$. It follows that a stable system must have real-valued simple poles of $G(s)$ in the left half of the s plane.

$\alpha = 0$ corresponds to a simple pole at the origin, having a corresponding time response that is a step $cH(t)$. A system having such a pole is said to be **marginally stable**; this does not ensure that a bounded input will lead to a bounded output, since, for example, if such a system has an input that is a step d applied at time $t = 0$ then the response will be a ramp $cdtH(t)$, which is unbounded as $t \to \infty$.

Repeated simple factors of the form $(s + \alpha)^n$, with α real

This corresponds to a multiple pole at $s = -\alpha$, and will lead in the partial-fractions expansion of $G(s)$ to a term of the form $c/(s + \alpha)^n$ having corresponding time response $[c/(n-1)!]t^{n-1}\mathrm{e}^{-\alpha t}H(t)$. Again the response will decay to zero as $t \to \infty$ only if $\alpha > 0$, indicating that a stable system must have all real-valued repeated poles of $G(s)$ in the left half of the s plane.

Quadratic factors of the form $(s + \alpha)^2 + \beta^2$, with α and β real

This corresponds to a pair of complex conjugate poles at $s = -\alpha + \mathrm{j}\beta$, $s = -\alpha - \mathrm{j}\beta$, and will lead in the partial-fractions expansion of $G(s)$ to a term of the form

$$\frac{c(s + \alpha) + d\beta}{(s + \alpha)^2 + \beta^2}$$

having corresponding time response

$$\mathrm{e}^{-\alpha t}(c \cos \beta t + d \sin \beta t) \equiv A\,\mathrm{e}^{-\alpha t} \sin(\beta t + \gamma)$$

where $A = \sqrt{(c^2 + d^2)}$ and $\gamma = \tan^{-1}(c/d)$.

Again we see that poles in the left half of the s plane (corresponding to $\alpha > 0$) have corresponding time responses that die away, in the form of an exponentially damped sinusoid, as $t \to \infty$. A stable system must therefore have complex conjugate poles located in the left half of the s plane; that is, all complex poles must have a negative real part.

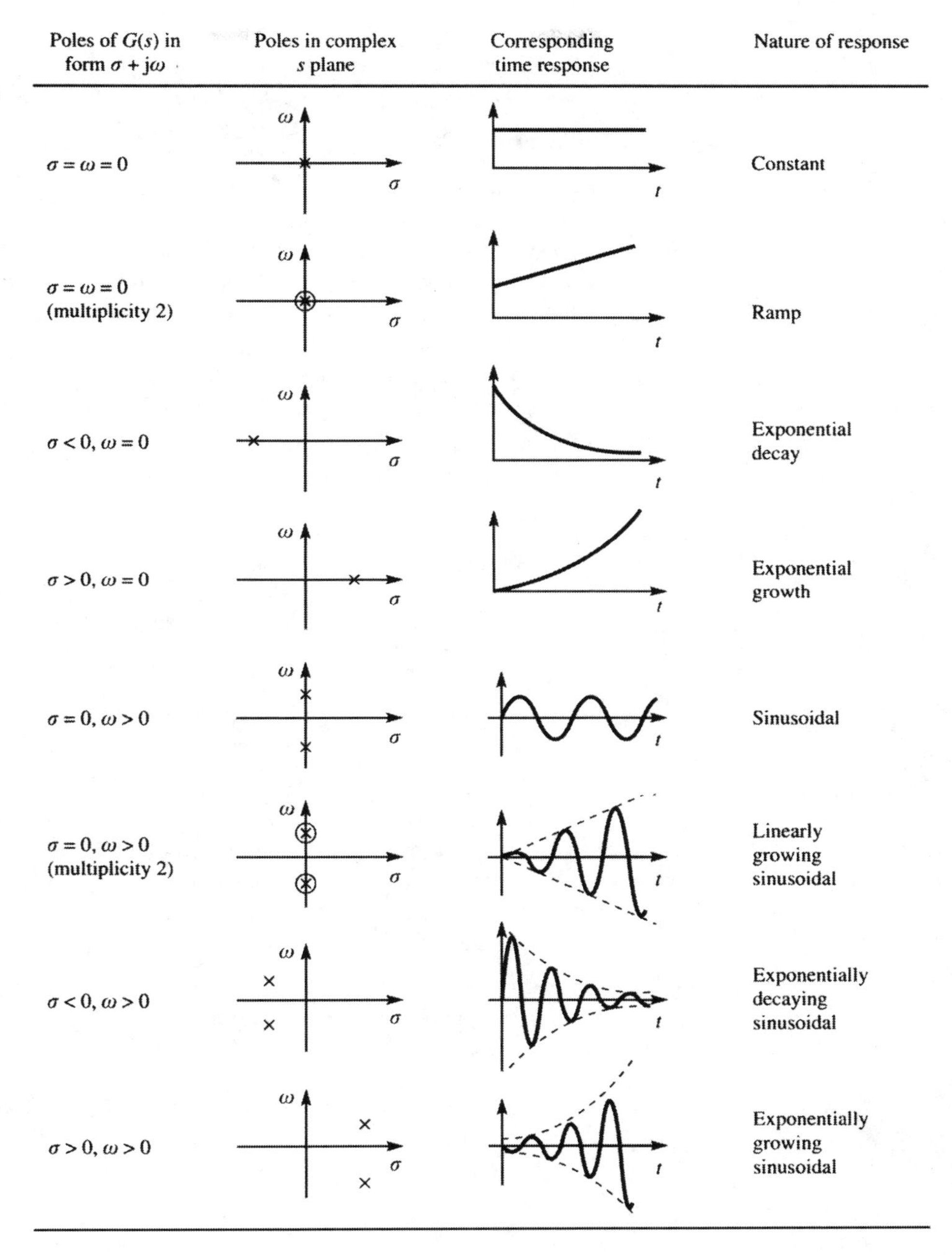

Figure 2.43 Relationship between transfer function poles and time response.

If $\alpha = 0$, the corresponding time response will be a periodic sinusoid, which will not die away as $t \to \infty$. Again this corresponds to a marginally stable system, and will, for example, give rise to a response that increases without bound as $t \to \infty$ when the input is a sinusoid at the same frequency β.

A summary of the responses corresponding to the various types of poles is given in Figure 2.43.

The concept of stability may be expressed in the form of Definition 2.3.

DEFINITION 2.3

A physically realizable causal time-invariant linear system with transfer function $G(s)$ is stable provided that all the poles of $G(s)$ are in the left half of the s plane.

The requirement in the definition that the system be physically realizable, that is $n \geqslant m$ in the transfer function $G(s)$ of (2.66), avoids terms of the form s^{m-n} in the partial-fractions expansion of $G(s)$. Such a term would correspond to differentiation of degree $m - n$, and were an input such as $\sin \omega t$ used to excite the system then the response would include a term such as $\omega^{m-n} \sin \omega t$ or $\omega^{m-n} \cos \omega t$, which could be made as large as desired by increasing the input frequency ω.

In terms of the poles of the transfer function $G(s)$, its abscissa of convergence σ_c corresponds to the real part of the pole located furthest to the right in the s plane. For example, if

$$G(s) = \frac{s+1}{(s+3)(s+2)}$$

then the abscissa of convergence $\sigma_c = -2$.

It follows from Definition 2.3 that the transfer function $G(s)$ of a stable system has abscissa of convergence $\sigma_c = -\alpha$, with $\alpha > 0$. Thus its region of convergence includes the imaginary axis, so that $G(s)$ exists when $s = j\omega$. We shall return to this result when considering the relationship between Laplace and Fourier transforms in Section 5.4.1.

According to Definition 2.3, in order to prove stability, we need to show that all the roots of the characteristic equation

$$Q(s) = a_n s^n + a_{n-1} s^{n-1} + \ldots + a_1 s + a_0 = 0 \tag{2.67}$$

have negative real parts (that is, they lie in the left half of the s plane). Various criteria exist to show that all the roots satisfy this requirement, and it is not necessary to solve the equation to prove stability. One widely used criterion is the **Routh–Hurwitz criterion**, which can be stated as follows:

A necessary and sufficient condition for all the roots of equation (2.67) to have negative real parts is that the determinants $\Delta_1, \Delta_2, \ldots, \Delta_n$ are all positive, where

$$\Delta_r = \begin{vmatrix} a_{n-1} & a_n & 0 & 0 & \cdots & 0 \\ a_{n-3} & a_{n-2} & a_{n-1} & a_n & \cdots & 0 \\ a_{n-5} & a_{n-4} & a_{n-3} & a_{n-2} & \cdots & 0 \\ \vdots & \vdots & \vdots & \vdots & & \vdots \\ a_{n-(2r-1)} & a_{n-2r} & a_{n-2r-1} & a_{n-2r-2} & \cdots & a_{n-r} \end{vmatrix} \tag{2.68}$$

it being understood that in each determinant all the as *with subscripts that are either negative or greater than* n *are to be replaced by zero.*

Example 2.51

Show that the roots of the characteristic equation

$$s^4 + 9s^3 + 33s^2 + 51s + 26 = 0$$

all have negative real parts.

Solution In this case $n = 4$, $a_0 = 26$, $a_1 = 51$, $a_2 = 33$, $a_3 = 9$, $a_4 = 1$ and $a_r = 0$ $(r > 4)$. The determinants of the Routh–Hurwitz criterion are

$$\Delta_1 = |a_{n-1}| = |a_3| = |9| = 9 > 0$$

$$\Delta_2 = \begin{vmatrix} a_{n-1} & a_n \\ a_{n-3} & a_{n-2} \end{vmatrix} = \begin{vmatrix} a_3 & a_4 \\ a_1 & a_2 \end{vmatrix} = \begin{vmatrix} 9 & 1 \\ 51 & 33 \end{vmatrix} = 246 > 0$$

$$\Delta_3 = \begin{vmatrix} a_{n-1} & a_n & 0 \\ a_{n-3} & a_{n-2} & a_{n-1} \\ a_{n-5} & a_{n-4} & a_{n-3} \end{vmatrix} = \begin{vmatrix} a_3 & a_4 & 0 \\ a_1 & a_2 & a_3 \\ a_{-1} & a_0 & a_1 \end{vmatrix} = \begin{vmatrix} 9 & 1 & 0 \\ 51 & 33 & 9 \\ 0 & 26 & 51 \end{vmatrix} = 10\,440 > 0$$

$$\Delta_4 = \begin{vmatrix} a_{n-1} & a_n & 0 & 0 \\ a_{n-3} & a_{n-2} & a_{n-1} & a_n \\ a_{n-5} & a_{n-4} & a_{n-3} & a_{n-2} \\ a_{n-7} & a_{n-6} & a_{n-5} & a_{n-4} \end{vmatrix} = \begin{vmatrix} a_3 & a_4 & 0 & 0 \\ a_1 & a_2 & a_3 & a_4 \\ a_{-1} & a_0 & a_1 & a_2 \\ a_{-3} & a_{-2} & a_{-1} & a_0 \end{vmatrix}$$

$$= \begin{vmatrix} 9 & 1 & 0 & 0 \\ 51 & 33 & 9 & 1 \\ 0 & 26 & 51 & 37 \\ 0 & 0 & 0 & 26 \end{vmatrix} = 26\Delta_3 > 0$$

Thus $\Delta_1 > 0$, $\Delta_2 > 0$, $\Delta_3 > 0$ and $\Delta_4 > 0$, so that all the roots of the given characteristic equation have negative real parts. This is readily checked, since the roots are -2, -1, $-3 + j2$ and $-3 - j2$.

Example 2.52 The steady motion of a steam-engine governor is modelled by the differential equations

$$m\ddot{\eta} + b\dot{\eta} + d\eta - e\omega = 0 \tag{2.69}$$

$$I_0\dot{\omega} = -f\eta \tag{2.70}$$

where η is a small fluctuation in the angle of inclination, ω a small fluctuation in the angular velocity of rotation, and m, b, d, e, f and I_0 are all positive constants. Show that the motion of the governor is stable provided that

$$\frac{bd}{m} > \frac{ef}{I_0}$$

Solution Differentiating (2.69) gives

$$m\dddot{\eta} + b\ddot{\eta} + d\dot{\eta} - e\dot{\omega} = 0$$

which, on using (2.70), leads to

$$m\dddot{\eta} + b\ddot{\eta} + d\dot{\eta} + \frac{ef}{I_0}\eta = 0$$

for which the corresponding characteristic equation is

$$ms^3 + bs^2 + ds + \frac{ef}{I_0} = 0$$

This is a cubic polynomial, so the parameters of (2.67) are

$$n = 3, \quad a_0 = \frac{ef}{I_0}, \quad a_1 = d, \quad a_2 = b, \quad a_3 = m \quad (a_r = 0, r > 3)$$

The determinants (2.68) of the Routh–Hurwitz criterion are

$$\Delta_1 = |a_2| = b > 0$$

$$\Delta_2 = \begin{vmatrix} a_2 & a_3 \\ a_0 & a_1 \end{vmatrix} = \begin{vmatrix} b & m \\ ef/I_0 & d \end{vmatrix} = bd - \frac{mef}{I_0}$$

(and so $\Delta_2 > 0$ provided that $bd - mef/I_0 > 0$ or $bd/m > ef/I_0$), and

$$\Delta_3 = \begin{vmatrix} a_2 & a_3 & 0 \\ a_0 & a_1 & a_2 \\ 0 & 0 & a_0 \end{vmatrix} = a_0\Delta_2 > 0 \quad \text{if } \Delta_2 > 0$$

Thus the action of the governor is stable provided that $\Delta_2 > 0$; that is,

$$\frac{bd}{m} > \frac{ef}{I_0}$$

2.6.3 Impulse response

From (2.66), we find that for a system having transfer function $G(s)$ the response $x(t)$ of the system, initially in a quiescent state, to an input $u(t)$ is determined by the transformed relationship

$$X(s) = G(s)U(s)$$

If the input $u(t)$ is taken to be the unit impulse function $\delta(t)$ then the system response will be determined by

$$X(s) = G(s)\mathscr{L}\{\delta(t)\} = G(s)$$

Taking inverse Laplace transforms leads to the corresponding time response $h(t)$, which is called the **impulse response** of the system (it is also sometimes referred to as the **weighting function** of the system); that is, the impulse response is given by

$$h(t) = \mathscr{L}^{-1}\{X(s)\} = \mathscr{L}^{-1}\{G(s)\} \tag{2.71}$$

We therefore have the following definition.

DEFINITION 2.4: Impulse response

The impulse response $h(t)$ of a linear time-invariant system is the response of the system to a unit impulse applied at time $t = 0$ when all the initial conditions are zero. It is such that $\mathscr{L}\{h(t)\} = G(s)$, where $G(s)$ is the system transfer function.

Since the impulse response is the inverse Laplace transform of the transfer function, it follows that both the impulse response and the transfer function carry the same information about the dynamics of a linear time-invariant system. Theoretically, therefore, it is possible to determine the complete information about the system by exciting it with an impulse and measuring the response. For this reason, it is common practice in engineering to regard the transfer function as being the Laplace transform of the impulse response, since this places greater emphasis on the parameters of the system when considering system design.

We saw in Section 2.6.2 that, since the transfer function $G(s)$ completely characterizes a linear time-invariant system, it can be used to specify conditions for system stability, which are that all the poles of $G(s)$ lie in the left half of the s plane. Alternatively, characterizing the system by its impulse response, we can say that the system is stable provided that its impulse response decays to zero as $t \to \infty$.

Example 2.53

Determine the impulse response of the linear system whose response $x(t)$ to an input $u(t)$ is determined by the differential equation

$$\frac{d^2x}{dt^2} + 5\frac{dx}{dt} + 6x = 5u(t) \tag{2.72}$$

Solution

The impulse response $h(t)$ is the system response to $u(t) = \delta(t)$ when all the initial conditions are zero. It is therefore determined as the solution of the differential equation

$$\frac{d^2h}{dt^2} + 5\frac{dh}{dt} + 6h = 5\delta(t) \tag{2.73}$$

subject to the initial conditions $h(0) = \dot{h}(0) = 0$. Taking Laplace transforms in (2.73) gives

$$(s^2 + 5s + 6)H(s) = 5\mathscr{L}\{\delta(t)\} = 5$$

so that

$$H(s) = \frac{5}{(s+3)(s+2)} = \frac{5}{s+2} - \frac{5}{s+3}$$

which, on inversion, gives the desired impulse response

$$h(t) = 5(e^{-2t} - e^{-3t})$$

Alternatively, the transfer function $G(s)$ of the system determined by (2.72) is

$$G(s) = \frac{5}{s^2 + 5s + 6}$$

so that $h(t) = \mathscr{L}^{-1}\{G(s)\} = 5(e^{-2t} - e^{-3t})$ as before.

Note: This example serves to illustrate the necessity for incorporating 0^- as the lower limit in the Laplace transform integral, in order to accommodate for an impulse applied at $t = 0$. The effect of the impulse is to cause a step change in $\dot{x}(t)$ at $t = 0$, with the initial condition accounting for what happens up to 0^-.

In MATLAB a plot of the impulse response is obtained using the commands

```
s=tf('s')
G=G(s)
impulse(G)
```

2.6.4 Initial- and final-value theorems

The initial- and final-value theorems are two useful theorems that enable us to predict system behaviour as $t \to 0$ and $t \to \infty$ without actually inverting Laplace transforms.

Theorem 2.6 **The initial-value theorem**

If $f(t)$ and $f'(t)$ are both Laplace-transformable and if $\lim_{s\to\infty} sF(s)$ exists then

$$\lim_{t\to 0^+} f(t) = f(0^+) = \lim_{s\to\infty} sF(s)$$

Proof From (2.13),

$$\mathscr{L}\{f'(t)\} = \int_{0^-}^{\infty} f'(t)\,\mathrm{e}^{-st}\,\mathrm{d}t = sF(s) - f(0^-)$$

where we have highlighted the fact that the lower limit is 0^-. Hence

$$\begin{aligned}\lim_{s\to\infty} [sF(s) - f(0^-)] &= \lim_{s\to\infty} \int_{0^-}^{\infty} f'(t)\,\mathrm{e}^{-st}\,\mathrm{d}t \\ &= \lim_{s\to\infty} \int_{0^-}^{0^+} f'(t)\,\mathrm{e}^{-st}\,\mathrm{d}t + \lim_{s\to\infty} \int_{0^+}^{\infty} f'(t)\,\mathrm{e}^{-st}\,\mathrm{d}t \qquad (2.74)\end{aligned}$$

If $f(t)$ is discontinuous at the origin, so that $f(0^+) \neq f(0^-)$, then, from (2.59), $f'(t)$ contains an impulse term $[f(0^+) - f(0^-)]\delta(t)$, so that

$$\lim_{s\to\infty} \int_{0^-}^{0^+} f'(t)\,\mathrm{e}^{-st}\,\mathrm{d}t = f(0^+) - f(0^-)$$

Also, since the Laplace transform of $f'(t)$ exists, it is of exponential order and we have

$$\lim_{s\to\infty} \int_{0^+}^{\infty} f'(t)\,\mathrm{e}^{-st}\,\mathrm{d}t = 0$$

so that (2.74) becomes

$$\lim_{s\to\infty} sF(s) - f(0^-) = f(0^+) - f(0^-)$$

giving the required result:

$$\lim_{s\to\infty} sF(s) = f(0^+)$$

If $f(t)$ is continuous at the origin then $f'(t)$ does not contain an impulse term, and the right-hand side of (2.74) is zero, giving

$$\lim_{s\to\infty} sF(s) = f(0^-) = f(0^+)$$

end of theorem

It is important to recognize that the initial-value theorem does not give the initial value $f(0^-)$ used when determining the Laplace transform, but rather gives the value of $f(t)$ as $t \to 0^+$. This distinction is highlighted in the following example.

Example 2.54

The circuit of Figure 2.44 consists of a resistance R and a capacitance C connected in series together with constant voltage source E. Prior to closing the switch at time $t = 0$, both the charge on the capacitor and the resulting current in the circuit are zero. Determine the current $i(t)$ in the circuit at time t after the switch is closed, and investigate the use of the initial-value theorem.

Solution

Applying Kirchhoff's law to the circuit of Figure 2.44, we have

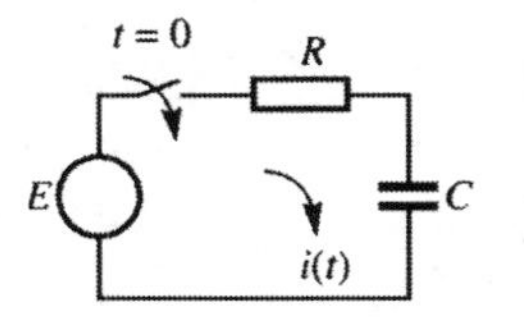

Figure 2.44 *RC* circuit of Example 2.54.

$$Ri + \frac{1}{C}\int i \, \mathrm{d}t = E_0$$

which, on taking Laplace transforms, gives the transformed equation

$$RI(s) + \frac{1}{C}\frac{I(s)}{s} = \frac{E_0}{s}$$

Therefore

$$I(s) = \frac{E_0/R}{s + 1/RC}$$

Taking inverse transforms gives the current $i(t)$ at $t \geqslant 0$ as

$$i(t) = \frac{E_0}{R}\mathrm{e}^{-t/RC} \tag{2.75}$$

Applying the initial-value theorem,

$$\lim_{t \to 0^+} i(t) = \lim_{s \to \infty} sI(s) = \lim_{s \to \infty} \frac{sE_0/R}{s + 1/RC} = \lim_{s \to \infty} \frac{E_0/R}{1 + 1/RCs} = \frac{E_0}{R}$$

That is,

$$i(0^+) = \frac{E_0}{R}$$

a result that is readily confirmed by allowing $t \to 0^+$ in (2.75). We note that this is not the same as the initial state $i(0) = 0$ owing to the fact that there is a step change in $i(t)$ at $t = 0$.

Theorem 2.7 **The final-value theorem**

If $f(t)$ and $f'(t)$ are both Laplace-transformable and $\lim_{t \to \infty} f(t)$ exists then

$$\lim_{t \to \infty} f(t) = \lim_{s \to 0} sF(s)$$

Proof From (2.13),

$$\mathcal{L}\{f'(t)\} = \int_{0^-}^{\infty} f'(t)\,\mathrm{e}^{-st}\,\mathrm{d}t = sF(s) - f(0^-)$$

Taking limits, we have

$$\begin{aligned}\lim_{s\to 0}\,[sF(s) - f(0^-)] &= \lim_{s\to 0}\int_{0^-}^{\infty} f'(t)\,\mathrm{e}^{-st}\,\mathrm{d}t \\ &= \int_{0^-}^{\infty} f'(t)\,\mathrm{d}t = [f(t)]_{0^-}^{\infty} \\ &= \lim_{t\to\infty} f(t) - f(0^-)\end{aligned}$$

giving the required result:

$$\lim_{t\to\infty} f(t) = \lim_{s\to 0} sF(s)$$

end of theorem

The restriction that $\lim_{t\to\infty} f(t)$ must exist means that the theorem does not hold for functions such as e^t, which tends to infinity as $t \to \infty$, or $\sin \omega t$, whose limit is undefined. Since in practice the final-value theorem is used to obtain the behaviour of $f(t)$ as $t \to \infty$ from knowledge of the transform $F(s)$, it is more common to express the restriction in terms of restrictions on $F(s)$, which are that $sF(s)$ must have all its poles in the left half of the s plane; that is, $sF(s)$ must represent a stable transfer function. It is important that the theorem be used with caution and that this restriction be fully recognized, since the existence of $\lim_{s\to 0} sF(s)$ does *not* imply that $f(t)$ has a limiting value as $t \to \infty$.

Example 2.55 Investigate the application of the final-value theorem to the transfer function

$$F(s) = \frac{1}{(s+2)(s-3)} \tag{2.76}$$

Solution

$$\lim_{s\to 0} sF(s) = \lim_{s\to 0} \frac{s}{(s+2)(s-3)} = 0$$

so the use of the final-value theorem implies that for the time function $f(t)$ corresponding to $F(s)$ we have

$$\lim_{t\to\infty} f(t) = 0$$

However, taking inverse transforms in (2.76) gives

$$f(t) = \frac{1}{s}(\mathrm{e}^{3t} - \mathrm{e}^{-2t})$$

implying that $f(t)$ tends to infinity as $t \to \infty$. This implied contradiction arises since the theorem is not valid in this case. Although $\lim_{s\to 0} sF(s)$ exists, $sF(s)$ has a pole at $s = 3$, which is not in the left half of the s plane.

The final-value theorem provides a useful vehicle for determining a system's **steady-state gain (SSG)** and the **steady-state errors**, or **offsets**, in feedback control systems, both of which are important features in control system design.

The SSG of a stable system is the system's steady-state response, that is the response as $t \to \infty$, to a unit step input. For a system with transfer function $G(s)$ we have, from (2.66), that its response $x(t)$ is related to the input $u(t)$ by the transformed equation

$$X(s) = G(s)U(s)$$

For a unit step input

$$u(t) = 1H(t) \quad \text{giving} \quad U(s) = \frac{1}{s}$$

so that

$$X(s) = \frac{G(s)}{s}$$

From the final-value theorem, the steady-state gain is

$$\text{SSG} = \lim_{t\to\infty} x(t) = \lim_{s\to 0} sX(s) = \lim_{s\to 0} G(s)$$

Example 2.56

Determine the steady-state gain of a system having transfer function

$$G(s) = \frac{20(1+3s)}{s^2+7s+10}$$

Solution

The response $x(t)$ to a unit step input $u(t) = 1H(t)$ is given by the transformed equation

$$X(s) = G(s)U(s) = \frac{20(1+3s)}{s^2+7s+10}\frac{1}{s}$$

Then, by the final-value theorem, the steady-state gain is given by

$$\text{SSG} = \lim_{t\to\infty} x(t) = \lim_{s\to 0} sX(s) = \lim_{s\to 0} \frac{20(1+3s)}{s^2+7s+10} = 2$$

Note that for a step input of magnitude K, that is $u(t) = KH(t)$, the steady-state response will be $\lim_{s\to 0} kG(s) = 2K$; that is,

steady-state response to step input = SSG × magnitude of step input

---

A unity feedback control system having forward-path transfer function $G(s)$, reference input or desired output $r(t)$ and actual output $x(t)$ is illustrated by the block diagram of Figure 2.45. Defining the error to be $e(t) = r(t) - x(t)$, it follows that

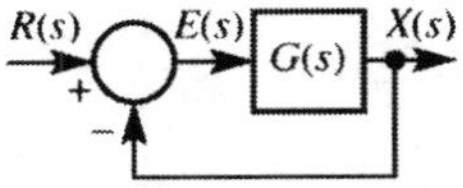

Figure 2.45 Unity feedback control system.

$$G(s)E(s) = X(s) = R(s) - E(s)$$

giving

$$E(s) = \frac{R(s)}{1+G(s)}$$

Thus, from the final-value theorem, the steady-state error (SSE) is

$$\text{SSE} = \lim_{t\to\infty} e(t) = \lim_{s\to 0} sE(s) = \lim_{s\to 0} \frac{sR(s)}{1+G(s)} \tag{2.77}$$

Example 2.57 Determine the SSE for the system of Figure 2.45 when $G(s)$ is the same as in Example 2.50 and $r(t)$ is a step of magnitude K.

Solution Since $r(t) = KH(t)$, we have $R(s) = K/s$, so, using (2.77),

$$\text{SSE} = \lim_{s\to 0} \frac{sK/s}{1+G(s)} = \frac{K}{1+\text{SSG}}$$

where SSG = 2 as determined in Example 2.56. Thus

$$\text{SSE} = \tfrac{1}{3}K$$

It is clear from Example 2.57 that if we are to reduce the SSE, which is clearly desirable in practice, then the SSG needs to be increased. However, such an increase could lead to an undesirable transient response, and in system design a balance must be achieved. Detailed design techniques for alleviating such problems are not considered here; for such a discussion the reader is referred to specialist texts (see for example J. Schwarzenbach and K. F. Gill, *System Modelling and Control*, Edward Arnold, London, 1984).

2.6.5 Exercises

34 The response $x(t)$ of a system to a forcing function $u(t)$ is determined by the differential equation model

$$\frac{d^2x}{dt^2} + 2\frac{dx}{dt} + 5x = 3\frac{du}{dt} + 2u$$

(a) Determine the transfer function characterizing the system.

(b) Write down the characteristic equation of the system. What is the order of the system?

(c) Determine the transfer function poles and zeros, and illustrate them diagrammatically in the s plane.

35 Repeat Exercise 34 for a system whose response $x(t)$ to an input $u(t)$ is determined by the differential equation

$$\frac{d^3x}{dt^3} + 5\frac{d^2x}{dt^2} + 17\frac{dx}{dt} + 13x = \frac{d^2u}{dt^2} + 5\frac{du}{dt} + 6$$

36 Which of the following transfer functions represent stable systems and which represent unstable systems?

(a) $\dfrac{s-1}{(s+2)(s^2+4)}$ (b) $\dfrac{(s+2)(s-2)}{(s+1)(s-1)(s+4)}$

(c) $\dfrac{s-1}{(s+2)(s+4)}$ (d) $\dfrac{6}{(s^2+s+1)(s+1)^2}$

(e) $\dfrac{5(s+10)}{(s+5)(s^2-s+10)}$

37 Which of the following characteristic equations are representative of stable systems?

(a) $s^2 - 4s + 13 = 0$

(b) $5s^3 + 13s^2 + 31s + 15 = 0$

(c) $s^3 + s^2 + s + 1 = 0$

(d) $24s^4 + 11s^3 + 26s^2 + 45s + 36 = 0$

(e) $s^3 + 2s^2 + 2s + 1 = 0$

38 The differential equation governing the motion of a mass–spring–damper system with controller is

$$m\frac{d^3x}{dt^3} + c\frac{d^2x}{dt^2} + K\frac{dx}{dt} + Krx = 0$$

where m, c, K and r are positive constants. Show that the motion of the system is stable provided that $r < c/m$.

39 The behaviour of a system having a gain controller is characterized by the characteristic equation

$$s^4 + 2s^3 + (K + 2)s^2 + 7s + K = 0$$

where K is the controller gain. Show that the system is stable provided that $K > 2.1$.

40 A feedback control system has characteristic equation

$$s^3 + 15Ks^2 + (2K - 1)s + 5K = 0$$

where K is a constant gain factor. Determine the range of positive values of K for which the system will be stable.

41 Determine the impulse responses of the linear systems whose response $x(t)$ to an input $u(t)$ is determined by the following differential equations:

(a) $\dfrac{d^2x}{dt^2} + 15\dfrac{dx}{dt} + 56x = 3u(t)$

(b) $\dfrac{d^2x}{dt^2} + 8\dfrac{dx}{dt} + 25x = u(t)$

(c) $\dfrac{d^2x}{dt^2} - 2\dfrac{dx}{dt} - 8x = 4u(t)$

(d) $\dfrac{d^2x}{dt^2} - 4\dfrac{dx}{dt} + 13x = u(t)$

What can be said about the stability of each of the systems?

42 The response of a given system to a unit step $u(t) = 1H(t)$ is given by

$$x(t) = 1 - \tfrac{7}{3}e^{-t} + \tfrac{3}{2}e^{-2t} - \tfrac{1}{6}e^{-4t}$$

What is the transfer function of the system?

43 Verify the initial-value theorem for the functions

(a) $2 - 3\cos t$ (b) $(3t - 1)^2$ (c) $t + 3\sin 2t$

44 Verify the final-value theorem for the functions

(a) $1 + 3e^{-t}\sin 2t$ (b) t^2e^{-2t}

(c) $3 - 2e^{-3t} + e^{-t}\cos 2t$

45 Using the final-value theorem, check the value obtained for $i_2(t)$ as $t \to \infty$ for the circuit of Example 2.28.

46 Discuss the applicability of the final-value theorem for obtaining the value of $i_2(t)$ as $t \to \infty$ for the circuit of Example 2.29.

47 Use the initial- and final-value theorems to find the jump at $t = 0$ and the limiting value as $t \to \infty$ for the solution of the initial-value problem

$$7\frac{dy}{dt} + 5y = 4 + e^{-3t} + 2\delta(t)$$

with $y(0^-) = -1$.

2.6.6 Convolution

Convolution is a useful concept that has many applications in various fields of engineering. In Section 2.6.7 we shall use it to obtain the response of a linear system to any input in terms of the impulse response.

DEFINITION 2.5: Convolution

Given two piecewise-continuous functions $f(t)$ and $g(t)$, the **convolution** of $f(t)$ and $g(t)$, denoted by $f * g(t)$, is defined as

$$f * g(t) = \int_{-\infty}^{\infty} f(\tau)g(t - \tau)\,d\tau$$

In the particular case when $f(t)$ and $g(t)$ are causal functions

$$f(\tau) = g(\tau) = 0 \quad (\tau < 0), \qquad g(t - \tau) = 0 \quad (\tau > t)$$

and we have

$$f * g(t) = \int_0^t f(\tau)g(t-\tau)\,d\tau \tag{2.78}$$

The notation $f * g(t)$ indicates that the convolution $f * g$ is a function of t; that is, it could also be written as $(f * g)(t)$. The integral $\int_{-\infty}^{\infty} f(\tau)g(t-\tau)\,d\tau$ is called the **convolution integral**. Alternative names are the **superposition integral**, **Duhamel integral**, **folding integral** and **faltung integral**.

Convolution can be considered as a generalized function, and as such it has many of the properties of multiplication. In particular, the commutative law is satisfied, so that

$$f * g(t) = g * f(t)$$

or, for causal functions,

$$\int_0^t f(\tau)g(t-\tau)\,d\tau = \int_0^t f(t-\tau)g(\tau)\,d\tau \tag{2.79}$$

This means that the convolution can be evaluated by time-shifting either of the two functions. The result (2.79) is readily proved, since by making the substitution $\tau_1 = t - \tau$ in (2.78) we obtain

$$f * g(t) = \int_t^0 f(t-\tau_1)g(\tau_1)(-d\tau_1) = \int_0^t f(t-\tau_1)g(\tau_1)\,d\tau_1 = g * f(t)$$

Example 2.58

For the two causal functions

$$f(t) = tH(t), \qquad g(t) = \sin 2t\,H(t)$$

show that $f * g(t) = g * f(t)$.

Solution

$$f * g(t) = \int_0^t f(\tau)g(t-\tau)\,d\tau = \int_0^t \tau \sin 2(t-\tau)\,d\tau$$

Integrating by parts gives

$$f * g(t) = [\tfrac{1}{2}\tau\cos 2(t-\tau) + \tfrac{1}{4}\sin 2(t-\tau)]_0^t = \tfrac{1}{2}t - \tfrac{1}{4}\sin 2t$$

$$g * f(t) = \int_0^t f(t-\tau)g(\tau)\,d\tau = \int_0^t (t-\tau)\sin 2\tau\,d\tau$$

$$= [-\tfrac{1}{2}(t-\tau)\cos 2\tau - \tfrac{1}{4}\sin 2\tau]_0^t = \tfrac{1}{2}t - \tfrac{1}{4}\sin 2t$$

so that $f * g(t) = g * f(t)$.

The importance of convolution in Laplace transform work is that it enables us to obtain the inverse transform of the product of two transforms. The necessary result for doing this is contained in the following theorem.

Theorem 2.8 **Convolution theorem for Laplace transforms**

If $f(t)$ and $g(t)$ are of exponential order σ, piecewise-continuous on $t \geq 0$ and have Laplace transforms $F(s)$ and $G(s)$ respectively, then, for $s > \sigma$,

$$\mathcal{L}\left\{\int_0^t f(\tau)g(t-\tau)\,\mathrm{d}\tau\right\} = \mathcal{L}\{f * g(t)\} = F(s)G(s)$$

or, in the more useful inverse form,

$$\mathcal{L}^{-1}\{F(s)G(s)\} = f * g(t) \quad \textbf{(2.80)}$$

Proof By definition,

$$F(s)G(s) = \mathcal{L}\{f(t)\}\mathcal{L}\{g(t)\} = \left[\int_0^\infty \mathrm{e}^{-sx}f(x)\,\mathrm{d}x\right]\left[\int_0^\infty \mathrm{e}^{-sy}g(y)\,\mathrm{d}y\right]$$

where we have used the 'dummy' variables x and y, rather than t, in the integrals to avoid confusion. This may now be expressed in the form of the double integral

$$F(s)G(s) = \int_0^\infty\int_0^\infty \mathrm{e}^{-s(x+y)}f(x)g(y)\,\mathrm{d}x\,\mathrm{d}y = \iint_R \mathrm{e}^{-s(x+y)}f(x)g(y)\,\mathrm{d}x\,\mathrm{d}y$$

where R is the first quadrant in the (x, y) plane, as shown in Figure 2.46(a). On making the substitution

$$x + y = t, \qquad y = \tau$$

the double integral is transformed into

$$F(s)G(s) = \iint_{R_1} \mathrm{e}^{-st}f(t-\tau)g(\tau)\,\mathrm{d}t\,\mathrm{d}\tau$$

where R_1 is the semi-infinite region in the (τ, t) plane bounded by the lines $\tau = 0$ and $\tau = t$, as shown in Figure 2.46(b). This may be written as

$$F(s)G(s) = \int_0^\infty \mathrm{e}^{-st}\left(\int_0^t f(t-\tau)\,g(\tau)\,\mathrm{d}\tau\right)\mathrm{d}t$$

$$= \int_0^\infty \mathrm{e}^{-st}\,[g * f(t)]\,\mathrm{d}t = \mathcal{L}\{g * f(t)\}$$

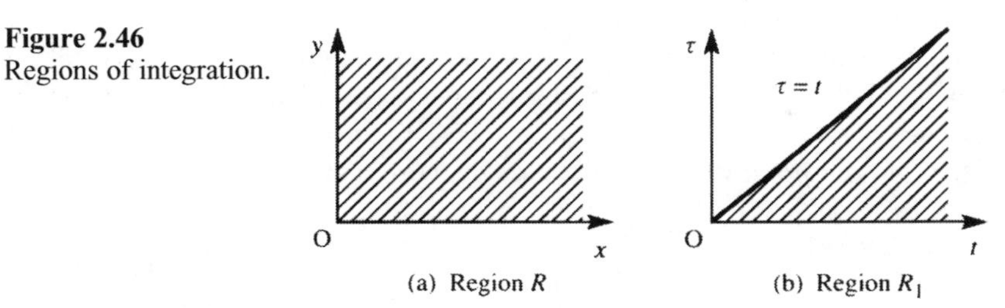

Figure 2.46
Regions of integration.

and, since convolution is commutative, we may write this as

$$F(s)G(s) = \mathscr{L}\{f * g(t)\}$$

which concludes the proof.

end of theorem

Example 2.59 Using the convolution theorem, determine $\mathscr{L}^{-1}\left\{\dfrac{1}{s^2(s+2)^2}\right\}$.

Solution We express $1/s^2(s+2)^2$ as $(1/s^2)[1/(s+2)^2]$; then, since

$$\mathscr{L}\{t\} = \frac{1}{s^2}, \qquad \mathscr{L}\{t\,e^{-2t}\} = \frac{1}{(s+2)^2}$$

taking $f(t) = t$ and $g(t) = t\,e^{-2t}$ in the convolution theorem gives

$$\mathscr{L}^{-1}\left\{\frac{1}{s^2}\frac{1}{(s+2)^2}\right\} = \int_0^t f(t-\tau)g(\tau)\,d\tau = \int_0^t (t-\tau)\tau\,e^{-2\tau}\,d\tau$$

which on integration by parts gives

$$\mathscr{L}^{-1}\left\{\frac{1}{s^2}\frac{1}{(s+2)^2}\right\} = [-\tfrac{1}{2}e^{-2\tau}[(t-\tau)\tau + \tfrac{1}{2}(t-2\tau) - \tfrac{1}{2}]]_0^t = \tfrac{1}{4}[t - 1 + (t+1)e^{-2t}]$$

We can check this result by first expressing the given transform in partial-fractions form and then inverting to give

$$\frac{1}{s^2(s+2)^2} = \frac{-\frac{1}{4}}{s} + \frac{\frac{1}{4}}{s^2} + \frac{\frac{1}{4}}{s+2} + \frac{\frac{1}{4}}{(s+2)^2}$$

so that

$$\mathscr{L}^{-1}\left\{\frac{1}{s^2(s+2)^2}\right\} = -\tfrac{1}{4} + \tfrac{1}{4}t + \tfrac{1}{4}e^{-2t} + \tfrac{1}{4}t\,e^{-2t} = \tfrac{1}{4}[t - 1 + (t+1)e^{-2t}]$$

as before.

2.6.7 System response to an arbitrary input

The impulse response of a linear time-invariant system is particularly useful in practice in that it enables us to obtain the response of the system to an arbitrary input using the convolution integral. This provides engineers with a powerful approach to the analysis of dynamical systems.

Let us consider a linear system characterized by its impulse response $h(t)$. Then we wish to determine the response $x(t)$ of the system to an arbitrary input $u(t)$ such as that illustrated in Figure 2.47(a). We first approximate the continuous function $u(t)$ by an infinite sequence of impulses of magnitude $u(n\Delta T)$, $n = 0, 1, 2, \dots$, as shown in Figure 2.47(b). This approximation for $u(t)$ may be written as

$$u(t) \simeq \sum_{n=0}^{\infty} u(n\Delta T)\delta(t - n\Delta T)\,\Delta T \qquad \textbf{(2.81)}$$

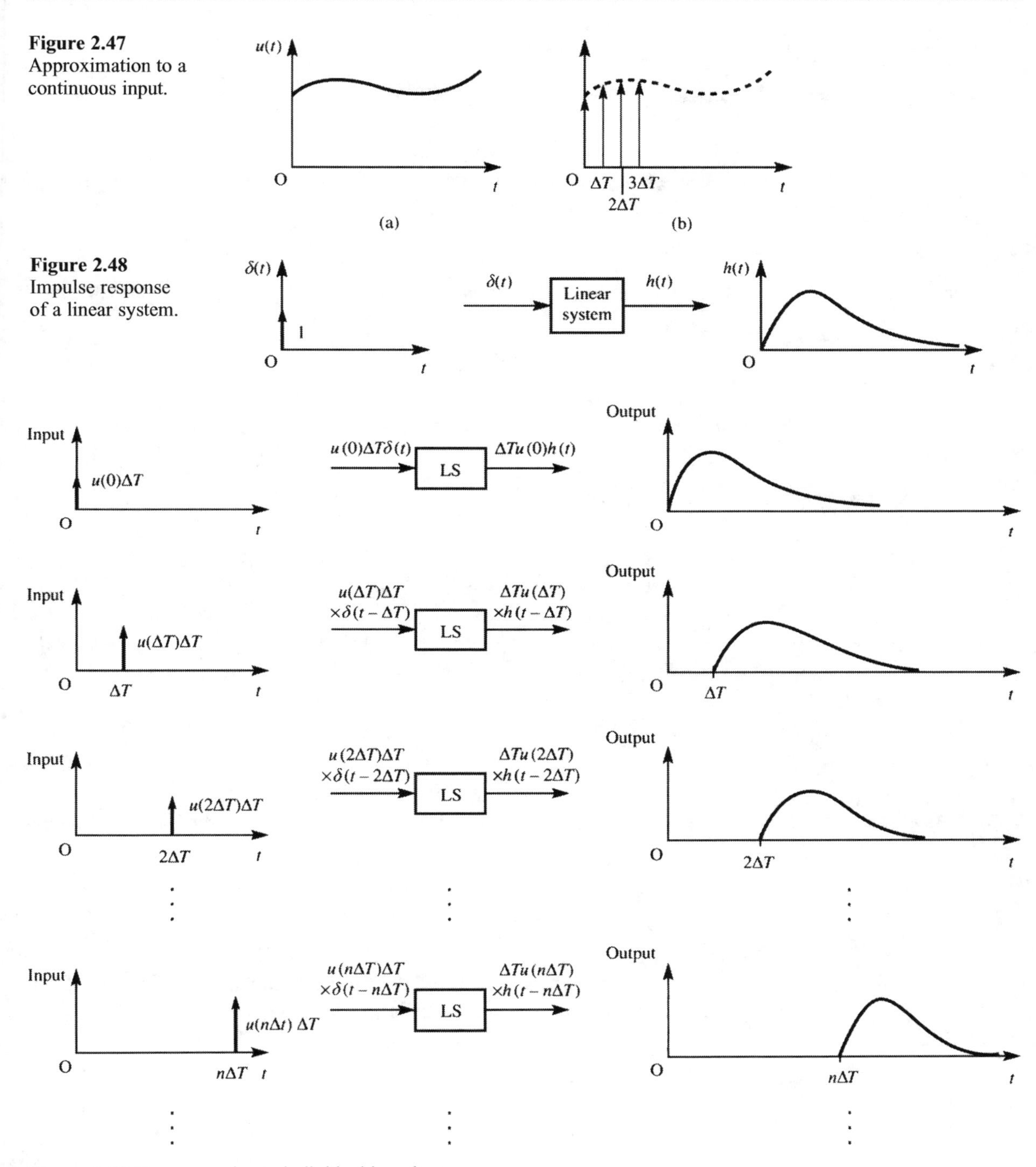

Figure 2.47 Approximation to a continuous input.

Figure 2.48 Impulse response of a linear system.

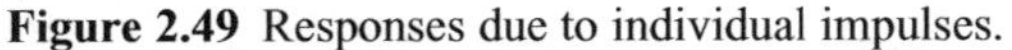

Figure 2.49 Responses due to individual impulses.

Since the system is linear, the **principle of superposition** holds, so that the response of the system to the sum of the impulses is equal to the sum of the responses of the system to each of the impulses acting separately. Depicting the impulse response $h(t)$ of the linear system by Figure 2.48, the responses due to the individual impulses forming the sum in (2.81) are illustrated in the sequence of plots in Figure 2.49.

Summing the individual responses, we find that the response due to the sum of the impulses is

$$\sum_{n=0}^{\infty} u(n\Delta T)h(t - n\Delta T)\,\Delta T \tag{2.82}$$

Allowing $\Delta T \to 0$, so that $n\Delta T$ approaches a continuous variable τ, the above sum will approach an integral that will be representative of the system response $x(t)$ to the continuous input $u(t)$. Thus

$$x(t) = \int_0^{\infty} u(\tau)h(t-\tau)\,\mathrm{d}\tau = \int_0^{t} u(\tau)h(t-\tau)\,\mathrm{d}\tau \quad \text{(since } h(t) \text{ is a causal function)}$$

That is,

$$x(t) = u * h(t)$$

Since convolution is commutative, we may also write

$$x(t) = h * u(t) = \int_0^{t} h(\tau)u(t-\tau)\,\mathrm{d}\tau$$

In summary, we have the result that if the impulse response of a linear time-invariant system is $h(t)$ then its response to an arbitrary input $u(t)$ is

$$x(t) = \int_0^{t} u(\tau)h(t-\tau)\,\mathrm{d}\tau = \int_0^{t} h(\tau)u(t-\tau)\,\mathrm{d}\tau \tag{2.83}$$

It is important to realize that this is the response of the system to the input $u(t)$ assuming it to be initially in a quiescent state.

Example 2.60

The response $\theta_o(t)$ of a system to a driving force $\theta_i(t)$ is given by the linear differential equation

$$\frac{\mathrm{d}^2\theta_o}{\mathrm{d}t^2} + \frac{2\mathrm{d}\theta_o}{\mathrm{d}t} + 5\theta_o = \theta_i$$

Determine the impulse response of the system. Hence, using the convolution integral, determine the response of the system to a unit step input at time $t = 0$, assuming that it is initially in a quiescent state. Confirm this latter result by direct calculation.

Solution The impulse response $h(t)$ is the solution of

$$\frac{\mathrm{d}^2 h}{\mathrm{d}t^2} + 2\frac{\mathrm{d}h}{\mathrm{d}t} + 5h = \delta(t)$$

subject to the initial conditions $h(0) = \dot{h}(0) = 0$. Taking Laplace transforms gives

$$(s^2 + 2s + 5)H(s) = \mathscr{L}\{\delta(t)\} = 1$$

so that

$$H(s) = \frac{1}{s^2 + 2s + 5} = \frac{1}{2}\,\frac{2}{(s+1)^2 + 2^2}$$

which, on inversion, gives the impulse response as

$$h(t) = \tfrac{1}{2}\,\mathrm{e}^{-t}\sin 2t$$

Using the convolution integral

$$\theta_o(t) = \int_0^t h(\tau)\theta_i(t-\tau)\,\mathrm{d}\tau$$

with $\theta_i(t) = 1H(t)$ gives the response to the unit step as

$$\theta_o(t) = \tfrac{1}{2}\int_0^t \mathrm{e}^{-\tau}\sin 2\tau\,\mathrm{d}\tau$$

Integrating by parts twice gives

$$\begin{aligned}\theta_o(t) &= -\tfrac{1}{2}\mathrm{e}^{-t}\sin 2t - \mathrm{e}^{-t}\cos 2t + 1 - 2\int_0^t \mathrm{e}^{-\tau}\sin 2\tau\,\mathrm{d}\tau \\ &= -\tfrac{1}{2}\mathrm{e}^{-t}\sin 2t - \mathrm{e}^{-t}\cos 2t + 1 - 4\theta_o(t)\end{aligned}$$

Hence

$$\theta_o(t) = \tfrac{1}{5}(1 - \mathrm{e}^{-t}\cos 2t - \tfrac{1}{2}\mathrm{e}^{-t}\sin 2t)$$

(Note that in this case, because of the simple form of $\theta_i(t)$, the convolution integral $\int_0^t h(\tau)\theta_i(t-\tau)\,\mathrm{d}\tau$ is taken in preference to $\int_0^t \theta_i(\tau)h(t-\tau)\,\mathrm{d}\tau$.)

To obtain the step response directly, we need to solve for $t \geqslant 0$ the differential equation

$$\frac{\mathrm{d}^2\theta_o}{\mathrm{d}t^2} + 2\frac{\mathrm{d}\theta_o}{\mathrm{d}t} + 5\theta_o = 1$$

subject to the initial conditions $\theta_o(0) = \dot{\theta}_o(0) = 0$. Taking Laplace transforms gives

$$(s^2 + 2s + 5)\Theta(s) = \frac{1}{s}$$

so that

$$\Theta = \frac{1}{s(s^2 + 2s + 5)} = \frac{\frac{1}{5}}{s} - \frac{1}{5}\frac{s+2}{(s+1)^2 + 4}$$

which, on inversion, gives

$$\theta_o(t) = \tfrac{1}{5} - \tfrac{1}{5}\mathrm{e}^{-t}(\cos 2t + \tfrac{1}{2}\sin 2t) = \tfrac{1}{5}(1 - \mathrm{e}^{-t}\cos 2t - \tfrac{1}{2}\mathrm{e}^{-t}\sin 2t)$$

confirming the previous result.

We therefore see that a linear time-invariant system may be characterized in the frequency domain (or s domain) by its transfer function $G(s)$ or in the time domain by its impulse response $h(t)$, as depicted in Figures 2.50(a) and (b) respectively. The response in the frequency domain is obtained by algebraic multiplication, while the

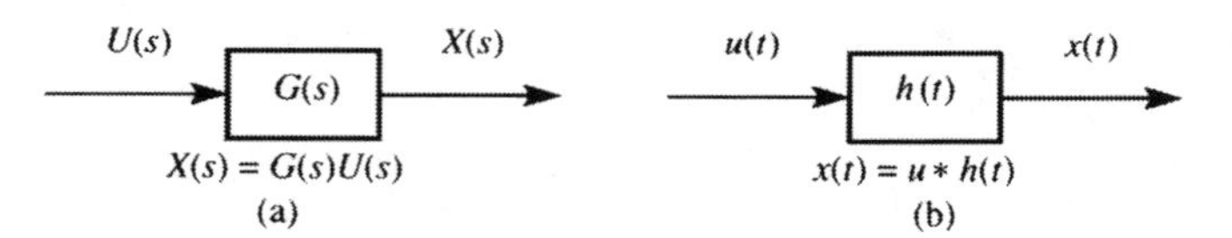

Figure 2.50 (a) Frequency-domain and (b) time-domain representations of a linear time-invariant system.

time-domain response involves a convolution. This equivalence of the operation of convolution in the time domain with algebraic multiplication in the frequency domain is clearly a powerful argument for the use of frequency-domain techniques in engineering design.

2.6.8 Exercises

48 For the following pairs of causal functions $f(t)$ and $g(t)$ show that $f * g(t) = g * f(t)$:

(a) $f(t) = t$, $\quad g(t) = \cos 3t$

(b) $f(t) = t + 1$, $\quad g(t) = e^{-2t}$

(c) $f(t) = t^2$, $\quad g(t) = \sin 2t$

(d) $f(t) = e^{-t}$, $\quad g(t) = \sin t$

49 Using the convolution theorem, determine the following inverse Laplace transforms. Check your results by first expressing the given transform in partial-fractions form and then inverting using the standard results:

(a) $\mathscr{L}^{-1}\left\{\dfrac{1}{s(s+3)^3}\right\}$

(b) $\mathscr{L}^{-1}\left\{\dfrac{1}{(s-2)^2(s+3)^2}\right\}$

(c) $\mathscr{L}^{-1}\left\{\dfrac{1}{s^2(s+4)}\right\}$

50 Taking $f(\lambda) = \lambda$ and $g(\lambda) = e^{-\lambda}$, use the inverse form (2.80) of the convolution theorem to show that the solution of the integral equation

$$y(t) = \int_0^t \lambda\, e^{-(t-\lambda)}\, d\lambda$$

is

$$y(t) = (t - 1) + e^{-t}.$$

51 Find the impulse response of the system characterized by the differential equation

$$\frac{d^2x}{dt^2} + 7\frac{dx}{dt} + 12x = u(t)$$

and hence find the response of the system to the pulse input $u(t) = A[H(t) - H(t - T)]$, assuming that it is initially in a quiescent state.

52 The response $\theta_o(t)$ of a servomechanism to a driving force $\theta_i(t)$ is given by the second-order differential equation

$$\frac{d^2\theta_o}{dt^2} + 4\frac{d\theta_o}{dt} + 5\theta_o = \theta_i \quad (t \geq 0)$$

Determine the impulse response of the system, and hence, using the convolution integral, obtain the response of the servomechanism to a unit step driving force, applied at time $t = 0$, given that the system is initially in a quiescent state.

Check your answer by directly solving the differential equation

$$\frac{d^2\theta_o}{dt^2} + 4\frac{d\theta_o}{dt} + 5\theta_o = 1$$

subject to the initial conditions $\theta_o = \dot{\theta}_o = 0$ when $t = 0$.

2.7 Engineering application: frequency response

Frequency-response methods provide a graphical approach for the analysis and design of systems. Traditionally these methods have evolved from practical considerations, and as such are still widely used by engineers, providing tremendous insight into overall system behaviour. In this section we shall illustrate how the frequency response can be readily obtained from the system transfer function $G(s)$ by simply replacing s by $j\omega$. Methods of representing it graphically will also be considered.

Consider the system depicted in Figure 2.41, with transfer function

$$G(s) = \frac{K(s-z_1)(s-z_2)\ldots(s-z_m)}{(s-p_1)(s-p_2)\ldots(s-p_n)} \quad (m \leqslant n) \tag{2.84}$$

When the input is the sinusoidally varying signal

$$u(t) = A\sin\omega t$$

applied at time $t = 0$, the system response $x(t)$ for $t \geqslant 0$ is determined by

$$X(s) = G(s)\mathscr{L}\{A\sin\omega t\}$$

That is,

$$\begin{aligned} X(s) &= G(s)\frac{A\omega}{s^2+\omega^2} \\ &= \frac{KA\omega(s-z_1)(s-z_2)\ldots(s-z_m)}{(s-p_1)(s-p_2)\ldots(s-p_n)(s-j\omega)(s+j\omega)} \end{aligned}$$

which, on expanding in partial fractions, gives

$$X(s) = \frac{\alpha_1}{s-j\omega} + \frac{\alpha_2}{s+j\omega} + \sum_{i=1}^{n}\frac{\beta_i}{s-p_i}$$

where $\alpha_1, \alpha_2, \beta_1, \beta_2, \ldots, \beta_n$ are constants. Here the first two terms in the summation are generated by the input and determine the steady-state response, while the remaining terms are generated by the transfer function and determine the system transient response.

Taking inverse Laplace transforms, the system response $x(t)$, $t \geqslant 0$, is given by

$$x(t) = \alpha_1 e^{j\omega t} + \alpha_2 e^{-j\omega t} + \sum_{i=1}^{n}\beta_i e^{p_i t} \quad (t \geqslant 0)$$

In practice we are generally concerned with systems that are stable, for which the poles p_i, $i = 1, 2, \ldots, n$, of the transfer function $G(s)$ lie in the left half of the s plane. Consequently, for practical systems the time-domain terms $\beta_i e^{p_i t}$, $i = 1, 2, \ldots, n$, decay to zero as t increases, and will not contribute to the steady-state response $x_{ss}(t)$ of the system. Thus for stable linear systems the latter is determined by the first two terms as

$$x_{ss}(t) = \alpha_1 e^{j\omega t} + \alpha_2 e^{-j\omega t}$$

Using the 'cover-up' rule for determining the coefficients α_1 and α_2 in the partial-fraction expansions gives

$$\alpha_1 = \left[\frac{(s - \mathrm{j}\omega)G(s)A\omega}{(s - \mathrm{j}\omega)(s + \mathrm{j}\omega)}\right]_{s=\mathrm{j}\omega} = \frac{A}{2\mathrm{j}}G(\mathrm{j}\omega)$$

$$\alpha_2 = \left[\frac{(s + \mathrm{j}\omega)G(s)A\omega}{(s - \mathrm{j}\omega)(s + \mathrm{j}\omega)}\right]_{s=-\mathrm{j}\omega} = -\frac{A}{2\mathrm{j}}G(-\mathrm{j}\omega)$$

so that the steady-state response becomes

$$x_{ss}(t) = \frac{A}{2\mathrm{j}}\,G(\mathrm{j}\omega)\,\mathrm{e}^{\mathrm{j}\omega t} - \frac{A}{2\mathrm{j}}\,G(-\mathrm{j}\omega)\,\mathrm{e}^{-\mathrm{j}\omega t} \qquad \textbf{(2.85)}$$

$G(\mathrm{j}\omega)$ can be expressed in the polar form

$$G(\mathrm{j}\omega) = |G(\mathrm{j}\omega)|\,\mathrm{e}^{\mathrm{j}\arg G(\mathrm{j}\omega)}$$

where $|G(\mathrm{j}\omega)|$ denotes the magnitude (or modulus) of $G(\mathrm{j}\omega)$. (Note that both the magnitude and argument vary with frequency ω.) Then, assuming that the system has real parameters,

$$G(-\mathrm{j}\omega) = |G(\mathrm{j}\omega)|\,\mathrm{e}^{-\mathrm{j}\arg G(\mathrm{j}\omega)}$$

and the steady-state response (2.85) becomes

$$\begin{aligned} x_{ss}(t) &= \frac{A}{2\mathrm{j}}\,[|G(\mathrm{j}\omega)|\mathrm{e}^{\mathrm{j}\arg G(\mathrm{j}\omega)}]\,\mathrm{e}^{\mathrm{j}\omega t} - \frac{A}{2\mathrm{j}}\,[|G(\mathrm{j}\omega)|\,\mathrm{e}^{-\mathrm{j}\arg G(\mathrm{j}\omega)}]\,\mathrm{e}^{-\mathrm{j}\omega t} \\ &= \frac{A}{2\mathrm{j}}\,|G(\mathrm{j}\omega)|[\mathrm{e}^{\mathrm{j}[\omega t+\arg G(\mathrm{j}\omega)]} - \mathrm{e}^{-\mathrm{j}[\omega t+\arg G(\mathrm{j}\omega)]}] \end{aligned}$$

That is,

$$x_{ss}(t) = A\,|G(\mathrm{j}\omega)|\sin[\omega t + \arg G(\mathrm{j}\omega)] \qquad \textbf{(2.86)}$$

This indicates that if a stable linear system with transfer function $G(s)$ is subjected to a sinusoidal input then

(a) the steady-state system response is also a sinusoid having the same frequency ω as the input;

(b) the amplitude of this response is $|G(\mathrm{j}\omega)|$ times the amplitude A of the input sinusoid; the input is said to be **amplified** if $|G(\mathrm{j}\omega)| > 1$ and **attenuated** if $|G(\mathrm{j}\omega)| < 1$;

(c) the phase shift between input and output is $\arg G(\mathrm{j}\omega)$. The system is said to **lead** if $\arg G(\mathrm{j}\omega) > 0$ and **lag** if $\arg G(\mathrm{j}\omega) < 0$.

The variations in both the magnitude $|G(\mathrm{j}\omega)|$ and argument $\arg G(\mathrm{j}\omega)$ as the frequency ω of the input sinusoid is varied constitute the **frequency response of the system**, the magnitude $|G(\mathrm{j}\omega)|$ representing the **amplitude gain** or **amplitude ratio** of the system for sinusoidal input with frequency ω, and the argument $\arg G(\mathrm{j}\omega)$ representing the **phase shift**.

The result (2.86) implies that the function $G(\mathrm{j}\omega)$ may be found experimentally by subjecting a system to sinusoidal excitations and measuring the amplitude gain and phase shift between output and input as the input frequency is varied over the range $0 < \omega < \infty$. In principle, therefore, frequency-response measurements may be used to determine the system transfer function $G(s)$.

In Chapters 4 and 5, dealing with Fourier series and Fourier transforms, we shall see that most functions can be written as sums of sinusoids, and consequently the response of a linear system to almost any input can be deduced in the form of the corresponding sinusoidal responses. It is important, however, to appreciate that the term 'response' in the expression 'frequency response' only relates to the steady-state response behaviour of the system.

The information contained in the system frequency response may be conveniently displayed in graphical form. In practice it is usual to represent it by two graphs: one showing how the amplitude $|G(j\omega)|$ varies with frequency and one showing how the phase shift $\arg G(j\omega)$ varies with frequency.

Example 2.61 Determine the frequency response of the *RC* filter shown in Figure 2.51. Sketch the amplitude and phase-shift plots.

Solution The input–output relationship is given by

$$E_o(s) = \frac{1}{RCs + 1} E_i(s)$$

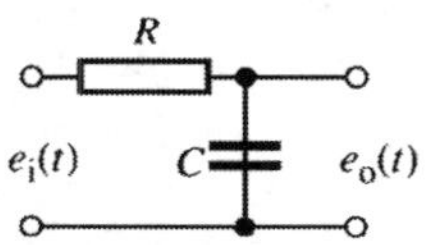

Figure 2.51 *RC* filter.

so that the filter is characterized by the transfer function

$$G(s) = \frac{1}{RCs + 1}$$

Therefore

$$G(j\omega) = \frac{1}{RCj\omega + 1} = \frac{1 - jRC\omega}{1 + R^2C^2\omega^2}$$

$$= \frac{1}{1 + R^2C^2\omega^2} - j\frac{RC\omega}{1 + R^2C^2\omega^2}$$

giving the frequency-response characteristics

$$\text{amplitude ratio} = |G(j\omega)|$$

$$= \sqrt{\left[\frac{1}{(1 + R^2C^2\omega^2)^2} + \frac{R^2C^2\omega^2}{(1 + R^2C^2\omega^2)^2}\right]}$$

$$= \frac{1}{\sqrt{(1 + R^2C^2\omega^2)}}$$

$$\text{phase shift} = \arg G(j\omega) = -\tan^{-1}(RC\omega)$$

Note that for $\omega = 0$

$$|G(j\omega)| = 1, \qquad \arg G(j\omega) = 0$$

and as $\omega \to \infty$

$$|G(j\omega)| \to 0, \qquad \arg G(j\omega) \to -\tfrac{1}{2}\pi$$

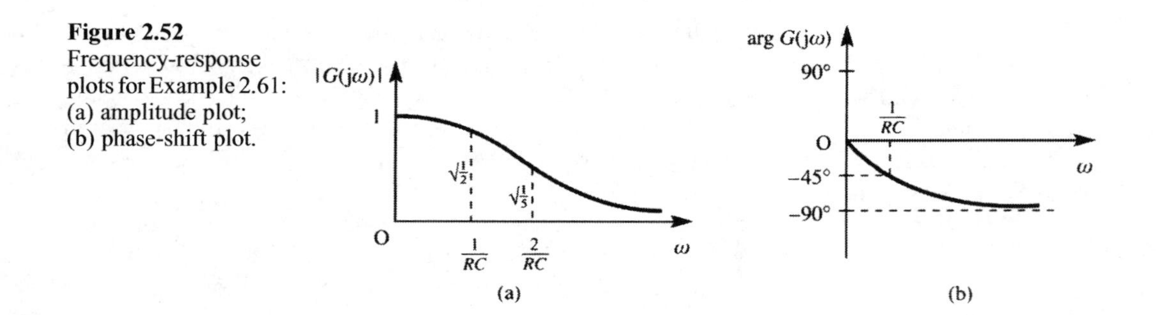

Figure 2.52 Frequency-response plots for Example 2.61: (a) amplitude plot; (b) phase-shift plot.

Plots of the amplitude and phase-shift curves are shown in Figures 2.52(a) and (b) respectively.

For the simple transfer function of Example 2.61, plotting the amplitude and phase-shift characteristics was relatively easy. For higher-order transfer functions it can be a rather tedious task, and it would be far more efficient to use a suitable computer package. However, to facilitate the use of frequency-response techniques in system design, engineers adopt a different approach, making use of **Bode plots** to display the relevant information. This approach is named after H. W. Bode, who developed the techniques at the Bell Laboratories in the late 1930s. Again it involves drawing separate plots of amplitude and phase shift, but in this case on semi-logarithmic graph paper, with frequency plotted on the horizontal logarithmic axis and amplitude, or phase, on the vertical linear axis. It is also normal to express the amplitude gain in decibels (dB); that is,

$$\text{amplitude gain in dB} = 20\log|G(j\omega)|$$

and the phase shift $\arg G(j\omega)$ in degrees. Thus the Bode plots consist of

(a) a plot of amplitude in decibels versus $\log\omega$, and

(b) a plot of phase shift in degrees versus $\log\omega$.

Note that with the amplitude gain measured in decibels, the input signal will be amplified if the gain is greater than zero and attenuated if it is less than zero.

The advantage of using Bode plots is that the amplitude and phase information can be obtained from the constituent parts of the transfer function by graphical addition. It is also possible to make simplifying approximations in which curves can be replaced by straight-line asymptotes. These can be drawn relatively quickly, and provide sufficient information to give an engineer a 'feel' for the system behaviour. Desirable system characteristics are frequently specified in terms of frequency-response behaviour, and since the approximate Bode plots permit quick determination of the effect of changes, they provide a good test for the system designer.

Example 2.62

Draw the approximate Bode plots corresponding to the transfer function

$$G(s) = \frac{4\times10^3(5+s)}{s(100+s)(20+s)} \tag{2.87}$$

Solution First we express the transfer function in what is known as the **standard form**, namely

$$G(s) = \frac{10(1 + 0.2s)}{s(1 + 0.01s)(1 + 0.05s)}$$

giving

$$G(\mathrm{j}\omega) = \frac{10(1 + \mathrm{j}0.2\omega)}{\mathrm{j}\omega(1 + \mathrm{j}0.01\omega)(1 + \mathrm{j}0.05\omega)}$$

Taking logarithms to base 10,

$$\begin{aligned} 20 \log |G(\mathrm{j}\omega)| &= 20 \log 10 + 20 \log |1 + \mathrm{j}0.2\omega| - 20 \log |\mathrm{j}\omega| \\ &\quad - 20 \log |1 + \mathrm{j}0.01\omega| - 20 \log |1 + \mathrm{j}0.05\omega| \\ \arg G(\mathrm{j}\omega) &= \arg 10 + \arg (1 + \mathrm{j}0.2\omega) - \arg \mathrm{j}\omega - \arg (1 + \mathrm{j}0.01\omega) \\ &\quad - \arg(1 + \mathrm{j}0.05\omega) \end{aligned} \tag{2.88}$$

The transfer function involves constituents that are again a simple zero and simple poles (including one at the origin). We shall now illustrate how the Bode plots can be built up from those of the constituent parts.

Consider first the amplitude gain plot, which is a plot of $20 \log |G(\mathrm{j}\omega)|$ versus $\log \omega$:

(a) for a simple gain k a plot of $20 \log k$ is a horizontal straight line, being above the 0 dB axis if $k > 1$ and below it if $k < 1$;

(b) for a simple pole at the origin a plot of $-20 \log \omega$ is a straight line with slope -20 dB/decade and intersecting the 0 dB axis at $\omega = 1$;

(c) for a simple zero or pole not at the origin we see that

$$20 \log |1 + \mathrm{j}\tau\omega| \to \begin{cases} 0 & \text{as } \omega \to 0 \\ 20 \log \tau\omega = 20 \log \omega - 20 \log(1/\tau) & \text{as } \omega \to \infty \end{cases}$$

Note that the graph of $20 \log \tau\omega$ is a straight line with slope 20 dB/decade and intersecting the 0 dB axis at $\omega = 1/\tau$. Thus the plot of $20 \log |1 + \mathrm{j}\tau\omega|$ may be approximated by two straight lines: one for $\omega < 1/\tau$ and one for $\omega > 1/\tau$. The frequency at intersection $\omega = 1/\tau$ is called the **breakpoint** or **corner frequency**; here $|1 + \mathrm{j}\tau\omega| = \sqrt{2}$, enabling the true curve to be indicated at this frequency. Using this approach, straight-line approximations to the amplitude plots of a simple zero and a simple pole, neither at zero, are shown in Figures 2.53(a) and (b) respectively (actual plots are also shown).

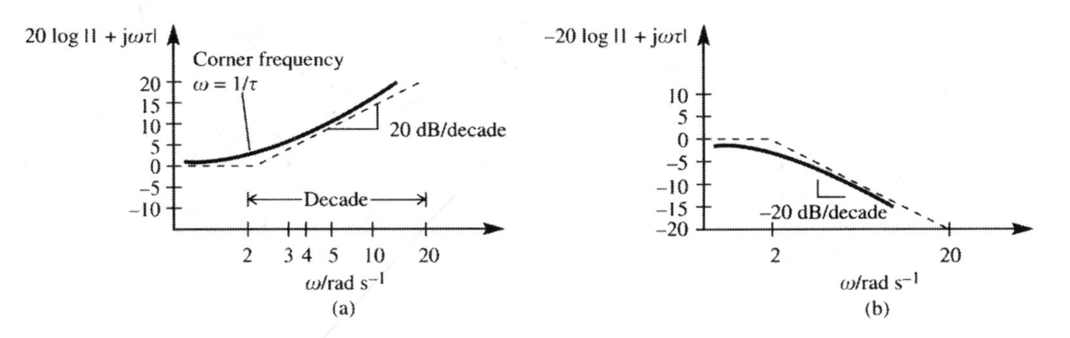

Figure 2.53 Straight-line approximations to Bode amplitude plots: (a) simple zero; (b) simple pole.

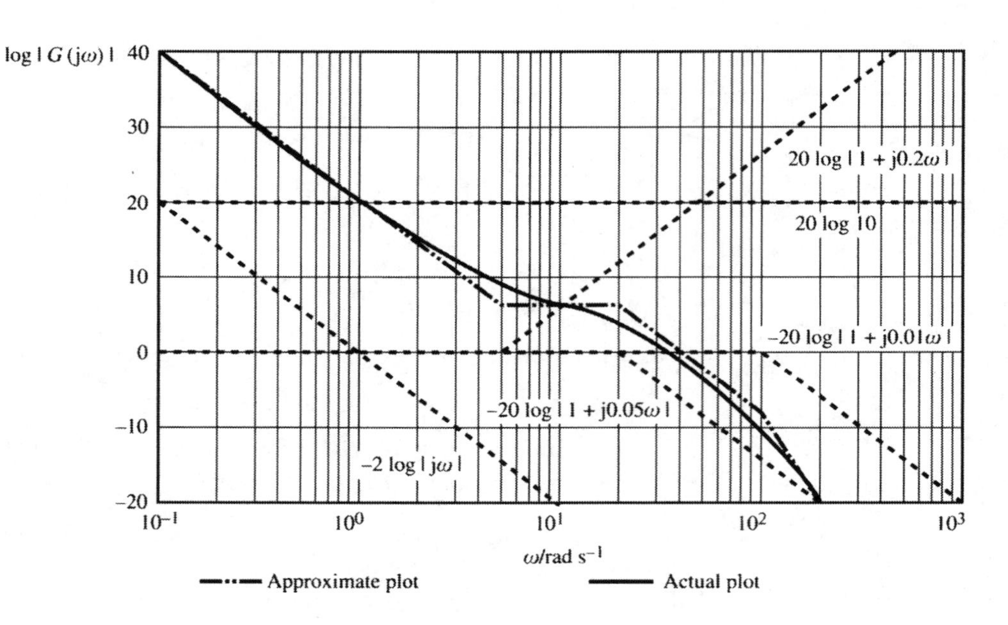

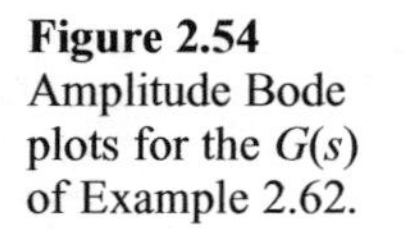
Figure 2.54 Amplitude Bode plots for the $G(s)$ of Example 2.62.

Using the approximation plots for the constituent parts as indicated in (a)–(c) earlier, we can build up the approximate amplitude gain plot corresponding to (2.87) by graphical addition as indicated in Figure 2.54. The actual amplitude gain plot, produced using a software package, is also shown.

The idea of using asymptotes can also be used to draw the phase-shift Bode plots, again taking account of the accumulated effects of the individual components making up the transfer function, namely that

(i) the phase shift associated with a constant gain k is zero;

(ii) the phase shift associated with a simple pole or zero at the origin is +90° or −90° respectively;

(iii) for a simple zero or pole not at the origin

$$\tan^{-1}(\omega\tau) \to \begin{cases} 0 & \text{as } \omega \to 0 \\ 90° & \text{as } \omega \to \infty \end{cases}$$

$$\tan^{-1}(\omega\tau) = 45° \quad \text{when } \omega\tau = 1$$

With these observations in mind, the following approximations are made. For frequencies ω less than one-tenth of the corner frequency $\omega = 1/\tau$ (that is, for $\omega < 1/10\tau$) the phase shift is assumed to be 0°, and for frequencies greater than ten times the corner frequency (that is, for $\omega > 10/\tau$) the phase shift is assumed to be ±90°. For frequencies between these limits (that is, $1/10\tau < \pi < 10/\tau$) the phase-shift plot is taken to be a straight line that passes through 0° at $\omega = 1/10\tau$, ±45° at $\omega = 1/\tau$, and ±90° at $\omega = 10/\tau$. In each case the plus sign is associated with a zero and the minus sign with a pole. With these assumptions, straight-line approximations to the phase-shift plots for a simple zero and pole, neither located at the origin, are shown in Figures 2.55(a) and (b) respectively (the actual plots are represented by the broken curves).

Using these approximations, a straight-line approximate phase-gain plot corresponding to (2.88) is shown in Figure 2.56. Again, the actual phase-gain plot, produced using a software package, is shown.

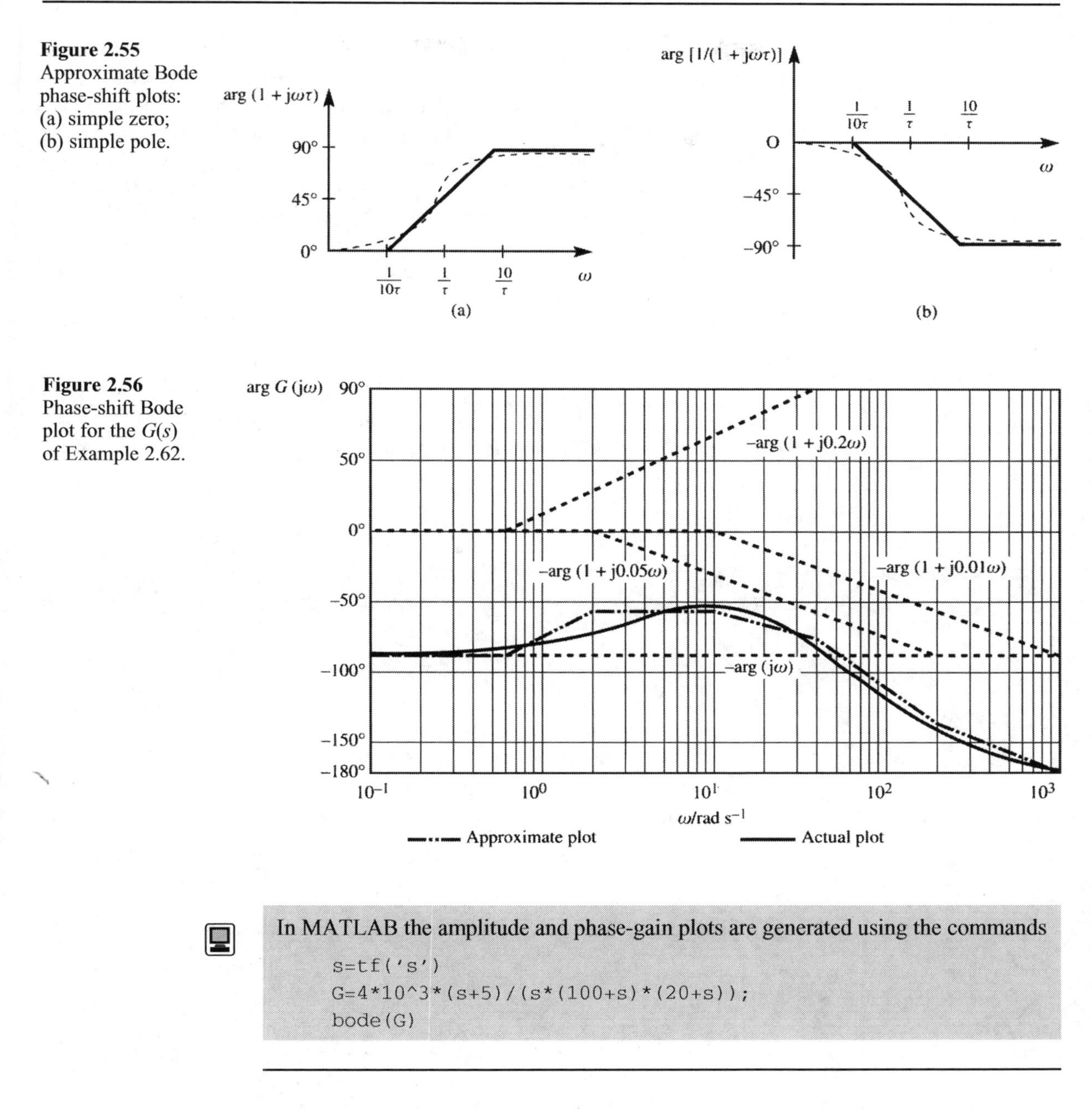

Figure 2.55 Approximate Bode phase-shift plots: (a) simple zero; (b) simple pole.

Figure 2.56 Phase-shift Bode plot for the $G(s)$ of Example 2.62.

In MATLAB the amplitude and phase-gain plots are generated using the commands

```
s=tf('s')
G=4*10^3*(s+5)/(s*(100+s)*(20+s));
bode(G)
```

In the graphical approach adopted in this section, separate plots of amplitude gain and phase shift versus frequency have been drawn. It is also possible to represent the frequency response graphically using only one plot. When this is done using the pair of polar coordinates ($|G(j\omega)|$, arg $G(j\omega)$) and allowing the frequency ω to vary, the resulting Argand diagram is referred to as the **polar plot** or **frequency-response plot**. Such a graphical representation of the transfer function forms the basis of the **Nyquist approach** to the analysis of feedback systems. In fact, the main use of frequency-response methods in practice is in the analysis and design of closed-loop control systems. For the unity feedback system of Figure 2.45 the frequency-response plot of the forward-path transfer function $G(s)$ is used to infer overall closed-loop system behaviour. The Bode plots are perhaps the quickest plots to construct, especially when straight-line approximations are made, and are useful when attempting to estimate a transfer function from a set of physical frequency-response measurements. Other plots used in practice are the **Nichols diagram** and the **inverse Nyquist** (or **polar**) **plot**, the first of these being useful for designing feedforward compensators and the second for designing feedback compensators. Although there is no simple mathematical relationship, it is also worth noting that transient behaviour may also be inferred from the various frequency-response plots. For example, the reciprocal of the inverse M circle centred on the −1 point in the inverse Nyquist plot gives an indication of the peak over-shoot in the transient behaviour (see, for example, G. Franklin, D. Powell and A. Naeini-Emami (1986), *Feedback Control of Dynamic Systems*, Reading, MA: Addison-Wesley).

Investigation of such design tools may be carried out in MATLAB, incorporating Control Toolbox, using the command `rltool(G)`.

2.8 Review exercises (1–30)

1 Solve, using Laplace transforms, the following differential equations:

(a) $\dfrac{d^2x}{dt^2} + 4\dfrac{dx}{dt} + 5x = 8\cos t$

subject to $x = \dfrac{dx}{dt} = 0$ at $t = 0$

(b) $5\dfrac{d^2x}{dt^2} - 3\dfrac{dx}{dt} - 2x = 6$

subject to $x = 1$ and $\dfrac{dx}{dt} = 1$ at $t = 0$

2 (a) Find the inverse Laplace transform of

$$\frac{1}{(s+1)(s+2)(s^2+2s+2)}$$

(b) A voltage source $Ve^{-t}\sin t$ is applied across a series LCR circuit with $L = 1$, $R = 3$ and $C = \frac{1}{2}$. Show that the current $i(t)$ in the circuit satisfies the differential equation

$$\frac{d^2i}{dt^2} + 3\frac{di}{dt} + 2i = Ve^{-t}\sin t$$

Find the current $i(t)$ in the circuit at time $t \geqslant 0$ if $i(t)$ satisfies the initial conditions $i(0) = 1$ and $(di/dt)(0) = 2$.

3 Use Laplace transform methods to solve the simultaneous differential equations

$$\frac{d^2x}{dt^2} - x + 5\frac{dy}{dt} = t$$

$$\frac{d^2y}{dt^2} - 4y - 2\frac{dx}{dt} = -2$$

subject to $x = y = \dfrac{dx}{dt} = \dfrac{dy}{dt} = 0$ at $t = 0$.

4 Solve the differential equation

$$\frac{d^2x}{dt^2} + 2\frac{dx}{dt} + 2x = \cos t$$

subject to the initial conditions $x = x_0$ and $dx/dt = x_1$ at $t = 0$. Identify the steady-state and transient solutions. Find the amplitude and phase shift of the steady-state solution.

5 Resistors of 5 and 20 Ω are connected to the primary and secondary coils of a transformer with inductances as shown in Figure 2.57. At time $t = 0$, with no currents flowing, a voltage $E = 100$ V is applied to the primary circuit. Show that subsequently the current in the secondary circuit is

$$\frac{20}{\sqrt{41}}\left(e^{-(11+\sqrt{41})t/2} - e^{-(11-\sqrt{41})t/2}\right)$$

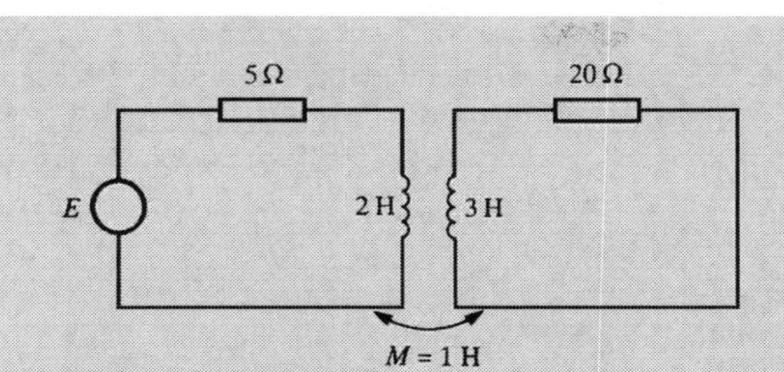

Figure 2.57 Circuit of Review exercise 5.

6 (a) Find the Laplace transforms of

(i) $\cos(\omega t + \phi)$ (ii) $e^{-\omega t}\sin(\omega t + \phi)$

(b) Using Laplace transform methods, solve the differential equation

$$\frac{d^2x}{dt^2} + 4\frac{dx}{dt} + 8x = \cos 2t$$

given that $x = 2$ and $dx/dt = 1$ when $t = 0$.

7 (a) Find the inverse Laplace transform of

$$\frac{s-4}{s^2+4s+13}$$

(b) Solve using Laplace transforms the differential equation

$$\frac{dy}{dt} + 2y = 2(2 + \cos t + 2\sin t)$$

given that $y = -3$ when $t = 0$.

8 Using Laplace transforms, solve the simultaneous differential equations

$$\frac{dx}{dt} + 5x + 3y = 5\sin t - 2\cos t$$

$$\frac{dy}{dt} + 3y + 5x = 6\sin t - 3\cos t$$

where $x = 1$ and $y = 0$ when $t = 0$.

9 The charge q on a capacitor in an inductive circuit is given by the differential equation

$$\frac{d^2q}{dt^2} + 300\frac{dq}{dt} + 2 \times 10^4 q = 200\sin 100t$$

and it is also known that both q and dq/dt are zero when $t = 0$. Use the Laplace transform method to find q. What is the phase difference between the steady-state component of the current dq/dt and the applied emf $200\sin 100t$ to the nearest half-degree?

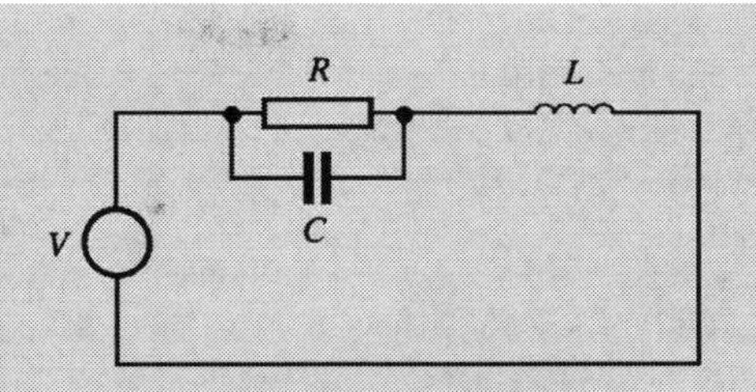

Figure 2.58 Circuit of Review exercise 12.

10 Use Laplace transforms to find the value of x given that

$$4\frac{dx}{dt} + 6x + y = 2\sin 2t$$

$$\frac{d^2x}{dt^2} + x - \frac{dy}{dt} = 3e^{-2t}$$

and that $x = 2$ and $dx/dt = -2$ when $t = 0$.

11 (a) Use Laplace transforms to solve the differential equation

$$\frac{d^2\theta}{dt^2} + 8\frac{d\theta}{dt} + 16\theta = \sin 2t$$

given that $\theta = 0$ and $d\theta/dt = 0$ when $t = 0$.

(b) Using Laplace transforms, solve the simultaneous differential equations

$$\frac{di_1}{dt} + 2i_1 + 6i_2 = 0$$

$$i_1 + \frac{di_2}{dt} - 3i_2 = 0$$

given that $i_1 = 1$, $i_2 = 0$ when $t = 0$.

12 The terminals of a generator producing a voltage V are connected through a wire of resistance R and a coil of inductance L (and negligible resistance). A capacitor of capacitance C is connected in parallel with the resistance R as shown in Figure 2.58. Show that the current i flowing through the resistance R is given by

$$LCR\frac{d^2i}{dt^2} + L\frac{di}{dt} + Ri = V$$

Suppose that

(i) $V = 0$ for $t < 0$ and $V = E$ (constant) for $t \geqslant 0$
(ii) $L = 2R^2C$
(iii) $CR = 1/2n$

and show that the equation reduces to

$$\frac{d^2i}{dt^2} + 2n\frac{di}{dt} + 2n^2 i = 2n^2\frac{E}{R}$$

Hence, assuming that $i = 0$ and $di/dt = 0$ when $t = 0$, use Laplace transforms to obtain an expression for i in terms of t.

13 Show that the currents in the coupled circuits of Figure 2.59 are determined by the simultaneous differential equations

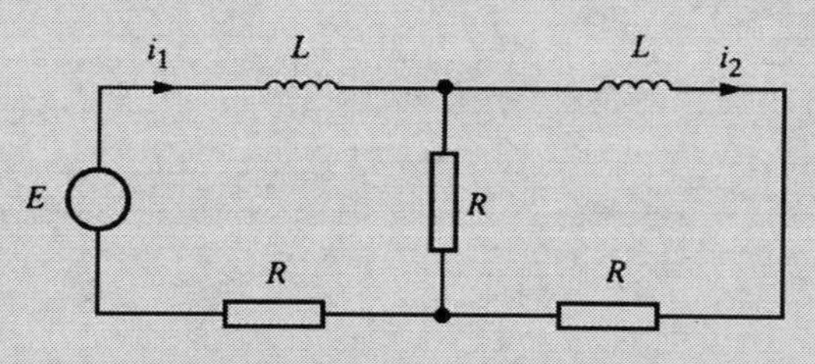

Figure 2.59 Circuit of Review exercise 13.

$$L\frac{di_1}{dt} + R(i_1 - i_2) + Ri_1 = E$$

$$L\frac{di_2}{dt} + Ri_2 - R(i_1 - i_2) = 0$$

Find i_1 in terms of t, L, E and R, given that $i_1 = 0$ and $di_1/dt = E/L$ at $t = 0$, and show that $i_1 \simeq \frac{2}{3}E/R$ for large t. What does i_2 tend to for large t?

14 A system consists of two unit masses lying in a straight line on a smooth surface and connected together to two fixed points by three springs. When a sinusoidal force is applied to the system, the displacements $x_1(t)$ and $x_2(t)$ of the respective masses from their equilibrium positions satisfy the equations

$$\frac{d^2x_1}{dt^2} = x_2 - 2x_1 + \sin 2t$$

$$\frac{d^2x_2}{dt^2} = -2x_2 + x_1$$

Given that the system is initially at rest in the equilibrium position ($x_1 = x_2 = 0$), use the Laplace transform method to solve the equations for $x_1(t)$ and $x_2(t)$.

15 (a) Obtain the inverse Laplace transforms of

(i) $\dfrac{s + 4}{s^2 + 2s + 10}$ (ii) $\dfrac{s - 3}{(s - 1)^2(s - 2)}$

(b) Use Laplace transforms to solve the differential equation

$$\frac{d^2y}{dt^2} + 2\frac{dy}{dt} + y = 3t\,e^{-t}$$

given that $y = 4$ and $dy/dt = 2$ when $t = 0$.

16 (a) Determine the inverse Laplace transform of

$$\frac{5}{s^2 - 14s + 53}$$

(b) The equation of motion of the moving coil of a galvanometer when a current i is passed thought it is of the form

$$\frac{d^2\theta}{dt^2} + 2K\frac{d\theta}{dt} + n^2\theta = \frac{n^2 i}{K}$$

where θ is the angle of deflection from the 'no-current' position and n and K are positive constants. Given that i is a constant and $\theta = 0 = d\theta/dt$ when $t = 0$, obtain an expression for the Laplace transform of θ.

In constructing the galvanometer, it is desirable to have it critically damped (that is, $n = K$). Use the Laplace transform method to solve the differential equation in this case, and sketch the graph of θ against t for positive values of t.

17 (a) Given that α is a positive constant, use the second shift theorem to

(i) show that the Laplace transform of $\sin t\, H(t - \alpha)$ is

$$e^{-\alpha s}\frac{\cos\alpha + s\sin\alpha}{s^2 + 1}$$

(ii) find the inverse transform of

$$\frac{s\,e^{-\alpha s}}{s^2 + 2s + 5}$$

(b) Solve the differential equation

$$\frac{d^2y}{dt^2} + 2\frac{dy}{dt} + 5y = \sin t - \sin t\, H(t - \pi)$$

given that $y = dy/dt = 0$ when $t = 0$.

18 Show that the Laplace transform of the voltage $v(t)$, with period T, defined by

$$v(t) = \begin{cases} 1 & (0 \leq t < \frac{1}{2}T) \\ -1 & (\frac{1}{2}T \leq t < T) \end{cases} \qquad v(t + T) = v(t)$$

is

$$V(s) = \frac{1}{s}\frac{1 - e^{-sT/2}}{1 + e^{-sT/2}}$$

This voltage is applied to a capacitor of 100 μF and a resistor of 250 Ω in series, with no charge initially on the capacitor. Show that the Laplace transform $I(s)$ of the current $i(t)$ flowing, for $t \geq 0$, is

$$I(s) = \frac{1}{250(s + 40)}\frac{1 - e^{-sT/2}}{1 + e^{-sT/2}}$$

and give an expression, involving Heaviside step functions, for $i(t)$ where $0 \leq t \leq 2T$. For $T = 10^{-3}$ s, is this a good representation of the steady-state response of the circuit? Briefly give a reason for your answer.

19 The response $x(t)$ of a control system to a forcing term $u(t)$ is given by the differential equation

$$\frac{d^2x}{dt^2} + 2\frac{dx}{dt} + 2x = u(t) \quad (t \geq 0)$$

Determine the impulse response of the system, and hence, using the convolution integral, obtain the response of the system to a unit step $u(t) = 1H(t)$ applied at $t = 0$, given that initially the system is in a quiescent state. Check your solution by directly solving the differential equation

$$\frac{d^2x}{dt^2} + 2\frac{dx}{dt} + 2x = 1 \quad (t \geq 0)$$

with $x = dx/dt = 0$ at $t = 0$.

20 A light horizontal beam, of length 5 m and constant flexural rigidity EI, built in at the left-hand end $x = 0$, is simply supported at the point $x = 4$ m and carries a distributed load with density function

$$W(x) = \begin{cases} 12\text{ kN m}^{-1} & (0 < x < 4) \\ 24\text{ kN m}^{-1} & (4 < x < 5) \end{cases}$$

Write down the fourth-order boundary-value problem satisfied by the deflection $y(x)$. Solve this problem to determine $y(x)$, and write down the resulting expressions for $y(x)$ for the cases $0 \leq x \leq 4$ and $4 \leq x \leq 5$. Calculate the end reaction and moment by evaluating appropriate derivatives of $y(x)$ at $x = 0$. Check that your results satisfy the equation of equilibrium for the beam as a whole.

21 (a) Sketch the function defined by

$$f(t) = \begin{cases} 0 & (0 \leq t < 1) \\ 1 & (1 \leq t < 2) \\ 0 & (t > 2) \end{cases}$$

Express $f(t)$ in terms of Heaviside step functions, and use the Laplace transform to solve the differential equation

$$\frac{dx}{dt} + x = f(t)$$

given that $x = 0$ at $t = 0$.

(b) The Laplace transform $I(s)$ of the current $i(t)$ in a certain circuit is given by

$$I(s) = \frac{E}{s[Ls + R/(1 + Cs)]}$$

where E, L, R and C are positive constants. Determine (i) $\lim_{t\to 0} i(t)$ and (ii) $\lim_{t\to\infty} i(t)$.

22 Show that the Laplace transform of the half-rectified sine-wave function

$$v(t) = \begin{cases} \sin t & (0 \leq t \leq \pi) \\ 0 & (\pi \leq t \leq 2\pi) \end{cases}$$

of period 2π, is

$$\frac{1}{(1 + s^2)(1 - e^{-\pi s})}$$

Such a voltage $v(t)$ is applied to a 1 Ω resistor and a 1 H inductor connected in series. Show that the resulting current, initially zero, is $\sum_{n=0}^{\infty} f(t - n\pi)$, where $f(t) = (\sin t - \cos t + e^{-t})H(t)$. Sketch a graph of the function $f(t)$.

23 (a) Find the inverse Laplace transform of $1/s^2(s + 1)^2$ by writing the expression in the form $(1/s^2)[1/(s + 1)^2]$ and using the convolution theorem.

(b) Use the convolution theorem to solve the integral equation

$$y(t) = t + 2\int_0^t y(u)\cos(t - u)\,du$$

and the integro-differential equation

$$\int_0^t y''(u)y'(t - u)\,du = y(t)$$

where $y(0) = 0$ and $y'(0) = y_1$. Comment on the solution of the second equation.

24 A beam of negligible weight and length $3l$ carries a point load W at a distance l from the left-hand end. Both ends are clamped horizontally at the same level. Determine the equation governing the deflection of the beam. If, in addition, the beam is now subjected to a load per unit length, w, over the shorter part of the beam, what will then be the differential equation determining the deflection?

25 (a) Using Laplace transforms, solve the differential equation

$$\frac{d^2x}{dt^2} - 3\frac{dx}{dt} + 3x = H(t-a) \qquad (a > 0)$$

where $H(t)$ is the Heaviside unit step function, given that $x = 0$ and $dx/dt = 0$ at $t = 0$.

(b) The output $x(t)$ from a stable linear control system with input $\sin \omega t$ and transfer function $G(s)$ is determined by the relationship

$$X(s) = G(s)\mathscr{L}\{\sin \omega t\}$$

where $X(s) = \mathscr{L}\{x(t)\}$. Show that, after a long time t, the output approaches $x_s(t)$, where

$$x_s(t) = \text{Re}\left(\frac{e^{j\omega t}G(j\omega)}{j}\right)$$

26 Consider the feedback system of Figure 2.60, where K is a constant feedback gain.

(a) In the absence of feedback (that is, $K = 0$) is the system stable?
(b) Write down the transfer function $G_1(s)$ for the overall feedback system.
(c) Plot the locus of poles of $G_1(s)$ in the s plane for both positive and negative values of K.
(d) From the plots in (c), specify for what range of values of K the feedback system is stable.
(e) Confirm your answer to (d) using the Routh–Hurwitz criterion.

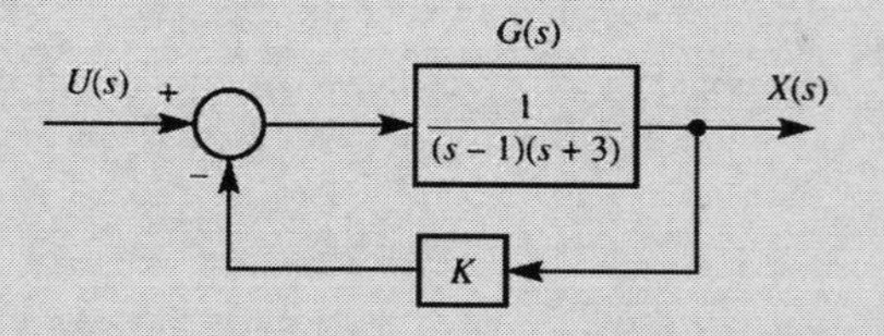

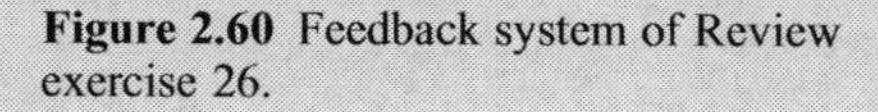
Figure 2.60 Feedback system of Review exercise 26.

27 (a) For the feedback control system of Figure 2.61(a) it is known that the impulse response is $h(t) = 2e^{-2t}\sin t$. Use this to determine the value of the parameter α.
(b) Consider the control system of Figure 2.61(b), having both proportional and rate feedback. Determine the critical value of the gain K for stability of the closed-loop system.

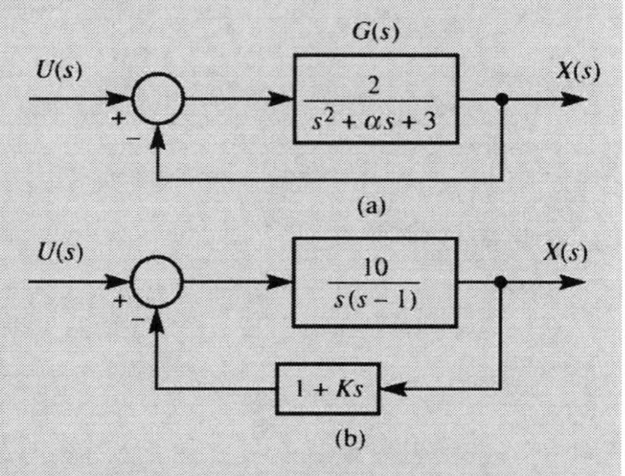

Figure 2.61 Feedback control systems of Review exercise 27.

28 (An extended problem) The transient response of a practical control system to a unit step input often exhibits damped oscillations before reaching steady state. The following properties are some of those used to specify the transient response characteristics of an underdamped system:

rise time, the time required for the response to rise from 0 to 100% of its final value;
peak time, the time required for the response to reach the first peak of the overshoot;
settling time, the time required for the response curve to reach and stay within a range about the final value of size specified by an absolute percentage of the final value (usually 2% or 5%);
maximum overshoot, the maximum peak value of the response measured from unity.

Consider the feedback control system of Figure 2.62 having both proportional and derivative feedback. It is desirable to choose the values of the gains K and K_1 so that the system unit step response has a maximum overshoot of 0.2 and a peak time of 1 s.

(a) Obtain the overall transfer function of the closed-loop system.

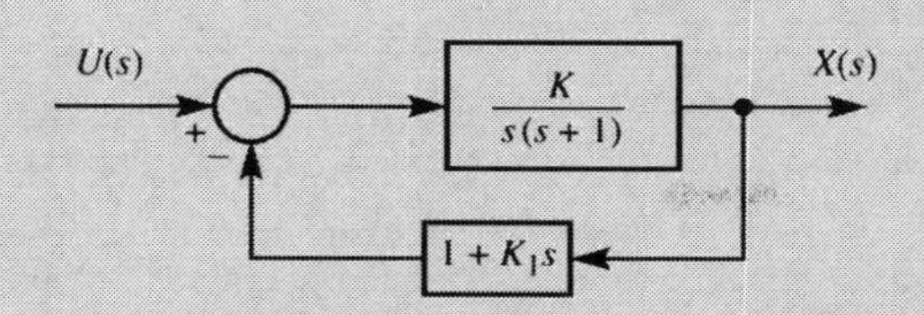

Figure 2.62 Feedback control system of Review exercise 28.

(b) Show that the unit step response of the system, assuming zero initial conditions, may be written in the form

$$x(t) = 1 - e^{-\omega_n \xi t}\left[\cos\omega_d t + \frac{\xi}{\sqrt{(1-\xi^2)}}\sin\omega_d t\right] \quad (t \geqslant 0)$$

where $\omega_d = \omega_n\sqrt{(1-\xi^2)}$, $\omega_n^2 = K$ and $2\omega_n\xi = 1 + KK_1$.

(c) Determine the values of the gains K and K_1 so that the desired characteristics are achieved.

(d) With these values of K and K_1, determine the rise time and settling time, comparing both the 2% and 5% criteria for the latter.

29 (An extended problem) The mass M_1 of the mechanical system of Figure 2.63(a) is subjected to a harmonic forcing term $\sin\omega t$. Determine the steady-state response of the system.

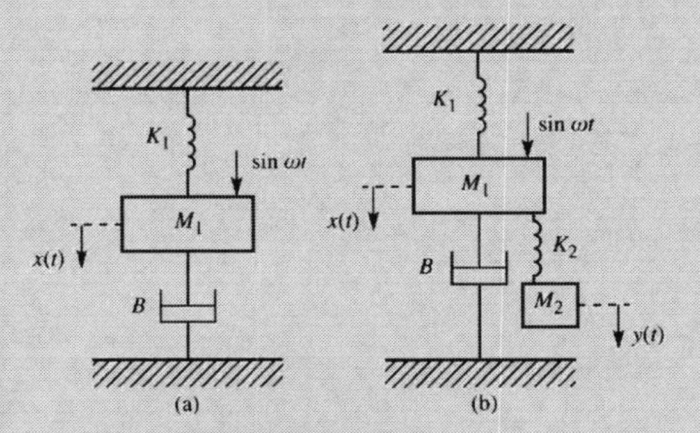

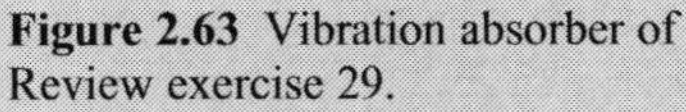

Figure 2.63 Vibration absorber of Review exercise 29.

It is desirable to design a vibration absorber to absorb the steady-state oscillations so that in the steady state $x(t) \equiv 0$. To achieve this, a secondary system is attached as illustrated in Figure 2.63(b).

(a) Show that, with an appropriate choice of M_2 and K_2, the desired objective may be achieved.

(b) What is the corresponding steady-state motion of the mass M_2?

(c) Comment on the practicality of your design.

30 (An extended problem) The electronic amplifier of Figure 2.64 has open-loop transfer function $G(s)$ with the following characteristics: a low-frequency gain of 120 dB and simple poles at 1 MHz, 10 MHz and 25 MHz. It may be assumed that the amplifier is ideal, so that $K/(1 + K\beta) \simeq 1/\beta$, where β is the feedback gain and K the steady-state gain associated with $G(s)$.

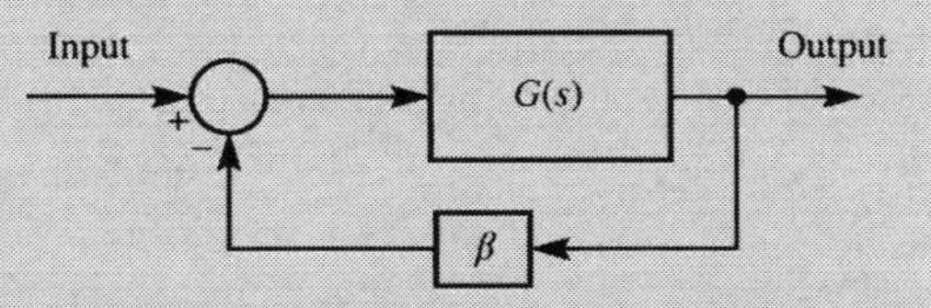

Figure 2.64 Electronic amplifier of Review exercise 30.

(a) Construct the magnitude versus log frequency and phase versus log frequency plots (Bode plots) for the open-loop system.

(b) Determine from the Bode plots whether or not the system is stable in the case of unity feedback (that is, $\beta = 1$).

(c) Determine the value of β for marginal stability, and hence the corresponding value of the closed-loop low-frequency gain.

(d) Feedback is now applied to the amplifier to reduce the overall closed-loop gain at low frequencies to 100 dB. Determine the gain and phase margin corresponding to this closed-loop configuration.

(e) Using the given characteristics, express $G(s)$ in the form

$$G(s) = \frac{K}{(1 + s\tau_1)(1 + s\tau_2)(1 + s\tau_3)}$$

and hence obtain the input–output transfer function for the amplifier.

(f) Write down the characteristic equation for the closed-loop system and, using the Routh–Hurwitz criterion, reconsider parts (b) and (c).

3 The *z* Transform

Chapter 3	Contents	

3.1 Introduction

In this chapter we focus attention on discrete-(time) processes. With the advent of fast and cheap digital computers, there has been renewed emphasis on the analysis and design of digital systems, which represent a major class of engineering systems. The main thrust of this chapter will be in this direction. However, it is a mistake to believe that the mathematical basis of this area of work is of such recent vintage. The first comprehensive text in English dealing with difference equations was *The Treatise of the Calculus of Finite Differences* due to George Boole and published in 1860. Much of the early impetus for the **finite calculus** was due to the need to carry out interpolation and to approximate derivatives and integrals. Later, numerical methods for the solution of differential equations were devised, many of which were based on **finite difference methods**, involving the approximation of the derivative terms to produce a **difference equation**. The underlying idea in each case so far discussed is some form of approximation of an underlying continuous function or continuous-time process. There are situations, however, where it is more appropriate to propose a discrete-time model from the start.

Digital systems operate on digital signals, which are usually generated by **sampling** a continuous-time signal, that is a signal defined for every instant of a possibly infinite time interval. The sampling process generates a **discrete-time signal**, defined only at the instants when sampling takes place so that a digital sequence is generated. After processing by a computer, the output digital signal may be used to construct a new continuous-time signal, perhaps by the use of a **zero-order hold** device, and this in turn might be used to control a plant or process. Digital signal processing devices have made a major impact in many areas of engineering, as well as in the home. For example, compact disc players, which operate using digital technology, offer such a significant improvement in reproduction quality that recent years have seen them rapidly take over from cassette tape players and vinyl record decks. DVD players are taking over from video players and digital radios are setting the standard for broadcasting. Both of these are based on digital technology.

We have seen in Chapter 2 that the Laplace transform was a valuable aid in the analysis of continuous-time systems, and in this chapter we develop the z transform, which will perform the same task for discrete-time systems. We introduce the transform in connection with the solution of difference equations, and later we show how difference equations arise as discrete-time system models.

The chapter includes two engineering applications. The first is on the design of digital filters, and highlights one of the major applications of transform methods as a design tool. It may be expected that whenever sampling is involved, performance will improve as sampling rate is increased. Engineers have found that this is not the full story, and the second application deals with some of the problems encountered. This leads on to an introduction to the unifying concept of the $\mathscr{D}$ transform, which brings together the theories of the Laplace and z transforms.

As in the previous chapter, operations that can be carried out in MATLAB are highlighted and basic commands introduced. Again, where appropriate, users are encouraged to use this facility to check their solutions to the exercises.

3.2 The z transform

Since z transforms relate to sequences, we first review the notation associated with sequences. A finite sequence $\{x_k\}_0^n$ is an ordered set of $n + 1$ real or complex numbers:

$$\{x_k\}_0^n = \{x_0, x_1, x_2, \ldots, x_n\}$$

Note that the set of numbers is ordered so that position in the sequence is important. The position is identified by the position index k, where k is an integer. If the number of elements in the set is infinite then this leads to the **infinite sequence**

$$\{x_k\}_0^\infty = \{x_0, x_1, x_2, \ldots\}$$

When dealing with sampled functions of time t, it is necessary to have a means of allowing for $t < 0$. To do this, we allow the sequence of numbers to extend to infinity on both sides of the initial position x_0, and write

$$\{x_k\}_{-\infty}^\infty = \{\ldots, x_{-2}, x_{-1}, x_0, x_1, x_2, \ldots\}$$

Sequences $\{x_k\}_{-\infty}^\infty$ for which $x_k = 0$ $(k < 0)$ are called **causal sequences**, by analogy with continuous-time causal functions $f(t)H(t)$ defined in Section 2.2.1 as

$$f(t)H(t) = \begin{cases} 0 & (t < 0) \\ f(t) & (t \geqslant 0) \end{cases}$$

While for some finite sequences it is possible to specify the sequence by listing all the elements of the set, it is normally the case that a sequence is specified by giving a formula for its general element x_k.

3.2.1 Definition and notation

The **z transform** of a sequence $\{x_k\}_{-\infty}^\infty$ is defined in general as

$$\mathscr{Z}\{x_k\}_{-\infty}^\infty = X(z) = \sum_{k=-\infty}^{\infty} \frac{x_k}{z^k} \qquad (3.1)$$

whenever the sum exists and where z is a complex variable, as yet undefined.

The process of taking the z transform of a sequence thus produces a function of a complex variable z, whose form depends upon the sequence itself. The symbol $\mathscr{Z}$ denotes the **z-transform operator**; when it operates on a sequence $\{x_k\}$ it transforms the latter into the function $X(z)$ of the complex variable z. It is usual to refer to $\{x_k\}$, $X(z)$ as a **z-transform pair**, which is sometimes written as $\{x_k\} \leftrightarrow X(z)$. Note the similarity to obtaining the Laplace transform of a function in Section 2.2.1. We shall return to consider the relationship between Laplace and z transforms in Section 3.7.

For sequences $\{x_k\}_{-\infty}^{\infty}$ that are *causal*, that is

$$x_k = 0 \quad (k < 0)$$

the z transform given in (3.1) reduces to

$$\mathscr{Z}\{x_k\}_0^{\infty} = X(z) = \sum_{k=0}^{\infty} \frac{x_k}{z^k} \tag{3.2}$$

In this chapter we shall be concerned with causal sequences, and so the definition given in (3.2) will be the one that we shall use henceforth. We shall therefore from now on take $\{x_k\}$ to denote $\{x_k\}_0^{\infty}$. Non-causal sequences, however, are of importance, and arise particularly in the field of digital image processing, among others.

Example 3.1 Determine the z transform of the sequence

$$\{x_k\} = \{2^k\} \quad (k \geqslant 0)$$

Solution From the definition (3.2),

$$\mathscr{Z}\{2^k\} = \sum_{k=0}^{\infty} \frac{2^k}{z^k} = \sum_{k=0}^{\infty} \left(\frac{2}{z}\right)^k$$

which we recognize as a geometric series, with common ratio $r = 2/z$ between successive terms. The series thus converges for $|z| > 2$, when

$$\sum_{k=0}^{\infty} \left(\frac{2}{z}\right)^k = \lim_{k\to\infty} \frac{1-(2/z)^k}{1-2/z} = \frac{1}{1-2/z}$$

leading to

$$\mathscr{Z}\{2^k\} = \frac{z}{z-2} \quad (|z| > 2) \tag{3.3}$$

so that

$$\left.\begin{aligned} \{x_k\} &= \{2^k\} \\ X(z) &= \frac{z}{z-2} \end{aligned}\right\}$$

is an example of a z-transform pair.

From Example 3.1, we see that the z transform of the sequence $\{2^k\}$ exists provided that we restrict the complex variable z so that it lies outside the circle $|z| = 2$ in the z plane. From another point of view, the function

$$X(z) = \frac{z}{z-2} \quad (|z|>2)$$

may be thought of as a **generating function** for the sequence $\{2^k\}$, in the sense that the coefficient of z^{-k} in the expansion of $X(z)$ in powers of $1/z$ *generates* the kth term of the sequence $\{2^k\}$. This can easily be verified, since

$$\frac{z}{z-2} = \frac{1}{1-2/z} = \left(1-\frac{2}{z}\right)^{-1}$$

and, since $|z| > 2$, we can expand this as

$$\left(1-\frac{2}{z}\right)^{-1} = 1 + \frac{2}{z} + \left(\frac{2}{z}\right)^2 + \ldots + \left(\frac{2}{z}\right)^k + \ldots$$

and we see that the coefficient of z^{-k} is indeed 2^k, as expected.

We can generalize the result (3.3) in an obvious way to determine $\mathscr{Z}\{a^k\}$, the z transform of the sequence $\{a^k\}$, where a is a real or complex constant. At once

$$\mathscr{Z}\{a^k\} = \sum_{k=0}^{\infty} \frac{a^k}{z^k} = \frac{1}{1-a/z} \quad (|z| > |a|)$$

so that

$$\mathscr{Z}\{a^k\} = \frac{z}{z-a} \quad (|z| > |a|) \tag{3.4}$$

Example 3.2 Show that

$$\mathscr{Z}\{(-\tfrac{1}{2})^k\} = \frac{2z}{2z+1} \quad (|z| > \tfrac{1}{2})$$

Solution Taking $a = -\frac{1}{2}$ in (3.4), we have

$$\mathscr{Z}\{(-\tfrac{1}{2})^k\} = \sum_{k=0}^{\infty} \frac{(-\frac{1}{2})^k}{z^k} = \frac{z}{z-(-\frac{1}{2})} \quad (|z| > \tfrac{1}{2})$$

so that

$$\mathscr{Z}\{(-\tfrac{1}{2})^k\} = \frac{2z}{2z+1} \quad (|z| > \tfrac{1}{2})$$

Further z-transform pairs can be obtained from (3.4) by formally differentiating with respect to a, which for the moment we regard as a parameter. This gives

$$\frac{\mathrm{d}}{\mathrm{d}a}\mathscr{Z}\{a^k\} = \mathscr{Z}\left\{\frac{\mathrm{d}a^k}{\mathrm{d}a}\right\} = \frac{\mathrm{d}}{\mathrm{d}a}\left(\frac{z}{z-a}\right)$$

leading to

$$\mathscr{Z}\{ka^{k-1}\} = \frac{z}{(z-a)^2} \quad (|z| > |a|) \tag{3.5}$$

In the particular case $a = 1$ this gives

$$\mathscr{Z}\{k\} = \frac{z}{(z-1)^2} \quad (|z| > 1) \tag{3.6}$$

Example 3.3 Find the z transform of the sequence

$$\{2k\} = \{0, 2, 4, 6, 8, \dots\}$$

Solution From (3.6),

$$\mathscr{Z}\{k\} = \mathscr{Z}\{0, 1, 2, 3, \dots\} = \sum_{k=0}^{\infty} \frac{k}{z^k} = \frac{z}{(z-1)^2}$$

Using the definition (3.1),

$$\mathscr{Z}\{0, 2, 4, 6, 8, \dots\} = 0 + \frac{2}{z} + \frac{4}{z^2} + \frac{6}{z^3} + \frac{8}{z^4} + \dots = 2\sum_{k=0}^{\infty} \frac{k}{z^k}$$

so that

$$\mathscr{Z}\{2k\} = 2\mathscr{Z}\{k\} = \frac{2z}{(z-1)^2} \tag{3.7}$$

Example 3.3 demonstrates the 'linearity' property of the z transform, which we shall consider further in Section 3.3.1.

A sequence of particular importance is the **unit pulse** or **impulse** sequence

$$\{\delta_k\} = \{1\} = \{1, 0, 0, \dots\}$$

It follows directly from the definition (3.4) that

$$\mathscr{Z}\{\delta_k\} = 1 \tag{3.8}$$

In MATLAB, using the Symbolic Math Toolbox, the z-transform of the sequence $\{x_k\}$ is obtained by entering the commands

```
syms k z
ztrans(x_k)
```

As for Laplace transforms (see Section 2.2.2), the answer may be simplified using the command `simple(ans)` and reformatted using the `pretty` command. Considering the sequence $\{x_k\} = \{2^k\}$ of Example 3.1, the commands

```
syms k z
ztrans(2^k)
```

return

```
ans=1/2*z/(1/2*z-1)
```

Entering the command

```
simple(ans)
```

returns

```
ans=z/(z-2)
```

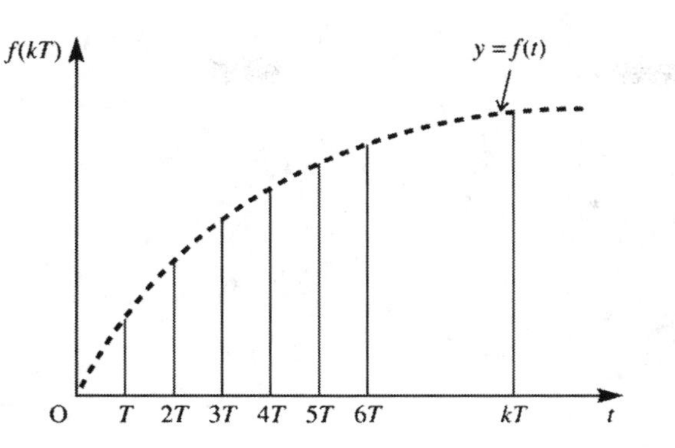

Figure 3.1 Sampling of a continuous-time signal.

3.2.2 Sampling: a first introduction

Sequences are often generated in engineering applications through the sampling of continuous-time signals, described by functions $f(t)$ of a continuous-time variable t. Here we shall not discuss the means by which a signal is sampled, but merely suppose this to be possible in idealized form.

Figure 3.1 illustrates the idealized sampling process in which a continuous-time signal $f(t)$ is sampled instantaneously and perfectly at uniform intervals T, the **sampling interval**. The idealized sampling process generates the sequence

$$\{f(kT)\} = \{f(0), f(T), f(2T), \dots, f(nT), \dots\} \tag{3.9}$$

Using the definition (3.1), we can take the z transform of the sequence (3.9) to give

$$\mathscr{Z}\{f(kT)\} = \sum_{k=0}^{\infty} \frac{f(kT)}{z^k} \tag{3.10}$$

whenever the series converges. This idea is simply demonstrated by an example.

Example 3.4

The signal $f(t) = e^{-t}H(t)$ is sampled at intervals T. What is the z transform of the resulting sequence of samples?

Solution

Sampling the causal function $f(t)$ generates the sequence

$$\begin{aligned}\{f(kT)\} &= \{f(0), f(T), f(2T), \dots, f(nT), \dots\}\\ &= \{1, e^{-T}, e^{-2T}, e^{-3T}, \dots, e^{-nT}, \dots\}\end{aligned}$$

Then, using (3.1),

$$\mathscr{Z}\{f(kT)\} = \sum_{k=0}^{\infty} \frac{e^{-kT}}{z^k} = \sum_{k=0}^{\infty} \left(\frac{e^{-T}}{z}\right)^k$$

so that

$$\mathscr{Z}\{e^{-kT}\} = \frac{z}{z - e^{-T}} \quad (|z| > e^{-T}) \tag{3.11}$$

It is important to note in Example 3.4 that the region of convergence depends on the sampling interval T.

In MATLAB the commands

```
syms k T z
ztrans(exp(-k*T));
pretty(simple(ans))
```

return

```
ans = z/(z-exp(-T))
```

which confirms (3.11).

3.2.3 Exercises

1. Calculate the z transform of the following sequences, stating the region of convergence in each case:

   (a) $\{(\frac{1}{4})^k\}$ (b) $\{3^k\}$ (c) $\{(-2)^k\}$

   (d) $\{-(2^k)\}$ (e) $\{3k\}$

2. The continuous-time signal $f(t) = e^{-2\omega t}$, where ω is a real constant, is sampled when $t \geqslant 0$ at intervals T. Write down the general term of the sequence of samples, and calculate the z transform of the sequence.

3.3 Properties of the z transform

In this section we establish the basic properties of the z transform that will enable us to develop further z-transform pairs, without having to compute them directly using the definition.

3.3.1 The linearity property

As for Laplace transforms, a fundamental property of the z transform is its linearity, which may be stated as follows.

If $\{x_k\}$ and $\{y_k\}$ are sequences having z transforms $X(z)$ and $Y(z)$ respectively and if α and β are any constants, real or complex, then

$$\mathscr{Z}\{\alpha x_k + \beta y_k\} = \alpha\mathscr{Z}\{x_k\} + \beta\mathscr{Z}\{y_k\} = \alpha X(z) + \beta Y(z) \tag{3.12}$$

As a consequence of this property, we say that the z-transform operator $\mathscr{Z}$ is a **linear operator**. A proof of the property follows readily from the definition (3.4), since

$$\mathscr{Z}\{\alpha x_k + \beta y_k\} = \sum_{k=0}^{\infty} \frac{\alpha x_k + \beta y_k}{z^k} = \alpha \sum_{k=0}^{\infty} \frac{x_k}{z^k} + \beta \sum_{k=0}^{\infty} \frac{y_k}{z^k}$$

$$= \alpha X(z) + \beta Y(z)$$

The region of existence of the z transform, in the z plane, of the linear sum will be the intersection of the regions of existence (that is, the region common to both) of the individual z transforms $X(z)$ and $Y(z)$.

Example 3.5 The continuous-time function $f(t) = \cos \omega t\, H(t)$, ω a constant, is sampled in the idealized sense at intervals T to generate the sequence $\{\cos k\omega T\}$. Determine the z transform of the sequence.

Solution Using the result $\cos k\omega T = \frac{1}{2}(e^{jk\omega T} + e^{-jk\omega T})$ and the linearity property, we have

$$\mathcal{Z}\{\cos k\omega T\} = \mathcal{Z}\{\tfrac{1}{2}e^{jk\omega T} + \tfrac{1}{2}e^{-jk\omega T}\} = \tfrac{1}{2}\mathcal{Z}\{e^{jk\omega T}\} + \tfrac{1}{2}\mathcal{Z}\{e^{-jk\omega T}\}$$

Using (3.7) and noting that $|e^{jk\omega T}| = |e^{-jk\omega T}| = 1$ gives

$$\mathcal{Z}\{\cos k\omega T\} = \tfrac{1}{2}\frac{z}{z - e^{j\omega T}} + \tfrac{1}{2}\frac{z}{z - e^{-j\omega T}} \quad (|z| > 1)$$

$$= \tfrac{1}{2}\frac{z(z - e^{-j\omega T}) + z(z - e^{j\omega T})}{z^2 - (e^{j\omega T} + e^{-j\omega T})z + 1}$$

leading to the z-transform pair

$$\mathcal{Z}\{\cos k\omega T\} = \frac{z(z - \cos \omega T)}{z^2 - 2z\cos \omega T + 1} \quad (|z| > 1) \tag{3.13}$$

In a similar manner to Example 3.5, we can verify the z-transform pair

$$\mathcal{Z}\{\sin k\omega T\} = \frac{z \sin \omega T}{z^2 - 2z\cos \omega T + 1} \quad (|z| > 1) \tag{3.14}$$

and this is left as an exercise for the reader (see Exercise 3).

Check that in MATLAB the commands

```
syms k z ω T
ztrans(cos(k*ω*T));
pretty(simple(ans))
```

return the transform given in (3.13).

3.3.2 The first shift property (delaying)

In this and the next section we introduce two properties relating the z transform of a sequence to the z transform of a shifted version of the same sequence. In this section we consider a delayed version of the sequence $\{x_k\}$, denoted by $\{y_k\}$, with

$$y_k = x_{k-k_0}$$

Here k_0 is the number of steps in the delay; for example, if $k_0 = 2$ then $y_k = x_{k-2}$, so that

$$y_0 = x_{-2}, \quad y_1 = x_{-1}, \quad y_2 = x_0, \quad y_3 = x_1$$

and so on. Thus the sequence $\{y_k\}$ is simply the sequence $\{x_k\}$ moved backward, or delayed, by two steps. From the definition (3.1),

$$\mathscr{Z}\{y_k\} = \sum_{k=0}^{\infty} \frac{y_k}{z^k} = \sum_{k=0}^{\infty} \frac{x_{k-k_0}}{z^k} = \sum_{p=-k_0}^{\infty} \frac{x_p}{z^{p+k_0}}$$

where we have written $p = k - k_0$. If $\{x_k\}$ is a causal sequence, so that $x_p = 0$ $(p < 0)$, then

$$\mathscr{Z}\{y_k\} = \sum_{p=0}^{\infty} \frac{x_p}{z^{p+k_0}} = \frac{1}{z^{k_0}} \sum_{p=0}^{\infty} \frac{x_p}{z^p} = \frac{1}{z^{k_0}} X(z)$$

where $X(z)$ is the z transform of $\{x_k\}$.

We therefore have the result

$$\mathscr{Z}\{x_{k-k_0}\} = \frac{1}{z^{k_0}} \mathscr{Z}\{x_k\} \tag{3.15}$$

which is referred to as the **first shift property** of z transforms.

If $\{x_k\}$ represents the sampled form, with uniform sampling interval T, of the continuous signal $x(t)$ then $\{x_{k-k_0}\}$ represents the sampled form of the continuous signal $x(t - k_0T)$ which, as illustrated in Figure 3.2, is the signal $x(t)$ delayed by a multiple k_0 of the sampling interval T. The reader will find it of interest to compare this result with the results for the Laplace transforms of integrals (2.16).

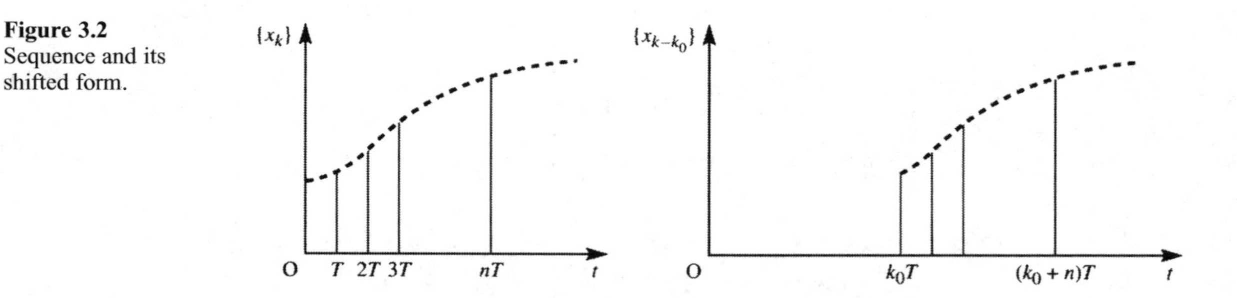

Figure 3.2 Sequence and its shifted form.

Example 3.6

The causal sequence $\{x_k\}$ is generated by

$$x_k = (\tfrac{1}{2})^k \quad (k \geqslant 0)$$

Determine the z transform of the shifted sequence $\{x_{k-2}\}$.

Solution

By the first shift property,

$$\mathscr{Z}\{x_{k-2}\} = \frac{1}{z^2} \mathscr{Z}\{(\tfrac{1}{2})^k\}$$

which, on using (3.4), gives

$$\mathscr{Z}\{x_{k-2}\} = \frac{1}{z^2}\frac{z}{z-\frac{1}{2}} \quad (|z| > \tfrac{1}{2}) \quad = \frac{1}{z^2}\frac{2z}{2z-1} = \frac{2}{z(2z-1)} \quad (|z| > \tfrac{1}{2})$$

We can confirm this result by direct use of the definition (3.1). From this, and the fact that $\{x_k\}$ is a causal sequence,

$$\{x_{k-2}\} = \{x_{-2}, x_{-1}, x_0, x_1, \dots\} = \{0, 0, 1, \tfrac{1}{2}, \tfrac{1}{4}, \dots\}$$

Thus,

$$\mathscr{Z}\{x_{k-2}\} = 0 + 0 + \frac{1}{z^2} + \frac{1}{2z^3} + \frac{1}{4z^4} + \dots = \frac{1}{z^2}\left(1 + \frac{1}{2z} + \frac{1}{4z^2} + \dots\right)$$

$$= \frac{1}{z^2}\frac{z}{z-\frac{1}{2}} \quad (|z| > \tfrac{1}{2}) \quad = \frac{z}{z(2z-1)} \quad (|z| > \tfrac{1}{2})$$

3.3.3 The second shift property (advancing)

In this section we seek a relationship between the z transform of an advanced version of a sequence and that of the original sequence. First we consider a single-step advance. If $\{y_k\}$ is the single-step advanced version of the sequence $\{x_k\}$ then $\{y_k\}$ is generated by

$$y_k = x_{k+1} \quad (k \geqslant 0)$$

Then

$$\mathscr{Z}\{y_k\} = \sum_{k=0}^{\infty}\frac{y_k}{z^k} = \sum_{k=0}^{\infty}\frac{x_{k+1}}{z^k} = z\sum_{k=0}^{\infty}\frac{x_{k+1}}{z^{k+1}}$$

and putting $p = k + 1$ gives

$$\mathscr{Z}\{y_k\} = z\sum_{p=1}^{\infty}\frac{x_p}{z^p} = z\left(\sum_{p=0}^{\infty}\frac{x_p}{z^p} - x_0\right) = zX(z) - zx_0$$

where $X(z)$ is the z transform of $\{x_k\}$.

We therefore have the result

$$\mathscr{Z}\{x_{k+1}\} = zX(z) - zx_0 \tag{3.16}$$

In a similar manner it is readily shown that for a two-step advanced sequence $\{x_{k+2}\}$

$$\mathscr{Z}\{x_{k+2}\} = z^2X(z) - z^2x_0 - zx_1 \tag{3.17}$$

Note the similarity in structure between (3.16) and (3.17) on the one hand and those for the Laplace transforms of first and second derivatives (Section 2.3.1). In general, it is readily proved by induction that for a k_0-step advanced sequence $\{x_{k+k_0}\}$

$$\mathscr{Z}\{x_{k+k_0}\} = z^{k_0}X(z) - \sum_{n=0}^{k_0-1} x_n z^{k_0-n} \tag{3.18}$$

In Section 3.5.2 we shall use these results to solve difference equations.

3.3.4 Some further properties

In this section we shall state some further useful properties of the z transform, leaving their verification to the reader as Exercises 9 and 10.

(i) *Multiplication by a^k*

If $Z\{x_k\} = X(z)$ then for a constant a

$$\mathscr{Z}\{a^k x_k\} = X(a^{-1}z) \tag{3.19}$$

(ii) *Multiplication by k^n*

If $\mathscr{Z}\{x_k\} = X(z)$ then for a positive integer n

$$\mathscr{Z}\{k^n x_k\} = \left(-z\frac{\mathrm{d}}{\mathrm{d}z}\right)^n X(z) \tag{3.20}$$

Note that in (3.20) the operator $-z\,\mathrm{d}/\mathrm{d}z$ means 'first differentiate with respect to z and then multiply by $-z$'. Raising to the power of n means 'repeat the operation n times'.

(iii) *Initial-value theorem*

If $\{x_k\}$ is a sequence with z transform $X(z)$ then the initial-value theorem states that

$$\lim_{z\to\infty} X(z) = x_0 \tag{3.21}$$

(iv) *Final-value theorem*

If $\{x_k\}$ is a sequence with z transform $X(z)$ then the final-value theorem states that

$$\lim_{k\to\infty} x_k = \lim_{z\to 1}(1 - z^{-1})X(z) \tag{3.22}$$

provided that the poles of $(1 - z^{-1})X(z)$ are inside the unit circle.

3.3.5 Table of z transforms

It is appropriate at this stage to draw together the results proved so far for easy access. This is done in the form of a table in Figure 3.3.

Figure 3.3 A short table of z transforms.

$\{x_k\}$ $(k \geqslant 0)$	$\mathscr{Z}\{x_k\}$	Region of existence
$x_k = \begin{cases} 1 & (k = 0) \\ 0 & (k > 0) \end{cases}$ (unit pulse sequence)	1	All z
$x_k = 1$ (unit step sequence)	$\dfrac{z}{z-1}$	$\lvert z \rvert > 1$
$x_k = a^k$ (a constant)	$\dfrac{z}{z-a}$	$\lvert z \rvert > \lvert a \rvert$
$x_k = k$	$\dfrac{z}{(z-1)^2}$	$\lvert z \rvert > 1$
$x_k = ka^{k-1}$ (a constant)	$\dfrac{z}{(z-a)^2}$	$\lvert z \rvert > a$
$x_k = e^{-kT}$ (T constant)	$\dfrac{z}{z-e^{-T}}$	$\lvert z \rvert > e^{-T}$
$x_k = \cos k\omega T$ (ω, T constants)	$\dfrac{z(z-\cos\omega T)}{z^2-2z\cos\omega T+1}$	$\lvert z \rvert > 1$
$x_k = \sin k\omega T$ (ω, T constants)	$\dfrac{z\sin\omega T}{z^2-2z\cos\omega T+1}$	$\lvert z \rvert > 1$

3.3.6 Exercises

3 Use the method of Example 3.5 to confirm (3.14), namely

$$\mathscr{Z}\{\sin k\omega T\} = \frac{z\sin\omega T}{z^2 - 2z\cos\omega T + 1}$$

where ω and T are constants.

4 Use the first shift property to calculate the z transform of the sequence $\{y_k\}$, with

$$y_k = \begin{cases} 0 & (k < 3) \\ x_{k-3} & (k \geqslant 3) \end{cases}$$

where $\{x_k\}$ is causal and $x_k = (\frac{1}{2})^k$. Confirm your result by direct evaluation of $\mathscr{Z}\{y_k\}$ using the definition of the z transform.

5 Determine the z transforms of the sequences

(a) $\{(-\frac{1}{5})^k\}$ (b) $\{\cos k\pi\}$

6 Determine $\mathscr{Z}\{(\frac{1}{2})^k\}$. Using (3.5), obtain the z transform of the sequence $\{k(\frac{1}{2})^k\}$.

7 Show that for a constant α

(a) $\mathscr{Z}\{\sinh k\alpha\} = \dfrac{z\sinh\alpha}{z^2 - 2z\cosh\alpha + 1}$

(b) $\mathscr{Z}\{\cosh k\alpha\} = \dfrac{z^2 - z\cosh\alpha}{z^2 - 2z\cosh\alpha + 1}$

8 Sequences are generated by sampling a causal continuous-time signal $u(t)$ $(t \geqslant 0)$ at uniform intervals T. Write down an expression for u_k, the general term of the sequence, and calculate the corresponding z transform when $u(t)$ is

(a) e^{-4t} (b) $\sin t$ (c) $\cos 2t$

9 Prove the initial- and final-value theorems given in (3.21) and (3.22).

10 Prove the multiplication properties given in (3.19) and (3.20).

3.4 The inverse z transform

In this section we consider the problem of recovering a causal sequence $\{x_k\}$ from knowledge of its z transform $X(z)$. As we shall see, the work on the inversion of Laplace transforms in Section 2.2.7 will prove a valuable asset for this task.

Formally the symbol $\mathscr{Z}^{-1}[X(z)]$ denotes a causal sequence $\{x_k\}$ whose z transform is $X(z)$; that is,

$$\text{if } \mathscr{Z}\{x_k\} = X(z) \quad \text{then} \quad \{x_k\} = \mathscr{Z}^{-1}[X(z)]$$

This correspondence between $X(z)$ and $\{x_k\}$ is called the **inverse z transformation**, $\{x_k\}$ being the **inverse transform** of $X(z)$, and $\mathscr{Z}^{-1}$ being referred to as the **inverse z-transform operator**.

As for the Laplace transforms in Section 2.2.8, the most obvious way of finding the inverse transform of $X(z)$ is to make use of a table of transforms such as that given in Figure 3.3. Sometimes it is possible to write down the inverse transform directly from the table, but more often than not it is first necessary to carry out some algebraic manipulation on $X(z)$. In particular, we frequently need to determine the inverse transform of a rational expression of the form $P(z)/Q(z)$, where $P(z)$ and $Q(z)$ are polynomials in z. In such cases the procedure, as for Laplace transforms, is first to resolve the expression, or a revised form of the expression, into partial fractions and then to use the table of transforms. We shall now illustrate the approach through some examples.

3.4.1 Inverse techniques

Example 3.7 Find

$$\mathscr{Z}^{-1}\left[\frac{z}{z-2}\right]$$

Solution From Figure 3.3, we see that $z/(z-2)$ is a special case of the transform $z/(z-a)$, with $a = 2$. Thus

$$\mathscr{Z}^{-1}\left[\frac{z}{z-2}\right] = \{2^k\}$$

Example 3.8 Find

$$\mathscr{Z}^{-1}\left[\frac{z}{(z-1)(z-2)}\right]$$

Solution Guided by our work on Laplace transforms, we might attempt to resolve

$$Y(z) = \frac{z}{(z-1)(z-2)}$$

into partial fractions. This approach does produce the correct result, as we shall show later. However, we notice that most of the entries in Figure 3.3 contain a factor z in the numerator of the transform. We therefore resolve

$$\frac{Y(z)}{z} = \frac{1}{(z-1)(z-2)}$$

into partial fractions, as

$$\frac{Y(z)}{z} = \frac{1}{z-2} - \frac{1}{z-1}$$

so that

$$Y(z) = \frac{z}{z-2} - \frac{z}{z-1}$$

Then using the result $\mathscr{Z}^{-1}[z/(z-a)] = \{a^k\}$ together with the linearity property, we have

$$\begin{aligned}\mathscr{Z}^{-1}[Y(z)] &= \mathscr{Z}^{-1}\left(\frac{z}{z-2} - \frac{z}{z-1}\right) = \mathscr{Z}^{-1}\left(\frac{z}{z-2}\right) - \mathscr{Z}^{-1}\left(\frac{z}{z-1}\right) \\ &= \{2^k\} - \{1^k\} \quad (k \geqslant 0)\end{aligned}$$

so that

$$\mathscr{Z}^{-1}\left[\frac{z}{(z-1)(z-2)}\right] = \{2^k - 1\} \quad (k \geqslant 0) \tag{3.23}$$

Suppose that in Example 3.8 we had not thought so far ahead and we had simply resolved $Y(z)$, rather than $Y(z)/z$, into partial fractions. Would the result be the same? The answer of course is 'yes', as we shall now show. Resolving

$$Y(z) = \frac{z}{(z-1)(z-2)}$$

into partial fractions gives

$$Y(z) = \frac{2}{z-2} - \frac{1}{z-1}$$

which may be written as

$$Y(z) = \frac{1}{z}\frac{2z}{z-2} - \frac{1}{z}\frac{z}{z-1}$$

Since

$$\mathscr{Z}^{-1}\left[\frac{2z}{z-2}\right] = 2\mathscr{Z}^{-1}\left(\frac{z}{z-2}\right) = 2\{2^k\}$$

it follows from the first shift property (3.15) that

$$\mathscr{Z}^{-1}\left[\frac{1}{z}\frac{2z}{z-2}\right] = \begin{cases}\{2 \cdot 2^{k-1}\} & (k > 0) \\ 0 & (k = 0)\end{cases}$$

Similarly,

$$\mathscr{Z}^{-1}\left[\frac{1}{z}\frac{z}{z-1}\right] = \begin{cases} \{1^{k-1}\} = \{1\} & (k > 0) \\ 0 & (k = 0) \end{cases}$$

Combining these last two results, we have

$$\mathscr{Z}^{-1}[Y(z)] = \mathscr{Z}^{-1}\left[\frac{1}{z}\frac{2z}{z-2}\right] - \mathscr{Z}^{-1}\left[\frac{1}{z}\frac{z}{z-1}\right]$$

$$= \begin{cases} \{2^k - 1\} & (k > 0) \\ 0 & (k = 0) \end{cases}$$

which, as expected, is in agreement with the answer obtained in Example 3.8.

We can see that adopting this latter approach, while producing the correct result, involved extra effort in the use of a shift theorem. When possible, we avoid this by 'extracting' the factor z as in Example 3.8, but of course this is not always possible, and recourse may be made to the shift property, as Example 3.9 illustrates.

The inverse z-transform $\{x_k\}$ of $X(z)$ is returned in MATLAB using the command

```
iztrans(X(z),k)
```

[*Note:* The command `iztrans(X(z))` by itself returns the inverse transform expressed in terms of n rather than k.]

For the z-transform in Example 3.8 the MATLAB command

```
iztrans(z/((z-1)*(z-2)),k)
```

returns

```
ans=-1+2^k
```

as required.

Example 3.9 Find

$$\mathscr{Z}^{-1}\left[\frac{2z+1}{(z+1)(z-3)}\right]$$

Solution In this case there is no factor z available in the numerator, and so we must resolve

$$Y(z) = \frac{2z+1}{(z+1)(z-3)}$$

into partial fractions, giving

$$Y(z) = \frac{1}{4}\frac{1}{z+1} + \frac{7}{4}\frac{1}{z-3} = \frac{1}{4}\frac{1}{z}\frac{z}{z+1} + \frac{7}{4}\frac{1}{z}\frac{z}{z-3}$$

Since

$$\mathscr{Z}^{-1}\left[\frac{z}{z+1}\right] = \{(-1)^k\} \quad (k \geqslant 0)$$

$$\mathscr{Z}^{-1}\left[\frac{z}{z-3}\right] = \{3^k\} \quad (k \geqslant 0)$$

it follows from the first shift property (3.15) that

$$\mathscr{Z}^{-1}\left[\frac{1}{z}\frac{z}{z+1}\right] = \begin{cases} \{(-1)^{k-1}\} & (k > 0) \\ 0 & (k = 0) \end{cases}$$

$$\mathscr{Z}^{-1}\left[\frac{1}{z}\frac{z}{z-3}\right] = \begin{cases} 3^{k-1} & (k > 0) \\ 0 & (k = 0) \end{cases}$$

Then, from the linearity property,

$$\mathscr{Z}^{-1}[Y(z)] = \tfrac{1}{4}\mathscr{Z}^{-1}\left[\frac{1}{z}\frac{z}{z+1}\right] + \tfrac{7}{4}\mathscr{Z}^{-1}\left[\frac{1}{z}\frac{z}{z-3}\right]$$

giving

$$\mathscr{Z}^{-1}\left[\frac{2z+1}{(z+1)(z-3)}\right] = \begin{cases} \{\tfrac{1}{4}(-1)^{k-1} + \tfrac{7}{4}3^{k-1}\} & (k > 0) \\ 0 & (k = 0) \end{cases}$$

In MATLAB the command

```
iztrans((2*z+1)/((z+1)*(z-3)),k)
```

returns

```
ans=-1/3*charfcn[0](k)-1/4*(-1)^k+7/12*3^k
```

[*Note:* The charfcn function is the characteristic function of the **set** A, and is defined to be

$$\text{charfcn}[A](k) = \begin{cases} 1 & \text{if } k \text{ is in } A \\ 0 & \text{if } k \text{ is not in } A \end{cases}$$

Thus charfcn $[0](k) = 1$ if $k = 0$ and 0 otherwise.]

It is left as an exercise to confirm that the answer provided using MATLAB concurs with the calculated answer.

It is often the case that the rational function $P(z)/Q(z)$ to be inverted has a quadratic term in the denominator. Unfortunately, in this case there is nothing resembling the first shift theorem of the Laplace transform which, as we saw in Section 2.2.9, proved so useful in similar circumstances. Looking at Figure 3.3, the only two transforms with quadratic terms in the denominator are those associated with the sequences $\{\cos k\omega T\}$ and $\{\sin k\omega T\}$. In practice these prove difficult to apply in the inverse form, and a 'first principles' approach is more appropriate. We illustrate this with two examples, demonstrating that all that is really required is the ability to handle complex numbers at the stage of resolution into partial fractions.

Example 3.10 Invert the z transform

$$Y(z) = \frac{z}{z^2 + a^2}$$

where a is a real constant.

Solution In view of the factor z in the numerator, we resolve $Y(z)/z$ into partial fractions, giving

$$\frac{Y(z)}{z} = \frac{1}{z^2 + a^2} = \frac{1}{(z + \mathrm{j}a)(z - \mathrm{j}a)} = \frac{1}{\mathrm{j}2a}\frac{1}{(z - \mathrm{j}a)} - \frac{1}{\mathrm{j}2a}\frac{1}{(z + \mathrm{j}a)}$$

That is

$$Y(z) = \frac{1}{\mathrm{j}2a}\left(\frac{z}{z - \mathrm{j}a} - \frac{z}{z + \mathrm{j}a}\right)$$

Using the result $\mathscr{Z}^{-1}[z/(z - a)] = \{a^k\}$, we have

$$\mathscr{Z}^{-1}\left[\frac{z}{z - \mathrm{j}a}\right] = \{(\mathrm{j}a)^k\} = \{\mathrm{j}^k a^k\}$$

$$\mathscr{Z}^{-1}\left[\frac{z}{z + \mathrm{j}a}\right] = \{(-\mathrm{j}a)^k\} = \{(-\mathrm{j})^k a^k\}$$

From the relation $\mathrm{e}^{\mathrm{j}\theta} = \cos\theta + \mathrm{j}\sin\theta$, we have

$$\mathrm{j} = \mathrm{e}^{\mathrm{j}\pi/2}, \qquad -\mathrm{j} = \mathrm{e}^{-\mathrm{j}\pi/2}$$

so that

$$\mathscr{Z}^{-1}\left[\frac{z}{z - \mathrm{j}a}\right] = \{a^k(\mathrm{e}^{\mathrm{j}\pi/2})^k\} = \{a^k \mathrm{e}^{\mathrm{j}k\pi/2}\} = \{a^k(\cos\tfrac{1}{2}k\pi + \mathrm{j}\sin\tfrac{1}{2}k\pi)\}$$

$$\mathscr{Z}^{-1}\left[\frac{z}{z + \mathrm{j}a}\right] = \{a^k(\cos\tfrac{1}{2}k\pi - \mathrm{j}\sin\tfrac{1}{2}k\pi)\}$$

The linearity property then gives

$$\mathscr{Z}^{-1}[Y(z)] = \left\{\frac{a^k}{\mathrm{j}2a}(\cos\tfrac{1}{2}k\pi + \mathrm{j}\sin\tfrac{1}{2}k\pi - \cos\tfrac{1}{2}k\pi + \mathrm{j}\sin\tfrac{1}{2}k\pi)\right\}$$

$$= \{a^{k-1}\sin\tfrac{1}{2}k\pi\}$$

Whilst MATLAB or MAPLE may be used to obtain the inverse z-transform when complex partial fractions are involved, it is difficult to convert results into a simple form, the difficult step being that of expressing complex exponentials in terms of trigonometric functions.

Example 3.11 Invert

$$Y(z) = \frac{z}{z^2 - z + 1}$$

Solution The denominator of the transform may be factorized as

$$z^2 - z + 1 = \left(z - \tfrac{1}{2} - \mathrm{j}\frac{\sqrt{3}}{2}\right)\left(z - \tfrac{1}{2} + \mathrm{j}\frac{\sqrt{3}}{2}\right)$$

In exponential form we have $\frac{1}{2} \pm \mathrm{j}\frac{1}{2}\sqrt{3} = \mathrm{e}^{\pm \mathrm{j}\pi/3}$, so the denominator may be written as

$$z^2 - z + 1 = (z - \mathrm{e}^{\mathrm{j}\pi/3})(z - \mathrm{e}^{-\mathrm{j}\pi/3})$$

We then have

$$\frac{Y(z)}{z} = \frac{1}{(z - \mathrm{e}^{\mathrm{j}\pi/3})(z - \mathrm{e}^{-\mathrm{j}\pi/3})}$$

which can be resolved into partial fractions as

$$\frac{Y(z)}{z} = \frac{1}{\mathrm{e}^{\mathrm{j}\pi/3} - \mathrm{e}^{-\mathrm{j}\pi/3}} \frac{1}{z - \mathrm{e}^{\mathrm{j}\pi/3}} + \frac{1}{\mathrm{e}^{-\mathrm{j}\pi/3} - \mathrm{e}^{\mathrm{j}\pi/3}} \frac{1}{z - \mathrm{e}^{-\mathrm{j}\pi/3}}$$

Noting that $\sin\theta = (\mathrm{e}^{\mathrm{j}\theta} - \mathrm{e}^{-\mathrm{j}\theta})/\mathrm{j}2$, this reduces to

$$\frac{Y(z)}{z} = \frac{1}{\mathrm{j}2 \sin \frac{1}{3}\pi} \frac{z}{z - \mathrm{e}^{\mathrm{j}\pi/3}} - \frac{1}{\mathrm{j}2 \sin \frac{1}{3}\pi} \frac{z}{z - \mathrm{e}^{-\mathrm{j}\pi/3}}$$

$$= \frac{1}{\mathrm{j}\sqrt{3}} \frac{z}{z - \mathrm{e}^{\mathrm{j}\pi/3}} - \frac{1}{\mathrm{j}\sqrt{3}} \frac{z}{z - \mathrm{e}^{-\mathrm{j}\pi/3}}$$

Using the result $\mathscr{Z}^{-1}[z/(z - a)] = \{a^k\}$, this gives

$$\mathscr{Z}^{-1}[Y(z)] = \frac{1}{\mathrm{j}\sqrt{3}}(\mathrm{e}^{\mathrm{j}k\pi/3} - \mathrm{e}^{-\mathrm{j}k\pi/3}) = \{2\sqrt{\tfrac{1}{3}} \sin \tfrac{1}{3}k\pi\}$$

We conclude this section with two further examples, illustrating the inversion technique applied to frequently occurring transform types.

Example 3.12 Find the sequence whose z transform is

$$F(z) = \frac{z^3 + 2z^2 + 1}{z^3}$$

Solution $F(z)$ is unlike any z transform treated so far in the examples. However, it is readily expanded in a power series in z^{-1} as

$$F(z) = 1 + \frac{2}{z} + \frac{1}{z^3}$$

Using (3.4), it is then apparent that

$$\mathscr{Z}^{-1}[F(z)] = \{f_k\} = \{1, 2, 0, 1, 0, 0, \dots\}$$

The MATLAB command

```
iztrans((z^3+2*z^2+1)/z^3,k)
```

returns

```
charfcn[0](k)+2*charfcn[1](k)+charfcn[3](k)
```

which corresponds to the sequence

$\{1, 2, 0, 1, 0, 0, \dots\}$

Example 3.13 Find $\mathscr{Z}^{-1}[G(z)]$ where

$$G(z) = \frac{z(1 - e^{-aT})}{(z - 1)(z - e^{-aT})}$$

where a and T are positive constants.

Solution Resolving into partial fractions,

$$\frac{G(z)}{z} = \frac{1}{z - 1} - \frac{1}{z - e^{-aT}}$$

giving

$$G(z) = \frac{1}{z - 1} - \frac{1}{z - e^{-aT}}$$

Using the result $\mathscr{Z}^{-1}[z/(z - a)] = \{a^k\}$, we have

$$\mathscr{Z}^{-1}[G(z)] = \{(1 - e^{-akT})\} \quad (k \geqslant 0)$$

In this particular example $G(z)$ is the z transform of a sequence derived by sampling the continuous-time signal

$$f(t) = 1 - e^{-at}$$

at intervals T.

The MATLAB commands

```
syms k z a T
iztrans((z*(1-exp(-a*T)))/((z-1)*(z-exp(-a*T))),k);
pretty(simple(ans))
```

return

```
ans=1-exp(-aT)^k
```

3.4.2 Exercises

Confirm your answers using MATLAB.

11 Invert the following z transforms. Give the general term of the sequence in each case.

(a) $\dfrac{z}{z-1}$ (b) $\dfrac{z}{z+1}$ (c) $\dfrac{z}{z-\frac{1}{2}}$

(d) $\dfrac{z}{3z+1}$ (e) $\dfrac{z}{z-\mathrm{j}}$ (f) $\dfrac{z}{z+\mathrm{j}\sqrt{2}}$

(g) $\dfrac{1}{z-1}$ (h) $\dfrac{z+2}{z+1}$

12 By first resolving $Y(z)/z$ into partial fractions, find $\mathscr{Z}^{-1}[Y(z)]$ when $Y(z)$ is given by

(a) $\dfrac{z}{(z-1)(z+2)}$ (b) $\dfrac{z}{(2z+1)(z-3)}$

(c) $\dfrac{z^2}{(2z+1)(z-1)}$ (d) $\dfrac{2z}{2z^2+z-1}$

(e) $\dfrac{z}{z^2+1}$ [*Hint:* $z^2+1=(z+\mathrm{j})(z-\mathrm{j})$]

(f) $\dfrac{z}{z^2-2\sqrt{3}z+4}$ (g) $\dfrac{2z^2-7z}{(z-1)^2(z-3)}$

(h) $\dfrac{z^2}{(z-1)^2(z^2-z+1)}$

13 Find $\mathscr{Z}^{-1}[Y(z)]$ when $Y(z)$ is given by

(a) $\dfrac{1}{z}+\dfrac{2}{z^7}$ (b) $1+\dfrac{3}{z^2}-\dfrac{2}{z^9}$

(c) $\dfrac{3z+z^2+5z^5}{z^5}$ (d) $\dfrac{1+z}{z^3}+\dfrac{3z}{3z+1}$

(e) $\dfrac{2z^3+6z^2+5z+1}{z^2(2z+1)}$ (f) $\dfrac{2z^2-7z+7}{(z-1)^2(z-2)}$

(g) $\dfrac{z-3}{z^2-3z+2}$

3.5 Discrete-time systems and difference equations

In Chapter 2 the Laplace transform technique was examined, first as a method for solving differential equations, then as a way of characterizing a continuous-time system. In fact, much could be deduced concerning the behaviour of the system and its properties by examining its transform-domain representation, without looking for specific time-domain responses at all. In this section we shall discuss the idea of a linear discrete-time system and its model, a **difference equation**. Later we shall see that the z transform plays an analogous role to the Laplace transform for such systems, by providing a transform-domain representation of the system.

3.5.1 Difference equations

First we illustrate the motivation for studying difference equations by means of an example.

Suppose that a sequence of observations $\{x_k\}$ is being recorded and we receive observation x_k at (time) step or index k. We might attempt to process (for example, smooth or filter) this sequence of observations $\{x_k\}$ using the discrete-time feedback system illustrated in Figure 3.4. At time step k the observation x_k enters the system as an input, and, after combination with the 'feedback' signal at the summing junction S, proceeds to the block labelled D. This block is a unit delay block, and its function is to hold its input signal until the 'clock' advances one step, to step $k+1$. At this time the input signal is passed without alteration to become the signal y_{k+1}, the $(k+1)$th member of the output sequence $\{y_k\}$. At the same time this signal is fed back through a scaling

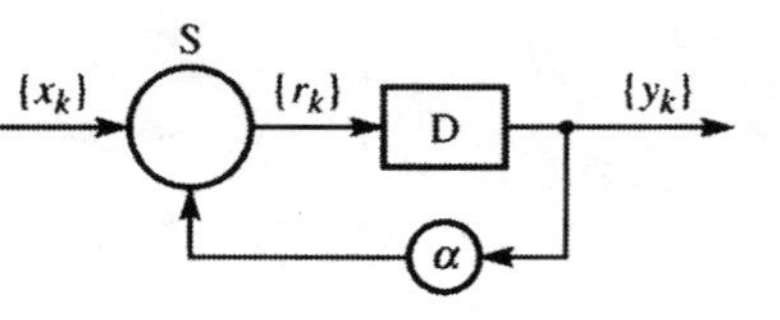

Figure 3.4 Discrete-time signal processing system.

block of amplitude α to the summing junction S. This process is instantaneous, and at S the feedback signal is subtracted from the next input observation x_{k+1} to provide the next input to the delay block D. The process then repeats at each 'clock' step.

To analyse the system, let $\{r_k\}$ denote the sequence of input signals to D; then, owing to the delay action of D, we have

$$y_{k+1} = r_k$$

Also, owing to the feedback action,

$$r_k = x_k - \alpha y_k$$

where α is the feedback gain. Combining the two expressions gives

$$y_{k+1} = x_k - \alpha y_k$$

or

$$y_{k+1} + \alpha y_k = x_k \tag{3.24}$$

Equation (3.24) is an example of a first-order difference equation, and it relates adjacent members of the sequence $\{y_k\}$ to each other and to the input sequence $\{x_k\}$.

A solution of the difference equation (3.24) is a formula for y_k, the general term of the output sequence $\{y_k\}$, and this will depend on both k and the input sequence $\{x_k\}$ as well as, in this case, the feedback gain α.

Example 3.14

Find a difference equation to represent the system shown in Figure 3.5, having input and output sequences $\{x_k\}$ and $\{y_k\}$ respectively, where D is the unit delay block and a and b are constant feedback gains.

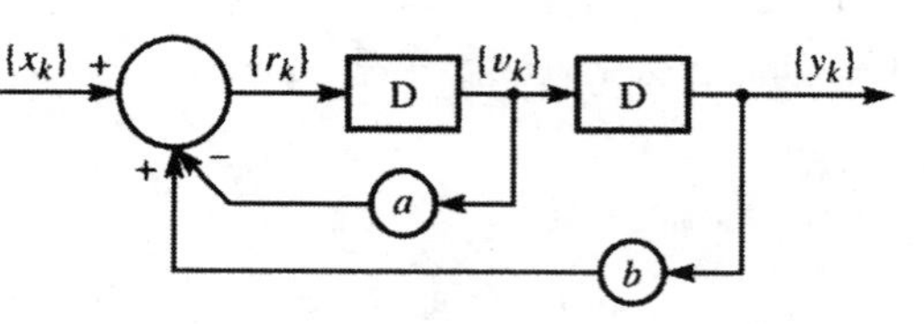

Figure 3.5 The system for Example 3.14.

Solution Introducing intermediate signal sequences $\{r_k\}$ and $\{v_k\}$ as shown in Figure 3.5, at each step the outputs of the delay blocks are

$$y_{k+1} = v_k \tag{3.25}$$

$$v_{k+1} = r_k \tag{3.26}$$

and at the summing junction

$$r_k = x_k - av_k + by_k \tag{3.27}$$

From (3.25),

$$y_{k+2} = v_{k+1}$$

which on using (3.26) gives

$$y_{k+2} = r_k$$

Substituting for r_k from (3.27) then gives

$$y_{k+2} = x_k - av_k + by_k$$

which on using (3.25) becomes

$$y_{k+2} = x_k - ay_{k+1} + by_k$$

Rearranging this gives

$$y_{k+2} + ay_{k+1} - by_k = x_k \tag{3.28}$$

as the difference equation representing the system.

The difference equation (3.28) is an example of a second-order linear constant-coefficient difference equation, and there are strong similarities between this and a second-order linear constant-coefficient differential equation. It is of second order because the term involving the greatest shift of the $\{y_k\}$ sequence is the term in y_{k+2}, implying a shift of two steps. As demonstrated by Example 3.14, the degree of shift, or the order of the equation, is closely related to the number of delay blocks in the block diagram.

3.5.2 The solution of difference equations

Difference equations arise in a variety of ways, sometimes from the direct modelling of systems in discrete time or as an approximation to a differential equation describing the behaviour of a system modelled as a continuous-time system. We do not discuss this further here; rather we restrict ourselves to the technique of solution but examples of applications will be apparent from the exercises. The z-transform method is based upon the second shift property (Section 3.3.3), and it will quickly emerge as a technique almost identical to the Laplace transform method for ordinary differential equations introduced in Section 2.3.3. We shall introduce the method by means of an example.

Example 3.15

If in Example 3.14, $a = 1$, $b = 2$ and the input sequence $\{x_k\}$ is the unit step sequence $\{1\}$, solve the resulting difference equation (3.28).

Solution

Substituting for a, b and $\{x_k\}$ in (3.28) leads to the difference equation

$$y_{k+2} + y_{k+1} - 2y_k = 1 \quad (k \geqslant 0) \tag{3.29}$$

Taking z transforms throughout in (3.29) gives

$$\mathscr{Z}\{y_{k+2} + y_{k+1} - 2y_k\} = \mathscr{Z}\{1, 1, 1, \dots\}$$

which, on using the linearity property and the result $\mathscr{Z}\{1\} = z/(z-1)$, may be written as

$$\mathscr{Z}\{y_{k+2}\} + \mathscr{Z}\{y_{k+1}\} - 2\mathscr{Z}\{y_k\} = \frac{z}{z-1}$$

Using (3.16) and (3.17) then gives

$$[z^2Y(z) - z^2y_0 - zy_1] + [zY(z) - zy_0] - 2Y(z) = \frac{z}{z-1}$$

which on rearranging leads to

$$(z^2 + z - 2)Y(z) = \frac{z}{z-1} + z^2y_0 + z(y_1 + y_0) \tag{3.30}$$

To proceed, we need some further information, namely the first and second terms y_0 and y_1 of the solution sequence $\{y_k\}$. Without this additional information, we cannot find a unique solution. As we saw in Section 2.3.3, this compares with the use of the Laplace transform method to solve second-order differential equations, where the values of the solution and its first derivative at time $t = 0$ are required.

Suppose that we know (or are given) that

$$y_0 = 0, \qquad y_1 = 1$$

Then (3.30) becomes

$$(z^2 + z - 2)Y(z) = z + \frac{z}{z-1}$$

or

$$(z+2)(z-1)Y(z) = z + \frac{z}{z-1}$$

and solving for $Y(z)$ gives

$$Y(z) = \frac{z}{(z+2)(z-1)} + \frac{z}{(z+2)(z-1)^2} = \frac{z^2}{(z+2)(z-1)^2} \tag{3.31}$$

To obtain the solution sequence $\{y_k\}$, we must take the inverse transform in (3.31). Proceeding as in Section 3.4, we resolve $Y(z)/z$ into partial fractions as

$$\frac{Y(z)}{z} = \frac{z}{(z+2)(z-1)^2} = \tfrac{1}{3}\frac{1}{(z-1)^2} + \tfrac{2}{9}\frac{1}{z-1} - \tfrac{2}{9}\frac{1}{z+2}$$

and so

$$Y(z) = \tfrac{1}{3}\frac{z}{(z-1)^2} + \tfrac{2}{9}\frac{z}{z-1} - \tfrac{2}{9}\frac{z}{z+2}$$

Using the results $\mathscr{Z}^{-1}[z/(z-a)] = \{a^k\}$ and $\mathscr{Z}^{-1}[z/(z-1)^2] = \{k\}$ from Figure 3.3, we obtain

$$\{y_k\} = \{\tfrac{1}{3}k + \tfrac{2}{9} - \tfrac{2}{9}(-2)^k\} \quad (k \geqslant 0)$$

as the solution sequence for the difference equation satisfying the conditions $y_0 = 0$ and $y_1 = 1$.

The method adopted in Example 3.15 is called the **z-transform method for solving linear constant-coefficient difference equations**, and is analogous to the Laplace transform method for solving linear constant-coefficient differential equations.

To conclude this section, two further examples are given to help consolidate understanding of the method.

Such difference equations can be solved directly in MAPLE using the `rsolve` command. In the current version of the Symbolic Math Toolbox in MATLAB there appears to be no equivalent command for directly solving a difference equation. However, as we saw in Section 2.5.5, using the `maple` command in MATLAB lets us access MAPLE commands directly. Hence, for the difference equation in Example 3.15, using the command

```
maple('rsolve({y(k+2)+y(k+1)-2*y(k)
=1,y(0)=0,y(1)=1},y(k))')
```

in MATLAB returns the calculated answer

```
-2/9*(-2)^k+2/9+1/3*k
```

Example 3.16

Solve the difference equation

$$8y_{k+2} - 6y_{k+1} + y_k = 9 \quad (k \geqslant 0)$$

given that $y_0 = 1$ and $y_1 = \frac{3}{2}$.

Solution

Taking z transforms

$$8\mathscr{Z}\{y_{k+2}\} - 6\mathscr{Z}\{y_{k+1}\} + \mathscr{Z}\{y_k\} = 9\mathscr{Z}\{1\}$$

Using (3.16) and (3.17) and the result $\mathscr{Z}\{1\} = z/(z-1)$ gives

$$8[z^2Y(z) - z^2y_0 - zy_1] - 6[zY(z) - zy_0] + Y(z) = \frac{9z}{z-1}$$

which on rearranging leads to

$$(8z^2 - 6z + 1)Y(z) = 8z^2y_0 + 8zy_1 - 6zy_0 + \frac{9z}{z-1}$$

We are given that $y_0 = 1$ and $y_1 = \frac{3}{2}$, so

$$(8z^2 - 6z + 1)Y(z) = 8z^2 + 6z + \frac{9z}{z-1}$$

or

$$\begin{aligned}\frac{Y(z)}{z} &= \frac{8z+6}{(4z-1)(2z-1)} + \frac{9}{(4z-1)(2z-1)(z-1)} \\ &= \frac{z+\frac{3}{4}}{(z-\frac{1}{4})(z-\frac{1}{2})} + \frac{\frac{9}{8}}{(z-\frac{1}{4})(z-\frac{1}{2})(z-1)}\end{aligned}$$

Resolving into partial fractions gives

$$\frac{Y(z)}{z} = \frac{5}{z-\frac{1}{2}} - \frac{4}{z-\frac{1}{4}} + \frac{6}{z-\frac{1}{4}} - \frac{9}{z-\frac{1}{2}} + \frac{3}{z-1}$$

$$= \frac{2}{z-\frac{1}{4}} - \frac{4}{z-\frac{1}{2}} + \frac{3}{z-1}$$

and so

$$Y(z) = \frac{2z}{z-\frac{1}{4}} - \frac{4z}{z-\frac{1}{2}} + \frac{3z}{z-1}$$

Using the result $\mathscr{Z}^{-1}\{z/(z-a)\} = \{a^k\}$ from Figure 3.3, we take inverse transforms, to obtain

$$\{y_k\} = \{2(\tfrac{1}{4})^k - 4(\tfrac{1}{2})^k + 3\} \quad (k \geq 0)$$

as the required solution.

Check that in MATLAB the command

```
maple('rsolve({8*y(k+2)-6*y(k+1)+y(k)=9,y(0)=1,y(1)=
3/2},y(k))')
```

returns the calculated answer.

Example 3.17 Solve the difference equation

$$y_{k+2} + 2y_k = 0 \quad (k \geq 0)$$

given that $y_0 = 1$ and $y_1 = \sqrt{2}$.

Solution Taking z transforms, we have

$$[z^2Y(z) - z^2y_0 - zy_1] + 2Y(z) = 0$$

and substituting the given values of y_0 and y_1 gives

$$z^2Y(z) - z^2 - \sqrt{2}z + 2Y(z) = 0$$

or

$$(z^2 + 2)Y(z) = z^2 + \sqrt{2}z$$

Resolving $Y(z)/z$ into partial fractions gives

$$\frac{Y(z)}{z} = \frac{z+\sqrt{2}}{z^2+2} = \frac{z+\sqrt{2}}{(z+\mathrm{j}\sqrt{2})(z-\mathrm{j}\sqrt{2})}$$

Following the approach adopted in Example 3.13, we write

$$\mathrm{j}\sqrt{2} = \sqrt{2}\,\mathrm{e}^{\mathrm{j}\pi/2}, \qquad -\mathrm{j}\sqrt{2} = \sqrt{2}\,\mathrm{e}^{-\mathrm{j}\pi/2}$$

$$\frac{Y(z)}{z} = \frac{z+\sqrt{2}}{(z-\sqrt{2}\,\mathrm{e}^{\mathrm{j}\pi/2})(z-\sqrt{2}\,\mathrm{e}^{-\mathrm{j}\pi/2})} = \frac{(1+\mathrm{j})/\mathrm{j}2}{z-\sqrt{2}\,\mathrm{e}^{\mathrm{j}\pi/2}} - \frac{(1-\mathrm{j})/\mathrm{j}2}{z-\sqrt{2}\,\mathrm{e}^{-\mathrm{j}\pi/2}}$$

Thus

$$Y(z) = \frac{1}{j2}\left[(1+j)\frac{z}{z-\sqrt{2}\,e^{j\pi/2}} - (1-j)\frac{z}{z-\sqrt{2}\,e^{-j\pi/2}}\right]$$

which on taking inverse transforms gives

$$\{y_k\} = \left\{\frac{2^{k/2}}{j2}\left[(1+j)\,e^{jk\pi/2} - (1-j)\,e^{-jk\pi/2}\right]\right\}$$

$$= \{2^{k/2}(\cos\tfrac{1}{2}k\pi + \sin\tfrac{1}{2}k\pi)\} \quad (k \geqslant 0)$$

as the required solution.

The solution in Example 3.17 was found to be a real-valued sequence, and this comes as no surprise because the given difference equation and the 'starting' values y_0 and y_1 involved only real numbers. This observation provides a useful check on the algebra when complex partial fractions are involved.

If complex partial fractions are involved then, as was mentioned at the end of Example 3.10, it is difficult to simplify answers when determining inverse z transforms using MATLAB. When such partial fractions arise in the solution of difference equations use of the command `evalc` alongside `rsolve` in MAPLE attempts to express complex exponentials in terms of trigonometric functions, leading in most cases to simplified answers.

Considering the difference equation of Example 3.17, using the command

```
maple('rsolve({y(k+2)+2*y(k)=0,y(0)=1,y(1)
=2^(1/2)},y(k))')
```

in MATLAB returns the answer

```
(1/2+1/2*i)*(-i*2^(1/2))^k+(1/2-1/2*i)*(i*2^(1/2))^k
```

whilst using the command

```
maple('evalc(rsolve({y(k+2)+2*y(k)=0,y(0)=1,y(1)
=2^(1/2)},y(k)))')
```

returns the answer

```
exp(1/2*log(2)*k)*cos(1/2*k*pi)+exp(1/2*log(2)*k)
*sin(1/2*k*pi)
```

Noting that $e^{\log 2} = 2$ it is readily seen that this corresponds to the calculated answer

$$2^{k/2}(\cos\tfrac{1}{2}k\pi + \sin\tfrac{1}{2}k\pi)$$

3.5.3 Exercises

When appropriate confirm your answers using MATLAB.

14 Find difference equations representing the discrete-time systems shown in Figure 3.6.

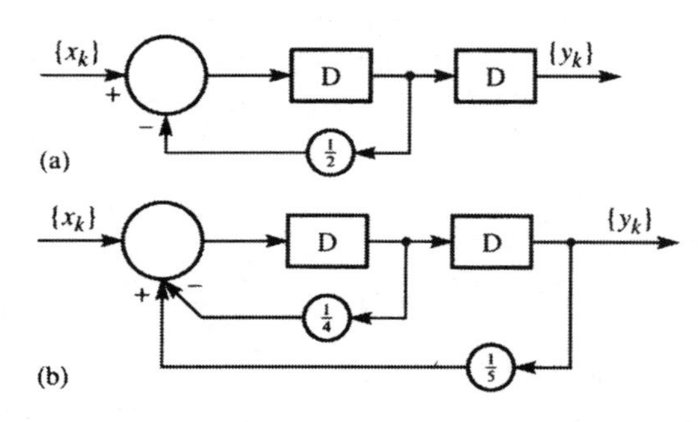

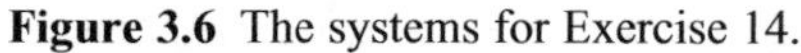

Figure 3.6 The systems for Exercise 14.

15 Using z-transform methods, solve the following difference equations:

(a) $y_{k+2} - 2y_{k+1} + y_k = 0$ subject to $y_0 = 0, y_1 = 1$

(b) $y_{n+2} - 8y_{n+1} - 9y_n = 0$ subject to $y_0 = 2, y_1 = 1$

(c) $y_{k+2} + 4y_k = 0$ subject to $y_0 = 0, y_1 = 1$

(d) $2y_{k+2} - 5y_{k+1} - 3y_k = 0$ subject to $y_0 = 3, y_1 = 2$

16 Using z-transform methods, solve the following difference equations:

(a) $6y_{k+2} + y_{k+1} - y_k = 3$ subject to $y_0 = y_1 = 0$

(b) $y_{k+2} - 5y_{k+1} + 6y_k = 5$ subject to $y_0 = 0, y_1 = 1$

(c) $y_{n+2} - 5y_{n+1} + 6y_n = (\frac{1}{2})^n$ subject to $y_0 = y_1 = 0$

(d) $y_{n+2} - 3y_{n+1} + 3y_n = 1$ subject to $y_0 = 1, y_1 = 0$

(e) $2y_{n+2} - 3y_{n+1} - 2y_n = 6n + 1$ subject to $y_0 = 1$, $y_1 = 2$

(f) $y_{n+2} - 4y_n = 3n - 5$ subject to $y_0 = y_1 = 0$

17 A person's capital at the beginning of and expenditure during, a given year k are denoted by C_k and E_k respectively, and satisfy the difference equations

$$C_{k+1} = 1.5C_k - E_k$$

$$E_{k+1} = 0.21C_k + 0.5E_k$$

(a) Show that eventually the person's capital grows at 20% per annum.

(b) If the capital at the beginning of year 1 is £6000 and the expenditure during year 1 is £3720 then find the year in which the expenditure is a minimum and the capital at the beginning of that year.

18 The dynamics of a discrete-time system are determined by the difference equation

$$y_{k+2} - 5y_{k+1} + 6y_k = u_k$$

Determine the response of the system to the unit step input

$$u_k = \begin{cases} 0 & (k < 0) \\ 1 & (k \geqslant 0) \end{cases}$$

given that $y_0 = y_1 = 1$.

19 As a first attempt to model the national economy, it is assumed that the national income I_k at year k is given by

$$I_k = C_k + P_k + G_k$$

where C_k is the consumer expenditure, P_k is private investment and G_k is government expenditure. It is also assumed that the consumer spending is proportional to the national income in the previous year, so that

$$C_k = aI_{k-1} \quad (0 < a < 1)$$

It is further assumed that private investment is proportional to the change in consumer spending over the previous year, so that

$$P_k = b(C_k - C_{k-1}) \quad (0 < b \leqslant 1)$$

Show that under these assumptions the national income I_k is determined by the difference equation

$$I_{k+2} - a(1 + b)I_{k+1} + abI_k = G_{k+2}$$

If $a = \frac{1}{2}$, $b = 1$, government spending is at a constant level (that is, $G_k = G$ for all k) and $I_0 = 2G$, $I_1 = 3G$, show that

$$I_k = 2[1 + (\tfrac{1}{2})^{k/2} \sin \tfrac{1}{4}k\pi]G$$

Discuss what happens as $k \to \infty$.

20 The difference equation for current in a particular ladder network of N loops is

$$R_1 i_{n+1} + R_2(i_{n+1} - i_n) + R_2(i_{n+1} - i_{n+2}) = 0$$

$$(0 \leqslant n \leqslant N - 2)$$

where i_n is the current in the $(n + 1)$th loop, and R_1 and R_2 are constant resistors.

(a) Show that this may be written as

$$i_{n+2} - 2\cosh\alpha i_{n+1} + i_n = 0 \quad (0 \leqslant n \leqslant N-2)$$

where

$$\alpha = \cosh^{-1}\left(1 + \frac{R_1}{2R_2}\right)$$

(b) By solving the equation in (a), show that

$$i_n = \frac{i_1 \sinh n\alpha - i_0 \sinh(n-1)\alpha}{\sinh\alpha} \quad (2 \leqslant n \leqslant N)$$

3.6 Discrete linear systems: characterization

In this section we examine the concept of a discrete-time linear system and its difference equation model. Ideas developed in Chapter 2 for continuous-time system modelling will be seen to carry over to discrete-time systems, and we shall see that the z transform is the key to the understanding of such systems.

3.6.1 *z* transfer functions

In Section 2.6, when considering continuous-time linear systems modelled by differential equations, we introduced the concept of the system (Laplace) transfer function. This is a powerful tool in the description of such systems, since it contains all the information on system stability and also provides a method of calculating the response to an arbitrary input signal using a convolution integral. In the same way, we can identify a z transfer function for a discrete-time linear time-invariant system modelled by a difference equation, and we can arrive at results analogous to those of Chapter 2.

Let us consider the general linear constant-coefficient difference equation model for a linear time-invariant system, with input sequence $\{u_k\}$ and output sequence $\{y_k\}$. Both $\{u_k\}$ and $\{y_k\}$ are causal sequences throughout. Such a difference equation model takes the form

$$a_n y_{k+n} + a_{n-1} y_{k+n-1} + a_{n-2} y_{k+n-2} + \ldots + a_0 y_k$$
$$= b_m u_{k+m} + b_{m-1} u_{k+m-1} + b_{m-2} u_{k+m-2} + \ldots + b_0 u_k \quad (3.32)$$

where $k \geqslant 0$ and n, m (with $n \geqslant m$) are positive integers and the a_i and b_j are constants. The difference equation (3.32) differs in one respect from the examples considered in Section 3.5 in that the possibility of delayed terms in the input sequence $\{u_k\}$ is also allowed for. The order of the difference equation is n if $a_n \neq 0$, and for the system to be physically realizable, $n \geqslant m$.

Assuming the system to be initially in a quiescent state, we take z transforms throughout in (3.32) to give

$$(a_n z^n + a_{n-1} z^{n-1} + \ldots + a_0) Y(z) = (b_m z^m + b_{m-1} z^{m-1} + \ldots + b_0) U(z)$$

where $Y(z) = \mathscr{Z}\{y_k\}$ and $U(z) = \mathscr{Z}\{u_k\}$. The **system discrete** or ***z* transfer function** $G(z)$ is defined as

$$G(z) = \frac{Y(z)}{U(z)} = \frac{b_m z^m + b_{m-1} z^{m-1} + \ldots + b_0}{a_n z^n + a_{n-1} z^{n-1} + \ldots + a_0} \quad (3.33)$$

and is normally rearranged (by dividing numerator and denominator by a_n) so that the coefficient of z^n in the denominator is 1. In deriving $G(z)$ in this form, we have assumed that the system was initially in a quiescent state. This assumption is certainly valid for the system (3.32) if

$$y_0 = y_1 = \ldots = y_{n-1} = 0$$

$$u_0 = u_1 = \ldots = u_{m-1} = 0$$

This is not the end of the story, however, and we shall use the term 'quiescent' to mean that no non-zero values are stored on the delay elements before the initial time.

On writing

$$P(z) = b_m z^m + b_{m-1} z^{m-1} + \ldots + b_0$$

$$Q(z) = a_n z^n + a_{n-1} z^{n-1} + \ldots + a_0$$

the discrete transfer function may be expressed as

$$G(z) = \frac{P(z)}{Q(z)}$$

As for the continuous model in Section 2.6.1, the equation $Q(z) = 0$ is called the **characteristic equation** of the discrete system, its order, n, determines the **order of the system**, and its roots are referred to as the **poles** of the discrete transfer function. Likewise, the roots of $P(z) = 0$ are referred to as the **zeros** of the discrete transfer function.

Example 3.18

Draw a block diagram to represent the system modelled by the difference equation

$$y_{k+2} + 3y_{k+1} - y_k = u_k \qquad \textbf{(3.34)}$$

and find the corresponding z transfer function.

Solution

The difference equation may be thought of as a relationship between adjacent members of the solution sequence $\{y_k\}$. Thus at each time step k we have from (3.34)

$$y_{k+2} = -3y_{k+1} + y_k + u_k \qquad \textbf{(3.35)}$$

which provides a formula for y_{k+2} involving y_k, y_{k+1} and the input u_k. The structure shown in Figure 3.7(a) illustrates the generation of the sequence $\{y_k\}$ from $\{y_{k+2}\}$ using two delay blocks.

We now use (3.35) as a prescription for generating the sequence $\{y_{k+2}\}$ and arrange for the correct combination of signals to be formed at each step k at the input summing junction S of Figure 3.7(a). This leads to the structure shown in Figure 3.7(b), which is the required block diagram.

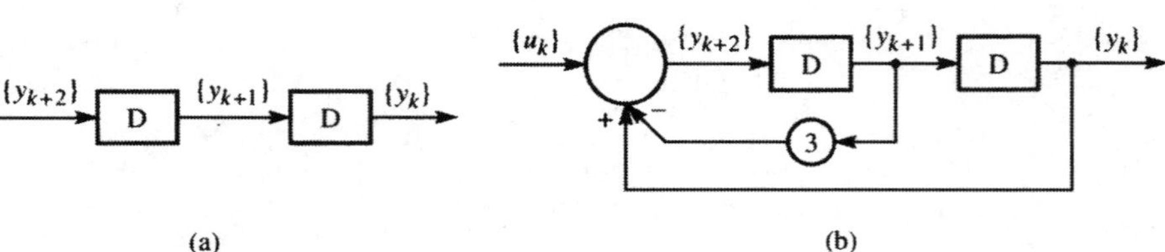

Figure 3.7
(a) The basic second-order block diagram substructure; (b) block diagram representation of (3.34).

We can of course produce a block diagram in the z-transform domain, using a similar process. Taking the z transform throughout in (3.34), under the assumption of a quiescent initial state, we obtain

$$z^2Y(z) + 3zY(z) - Y(z) = U(z) \tag{3.36}$$

or

$$z^2Y(z) = -3zY(z) + Y(z) + U(z) \tag{3.37}$$

The representation (3.37) is the transform-domain version of (3.35), and the z-transform domain basic structure corresponding to the time-domain structure of Figure 3.7(a) is shown in Figure 3.8(a).

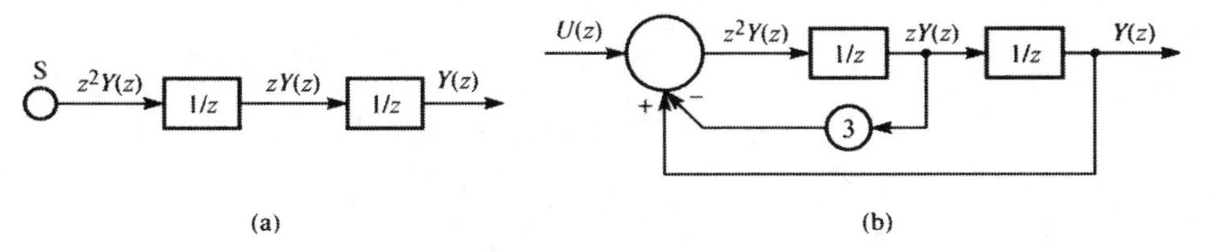

Figure 3.8 (a) The z-transform domain basic second-order block diagram substructure; (b) the z-transform domain block diagram representation of (3.34).

The unit delay blocks, labelled D in Figure 3.7(a), become '$1/z$' elements in the z-transform domain diagram, in line with the first shift property (3.15), where a number k_0 of delay steps involves multiplication by z^{-k_0}.

It is now a simple matter to construct the 'signal' transform $z^2Y(z)$ from (3.37) and arrange for it to be available at the input to the summing junction S in Figure 3.8(a). The resulting block diagram is shown in Figure 3.8(b).

The z transfer function follows at once from (3.36) as

$$G(z) = \frac{Y(z)}{U(z)} = \frac{1}{z^2 + 3z - 1} \tag{3.38}$$

Example 3.19

A system is specified by its z transfer function

$$G(z) = \frac{z - 1}{z^2 + 3z + 2}$$

What is the order n of the system? Can it be implemented using only n delay elements? Illustrate this.

Solution

If $\{u_k\}$ and $\{y_k\}$ denote respectively the input and output sequences to the system then

$$G(z) = \frac{Y(z)}{U(z)} = \frac{z - 1}{z^2 + 3z + 2}$$

so that

$$(z^2 + 3z + 2)Y(z) = (z - 1)U(z)$$

Taking inverse transforms, we obtain the corresponding difference equation model assuming the system is initially in a quiescent state

$$y_{k+2} + 3y_{k+1} + 2y_k = u_{k+1} - u_k \tag{3.39}$$

The difference equation (3.39) has a more complex right-hand side than the difference equation (3.34) considered in Example 3.18. This results from the existence of z terms in the numerator of the transfer function. By definition, the order of the difference equation (3.39) is still 2. However, realization of the system with two delay blocks is not immediately apparent, although this can be achieved, as we shall now illustrate.

Introduce a new signal sequence $\{r_k\}$ such that

$$(z^2 + 3z + 2)R(z) = U(z) \tag{3.40}$$

where $R(z) = \mathscr{Z}\{r_k\}$. In other words, $\{r_k\}$ is the output of the system having transfer function $1/(z^2 + 3z + 2)$.

Multiplying both sides of (3.40) by z, we obtain

$$z(z^2 + 3z + 2)R(z) = zU(z)$$

or

$$(z^2 + 3z + 2)zR(z) = zU(z) \tag{3.41}$$

Subtracting (3.40) from (3.41) we have

$$(z^2 + 3z + 2)zR(z) - (z^2 + 3z + 2)R(z) = zU(z) - U(z)$$

giving

$$(z^2 + 3z + 2)[zR(z) - R(z)] = (z - 1)U(z)$$

Finally, choosing

$$Y(z) = zR(z) - R(z) \tag{3.42}$$

$$(z^2 + 3z + 2)Y(z) = (z - 1)U(z)$$

which is a realization of the given transfer function.

To construct a block diagram realization of the system, we first construct a block diagram representation of (3.40) as in Figure 3.9(a). We now 'tap off' appropriate signals to generate $Y(z)$ according to (3.42) to construct a block diagram representation of the specified system. The resulting block diagram is shown in Figure 3.9(b).

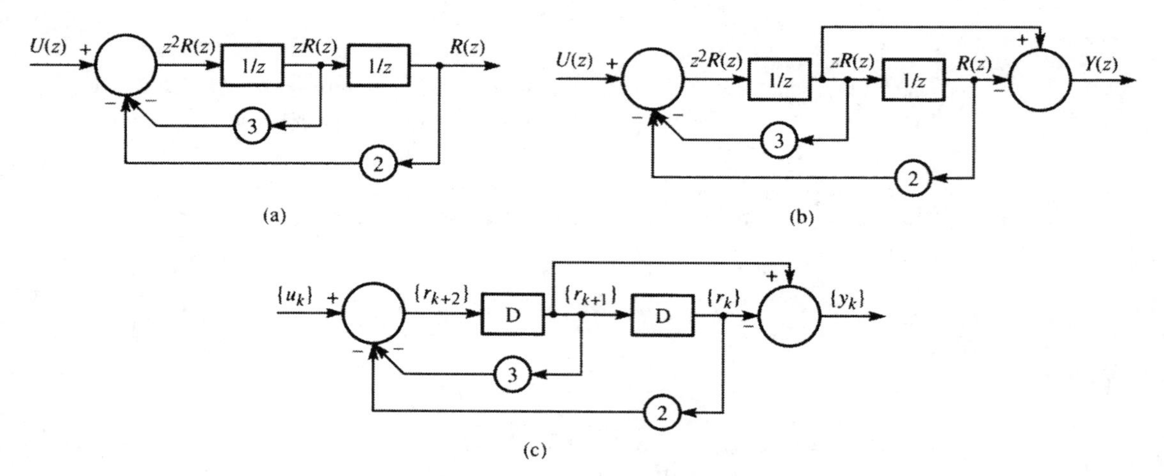

Figure 3.9 The z-transform block diagrams for (a) the system (3.40), (b) the system (3.39), and (c) the time-domain realization of the system in Example 3.19.

In order to implement the system, we must exhibit a physically realizable time-domain structure, that is one containing only D elements. Clearly, since Figure 3.9(b) contains only '$1/z$' blocks, we can immediately produce a realizable time-domain structure as shown in Figure 3.9(c), where, as before, D is the unit delay block.

Example 3.20

A system is specified by its z transfer function

$$G(z) = \frac{z}{z^2 + 0.3z + 0.02}$$

Draw a block diagram to illustrate a time-domain realization of the system. Find a second structure that also implements the system.

Solution

We know that if $\mathscr{Z}\{u_k\} = U\{z\}$ and $\mathscr{Z}\{y_k\} = Y(z)$ are the z transforms of the input and output sequences respectively then, by definition,

$$G(z) = \frac{Y(z)}{U(z)} = \frac{z}{z^2 + 0.3z + 0.02} \tag{3.43}$$

which may be rewritten as

$$(z^2 + 0.3z + 0.02)Y(z) = zU(z)$$

Noting the presence of the factor z on the right-hand side, we follow the procedure of Example 3.19 and consider the system

$$(z^2 + 0.3z + 0.02)R(z) = U(z) \tag{3.44}$$

Multiplying both sides by z, we have

$$(z^2 + 0.3z + 0.02)zR(z) = zU(z)$$

and so, if the output $Y(z) = zR(z)$ is extracted from the block diagram corresponding to (3.44), we have the block diagram representation of the given system (3.43). This is illustrated in Figure 3.10(a), with the corresponding time-domain implementation shown in Figure 3.10(b).

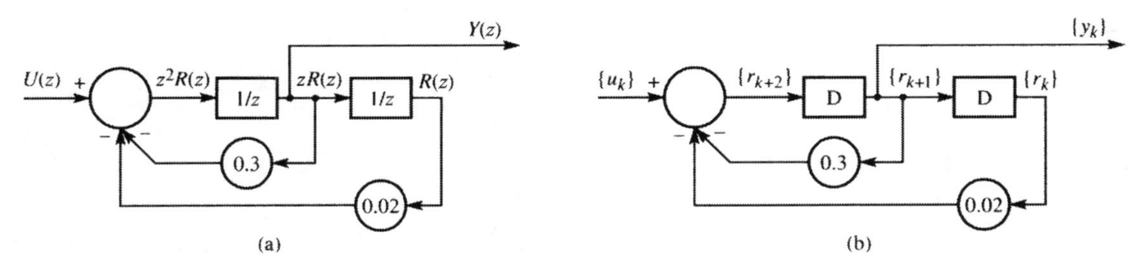

Figure 3.10 (a) The z-transform block diagram for the system of Example 3.20; and (b) the time-domain implementation of (a).

To discover a second form of time-domain implementation, note that

$$G(z) = \frac{z}{z^2 + 0.3z + 0.02} = \frac{2}{z + 0.2} - \frac{1}{z + 0.1}$$

We may therefore write

$$Y(z) = G(z)U(z) = \left(\frac{2}{z + 0.2} - \frac{1}{z + 0.1}\right)U(z)$$

so that

$$Y(z) = R_1(z) - R_2(z)$$

where

$$R_1(z) = \frac{2}{z + 0.2}U(z) \quad \textbf{(3.45a)}$$

$$R_2(z) = \frac{1}{z + 0.1}U(z) \quad \textbf{(3.45b)}$$

From (3.45a), we have

$$(z + 0.2)R_1(z) = 2U(z)$$

which can be represented by the block diagram shown in Figure 3.11(a). Likewise, (3.45b) may be represented by the block diagram shown in Figure 3.11(b).

Recalling that $Y(z) = R_1(z) - R_2(z)$, it is clear that the given system can be represented and then implemented by an obvious coupling of the two subsystems represented by (3.45a, b). The resulting z-transform block diagram is shown in Figure 3.11(c). The time-domain version is readily obtained by replacing the '$1/z$' blocks by D and the transforms $U(z)$ and $Y(z)$ by their corresponding sequences $\{u_k\}$ and $\{y_k\}$ respectively.

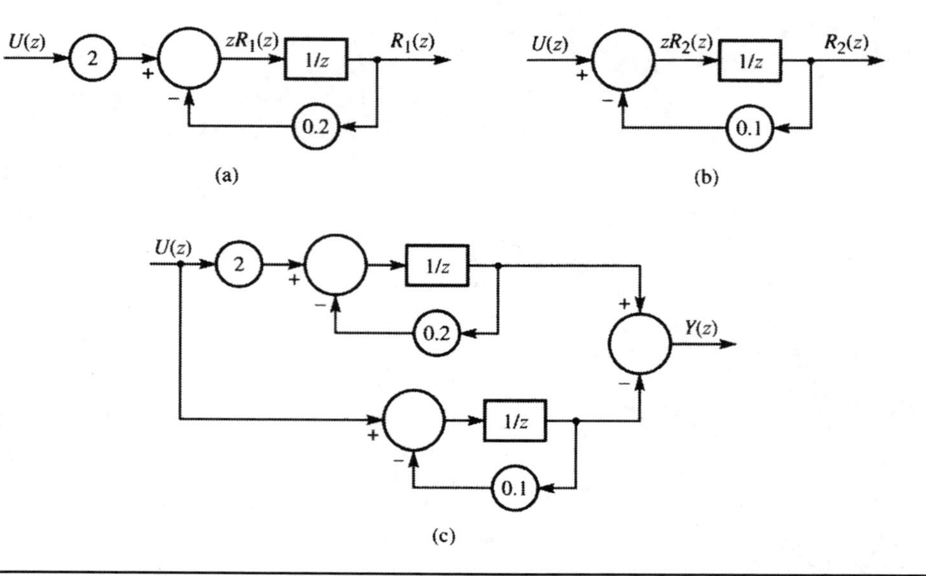

Figure 3.11 The block diagrams for (a) the subsystem (3.45a), (b) the subsystem (3.45b), and (c) an alternative z-transform block diagram for the system of Example 3.20.

3.6.2 The impulse response

In Example 3.20 we saw that two quite different realizations were possible for the same transfer function $G(z)$, and others are possible. Whichever realization of the transfer function is chosen, however, when presented with the same input sequence $\{u_k\}$, the same output sequence $\{y_k\}$ will be produced. Thus we identify the system as characterized by its transfer function as the key concept, rather than any particular implementation. This idea is reinforced when we consider the impulse response sequence for a discrete-time linear time-invariant system, and its role in convolution sums.

Consider the sequence

$$\{\delta_k\} = \{1, 0, 0, \dots\}$$

that is, the sequence consisting of a single 'pulse' at $k = 0$, followed by a train of zeros. As we saw in Section 3.2.1, the z transform of this sequence is easily found from the definition (3.1) as

$$\mathscr{Z}\{\delta_k\} = 1 \tag{3.46}$$

The sequence $\{\delta_k\}$ is called the **impulse sequence**, by analogy with the continuous-time counterpart $\delta(t)$, the impulse function. The analogy is perhaps clearer on considering the transformed version (3.46). In continuous-time analysis, using Laplace transform methods, we observed that $\mathscr{L}\{\delta(t)\} = 1$, and (3.46) shows that the 'entity' with z transform equal to unity is the sequence $\{\delta_k\}$. It is in fact the property that $\mathscr{Z}\{\delta_k\} = 1$ that makes the impulse sequence of such great importance.

Consider a system with transfer function $G(z)$, so that the z transform $Y(z)$ of the output sequence $\{y_k\}$ corresponding to an input sequence $\{u_k\}$ with z transform $U(z)$ is

$$Y(z) = G(z)U(z) \tag{3.47}$$

If the input sequence $\{y_k\}$ is the impulse sequence $\{\delta_k\}$ and the system is initially quiescent, then the output sequence $\{y_{\delta_k}\}$ is called the impulse response of the system. Hence

$$\mathscr{Z}\{y_{\delta_k}\} = Y_\delta(z) = G(z) \tag{3.48}$$

That is, the z transfer function of the system is the z transform of the impulse response. Alternatively, we can say that the impulse response of a system is the inverse z transform of the system transfer function. This compares with the definition of the impulse response for continuous systems given in Section 2.6.3.

Substituting (3.48) into (3.47), we have

$$Y(z) = Y_\delta(z)U(z) \tag{3.49}$$

Thus the z transform of the system output in response to any input sequence $\{u_k\}$ is the product of the transform of the input sequence with the transform of the system impulse response. The result (3.49) shows the underlying relationship between the concepts of impulse response and transfer function, and explains why the impulse response (or the transfer function) is thought of as characterizing a system. In simple terms, if either of these is known then we have all the information about the system for any analysis we may wish to do.

Example 3.21 Find the impulse response of the system with z transfer function

$$G(z) = \frac{z}{z^2 + 3z + 2}$$

Solution Using (3.48),

$$Y_\delta(z) = \frac{z}{z^2 + 3z + 2} = \frac{z}{(z+2)(z+1)}$$

Resolving $Y_\delta(z)/z$ into partial fractions gives

$$\frac{Y_\delta(z)}{z} = \frac{1}{(z+2)(z+1)} = \frac{1}{z+1} - \frac{1}{z+2}$$

which on inversion gives the impulse response sequence

$$\begin{aligned}\{Y_{\delta_k}\} &= \mathscr{Z}^{-1}\left[\frac{z}{z+1} - \frac{z}{z+2}\right] \\ &= \{(-1)^k - (-2)^k\} \quad (k \geqslant 0)\end{aligned}$$

Since the impulse response of a system is the inverse z transform of its transfer function $G(z)$ it can be obtained in MATLAB using the command

```
syms k z
iztrans(G(z),k)
```

so for the $G(z)$ of Example 3.21

```
syms k z
iztrans(z/(z^2+3*z+2),k)
```

returns

```
ans=(-1)^k-(-2)^k
```

A plot of the impulse response is obtained using the commands

```
z=tf('z',1);
G=G(z);
impulse(G)
```

Example 3.22 A system has the impulse response sequence

$$\{y_{\delta_k}\} = \{a^k - 0.5^k\}$$

where $a > 0$ is a real constant. What is the nature of this response when (a) $a = 0.4$, (b) $a = 1.2$? Find the step response of the system in both cases.

Solution When $a = 0.4$

$$\{y_{\delta_k}\} = \{0.4^k - 0.5^k\}$$

and, since both $0.4^k \to 0$ as $k \to \infty$ and $0.5^k \to 0$ as $k \to \infty$, we see that the terms of the impulse response sequence go to zero as $k \to \infty$.

On the other hand, when $a = 1.2$, since $(1.2)^k \to \infty$ as $k \to \infty$, we see that in this case the impulse response sequence terms become unbounded, implying that the system 'blows up'.

In order to calculate the step response, we first determine the system transfer function $G(z)$, using (3.48), as

$$G(z) = Y_\delta(z) = \mathscr{Z}\{a^k - 0.5^k\}$$

giving

$$G(z) = \frac{z}{z-a} - \frac{z}{z-0.5}$$

The system step response is the system response to the unit step sequence $\{h_k\} = \{1, 1, 1, \dots\}$ which, from Figure 3.3, has z transform

$$\mathscr{Z}\{h_k\} = \frac{z}{z-1}$$

Hence, from (3.46), the step response is determined by

$$Y(z) = G(z)\mathscr{Z}\{h_k\} = \left(\frac{z}{z-a} - \frac{z}{z-0.5}\right)\frac{z}{z-1}$$

so that

$$\frac{Y(z)}{z} = \frac{z}{(z-a)(z-1)} - \frac{z}{(z-0.5)(z-1)}$$

$$= \frac{a}{a-1}\frac{1}{z-a} - \frac{1}{z-0.5} + \left(-2 + \frac{1}{1-a}\right)\frac{1}{z-1}$$

giving

$$Y(z) = \frac{a}{a-1}\frac{z}{z-a} - \frac{z}{z-0.5} + \left(-2 + \frac{1}{1-a}\right)\frac{z}{z-1}$$

which on taking inverse transforms gives the step response as

$$\{y_k\} = \left\{\frac{a}{a-1}a^k - (0.5)^k + \left(-2 + \frac{1}{1-a}\right)\right\} \quad \textbf{(3.50)}$$

Considering the output sequence (3.50), we see that when $a = 0.4$, since $(0.4)^k \to 0$ as $k \to \infty$ (and $(0.5)^k \to 0$ as $k \to \infty$), the output sequence terms tend to the constant value

$$-2 + \frac{1}{1-0.4} = 0.3333$$

In the case of $a = 1.2$, since $(1.2)^k \to \infty$ as $k \to \infty$, the output sequence is unbounded, and again the system 'blows up'.

3.6.3 Stability

Example 3.22 illustrated the concept of system stability for discrete systems. When $a = 0.4$, the impulse response decayed to zero with increasing k, and we observed that the step response remained bounded (in fact, the terms of the sequence approached a constant limiting value). However, when $a = 1.2$, the impulse response became unbounded, and we observed that the step response also increased without limit. In fact, as we saw for continuous systems in Section 2.6.3, a linear constant-coefficient discrete-time system is stable provided that its impulse response goes to zero as $t \to \infty$. As for the continuous case, we can relate this definition to the poles of the system transfer function

$$G(z) = \frac{P(z)}{Q(z)}$$

As we saw in Section 3.6.1, the system poles are determined as the n roots of its characteristic equation

$$Q(z) = a_n z^n + a_{n-1} z^{n-1} + \ldots + a_0 = 0 \tag{3.51}$$

For instance, in Example 3.19 we considered a system with transfer function

$$G(z) = \frac{z - 1}{z^2 + 3z + 2}$$

having poles determined by $z^2 + 3z + 2 = 0$, that is poles at $z = -1$ and $z = -2$. Since the impulse response is the inverse transform of $G(z)$, we expect this system to 'blow up' or, rather, be unstable, because its impulse response sequence would be expected to contain terms of the form $(-1)^k$ and $(-2)^k$, neither of which goes to zero as $k \to \infty$. (Note that the term in $(-1)^k$ neither blows up nor goes to zero, simply alternating between $+1$ and -1; however, $(-2)^k$ certainly becomes unbounded as $k \to \infty$.) On the other hand, in Example 3.20 we encountered a system with transfer function

$$G(z) = \frac{z}{z^2 + 0.3z + 0.02}$$

having poles determined by

$$Q(z) = z^2 + 0.3z + 0.02 = (z + 0.2)(z + 0.1) = 0$$

that is poles at $z = -0.2$ and $z = -0.1$. Clearly, this system is stable, since its impulse response contains terms in $(-0.2)^k$ and $(-0.1)^k$, both of which go to zero as $k \to \infty$.

Both of these illustrative examples gave rise to characteristic polynomials $Q(z)$ that were quadratic in form and that had real coefficients. More generally, $Q(z) = 0$ gives rise to a polynomial equation of order n, with real coefficients. From the theory of polynomial equations, we know that $Q(z) = 0$ has n roots α_i $(i = 1, 2, \ldots, n)$, which may be real or complex (with complex roots occurring in conjugate pairs).

Hence the characteristic equation may be written in the form

$$Q(z) = a_n(z - \alpha_1)(z - \alpha_2) \ldots (z - \alpha_n) = 0 \tag{3.52}$$

The system poles α_i $(i = 1, 2, \ldots, n)$ determined by (3.52) may be expressed in the polar form

$$\alpha_i = r_i \, e^{j\theta_i} \quad (i = 1, 2, \ldots, n)$$

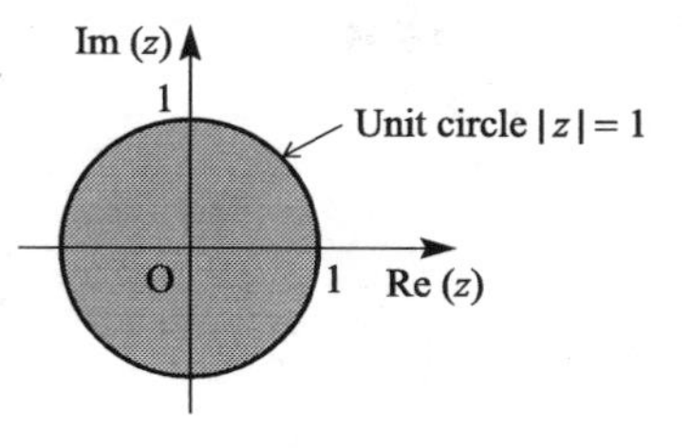

Figure 3.12 Region of stability in the z plane.

where $\theta_i = 0$ or π if α_i is real. From the interpretation of the impulse response as the inverse transform of the transfer function $G(z) = P(z)/Q(z)$, it follows that the impulse response sequence of the system will contain terms in

$$r_1^k\, e^{jk\theta_1},\ r_2^k\, e^{jk\theta_2},\ \ldots,\ r_n^k\, e^{jk\theta_n}$$

Since, for stability, terms in the impulse response sequence must tend to zero as $k \to \infty$, it follows that a system having characteristic equation $Q(z) = 0$ will be stable provided that

$$r_i < 1 \quad \text{for} \quad i = 1, 2, \ldots, n$$

Therefore a linear constant-coefficient discrete-time system with transfer function $G(z)$ is stable if and only if all the poles of $G(z)$ lie within the unit circle $|z| < 1$ in the complex z plane, as illustrated in Figure 3.12. If one or more poles lie outside this unit circle then the system will be unstable. If one or more distinct poles lie on the unit circle $|z| = 1$, with all the other poles inside, then the system is said to be **marginally stable**.

Example 3.23

Which of the following systems, specified by their transfer function $G(z)$, are stable?

(a) $G(z) = \dfrac{1}{z + 0.25}$ (b) $G(z) = \dfrac{z}{z^2 - z + 0.5}$ (c) $G(z) = \dfrac{z^2}{z^3 - 3z^2 + 2.5z - 1}$

Solution

(a) The single pole is at $z = -0.25$, so $r_1 = 0.25 < 1$, and the system is stable.

(b) The system poles are determined by

$$z^2 - z + 0.5 = [z - 0.5(1 + j)][z - 0.5(1 - j)] = 0$$

giving the poles as the conjugate pair $z_1 = 0.5(1 + j)$, $z_2 = 0.5(1 - j)$. The amplitudes $r_1 = r_2 = 0.707 < 1$, and again the system is stable.

(c) The system poles are determined by

$$z^3 - 3z^2 + 2.5z - 1 = (z - 2)[z - 0.5(1 + j)][z - 0.5(1 - j)]$$

giving the poles as $z_1 = 2$, $z_2 = 0.5(1 + j)$, $z_3 = 0.5(1 - j)$, and so their amplitudes are $r_1 = 2$, $r_2 = r_3 = 0.707$. Since $r_1 > 1$, it follows that the system is unstable.

Figure 3.13 Jury stability table for the polynomial equation (3.53).

Row	z^n	z^{n-1}	z^{n-2}	...	z^{n-k}	...	z^2	z^1	z^0
1	1	a_{n-1}	a_{n-2}	...	a_{n-k}	...	a_2	a_1	a_0
2	a_0	a_1	a_2	...	a_k	...	a_{n-2}	a_{n-1}	1
3	$\Delta_1 = b_0$	b_1	b_2	...	b_k	...	b_{n-2}	b_{n-1}	
4	b_{n-1}	b_{n-2}	b_{n-3}	...	b_{n-1-k}	...	b_1	b_0	
5	$\Delta_2 = c_0$	c_1	c_2	...	c_k	...	c_{n-2}		
6	c_{n-2}	c_{n-3}	c_{n-4}	...	c_{n-2-k}	...	c_0		
7	$\Delta_3 = d_0$	d_1	d_2	...	d_k	...			
8	d_{n-3}	d_{n-4}	d_{n-5}	...	d_{n-3-k}	...			
⋮									
⋮									
$2n-5$	$\Delta_{n-3} = s_0$	s_1	s_2	s_3					
$2n-4$	s_3	s_2	s_1	s_0					
$2n-3$	$\Delta_{n-2} = r_0$	r_1	r_2						
$2n-2$	r_2	r_1	r_0						
$2n-1$	$\Delta_{n-1} = t_0$								

According to our definition, it follows that to prove stability we must show that all the roots of the characteristic equation

$$Q(z) = z^n + a_{n-1}z^{n-1} + \ldots + a_0 = 0 \tag{3.53}$$

lie within the unit circle $|z| = 1$ (note that for convenience we have arranged for the coefficient of z^n to be unity in (3.53)). Many mathematical criteria have been developed to test for this property. One such method, widely used in practice, is the **Jury stability criterion** introduced by E. I. Jury in 1963. This procedure gives necessary and sufficient conditions for the polynomial equation (3.53) to have all its roots inside the unit circle $|z| = 1$.

The first step in the procedure is to set up a table as in Figure 3.13 using information from the given polynomial equation (3.53) and where

$$b_k = \begin{vmatrix} 1 & a_k \\ a_0 & a_{n-k} \end{vmatrix}, \quad c_k = \begin{vmatrix} b_0 & b_{n-1-k} \\ b_{n-1} & b_k \end{vmatrix}, \quad d_k = \begin{vmatrix} c_0 & c_{n-2-k} \\ c_{n-2} & c_k \end{vmatrix}, \quad \ldots,$$

$$t_0 = \begin{vmatrix} r_0 & r_2 \\ r_2 & r_0 \end{vmatrix}$$

Note that the elements of row $2j + 2$ consist of the elements of row $2j + 1$ written in the reverse order for $j = 0, 1, 2, \ldots, n$; that is, the elements of the even rows consist of the elements of the odd rows written in reverse order. Necessary and sufficient conditions for the polynomial equation (3.53) to have all its roots inside the unit circle $|z| = 1$ are then given by

$$\begin{aligned} &\text{(i)} \quad Q(1) > 0, \quad (-1)^n Q(-1) > 0 \\ &\text{(ii)} \quad \Delta_1 > 0, \quad \Delta_2 > 0, \quad \Delta_3 > 0, \quad \ldots, \quad \Delta_{n-2} > 0, \quad \Delta_{n-1} > 0 \end{aligned} \tag{3.54}$$

Example 3.24

Show that all the roots of the polynomial equation

$$F(z) = z^3 + \tfrac{1}{3}z^2 - \tfrac{1}{4}z - \tfrac{1}{12} = 0$$

lie within the unit circle $|z| = 1$.

Figure 3.14 Jury stability table for Example 3.24.

Row	z^3	z^2	z^1	z^0
1	1	$\frac{1}{3}$	$-\frac{1}{4}$	$-\frac{1}{12}$
2	$-\frac{1}{12}$	$-\frac{1}{4}$	$\frac{1}{3}$	1
3	$\Delta_1 = \begin{vmatrix} 1 & -\frac{1}{12} \\ -\frac{1}{12} & 1 \end{vmatrix} = \frac{143}{144}$	$\begin{vmatrix} 1 & -\frac{1}{4} \\ -\frac{1}{12} & \frac{1}{3} \end{vmatrix} = \frac{5}{16}$	$\begin{vmatrix} 1 & \frac{1}{3} \\ -\frac{1}{12} & -\frac{1}{4} \end{vmatrix} = -\frac{2}{9}$	
4	$-\frac{2}{9}$	$\frac{5}{16}$	$\frac{143}{144}$	
5	$\Delta_2 = \begin{vmatrix} \frac{143}{144} & -\frac{2}{9} \\ -\frac{2}{9} & \frac{143}{144} \end{vmatrix} = 0.936\,78$			

Solution The corresponding Jury stability table is shown in Figure 3.14. In this case

(i) $F(1) = 1 + \frac{1}{3} - \frac{1}{4} - \frac{1}{12} > 0$

$(-1)^n F(-1) = (-1)^3(-1 + \frac{1}{3} + \frac{1}{4} - \frac{1}{12}) > 0$

(ii) $\Delta_1 = \frac{143}{144} > 0, \quad \Delta_2 = (\frac{143}{144})^2 - \frac{4}{81} > 0$

Thus, by the criteria (3.54), all the roots lie within the unit circle. In this case this is readily confirmed, since the polynomial $F(z)$ may be factorized as

$$F(z) = (z - \tfrac{1}{2})(z + \tfrac{1}{2})(z + \tfrac{1}{3}) = 0$$

So the roots are $z_1 = \frac{1}{2}$, $z_2 = -\frac{1}{2}$ and $z_3 = -\frac{1}{3}$.

The Jury stability table may also be used to determine how many roots of the polynomial equation (3.53) lie outside the unit circle. The number of such roots is determined by the number of changes in sign in the sequence

$$1, \quad \Delta_1, \quad \Delta_2, \quad \ldots, \quad \Delta_{n-1}$$

Example 3.25

Show that the polynomial equation

$$F(z) = z^3 - 3z^2 - \tfrac{1}{4}z + \tfrac{3}{4} = 0$$

has roots that lie outside the unit circle $|z| = 1$. Determine how many such roots there are.

Figure 3.15 Jury stability table for Example 3.25.

Row	z^3	z^2	z^1	z^0
1	1	-3	$-\frac{1}{4}$	$\frac{3}{4}$
2	$\frac{3}{4}$	$-\frac{1}{4}$	-3	1
3	$\Delta_1 = \frac{7}{16}$	$-\frac{45}{16}$	2	
4	2	$-\frac{45}{16}$	$\frac{7}{16}$	
5	$\Delta_2 = -\frac{5}{16}$			

Solution The corresponding Jury stability table is shown in Figure 3.15. Hence, in this case

$$F(z) = 1 - 3 - \tfrac{1}{4} + \tfrac{3}{4} = -\tfrac{3}{2}$$

$$(-1)^n F(-1) = (-1)^3(-1 - 3 + \tfrac{1}{4} + \tfrac{3}{4}) = 3$$

As $F(1) < 0$, it follows from (3.54) that the polynomial equation has roots outside the unit circle $|z| = 1$. From Figure 3.15, the sequence $1, \Delta_1, \Delta_2$ is $1, \frac{7}{16}, -\frac{15}{16}$, and since there is only one sign change in the sequence, it follows that one root lies outside the unit circle. Again this is readily confirmed, since $F(z)$ may be factorized as

$$F(z) = (z - \tfrac{1}{2})(z + \tfrac{1}{2})(z - 3) = 0$$

showing that there is indeed one root outside the unit circle at $z = 3$.

3.6.4 Convolution

Here we shall briefly extend the concept of convolution introduced in Section 2.6.6 to discrete-time systems. From (3.45), for an initially quiescent system with an impulse response sequence $\{y_{\delta_k}\}$ with z transform $Y_\delta(z)$, the z transform $Y(z)$ of the output sequence $\{y_k\}$ in response to an input sequence $\{u_k\}$ with z transform $U(z)$ is given by

$$Y(z) = Y_\delta(z)U(z) \tag{3.49}$$

For the purposes of solving a particular problem, the best approach to determining $\{y_k\}$ for a given $\{u_k\}$ is to invert the right-hand side of (3.49) as an ordinary z transform with no particular thought as to its structure. However, to understand more of the theory of linear systems in discrete time, it is worth exploring the general situation a little further. To do this, we revert to the time domain.

Suppose that a linear discrete-time time-invariant system has impulse response sequence $\{y_{\delta_k}\}$, and suppose that we wish to find the system response $\{y_k\}$ to an input sequence $\{u_k\}$, with the system initially in a quiescent state. First we express the input sequence

$$\{u_k\} = \{u_0, u_1, u_2, \ldots u_n, \ldots\} \tag{3.55}$$

as

$$\{u_k\} = u_0\{\delta_k\} + u_1\{\delta_{k-1}\} + u_2\{\delta_{k-2}\} + \ldots + u_n\{\delta_{k-n}\} + \ldots \tag{3.56}$$

where

$$\delta_{k-j} = \begin{cases} 0 & (k \neq j) \\ 1 & (k = j) \end{cases}$$

In other words, $\{\delta_{k-j}\}$ is simply an impulse sequence with the pulse shifted to $k = j$. Thus, in going from (3.55) to (3.56), we have decomposed the input sequence $\{u_k\}$ into a weighted sum of shifted impulse sequences. Under the assumption of an initially quiescent system, linearity allows us to express the response $\{y_k\}$ to the input sequence $\{u_k\}$ as the appropriately weighted sum of shifted impulse responses. Thus, since the impulse response is $\{y_{\delta_k}\}$, the response to the shifted impulse sequence $\{\delta_{k-j}\}$ will be $\{y_{\delta_{k-j}}\}$, and the response to the weighted impulse sequence $u_j\{\delta_{k-j}\}$ will be simply $u_j\{y_{\delta_{k-j}}\}$. Summing the contributions from all the sequences in (3.56), we obtain

$$\{y_k\} = \sum_{j=0}^{\infty} u_j\{y_{\delta_{k-j}}\} \tag{3.57}$$

as the response of the system to the input sequence $\{u_k\}$. Expanding (3.57), we have

$$\begin{aligned}
\{y_k\} &= u_0\{y_{\delta_k}\} + u_1\{y_{\delta_{k-1}}\} + \ldots + u_j\{y_{\delta_{k-j}}\} + \ldots \\
&= u_0\{y_{\delta_0},\ y_{\delta_1},\ y_{\delta_2}, \ldots,\quad y_{\delta_h},\ \ldots\} \\
&\quad + u_1\{0,\ y_{\delta_0},\ y_{\delta_1}, \ldots,\quad y_{\delta_{h-1}}, \ldots\} \\
&\quad + u_2\{0,\ 0,\ y_{\delta_0}, \ldots,\quad y_{\delta_{h-2}}, \ldots\} \\
&\quad \vdots \\
&\quad + u_h\{0,\ 0,\ 0,\ \ldots, 0,\ \underset{\substack{\uparrow \\ h\text{th position}}}{y_{\delta_0}},\ y_{\delta_1}, \ldots\} \\
&\quad + \ldots
\end{aligned}$$

From this expansion, we find that the hth term of the output sequence is determined by

$$y_h = \sum_{j=0}^{h} u_j y_{\delta_{h-j}} \tag{3.58}$$

That is,

$$\{y_k\} = \left\{\sum_{j=0}^{k} u_j y_{\delta_{k-j}}\right\} \tag{3.59}$$

The expression (3.58) is called the **convolution sum**, and the result (3.59) is analogous to (2.83) for continuous systems.

Example 3.26

A system has z transfer function

$$G(z) = \frac{z}{z + \frac{1}{2}}$$

What is the system step response? Verify the result using (3.59).

Solution From (3.46), the system step response is

$$Y(z) = G(z)\mathscr{Z}\{h_k\}$$

where $\{h_k\} = \{1, 1, 1, \dots\}$. From Figure 3.3, $\mathscr{Z}\{h_k\} = z/(z-1)$, so

$$Y(z) = \frac{z}{z+\frac{1}{2}}\frac{z}{z-1}$$

Resolving $Y(z)/z$ into partial fractions gives

$$\frac{Y(z)}{z} = \frac{z}{(z+\frac{1}{2})(z-1)} = \frac{2}{3}\frac{1}{z-1} + \frac{1}{3}\frac{1}{z+\frac{1}{2}}$$

so

$$Y(z) = \frac{2}{3}\frac{z}{z-1} + \frac{1}{3}\frac{z}{z+\frac{1}{2}}$$

Taking inverse transforms then gives the step response as

$$\{y_k\} = \{\tfrac{2}{3} + \tfrac{1}{3}(-\tfrac{1}{2})^k\}$$

Using (3.59), we first have to find the impulse response, which, from (3.48), is given by

$$\{y_{\delta_k}\} = \mathscr{Z}^{-1}[G(z)] = \mathscr{Z}^{-1}\left[\frac{z}{z+\frac{1}{2}}\right]$$

so that

$$\{y_{\delta_k}\} = \{(-\tfrac{1}{2})^k\}$$

Taking $\{u_k\}$ to be the unit step sequence $\{h_k\}$, where $h_k = 1$ $(k \geqslant 0)$, the step response may then be determined from (3.59) as

$$\{y_k\} = \left\{\sum_{j=0}^{k} u_j y_{\delta_{k-j}}\right\} = \left\{\sum_{j=0}^{k} 1 \cdot (-\tfrac{1}{2})^{k-j}\right\}$$

$$= \left\{(-\tfrac{1}{2})^k \sum_{j=0}^{k} (-\tfrac{1}{2})^{-j}\right\} = \left\{(-\tfrac{1}{2})^k \sum_{j=0}^{k} (-2)^j\right\}$$

Recognizing the sum as the sum to $k+1$ terms of a geometric series with common ratio -2, we have

$$\{y_k\} = \left\{(-\tfrac{1}{2})^k \frac{1-(-2)^{k+1}}{1-(-2)}\right\} = \{\tfrac{1}{3}((-\tfrac{1}{2})^k + 2)\} = \{\tfrac{2}{3} + \tfrac{1}{3}(-\tfrac{1}{2})^k\}$$

which concurs with the sequence obtained by direct evaluation.

Example 3.26 reinforces the remark made earlier that the easiest approach to obtaining the response is by direct inversion of (3.32). However, (3.59), together with the argument leading to it, provides a great deal of insight into the way in which the response sequence $\{y_k\}$ is generated. It also serves as a useful 'closed form' for the output of the system, and readers should consult specialist texts on signals and systems for a full discussion (P. Kraniauskas, *Transforms in Signals and Systems*, Addison-Wesley, Wokingham, 1992).

The astute reader will recall that we commenced this section by suggesting that we were about to study the implications of the input–output relationship (3.49), namely

$$Y(z) = Y_\delta(z)U(z)$$

We have in fact explored the time-domain input–output relationship for a linear system, and we now proceed to link this approach with our work in the transform domain. By definition,

$$U(z) = \sum_{k=0}^{\infty} u_k z^{-k} = u_0 + \frac{u_1}{z} + \frac{u_2}{z^2} + \ldots + \frac{u_k}{z^k} + \ldots$$

$$Y_\delta(z) = \sum_{k=0}^{\infty} y_{\delta_k} z^{-k} = y_{\delta_0} + \frac{y_{\delta_1}}{z} + \frac{y_{\delta_2}}{z^2} + \ldots + \frac{y_{\delta_k}}{z^k} + \ldots$$

so

$$Y_\delta(z)U(z) = u_0 y_{\delta_0} + (u_0 y_{\delta_1} + u_1 y_{\delta_0})\frac{1}{z} + (u_0 y_{\delta_2} + u_1 y_{\delta_1} + u_2 y_{\delta_0})\frac{1}{z^2} + \ldots \tag{3.60}$$

Considering the kth term of (3.60), we see that the coefficient of z^{-k} is simply

$$\sum_{j=0}^{k} u_j y_{\delta_{k-j}}$$

However, by definition, since $Y(z) = Y_\delta(z)U(z)$, this is also $y(k)$, the kth term of the output sequence, so that the latter is

$$\{y_k\} = \left\{\sum_{j=0}^{k} u_j y_{\delta_{k-j}}\right\}$$

as found in (3.59). We have thus shown that the time-domain and transform-domain approaches are equivalent, and, in passing, we have established the z transform of the convolution sum as

$$\mathscr{Z}\left\{\sum_{j=0}^{k} u_j v_{k-j}\right\} = U(z)V(z) \tag{3.61}$$

where

$$\mathscr{Z}\{u_k\} = U(z), \quad \mathscr{Z}\{v_k\} = V(z)$$

Putting $p = k - j$ in (3.61) shows that

$$\sum_{j=0}^{k} u_j v_{k-j} = \sum_{p=0}^{k} u_{k-p} v_p \tag{3.62}$$

confirming that the convolution process is commutative.

3.6.5 Exercises

21 Find the transfer functions of each of the following discrete-time systems, given that the system is initially in a quiescent state:

(a) $y_{k+2} - 3y_{k+1} + 2y_k = u_k$

(b) $y_{k+2} - 3y_{k+1} + 2y_k = u_{k+1} - u_k$

(c) $y_{k+3} - y_{k+2} + 2y_{k+1} + y_k = u_k + u_{k-1}$

22 Draw a block diagram representing the discrete-time system

$$y_{k+2} + 0.5y_{k+1} + 0.25y_k = u_k$$

Hence find a block diagram representation of the system

$$y_{k+2} + 0.5y_{k+1} + 0.25y_k = u_k - 0.6u_{k+1}$$

23 Find the impulse response for the systems with z transfer function

(a) $\dfrac{z}{8z^2 + 6z + 1}$ (b) $\dfrac{z^2}{z^2 - 3z + 3}$

(c) $\dfrac{z^2}{z^2 - 0.2z - 0.08}$ (d) $\dfrac{5z^2 - 12z}{z^2 - 6z + 8}$

24 Obtain the impulse response for the systems of Exercises 21(a, b).

25 Which of the following systems are stable?

(a) $9y_{k+2} + 9y_{k+1} + 2y_k = u_k$

(b) $9y_{k+2} - 3y_{k+1} - 2y_k = u_k$

(c) $2y_{k+2} - 2y_{k+1} + y_k = u_{k+1} - u_k$

(d) $2y_{k+2} + 3y_{k+1} - y_k = u_k$

(e) $4y_{k+2} - 3y_{k+1} - y_k = u_{k+1} - 2u_k$

26 Use the method of Example 3.26 to calculate the step response of the system with transfer function

$$\frac{z}{z - \frac{1}{2}}$$

Verify the result by direct calculation.

27 A sampled data system described by the difference equation

$$y_{n+1} - y_n = u_n$$

is controlled by making the input u_n proportional to the previous error according to

$$u_n = K\left(\frac{1}{2^n} - y_{n-1}\right)$$

where K is a positive gain. Determine the range of values of K for which the system is stable. Taking $K = \frac{2}{9}$, determine the response of the system given $y_0 = y_1 = 0$.

28 Show that the system

$$y_{n+2} + 2y_{n+1} + 2y_n = u_{n+1} \quad (n \geq 0)$$

has transfer function

$$D(z) = \frac{z}{z^2 + 2z + 2}$$

Show that the poles of the system are at $z = -1 + \mathrm{j}$ and $z = -1 - \mathrm{j}$. Hence show that the impulse response of the system is given by

$$h_n = \mathscr{Z}^{-1}D(z) = 2^{n/2} \sin \tfrac{3}{4} n\pi$$

3.7 The relationship between Laplace and z transforms

Throughout this chapter we have attempted to highlight similarities, where they occur, between results in Laplace transform theory and those for z transforms. In this section we take a closer look at the relationship between the two transforms. In Section 3.2.2 we introduced the idea of sampling a continuous-time signal $f(t)$ instantaneously at uniform intervals T to produce the sequence

$$\{f(nT)\} = \{f(0), f(T), f(2T), \ldots, f(nT), \ldots\} \tag{3.63}$$

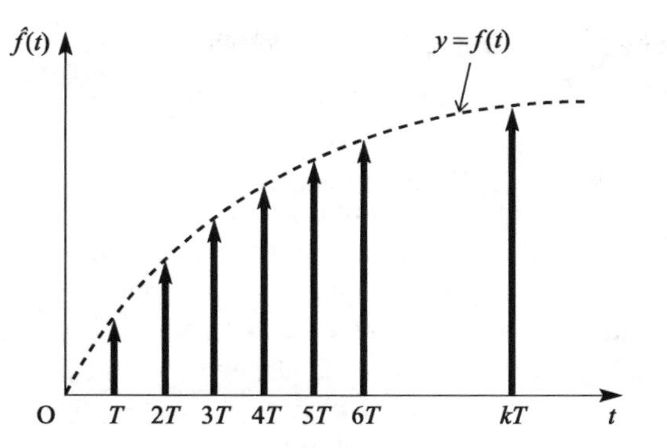

Figure 3.16 Sampled function $f(t)$.

An alternative way of representing the sampled function is to define the continuous-time sampled version of $f(t)$ as $\hat{f}(t)$ where

$$\hat{f}(t) = \sum_{n=0}^{\infty} f(t)\delta(t - nT) = \sum_{n=0}^{\infty} f(nT)\delta(t - nT) \tag{3.64}$$

The representation (3.64) may be interpreted as defining a row of impulses located at the sampling points and weighted by the appropriate sampled values (as illustrated in Figure 3.16). Taking the Laplace transform of $\hat{f}(t)$, following the results of Section 2.5.10, we have

$$\mathscr{L}\{\hat{f}(t)\} = \int_{0^-}^{\infty} \left[\sum_{k=0}^{\infty} f(kT)\delta(t - kT)\right] e^{-st}\, dt$$

$$= \sum_{k=0}^{\infty} f(kT) \int_{0^-}^{\infty} \delta(t - kT)\, e^{-st}\, dt$$

giving

$$\mathscr{L}\{\hat{f}(t)\} = \sum_{k=0}^{\infty} f(kT)\, e^{-ksT} \tag{3.65}$$

Making the change of variable $z = e^{sT}$ in (3.65) leads to the result

$$\mathscr{L}\{\hat{f}(t)\} = \sum_{k=0}^{\infty} f(kT)\, z^{-k} = F(z) \tag{3.66}$$

where, as in (3.10), $F(z)$ denotes the z transform of the sequence $\{f(kT)\}$. We can therefore view the z transform of a sequence of samples in discrete time as the Laplace transform of the continuous-time sampled function $\hat{f}(t)$ with an appropriate change of variable

$$z = e^{sT} \quad \text{or} \quad s = \frac{1}{T} \ln z$$

In Chapter 1 we saw that under this transformation the left half of the s plane, $\text{Re}(s) < 0$, is mapped onto the region inside the unit circle in the z plane, $|z| < 1$. This is consistent with our stability criteria in the s and z domains.

3.8 Engineering application: design of discrete-time systems

An important development in many areas of modern engineering is the replacement of analogue devices by digital ones. Perhaps the most widely known example is the compact disc player, in which mechanical transcription followed by analogue signal processing has been superseded by optical technology and digital signal processing. Also, as stated in the introduction, DVD players and digital radios are setting new standards in home entertainment. There are other examples in many fields of engineering, particularly where automatic control is employed.

3.8.1 Analogue filters

At the centre of most signal processing applications are **filters**. These have the effect of changing the spectrum of input signals; that is, attenuating components of signals by an amount depending on the frequency of the component. For example, an analogue **ideal low-pass filter** passes without attenuation all signal components at frequencies less than a critical frequency $\omega = \omega_c$ say. The amplitude of the frequency response $|G(j\omega)|$ (see Section 2.7) of such an ideal filter is shown in Figure 3.17.

One class of analogue filters whose frequency response approximates that of the ideal low-pass filter comprises those known as **Butterworth filters**. As well as having 'good' characteristics, these can be implemented using a network as illustrated in Figure 3.18 for the second-order filter.

It can be shown (see M. J. Chapman, D. P. Goodall and N. C. Steele, *Signal Processing in Electronic Communication*, Horwood Publishing, Chichester, 1997) that the transfer function $G_n(s)$ of the nth-order filter is

$$G_n(s) = \frac{1}{B_n(x)} \quad \text{where} \quad B_n(x) = \sum_{k=0}^{n} a_k x^k$$

with

$$x = \frac{s}{\omega_c}, \qquad a_k = \prod_{r=1}^{k} \frac{\cos(r-1)\alpha}{\sin r\alpha}, \qquad \alpha = \frac{\pi}{2n}$$

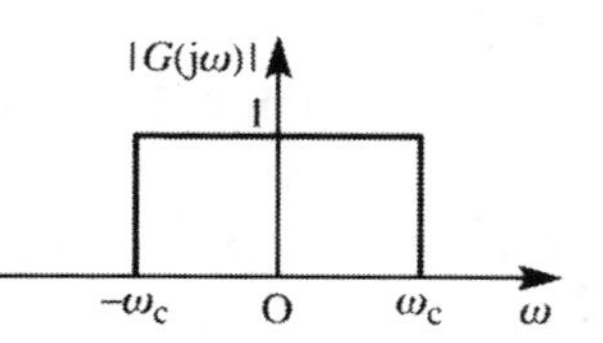

Figure 3.17 Amplitude response for an ideal low-pass filter.

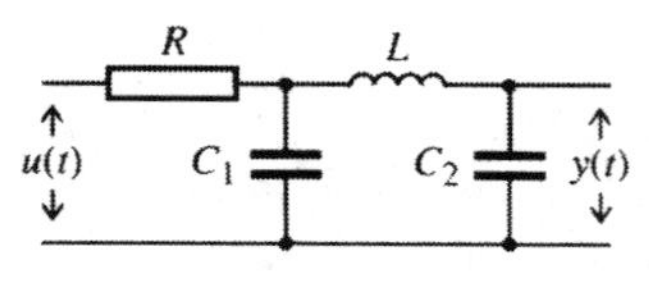

Figure 3.18 *LCR* network for implementing a second-order Butterworth filter.

Using these relations, it is readily shown that

$$G_2(s) = \frac{\omega_c^2}{s^2 + \sqrt{2}\omega_c s + \omega_c^2} \tag{3.67}$$

$$G_3(s) = \frac{\omega_c^3}{s^3 + 2\omega_c s^2 + 2\omega_c^2 s + \omega_c^3} \tag{3.68}$$

and so on. On sketching the amplitudes of the frequency responses $G_n(j\omega)$, it becomes apparent that increasing n improves the approximation to the response of the ideal low-pass filter of Figure 3.17.

3.8.2 Designing a digital replacement filter

Suppose that we now wish to design a discrete-time system, to operate on samples taken from an input signal, that will operate in a similar manner to a Butterworth filter. We shall assume that the input signal $u(t)$ and the output signal $y(t)$ of the analogue filter are both sampled at the same intervals T to generate the input sequence $\{u(kT)\}$ and the output sequence $\{y(kT)\}$ respectively. Clearly, we need to specify what is meant by 'operate in a similar manner'. In this case, we shall select as our design strategy a method that matches the impulse response sequence of the digital design with a sequence of samples, drawn at the appropriate instants T from the impulse response of an analogue 'prototype'. We shall select the prototype from one of the Butterworth filters discussed in Section 3.8.1, although there are many other possibilities.

Let us select the first-order filter, with cut-off frequency ω_c, as our prototype. Then the first step is to calculate the impulse response of this filter. The Laplace transfer function of the filter is

$$G(s) = \frac{\omega_c}{s + \omega_c}$$

So, from (2.71), the impulse response is readily obtained as

$$h(t) = \omega_c e^{-\omega_c T} \quad (t \geq 0) \tag{3.69}$$

Next, we sample this response at intervals T to generate the sequence

$$\{h(kT)\} = \{\omega_c e^{-\omega_c kT}\}$$

which on taking the z transform, gives

$$\mathscr{Z}\{h(kT)\} = H(z) = \omega_c \frac{z}{z - e^{-\omega_c T}}$$

Finally, we choose $H(z)$ to be the transfer function of our digital system. This means simply that the input–output relationship for the design of the digital system will be

$$Y(z) = H(z)U(z)$$

where $Y(z)$ and $U(z)$ are the z transforms of the output and input sequences $\{y(kT)\}$ and $\{u(kT)\}$ respectively. Thus we have

$$Y(z) = \omega_c \frac{z}{z - e^{-\omega_c T}} U(z) \tag{3.70}$$

Our digital system is now defined, and we can easily construct the corresponding difference equation model of the system as

$$(z - e^{-\omega_c T})Y(z) = \omega_c z U(z)$$

that is

$$zY(z) - e^{-\omega_c T} Y(z) = \omega_c z U(z)$$

Under the assumption of zero initial conditions, we can take inverse transforms to obtain the first-order difference equation model

$$y(k + 1) - e^{-\omega_c T} y(k) = \omega_c u(k + 1) \tag{3.71}$$

A block diagram implementation of (3.71) is shown in Figure 3.19.

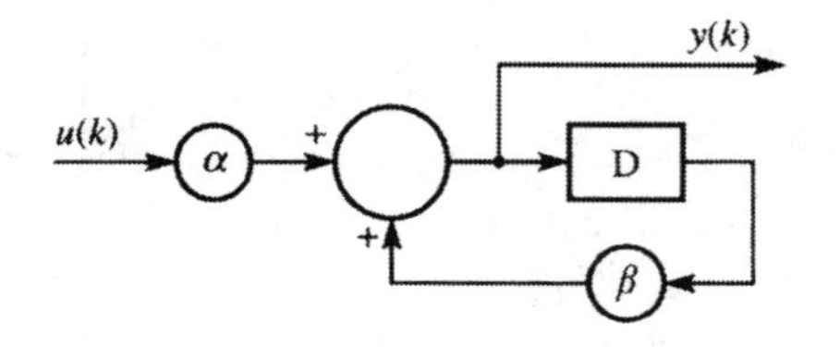

Figure 3.19 Block diagram for the digital replacement filter, $\alpha = k\omega_c$, $\beta = e^{-\omega_c t}$.

3.8.3 Possible developments

The design method we have considered is called the **impulse invariant technique**, and is only one of many available. The interested reader may develop this study in various ways:

(1) Write a computer program to evaluate the sequence generated by (3.71) with $\omega_c = 1$, and compare with values obtained at the sampling instants for the impulse response (3.69) of the prototype analogue filter.

(2) Repeat the design process for the second-order Butterworth filter.

(3) By setting $s = j\omega$ in the Laplace transfer function of the prototype, and $z = e^{j\omega T}$ in the z transfer function of the digital design, compare the amplitude of the frequency responses in both cases. For an explanation of the results obtained, see Chapter 5.

(4) An alternative design strategy is to replace s in the Laplace transfer function with

$$\frac{2}{T}\frac{z - 1}{z + 1}$$

(this is a process that makes use of the trapezoidal method of approximate integration). Design alternative digital filters using this technique.

(5) Show that filters designed using either of these techniques will be stable provided that the prototype design is itself stable.

3.9 Engineering application: the delta operator and the $\mathscr{D}$ transform

3.9.1 Introduction

In recent years, sampling rates for digital systems have increased many-fold, and traditional model formulations based on the z transform have produced unsatisfactory results in some applications. It is beyond the scope of this text to describe this situation in detail, but it is possible to give a brief introduction to the problem and to suggest an approach to the solution. For further details see R. M. Middleton and G. C. Goodwin, *Digital Control and Estimation, A Unified Approach* (Prentice Hall, Englewood Cliffs, NJ, 1990) or W. Forsythe and R. M. Goodall, *Digital Control* (Macmillan, London, 1991). The contribution of Colin Paterson to the development of this application is gratefully acknowledged.

3.9.2 The q or shift operator and the δ operator

In the time domain we define the shift operator q in terms of its effect on a sequence $\{x_k\}$ as

$$\mathrm{q}\{x_k\} = \{x_{k+1}\}$$

That is, the effect of the shift operator is to shift the sequence by one position, so that the kth term of the new sequence is the $(k+1)$th term of the original sequence. It is then possible to write the difference equation

$$y_{k+2} + 2y_{k+1} + 5y_k = u_{k+1} - u_k$$

as

$$\mathrm{q}^2 y_k + 2\mathrm{q}\,y_k + 5y_k = \mathrm{q}u_k - u_k$$

or

$$(\mathrm{q}^2 + 2\mathrm{q} + 5)y_k = (\mathrm{q} - 1)u_k \tag{3.72}$$

Note that if we had taken the z transform of the difference equation, with an initially quiescent system, we would have obtained

$$(z^2 + 2z + 5)Y(z) = (z - 1)U(z)$$

We see at once the correspondence between the time-domain q operator and the z-transform operator $\mathscr{Z}$.

The next step is to introduce the δ operator, defined as

$$\delta = \frac{\mathrm{q} - 1}{\Delta}$$

where Δ has the dimensions of time and is often chosen as the sampling period T. Note that

$$\delta y_k = \frac{(\mathrm{q} - 1)y_k}{\Delta} = \frac{y_{k+1} - y_k}{\Delta}$$

so that if $\Delta = T$ then, in the limit of rapid sampling,

$$\delta y_k \simeq \frac{\mathrm{d}y}{\mathrm{d}t}$$

Solving for q we see that

$$\mathrm{q} = 1 + \Delta\delta$$

The difference equation (3.72) can thus be written as

$$((1 + \Delta\delta)^2 + 2(1 + \Delta\delta) + 5)y_k = [(1 + \Delta\delta) - 1]u_k$$

or

$$[(\Delta\delta)^2 + 4\Delta\delta + 8]y_k = \Delta\delta u_k$$

or, finally, as

$$\left(\delta^2 + \frac{4\delta}{\Delta} + \frac{8}{\Delta^2}\right)y_k = \frac{\delta}{\Delta}u_k$$

3.9.3 Constructing a discrete-time system model

So far, we have simply demonstrated a method of rewriting a difference equation in an alternative form. We now examine the possible advantages of constructing discrete-time system models using the δ operator. To do this, we consider a particular example, in which we obtain two different discrete-time forms of the second-order Butterworth filter, both based on the bilinear transform method, sometimes known as **Tustin's method**. This method has its origins in the trapezoidal approximation to the integration process; full details are given in M. J. Chapman, D. P. Goodall and N. C. Steele, *Signal Processing in Electronic Communication* (Horwood Publishing, Chichester, 1997).

The continuous-time second-order Butterworth filter with cut-off frequency $\omega_c = 1$ is modelled, as indicated by (3.67), by the differential equation

$$\frac{\mathrm{d}^2y}{\mathrm{d}t^2} + 1.414\,21\frac{\mathrm{d}y}{\mathrm{d}t} + y = u(t) \quad \textbf{(3.73)}$$

where $u(t)$ is the input and $y(t)$ the filter response. Taking Laplace transforms throughout on the assumption of quiescent initial conditions, that is $y(0) = (\mathrm{d}y/\mathrm{d}t)(0) = 0$, we obtain the transformed equation

$$(s^2 + 1.414\,21s + 1)Y(s) = U(s) \quad \textbf{(3.74)}$$

This represents a stable system, since the system poles, given by

$$s^2 + 1.414\,21s + 1 = 0$$

are located at $s = -0.707\,10 \pm \mathrm{j}0.707\,10$ and thus lie in the left half-plane of the complex s plane.

We now seek a discrete-time version of the differential equation (3.73). To do this, we first transform (3.74) into the z domain using the **bilinear transform method**, which involves replacing s by

$$\frac{2}{T}\frac{z-1}{z+1}$$

Equation (3.74) then becomes

$$\left[\frac{4}{T^2}\left(\frac{z-1}{z+1}\right)^2 + 1.414\,21\frac{2}{T}\left(\frac{z-1}{z+1}\right) + 1\right]Y(z) = U(z)$$

or

$$[(\tfrac{1}{4}T^2 + 1.414\,21 \times \tfrac{1}{2}T + 4)z^2 + (\tfrac{1}{2}T^2 - 8)z + \tfrac{1}{4}T^2 - 1.414\,21 \times \tfrac{1}{2}T + 4]Y(z)$$
$$= \tfrac{1}{4}T^2(z^2 + 2z + 1)U(z) \tag{3.75}$$

We can now invert this transformed equation to obtain the time-domain model

$$(\tfrac{1}{4}T^2 + 1.414\,21 \times \tfrac{1}{2}T + 4)y_{k+2} + (\tfrac{1}{2}T^2 - 8)y_{k+1} + (\tfrac{1}{4}T^2 - 1.414\,21 \times \tfrac{1}{2}T + 4)y_k$$
$$= \tfrac{1}{4}T^2(u_{k+2} + 2u_{k+1} + u_k) \tag{3.76}$$

For illustrative purposes we set $T = 0.1$ s in (3.76) to obtain

$$4.073\,21y_{k+2} - 7.995\,00y_{k+1} + 3.931\,79y_k = 0.025\,00(u_{k+2} + 2u_{k+1} + u_k)$$

Note that the roots of the characteristic equation have modulus of about 0.9825, and are thus quite close to the stability boundary.

When $T = 0.01$ s, (3.76) becomes

$$4.007\,10y_{k+2} - 7.999\,95y_{k+1} + 3.992\,95y_k = 0.000\,03(u_{k+2} + 2u_{k+1} + u_k)$$

In this case the roots have modulus of about 0.9982, and we see that increasing the sampling rate has moved them even closer to the stability boundary, and that *high accuracy in the coefficients is essential*, thus adding to the expense of implementation.

An alternative method of proceeding is to avoid the intermediate stage of obtaining the z-domain model (3.75) and to proceed directly to a discrete-time representation from (3.73), using the transformation

$$s \to \frac{2}{T}\frac{\text{q}-1}{\text{q}+1}$$

leading to the same result as in (3.76). Using the δ operator instead of the shift operator q, noting that $\text{q} = 1 + \Delta\delta$, we make the transformation

$$s \to \frac{2}{T}\frac{\Delta\delta}{2+\Delta\delta}$$

or, if $T = \Delta$, the transformation

$$s \to \frac{2\delta}{2+\Delta\delta}$$

in (3.74), which becomes

$$[\delta^2 + 1.414\,21 \times \tfrac{1}{2}\delta(2 + \Delta\delta) + \tfrac{1}{4}(2 + \Delta\delta)^2]y_k = \tfrac{1}{4}(2 + \Delta\delta)^2 u_k$$

Note that in this form it is easy to see that in the limit as $\Delta \to 0$ (that is, as sampling becomes very fast) we regain the original differential equation model. Rearranging this equation, we have

$$\left[\delta^2 + \frac{(1.414\,21 + \Delta)}{(1 + 1.414\,21 \times \frac{1}{2}\Delta + \frac{1}{4}\Delta^2)}\delta + \frac{1}{(1 + 1.414\,21 \times \frac{1}{2}\Delta + \frac{1}{4}\Delta^2)}\right]y_k$$

$$= \frac{(2 + \Delta\delta)^2}{4(1 + 1.414\,21 \times \frac{1}{2}\Delta + \frac{1}{4}\Delta^2)}u_k \tag{3.77}$$

In order to assess stability, it is helpful to introduce a transform variable γ associated with the δ operator. This is achieved by defining γ in terms of z as

$$\gamma = \frac{z - 1}{\Delta}$$

The region of stability in the z plane, $|z| < 1$, thus becomes

$$|1 + \Delta\gamma| < 1$$

or

$$\left|\frac{1}{\Delta} + \gamma\right| < \frac{1}{\Delta} \tag{3.78}$$

This corresponds to a circle in the γ domain, centre $(-1/\Delta, 0)$ and radius $1/\Delta$. As $\Delta \to 0$, we see that this circle expands in such a way that the stability region is the entire open left half-plane, and coincides with the stability region for continuous-time systems.

Let us examine the pole locations for the two cases previously considered, namely $T = 0.1$ and $T = 0.01$. With $\Delta = T = 0.1$, the characteristic equation has the form

$$\gamma^2 + 1.410\,92\gamma + 0.931\,78 = 0$$

with roots, corresponding to poles of the system, at $-0.705\,46 \pm \text{j}0.658\,87$. The centre of the circular stability region is now at $-1/0.1 = -10$, with radius 10, and these roots lie at a radial distance of about 9.3178 from this centre. Note that the distance of the poles from the stability boundary is just less than 0.7. The poles of the original continuous-time model were also at about this distance from the appropriate boundary, and we observe the sharp contrast from our first discretized model, when the discretization process itself moved the pole locations very close to the stability boundary. In that approach the situation became exacerbated when the sampling rate was increased, to $T = 0.01$, and the poles moved nearer to the boundary. Setting $T = 0.01$ in the new formulation, we find that the characteristic equation becomes

$$\gamma^2 + 1.414\,13\gamma + 0.992\,95 = 0$$

with roots at $-0.707\,06 \pm \text{j}0.702\,14$. The stability circle is now centred at -100, with radius 100, and the radial distance of the poles is about 99.2954. Thus the distance from the boundary remains at about 0.7. Clearly, in the limit as $\Delta \to 0$, the pole locations become those of the continuous-time model, with the stability circle enlarging to become the entire left half of the complex γ plane.

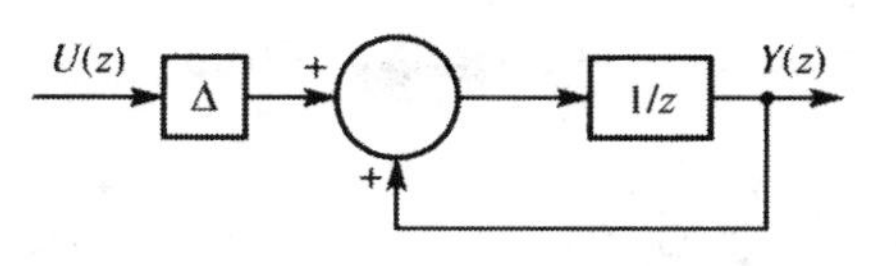

Figure 3.20 The δ^{-1} block.

3.9.4 Implementing the design

The discussion so far serves to demonstrate the utility of the δ operator formulation, but the problem of implementation of the design remains. It is possible to construct a δ^{-1} block based on delay or $1/z$ blocks, as shown in Figure 3.20. Systems can be realized using these structures in cascade or otherwise, and simulation studies have produced successful results. An alternative approach is to make use of the **state-space form** of the system model. We demonstrate this approach again for the case $T = 0.01$, when, with $T = \Delta = 0.01$, (3.77) becomes

$$(\delta^2 + 1.414\,13\delta + 0.992\,95)y_k = (0.000\,02\delta^2 + 0.009\,30\delta + 0.992\,95)u_k \quad \textbf{(3.79a)}$$

Based on (3.79a) we are led to consider the equation

$$(\delta^2 + 1.414\,13\delta + 0.992\,95)p_k = u_k \quad \textbf{(3.79b)}$$

Defining the state variables

$$x_{1,k} = p_k, \qquad x_{2,k} = \delta p_k$$

equation (3.79b) can be represented by the pair of equations

$$\delta x_{1,k} = x_{2,k}$$

$$\delta x_{2,k} = -0.992\,95x_{1,k} - 1.414\,13x_{2,k} + u_k$$

Choosing

$$y_k = 0.992\,95p_k + 0.009\,30\delta p_k + 0.000\,002\delta^2 p_k \quad \textbf{(3.79c)}$$

equations (3.79b) and (3.79c) are equivalent to (3.79a). In terms of the state variables we see that

$$y_k = 0.992\,93x_{1,k} + 0.009\,72x_{2,k} + 0.000\,02u_k$$

Defining the vectors $\boldsymbol{x}_k = [x_{1,k} \quad x_{2,k}]^{\mathrm{T}}$ and $\delta\boldsymbol{x}_k = [\delta x_{1,k} \quad \delta x_{2,k}]^{\mathrm{T}}$, equation (3.79a) can be represented in matrix form as

$$\delta\boldsymbol{x}_k = \begin{bmatrix} 0 & 1 \\ -0.992\,95 & -1.414\,13 \end{bmatrix}\boldsymbol{x}_k + \begin{bmatrix} 0 \\ 1 \end{bmatrix}u_k \quad \textbf{(3.80a)}$$

with

$$y_k = [0.992\,93 \quad 0.009\,72]\boldsymbol{x}_k + 0.000\,02u_k \quad \textbf{(3.80b)}$$

We now return to the q form to implement the system. Recalling that $\delta = (\mathrm{q} - 1)/\Delta$, (3.80a) becomes

$$\mathrm{q}\boldsymbol{x}_k = \boldsymbol{x}_{k+1} = \boldsymbol{x}_k + \Delta\left(\begin{bmatrix} 0 & 1 \\ -0.992\,95 & -1.414\,13 \end{bmatrix}\boldsymbol{x}_k + \begin{bmatrix} 0 \\ 1 \end{bmatrix}u_k\right) \quad \textbf{(3.81)}$$

with (3.80b) remaining the same and where $\Delta = 0.01$, in this case. Equations (3.81) and (3.80b) may be expressed in the vector–matrix form

$$\boldsymbol{x}_{k+1} = \boldsymbol{x}_k + \Delta[\boldsymbol{A}(\Delta)\boldsymbol{x}_k + \boldsymbol{b}u_k]$$

$$y = \boldsymbol{c}^{\mathrm{T}}(\Delta)\boldsymbol{x}_k + d(\Delta)u_k$$

This matrix difference equation can now be implemented without difficulty using standard delay blocks, and has a form similar to the result of applying a simple Euler discretization of the original continuous-time model expressed in state-space form.

3.9.5 The $\mathscr{D}$ transform

In Section 3.9.3 we introduced a transform variable

$$\gamma = \frac{z-1}{\Delta}$$

The purpose of this was to enable us to analyse the stability of systems described in the δ form. We now define a transform in terms of the z transform using the notation given by R. M. Middleton and G. C. Goodwin, *Digital Control and Estimation, A Unified Approach* (Prentice Hall, Englewood Cliffs, NJ, 1990). Let the sequence $\{f_k\}$ have z transform $F(z)$; then the new transform is given by

$$\begin{aligned} F'_{\Delta}(\gamma) &= F(z)|_{z=\Delta\gamma+1} \\ &= \sum_{k=0}^{\infty} \frac{f_k}{(1+\Delta\gamma)^k} \end{aligned}$$

The $\mathscr{D}$ transform is formally defined as a slight modification to this form, as

$$\mathscr{D}(f_k) = F_{\Delta}(\gamma) = \Delta F'_{\Delta}(\gamma) = \Delta \sum_{k=0}^{\infty} \frac{f_k}{(1+\Delta\gamma)^k}$$

The purpose of this modification is to permit the construction of a *unified theory of transforms* encompassing both continuous- and discrete-time models in the same structure. These developments are beyond the scope of the text, but may be pursued by the interested reader in the reference given above. We conclude the discussion with an example to illustrate the ideas. The ramp sequence $\{u_k\} = \{k\Delta\}$ can be obtained by sampling the continuous-time function $f(t) = t$ at intervals Δ. This sequence has z transform

$$U(z) = \frac{\Delta z}{(z-1)^2}$$

and the corresponding $\mathscr{D}$ transform is then

$$\Delta U'_{\Delta}(\gamma) = \frac{1+\Delta\gamma}{\gamma^2}$$

Note that on setting $\Delta = 0$ and $\gamma = s$ one recovers the Laplace transform of $f(t)$.

3.9.6 Exercises

29 A continuous-time system having input $y(t)$ and output $y(t)$ is defined by its transfer function

$$H(s) = \frac{1}{(s+1)(s+2)}$$

Use the methods described above to find the q and δ form of the discrete-time system model obtained using the transformation

$$s \rightarrow \frac{2}{\Delta}\frac{z-1}{z+1}$$

where Δ is the sampling interval. Examine the stability of the original system and that of the discrete-time systems when $\Delta = 0.1$ and when $\Delta = 0.01$.

30 Use the formula in equation (3.68) to obtain the transfer function of the third-order Butterworth filter with $\omega_c = 1$, and obtain the corresponding δ form discrete-time system when $T = \Delta$.

31 Make the substitution

$$x_1(t) = y(t)$$

$$x_2(t) = \frac{dy(t)}{dt}$$

in Exercise 29 to obtain the state-space form of the system model,

$$\dot{x}(t) = \boldsymbol{A}x(t) + bu(t)$$

$$y(t) = c^{T}x(t) + du(t)$$

The **Euler discretization technique** replaces $\dot{x}(t)$ by

$$\frac{x((k+1)\Delta) - x(k\Delta)}{\Delta}$$

Show that this corresponds to the model obtained above with $\boldsymbol{A} = \boldsymbol{A}(0)$, $c = c(0)$ and $d = d(0)$.

32 The discretization procedure used in Section 3.9.3 has been based on the bilinear transform method, derived from the trapezoidal approximation to the integration process. An alternative approximation is the Adams–Bashforth procedure, and it can be shown that this means that we should make the transformation

$$s \rightarrow \frac{12}{\Delta}\frac{z^2 - z}{5z^2 + 8z - 1}$$

where Δ is the sampling interval (see W. Forsythe and R. M. Goodall, *Digital Control*, Macmillan, London, 1991). Use this transformation to discretize the system given by

$$H(s) = \frac{s}{s+1}$$

when $\Delta = 0.1$ in

(a) the z form, and
(b) the γ form.

3.10 Review exercises (1–16)

1 The signal $f(t) = t$ is sampled at intervals T to generate the sequence $\{f(kT)\}$. Show that

$$\mathscr{Z}\{f(kT)\} = \frac{Tz}{(z-1)^2}$$

2 Show that

$$\mathscr{Z}\{a^k \sin k\omega\} = \frac{az \sin \omega}{z^2 - 2az \cos \omega + a^2} \quad (a > 0)$$

3 Show that

$$\mathscr{Z}\{k^2\} = \frac{z(z+1)}{(z-1)^3}$$

4 Find the impulse response for the system with transfer function

$$H(z) = \frac{(3z^2 - z)}{z^2 - 2z + 1}$$

5 Calculate the step response for the system with transfer function

$$H(z) = \frac{1}{z^2 + 3z + 2}$$

6 A process with Laplace transfer function $H(s) = 1/(s+1)$ is in cascade with a zero-order hold device with Laplace transfer function

$G(s) = (1 - e^{-sT})/s$. The overall transfer function is then

$$\frac{1 - e^{-sT}}{s(s + 1)}$$

Write $F(s) = 1/s(s + 1)$, and find $f(t) = \mathscr{L}^{-1}\{F(s)\}$. Sample $f(t)$ at intervals T to produce the sequence $\{f(kT)\}$ and find $\tilde{F}(z) = \mathscr{Z}\{f(kT)\}$. Deduce that

$$e^{-sT}F(s) \rightarrow \frac{1}{z}\tilde{F}(z)$$

and hence show that the overall z transfer function for the process and zero-order hold is

$$\frac{1 - e^{-T}}{z - e^{-T}}$$

7 A system has Laplace transfer function

$$H(s) = \frac{s + 1}{(s + 2)(s + 3)}$$

Calculate the impulse response, and obtain the z transform of this response when sampled at intervals T.

8 It can be established that if $X(z)$ is the z transform of the sequence $\{x_n\}$ then the general term of that sequence is given by

$$x_n = \frac{1}{j2\pi}\oint_C X(z)z^{n-1}\,dz$$

where C is any closed contour containing all the singularities of $X(z)$. If we assume that all the singularities of $X(z)$ are poles located within a circle of finite radius then it is an easy application of the residue theorem to show that

$$x_n = \sum [\text{residues of } X(z)z^{n-1} \text{ at poles of } X(z)]$$

(a) Let $X(z) = z/(z - a)(z - b)$, with a and b real. Where are the poles of $X(z)$? Calculate the residues of $z^{n-1}X(z)$, and hence invert the transform to obtain $\{x_n\}$.

(b) Use the residue method to find

(i) $\mathscr{Z}^{-1}\left\{\dfrac{z}{(z - 3)^2}\right\}$ (ii) $\mathscr{Z}^{-1}\left\{\dfrac{z}{z^2 - z + 1}\right\}$

9 The impulse response of a certain discrete-time system is $\{(-1)^k - 2^k\}$. What is the step response?

10 A discrete-time system has transfer function

$$H(z) = \frac{z^2}{(z + 1)(z - 1)}$$

Find the response to the sequence $\{1, -1, 0, 0, \dots\}$.

11 Show that the response of the second-order system with transfer function

$$\frac{z^2}{(z - \alpha)(z - \beta)}$$

to the input $(1, -(\alpha + \beta), \alpha\beta, 0, 0, 0, \dots\}$ is

$$\{\delta_k\} = \{1, 0, 0, \dots\}$$

Deduce that the response of the system

$$\frac{z}{(z - \alpha)(z - \beta)}$$

to the same input will be

$$\{\delta_{k-1}\} = \{0, 1, 0, 0, \dots\}$$

12 A system is specified by its Laplace transfer function

$$H(s) = \frac{s}{(s + 1)(s + 2)}$$

Calculate the impulse response $y_\delta(t) = \mathscr{L}^{-1}\{H(s)\}$, and show that if this response is sampled at intervals T to generate the sequence $\{y_\delta(nT)\}$ $(n = 0, 1, 2, \dots)$ then

$$D(z) = \mathscr{Z}\{y_\delta(nT)\} = \frac{2z}{z - e^{-2T}} - \frac{z}{z - e^{-T}}$$

A discrete-time system is now constructed so that

$$Y(z) = TD(z)X(z)$$

where $X(z)$ is the z transform of the input sequence $\{x_n\}$ and $Y(z)$ that of the output sequence $\{y_n\}$, with $x_n = x(nT)$ and $y_n = y(nT)$. Show that if $T = 0.5$ s then the difference equation governing the system is

$$y_{n+2} - 0.9744y_{n+1} + 0.2231y_n$$
$$= 0.5x_{n+2} - 0.4226x_{n+1}$$

Sketch a block diagram for the discrete-time system modelled by the difference equation

$$p_{n+2} - 0.9744p_{n+1} + 0.2231p_n = x_n$$

and verify that the signal y_n, as defined above, is generated by taking $y_n = 0.5p_{n+2} - 0.4226p_{n+1}$ as output.

13 In a discrete-time position-control system the position y_n satisfies the difference equation

$$y_{n+1} = y_n + av_n \quad (a \text{ constant})$$

where v_n and u_n satisfy the difference equations

$$v_{n+1} = v_n + bu_n \quad (b \text{ constant})$$

$$u_n = k_1(x_n - y_n) - k_2v_n \quad (k_1, k_2 \text{ constants})$$

(a) Show that if $k_1 = 1/4ab$ and $k_2 = 1/b$ then the z transfer function of the system is

$$\frac{Y(z)}{X(z)} = \frac{1}{(1-2z)^2}$$

where $Y(z) = \mathscr{Z}\{y_n\}$ and $X(z) = \mathscr{Z}\{x_n\}$.

(b) If also $x_n = A$ (where A is a constant), determine the response sequence $\{y_n\}$ given that $y_0 = y_1 = 0$.

14 The step response of a continuous-time system is modelled by the differential equation

$$\frac{d^2y}{dt^2} + 3\frac{dy}{dt} + 2y = 1 \quad (t \geqslant 0)$$

with $y(0) = \dot{y}(0) = 0$. Use the backward-difference approximation

$$\frac{dy}{dt} \simeq \frac{y_k - y_{k-1}}{T}$$

$$\frac{d^2y}{dt^2} \simeq \frac{y_k - 2y_{k-1} + y_{k-2}}{T^2}$$

to show that this differential equation may be approximated by

$$\frac{y_k - 2y_{k-1} + y_{k-2}}{T^2} + 3\frac{y_k - y_{k-1}}{T} + 2y_k = 1$$

Take the z transform of this difference equation, and show that the system poles are at

$$z = \frac{1}{1+T}, \quad z = \frac{1}{1+2T}$$

Deduce that the general solution is thus

$$y_k = \alpha\left(\frac{1}{1+T}\right)^k + \beta\left(\frac{1}{1+2T}\right)^k + \gamma$$

Show that $\gamma = \frac{1}{2}$ and, noting that the initial conditions $y(0) = 0$ and $\dot{y}(0) = 0$ imply $y_0 = y_{-1} = 0$, deduce that

$$y_k = \tfrac{1}{2}\left[\left(\frac{1}{1+2T}\right)^k - 2\left(\frac{1}{1+T}\right)^k + 1\right]$$

Note that the z-transform method could be used to obtain this result if we redefine $\mathscr{Z}\{y_k\} = \sum_{j=-1}^{\infty}(y_j/z^j)$, with appropriate modifications to the formulae for $\mathscr{Z}\{y_{k+1}\}$ and $\mathscr{Z}\{y_{k+2}\}$.

Explain why the calculation procedure is always stable in theory, but note the pole locations for very small T.

Finally, verify that the solution of the differential equation is

$$y(t) = \tfrac{1}{2}(e^{-2t} - 2e^{-t} + 1)$$

and plot graphs of the exact and approximate solutions with $T = 0.1$ s and $T = 0.05$ s.

15 Again consider the step response of the system modelled by the differential equation

$$\frac{d^2y}{dt^2} + 3\frac{dy}{dt} + 2y = 1 \quad (t \geqslant 0)$$

with $y(0) = \dot{y}(0) = 0$. Now discretize using the bilinear transform method; that is, take the Laplace transform and make the transformation

$$s \to \frac{2}{T}\frac{z-1}{z+1}$$

where T is the sampling interval. Show that the poles of the resulting z transfer function are at

$$z = \frac{1-T}{1+T}, \quad z = \frac{2-T}{2+T}$$

Deduce that the general solution is then

$$y_k = \alpha\left(\frac{1-T}{1+T}\right)^k + \beta\left(\frac{2-T}{2+T}\right)^k + \gamma$$

Deduce that $\gamma = \frac{1}{2}$ and, using the conditions $y_0 = y_{-1} = 0$, show that

$$y_k = \tfrac{1}{2}\left[(1-T)\left(\frac{1-T}{1+T}\right)^k - (2-T)\left(\frac{2-T}{2+T}\right)^k + 1\right]$$

Plot graphs to illustrate the exact solution and the approximate solution when $T = 0.1$ s and $T = 0.05$ s.

16 Show that the z transform of the sampled version of the signal $f(t) = t^2$ is

$$F(z) = \frac{z(z+1)\Delta^2}{(z-1)^3}$$

where Δ is the sampling interval. Verify that the $\mathscr{D}$ transform is then

$$\frac{(1+\Delta v)(2+\Delta v)}{v^3}$$

4 Fourier Series

Chapter 4 Contents

4.1 Introduction

The representation of a function in the form of a series is fairly common practice in mathematics. Probably the most familiar expansions are power series of the form

$$f(x) = \sum_{n=0}^{\infty} a_n x^n$$

in which the resolved components or **base set** comprise the power functions

$$1, x, x^2, x^3, \ldots, x^n, \ldots$$

For example, we recall that the exponential function may be represented by the infinite series

$$e^x = 1 + x + \frac{x^2}{2!} + \frac{x^3}{3!} + \ldots + \frac{x^n}{n!} + \ldots = \sum_{n=0}^{\infty} \frac{x^n}{n!}$$

There are frequently advantages in expanding a function in such a series, since the first few terms of a good approximation are easy to deal with. For example, term-by-term integration or differentiation may be applied or suitable function approximations can be made.

Power functions comprise only one example of a base set for the expansion of functions: a number of other base sets may be used. In particular, a **Fourier series** is an expansion of a periodic function $f(t)$ of period $T = 2\pi/\omega$ in which the base set is the set of sine functions, giving an expanded representation of the form

$$f(t) = A_0 + \sum_{n=1}^{\infty} A_n \sin(n\omega t + \phi_n)$$

Although the idea of expanding a function in the form of such a series had been used by Bernoulli, D'Alembert and Euler (*c.* 1750) to solve problems associated with the vibration of strings, it was Joseph Fourier (1768–1830) who developed the approach to a stage where it was generally useful. Fourier, a French physicist, was interested in heat-flow problems: given an initial temperature at all points of a region, he was concerned with determining the change in the temperature distribution over time. When Fourier postulated in 1807 that an arbitrary function $f(x)$ could be represented by a trigonometric series of the form

$$\sum_{n=0}^{\infty} (A_n \cos nkx + B_n \sin nkx)$$

the result was considered so startling that it met considerable opposition from the leading mathematicians of the time, notably Laplace, Poisson and, more significantly, Lagrange, who is regarded as one of the greatest mathematicians of all time. They questioned his work because of its lack of rigour, and it was probably this opposition that delayed the publication of Fourier's work, his classic text *Théorie Analytique de la Chaleur* (The Analytical Theory of Heat) not appearing until 1822. This text has since become the source for the modern methods of solving practical problems associated with partial differential equations subject to prescribed boundary conditions. In addition to heat flow, this class of problems includes structural vibrations, wave propagation and diffusion. The task of giving Fourier's work a more rigorous mathematical underpinning was undertaken later by Dirichlet (*c.* 1830) and subsequently Riemann, his successor at the University of Göttingen.

In addition to its use in solving boundary-value problems associated with partial differential equations, Fourier series analysis is central to many other applications in engineering. In Chapter 2 we saw how the frequency response of a dynamical system, modelled by a linear differential equation with constant coefficients, is readily determined and the role that it plays in both system analysis and design. In such cases the frequency response, being the steady-state response to a sinusoidal input signal $A \sin \omega t$, is also a sinusoid having the same frequency as the input signal. As mentioned in Section 2.5.6, periodic functions, which are not purely sinusoidal, frequently occur as input signals in engineering applications, particularly in electrical engineering, since many electrical sources of practical value, such as electronic rectifiers, generate non-sinusoidal periodic waveforms. Fourier series provide the ideal framework for analysing the steady-state response to such periodic input signals, since they enable us to represent the signals as infinite sums of sinusoids. The steady-state response due to each sinusoid can then be determined as in Section 2.7, and, because of the linear character of the system, the desired steady-state response can be determined as the sum of the individual responses. As the Fourier series expansion will consist of sinusoids having frequencies $n\omega$ that are multiples of the input signal frequency ω, the steady-state response will also have components having such frequencies. If one of the multiple frequencies $n\omega$ happens to be close in value to the natural oscillating frequency of the system, then it will resonate with the system, and the component at this frequency will dominate the steady-state response. Thus a distinction of significant practical interest between a non-sinusoidal periodic input signal and a sinusoidal input signal is that although the signal may have a frequency considerably lower than the natural frequency of the system, serious problems can still arise owing to resonance. A Fourier series analysis helps to identify such a possibility.

In Chapter 5 we shall illustrate how Fourier series analysis may be extended to aperiodic functions by the use of Fourier transforms. The discrete versions of such transforms provide one of the most advanced methods for discrete signal analysis, and are widely used in such fields as communications theory and speech and image processing.

4.2 Fourier series expansion

In this section we develop the Fourier series expansion of periodic functions and discuss how closely they approximate the functions. We also indicate how symmetrical properties of the function may be taken advantage of in order to reduce the amount of mathematical manipulation involved in determining the Fourier series. First the properties of periodic functions are briefly reviewed.

4.2.1 Periodic functions

A function $f(t)$ is said to be **periodic** if its image values are repeated at regular intervals in its domain. Thus the graph of a periodic function can be divided into 'vertical strips'

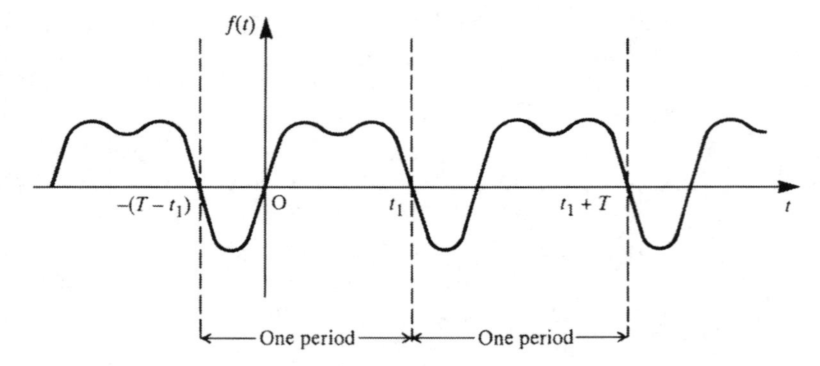

Figure 4.1 A periodic function with period T.

that are replicas of each other, as illustrated in Figure 4.1. The interval between two successive replicas is called the **period** of the function. We therefore say that a function $f(t)$ is periodic with period T if, for all its domain values t,

$$f(t + mT) = f(t)$$

for any integer m.

To provide a measure of the number of repetitions per unit of t, we define the **frequency** of a periodic function to be the reciprocal of its period, so that

$$\text{frequency} = \frac{1}{\text{period}} = \frac{1}{T}$$

The term **circular frequency** is also used in engineering, and is defined by

$$\text{circular frequency} = 2\pi \times \text{frequency} = \frac{2\pi}{T}$$

and is measured in radians per second. It is common to drop the term 'circular' and refer to this simply as the frequency when the context is clear.

4.2.2 Fourier's theorem

This theorem states that a periodic function that satisfies certain conditions can be expressed as the sum of a number of sine functions of different amplitudes, phases and periods. That is, if $f(t)$ is a periodic function with period T then

$$f(t) = A_0 + A_1 \sin(\omega t + \phi_1) + A_2 \sin(2\omega t + \phi_2) + \ldots$$
$$+ A_n \sin(n\omega t + \phi_n) + \ldots \quad \textbf{(4.1)}$$

where the As and ϕs are constants and $\omega = 2\pi/T$ is the frequency of $f(t)$. The term $A_1 \sin(\omega t + \phi_1)$ is called the **first harmonic** or the **fundamental mode**, and it has the same frequency ω as the parent function $f(t)$. The term $A_n \sin(n\omega t + \phi_n)$ is called the ***n*th harmonic**, and it has frequency $n\omega$, which is n times that of the fundamental. A_n denotes the **amplitude** of the nth harmonic and ϕ_n is its **phase angle**, measuring the lag or lead of the nth harmonic with reference to a pure sine wave of the same frequency.

Since

$$A_n \sin(n\omega t + \phi_n) \equiv (A_n \cos \phi_n) \sin n\omega t + (A_n \sin \phi_n) \cos n\omega t$$
$$\equiv b_n \sin n\omega t + a_n \cos n\omega t$$

where

$$b_n = A_n \cos \phi_n, \qquad a_n = A_n \sin \phi_n \tag{4.2}$$

the expansion (4.1) may be written as

$$f(t) = \tfrac{1}{2}a_0 + \sum_{n=1}^{\infty} a_n \cos n\omega t + \sum_{n=1}^{\infty} b_n \sin n\omega t \tag{4.3}$$

where $a_0 = 2A_0$ (we shall see later that taking the first term as $\frac{1}{2}a_0$ rather than a_0 is a convenience that enables us to make a_0 fit a general result). The expansion (4.3) is called the **Fourier series expansion** of the function $f(t)$, and the *a*s and *b*s are called the **Fourier coefficients**. In electrical engineering it is common practice to refer to a_n and b_n respectively as the **in-phase** and **phase quadrature components** of the *n*th harmonic, this terminology arising from the use of the phasor notation $e^{jn\omega t} = \cos n\omega t + j \sin n\omega t$. Clearly, (4.1) is an alternative representation of the Fourier series with the amplitude and phase of the *n*th harmonic being determined from (4.2) as

$$A_n = \sqrt{(a_n^2 + b_n^2)}, \qquad \phi_n = \tan^{-1}\left(\frac{a_n}{b_n}\right)$$

with care being taken over choice of quadrant.

4.2.3 The Fourier coefficients

Before proceeding to evaluate the Fourier coefficients, we first state the following integrals, in which $T = 2\pi/\omega$:

$$\int_d^{d+T} \cos n\omega t \, dt = \begin{cases} 0 & (n \neq 0) \\ T & (n = 0) \end{cases} \tag{4.4}$$

$$\int_d^{d+T} \sin n\omega t \, dt = 0 \quad (\text{all } n) \tag{4.5}$$

$$\int_d^{d+T} \sin m\omega t \sin n\omega t \, dt = \begin{cases} 0 & (m \neq n) \\ \frac{1}{2}T & (m = n \neq 0) \end{cases} \tag{4.6}$$

$$\int_d^{d+T} \cos m\omega t \cos n\omega t \, dt = \begin{cases} 0 & (m \neq n) \\ \frac{1}{2}T & (m = n \neq 0) \end{cases} \tag{4.7}$$

$$\int_d^{d+T} \cos m\omega t \sin n\omega t \, dt = 0 \quad (\text{all } m \text{ and } n) \tag{4.8}$$

The results (4.4)–(4.8) constitute the **orthogonality relations** for sine and cosine functions, and show that the set of functions

$$\{1, \cos \omega t, \cos 2\omega t, \ldots, \cos n\omega t, \sin \omega t, \sin 2\omega t, \ldots, \sin n\omega t\}$$

is an orthogonal set of functions on the interval $d \leq t \leq d + T$. The choice of d is arbitrary in these results, it only being necessary to integrate over a period of duration T.

Integrating the series (4.3) with respect to t over the period $t = d$ to $t = d + T$, and using (4.4) and (4.5), we find that each term on the right-hand side is zero except for the term involving a_0; that is, we have

$$\begin{aligned}\int_d^{d+T} f(t)\,\mathrm{d}t &= \tfrac{1}{2}a_0\int_d^{d+T}\mathrm{d}t + \sum_{n=1}^{\infty}\left(a_n\int_d^{d+T}\cos n\omega t\,\mathrm{d}t + b_n\int_d^{d+T}\sin n\omega t\,\mathrm{d}t\right)\\ &= \tfrac{1}{2}a_0(T) + \sum_{n=1}^{\infty}[a_n(0) + b_n(0)]\\ &= \tfrac{1}{2}Ta_0\end{aligned}$$

Thus

$$\tfrac{1}{2}a_0 = \frac{1}{T}\int_d^{d+T} f(t)\,\mathrm{d}t$$

and we can see that the constant term $\frac{1}{2}a_0$ in the Fourier series expansion represents the mean value of the function $f(t)$ over one period. For an electrical signal it represents the bias level or DC (direct current) component. Hence

$$a_0 = \frac{2}{T}\int_d^{d+T} f(t)\,\mathrm{d}t \tag{4.9}$$

To obtain this result, we have assumed that term-by-term integration of the series (4.3) is permissible. This is indeed so because of the convergence properties of the series – its validity is discussed in detail in more advanced texts.

To obtain the Fourier coefficient a_n $(n \neq 0)$, we multiply (4.3) throughout by $\cos m\omega t$ and integrate with respect to t over the period $t = d$ to $t = d + T$, giving

$$\begin{aligned}\int_d^{d+T} f(t)\cos m\omega t\,\mathrm{d}t &= \tfrac{1}{2}a_0\int_d^{d+T}\cos m\omega t\,\mathrm{d}t + \sum_{n=1}^{\infty}a_n\int_d^{d+T}\cos n\omega t\cos m\omega t\,\mathrm{d}t\\ &\quad + \sum_{n=1}^{\infty}b_n\int_d^{d+T}\cos m\omega t\sin n\omega t\,\mathrm{d}t\end{aligned}$$

Assuming term-by-term integration to be possible, and using (4.4), (4.7) and (4.8), we find that, when $m \neq 0$, the only non-zero integral on the right-hand side is the one that occurs in the first summation when $n = m$. That is, we have

$$\int_d^{d+T} f(t)\cos m\omega t\,\mathrm{d}t = a_m\int_d^{d+T}\cos m\omega t\cos m\omega t\,\mathrm{d}t = \tfrac{1}{2}a_mT$$

giving

$$a_m = \frac{2}{T}\int_d^{d+T} f(t)\cos m\omega t\,\mathrm{d}t$$

which, on replacing m by n, gives

$$a_n = \frac{2}{T}\int_d^{d+T} f(t)\cos n\omega t\,\mathrm{d}t \tag{4.10}$$

The value of a_0 given in (4.9) may be obtained by taking $n = 0$ in (4.10), so that we may write

$$a_n = \frac{2}{T}\int_d^{d+T} f(t)\cos m\omega t\,\mathrm{d}t \quad (n = 0, 1, 2, \dots) \tag{4.11}$$

This explains why the constant term in the Fourier series expansion was taken as $\frac{1}{2}a_0$ and not a_0, since this ensures compatibility of the results (4.9) and (4.10). Although a_0 and a_n satisfy the same formula, it is usually safer to work them out separately.

Finally, to obtain the Fourier coefficients b_n, we multiply (4.3) throughout by $\sin m\omega t$ and integrate with respect to t over the period $t = d$ to $t = d + T$, giving

$$\int_d^{d+T} f(t)\sin m\omega t\,\mathrm{d}t = \tfrac{1}{2}a_0\int_d^{d+T} \sin m\omega t\,\mathrm{d}t$$
$$+ \sum_{n=1}^{\infty}\left(a_n\int_d^{d+T} \sin m\omega t\cos n\omega t\,\mathrm{d}t + b_n\int_t^{d+T} \sin m\omega t\sin n\omega t\,\mathrm{d}t\right)$$

Assuming term-by-term integration to be possible, and using (4.5), (4.6) and (4.8), we find that the only non-zero integral on the right-hand side is the one that occurs in the second summation when $m = n$. That is, we have

$$\int_d^{d+T} f(t)\sin m\omega t\,\mathrm{d}t = b_m\int_d^{d+T} \sin m\omega t\sin m\omega t\,\mathrm{d}t = \tfrac{1}{2}b_m T$$

giving, on replacing m by n,

$$b_n = \frac{2}{T}\int_d^{d+T} f(t)\sin n\omega t\,\mathrm{d}t \quad (n = 1, 2, 3, \dots) \tag{4.12}$$

The equations (4.11) and (4.12) giving the Fourier coefficients are known as **Euler's formulae**.

Summary

In summary, we have shown that if a periodic function $f(t)$ of period $T = 2\pi/\omega$ can be expanded as a Fourier series then that series is given by

$$f(t) = \tfrac{1}{2}a_0 + \sum_{n=1}^{\infty} a_n\cos n\omega t + \sum_{n=1}^{\infty} b_n\sin n\omega t \tag{4.3}$$

where the coefficients are given by the Euler formulae

$$a_n = \frac{2}{T}\int_d^{d+T} f(t)\cos n\omega t\,\mathrm{d}t \quad (n = 0, 1, 2, \dots) \tag{4.11}$$

$$b_n = \frac{2}{T}\int_d^{d+T} f(t)\sin n\omega t\,\mathrm{d}t \quad (n = 1, 2, 3, \dots) \tag{4.12}$$

The limits of integration in Euler's formulae may be specified over any period, so that the choice of d is arbitrary, and may be made in such a way as to help in the calculation of a_n and b_n. In practice, it is common to specify $f(t)$ over either the period $-\frac{1}{2}T < t < \frac{1}{2}T$ or the period $0 < t < T$, leading respectively to the limits of integration being $-\frac{1}{2}T$ and $\frac{1}{2}T$ (that is, $d = -\frac{1}{2}T$) or 0 and T (that is, $d = 0$).

It is also worth noting that an alternative approach may simplify the calculation of a_n and b_n. Using the formula

$$\mathrm{e}^{\mathrm{j}n\omega t} = \cos n\omega t + \mathrm{j}\sin n\omega t$$

we have

$$a_n + \mathrm{j}b_n = \frac{2}{T}\int_d^{d+T} f(t)\,\mathrm{e}^{\mathrm{j}n\omega t}\,\mathrm{d}t \tag{4.13}$$

Evaluating this integral and equating real and imaginary parts on each side gives the values of a_n and b_n. This approach is particularly useful when only the amplitude $|a_n + \mathrm{j}b_n|$ of the nth harmonic is required.

4.2.4 Functions of period 2π

If the period T of the periodic function $f(t)$ is taken to be 2π then $\omega = 1$, and the series (4.3) becomes

$$f(t) = \tfrac{1}{2}a_0 + \sum_{n=1}^{\infty} a_n \cos nt + \sum_{n=1}^{\infty} b_n \sin nt \tag{4.14}$$

with the coefficients given by

$$a_n = \frac{1}{\pi}\int_d^{d+2\pi} f(t)\cos nt\,\mathrm{d}t \quad (n = 0, 1, 2, \dots) \tag{4.15}$$

$$b_n = \frac{1}{\pi}\int_d^{d+2\pi} f(t)\sin nt\,\mathrm{d}t \quad (n = 1, 2, \dots) \tag{4.16}$$

While a unit frequency may rarely be encountered in practice, consideration of this particular case reduces the amount of mathematical manipulation involved in determining the coefficients a_n and b_n. Also, there is no loss of generality in considering this case, since if we have a function $f(t)$ of period T, we may write $t_1 = 2\pi t/T$, so that

$$f(t) \equiv f\left(\frac{Tt_1}{2\pi}\right) \equiv F(t_1)$$

where $F(t_1)$ is a function of period 2π. That is, by a simple change of variable, a periodic function $f(t)$ of period T may be transformed into a periodic function $F(t_1)$ of period 2π. Thus, in order to develop an initial understanding and to discuss some of the properties of Fourier series, we shall first consider functions of period 2π, returning to functions of period other than 2π in Section 4.2.10.

Example 4.1 Obtain the Fourier series expansion of the periodic function $f(t)$ of period 2π defined by

$$f(t) = t \quad (0 < t < 2\pi), \qquad f(t) = f(t + 2\pi)$$

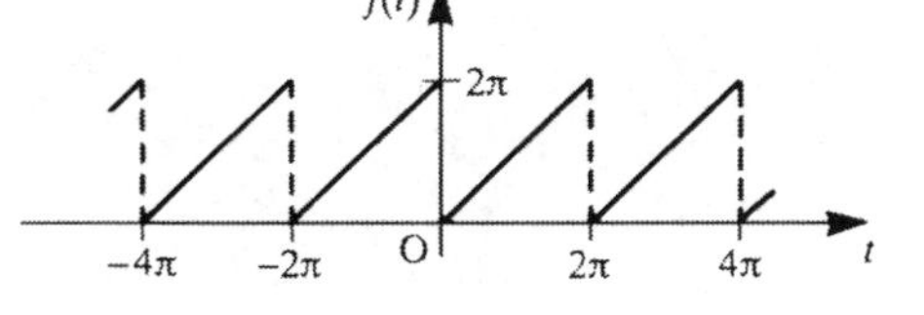

Figure 4.2 Sawtooth wave of Example 4.1.

Solution A sketch of the function $f(t)$ over the interval $-4\pi < t < 4\pi$ is shown in Figure 4.2. Since the function is periodic we only need to sketch it over one period, the pattern being repeated for other periods. Using (4.15) to evaluate the Fourier coefficients a_0 and a_n gives

$$a_0 = \frac{1}{\pi}\int_0^{2\pi} f(t)\,\mathrm{d}t = \frac{1}{\pi}\int_0^{2\pi} t\,\mathrm{d}t = \frac{1}{\pi}\left[\frac{t^2}{2}\right]_0^{2\pi} = 2\pi$$

and

$$\begin{aligned} a_n &= \frac{1}{\pi}\int_0^{2\pi} f(t)\cos nt\,\mathrm{d}t \quad (n = 1, 2, \ldots) \\ &= \frac{1}{\pi}\int_0^{2\pi} t\cos nt\,\mathrm{d}t \end{aligned}$$

which, on integration by parts, gives

$$a_n = \frac{1}{\pi}\left[t\frac{\sin nt}{n} + \frac{\cos nt}{n^2}\right]_0^{2\pi} = \frac{1}{\pi}\left(\frac{2\pi}{n}\sin 2n\pi + \frac{1}{n^2}\cos 2n\pi - \frac{\cos 0}{n^2}\right) = 0$$

since $\sin 2n\pi = 0$ and $\cos 2n\pi = \cos 0 = 1$. Note the need to work out a_0 separately from a_n in this case. The formula (4.16) for b_n gives

$$\begin{aligned} b_n &= \frac{1}{\pi}\int_0^{2\pi} f(t)\sin nt\,\mathrm{d}t \quad (n = 1, 2, \ldots) \\ &= \frac{1}{\pi}\int_0^{2\pi} t\sin nt\,\mathrm{d}t \end{aligned}$$

which, on integration by parts, gives

$$\begin{aligned} b_n &= \frac{1}{\pi}\left[-\frac{t}{n}\cos nt + \frac{\sin nt}{n^2}\right]_0^{2\pi} \\ &= \frac{1}{\pi}\left(-\frac{2\pi}{n}\cos 2n\pi\right) \quad (\text{since } \sin 2n\pi = \sin 0 = 0) \\ &= -\frac{2}{n} \quad (\text{since } \cos 2n\pi = 1) \end{aligned}$$

Hence from (4.14) the Fourier series expansion of $f(t)$ is

$$f(t) = \pi - \sum_{n=1}^{\infty} \frac{2}{n} \sin nt$$

or, in expanded form,

$$f(t) = \pi - 2\left(\sin t + \frac{\sin 2t}{2} + \frac{\sin 3t}{3} + \ldots + \frac{\sin nt}{n} + \ldots \right)$$

Example 4.2

A periodic function $f(t)$ with period 2π is defined by

$$f(t) = t^2 + t \quad (-\pi < t < \pi), \qquad f(t) = f(t + 2\pi)$$

Sketch a graph of the function $f(t)$ for values of t from $t = -3\pi$ to $t = 3\pi$ and obtain a Fourier series expansion of the function.

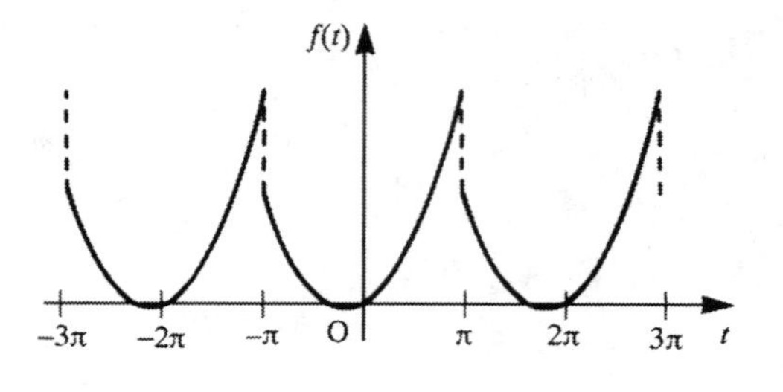

Figure 4.3 Graph of the function $f(t)$ of Example 4.2.

Solution A graph of the function $f(t)$ for $-3\pi < t < 3\pi$ is shown in Figure 4.3. From (4.15) we have

$$a_0 = \frac{1}{\pi}\int_{-\pi}^{\pi} f(t)\,dt = \frac{1}{\pi}\int_{-\pi}^{\pi} (t^2 + t)\,dt = \tfrac{2}{3}\pi^2$$

and

$$a_n = \frac{1}{\pi}\int_{-\pi}^{\pi} f(t)\cos nt\,dt \quad (n = 1, 2, 3, \ldots)$$

$$= \frac{1}{\pi}\int_{-\pi}^{\pi} (t^2 + t)\cos nt\,dt$$

which, on integration by parts, gives

$$a_n = \frac{1}{\pi}\left[\frac{t^2}{n}\sin nt + \frac{2t}{n^2}\cos nt - \frac{2}{n^3}\sin nt + \frac{t}{n}\sin nt + \frac{1}{n^2}\cos nt \right]_{-\pi}^{\pi}$$

$$= \frac{1}{\pi}\frac{4\pi}{n^2}\cos n\pi \quad \left(\text{since } \sin n\pi = 0 \text{ and } \left[\frac{1}{n^2}\cos nt \right]_{-\pi}^{\pi} = 0 \right)$$

$$= \frac{4}{n^2}(-1)^n \qquad (\text{since } \cos n\pi = (-1)^n)$$

From (4.16)

$$b_n = \frac{1}{\pi}\int_{-\pi}^{\pi} f(t)\sin nt\,dt \quad (n = 1, 2, 3, \dots)$$

$$= \frac{1}{\pi}\int_{-\pi}^{\pi} (t^2 + t)\sin nt\,dt$$

which, on integration by parts, gives

$$b_n = \frac{1}{\pi}\left[-\frac{t^2}{n}\cos nt + \frac{2t}{n^2}\sin nt + \frac{2}{n^3}\cos nt - \frac{t}{n}\cos nt + \frac{1}{n^2}\sin nt\right]_{-\pi}^{\pi}$$

$$= -\frac{2}{n}\cos n\pi = -\frac{2}{n}(-1)^n \quad (\text{since } \cos n\pi = (-1)^n)$$

Hence from (4.14) the Fourier series expansion of $f(t)$ is

$$f(t) = \tfrac{1}{3}\pi^2 + \sum_{n=1}^{\infty}\frac{4}{n^2}(-1)^n\cos nt - \sum_{n=1}^{\infty}\frac{2}{n}(-1)^n\sin nt$$

or, in expanded form,

$$f(t) = \tfrac{1}{3}\pi^2 + 4\left(-\cos t + \frac{\cos 2t}{2^2} - \frac{\cos 3t}{3^2} + \dots\right) + 2\left(\sin t - \frac{\sin 2t}{2} + \frac{\sin 3t}{3} \dots\right)$$

To illustrate the alternative approach, using (4.13) gives

$$a_n + \mathrm{j}b_n = \frac{1}{\pi}\int_{-\pi}^{\pi} f(t)\,\mathrm{e}^{\mathrm{j}nt}\,dt = \frac{1}{\pi}\int_{-\pi}^{\pi}(t^2 + t)\,\mathrm{e}^{\mathrm{j}nt}\,dt$$

$$= \frac{1}{\pi}\left(\left[\frac{t^2 + t}{\mathrm{j}n}\mathrm{e}^{\mathrm{j}nt}\right]_{-\pi}^{\pi} - \int_{-\pi}^{\pi}\frac{2t + 1}{\mathrm{j}n}\mathrm{e}^{\mathrm{j}nt}\,dt\right)$$

$$= \frac{1}{\pi}\left[\frac{t^2 + t}{\mathrm{j}n}\mathrm{e}^{\mathrm{j}nt} - \frac{2t + 1}{(\mathrm{j}n)^2}\mathrm{e}^{\mathrm{j}nt} + \frac{2\mathrm{e}^{\mathrm{j}nt}}{(\mathrm{j}n)^3}\right]_{-\pi}^{\pi}$$

Since

$$\mathrm{e}^{\mathrm{j}n\pi} = \cos n\pi + \mathrm{j}\sin n\pi = (-1)^n$$

$$\mathrm{e}^{-\mathrm{j}n\pi} = \cos n\pi - \mathrm{j}\sin n\pi = (-1)^n$$

and

$$1/\mathrm{j} = -\mathrm{j}$$

$$a_n + \mathrm{j}b_n = \frac{(-1)^n}{\pi}\left(-\mathrm{j}\frac{\pi^2 + \pi}{n} + \frac{2\pi + 1}{n^2} + \frac{\mathrm{j}2}{n^3} + \mathrm{j}\frac{\pi^2 - \pi}{n} - \frac{1 - 2\pi}{n^2} - \frac{\mathrm{j}2}{n^3}\right)$$

$$= (-1)^n\left(\frac{4}{n^2} - \mathrm{j}\frac{2}{n}\right)$$

Equating real and imaginary parts gives, as before,

$$a_n = \frac{4}{n^2}(-1)^n, \qquad b_n = -\frac{2}{n}(-1)^n$$

A periodic function $f(t)$ may be specified in a piecewise fashion over a period, or, indeed, it may only be piecewise-continuous over a period, as illustrated in Figure 4.4. In order to calculate the Fourier coefficients in such cases, it is necessary to break up the range of integration in the Euler formulae to correspond to the various components of the function. For example, for the function shown in Figure 4.4, $f(t)$ is defined in the interval $-\pi < t < \pi$ by

$$f(t) = \begin{cases} f_1(t) & (-\pi < t < -p) \\ f_2(t) & (-p < t < q) \\ f_3(t) & (q < t < \pi) \end{cases}$$

and is periodic with period 2π. The Euler formulae (4.15) and (4.16) for the Fourier coefficients become

$$a_n = \frac{1}{\pi}\left[\int_{-\pi}^{-p} f_1(t)\cos nt\,\mathrm{d}t + \int_{-p}^{q} f_2(t)\cos nt\,\mathrm{d}t + \int_{q}^{\pi} f_3(t)\cos nt\,\mathrm{d}t\right]$$

$$b_n = \frac{1}{\pi}\left[\int_{-\pi}^{-p} f_1(t)\sin nt\,\mathrm{d}t + \int_{-p}^{q} f_2(t)\sin nt\,\mathrm{d}t + \int_{q}^{\pi} f_3(t)\sin nt\,\mathrm{d}t\right]$$

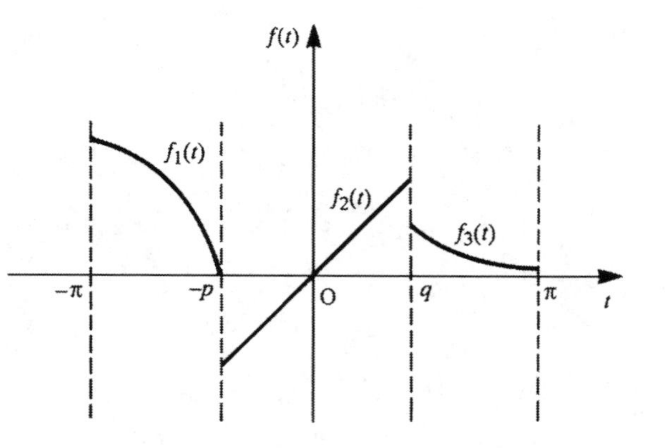

Figure 4.4 Piecewise-continuous function over a period.

Example 4.3

A periodic function $f(t)$ of period 2π is defined within the period $0 \leqslant t \leqslant 2\pi$ by

$$f(t) = \begin{cases} t & (0 \leqslant t \leqslant \frac{1}{2}\pi) \\ \frac{1}{2}\pi & (\frac{1}{2}\pi \leqslant t \leqslant \pi) \\ \pi - \frac{1}{2}t & (\pi \leqslant t \leqslant 2\pi) \end{cases}$$

Sketch a graph of $f(t)$ for $-2\pi \leqslant t \leqslant 3\pi$ and find a Fourier series expansion of it.

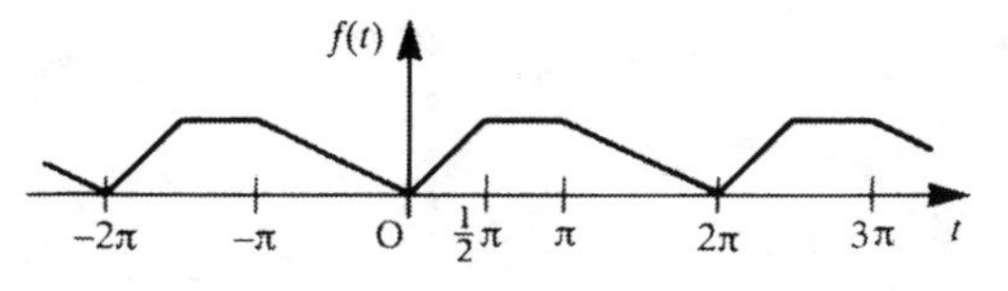

Figure 4.5 Graph of the function $f(t)$ of Example 4.3.

Solution A graph of the function $f(t)$ for $-2\pi \leqslant t \leqslant 3\pi$ is shown in Figure 4.5. From (4.15),

$$a_0 = \frac{1}{\pi}\int_0^{2\pi} f(t)\,dt = \frac{1}{\pi}\left[\int_0^{\pi/2} t\,dt + \int_{\pi/2}^{\pi} \tfrac{1}{2}\pi\,dt + \int_{\pi}^{2\pi} (\pi - \tfrac{1}{2}t)\,dt\right] = \tfrac{5}{8}\pi$$

and

$$\begin{aligned}
a_n &= \frac{1}{\pi}\int_0^{2\pi} f(t)\cos nt\,dt \quad (n = 1, 2, 3, \dots)\\
&= \frac{1}{\pi}\left[\int_0^{\pi/2} t\cos nt\,dt + \int_{\pi/2}^{\pi} \tfrac{1}{2}\pi\cos nt\,dt + \int_{\pi}^{2\pi} (\pi - \tfrac{1}{2}t)\cos nt\,dt\right]\\
&= \frac{1}{\pi}\left(\left[\frac{t}{n}\sin nt + \frac{\cos nt}{n^2}\right]_0^{\pi/2} + \left[\frac{\pi}{2n}\sin nt\right]_{\pi/2}^{\pi} + \left[\frac{2\pi - t}{2}\frac{\sin nt}{n} - \frac{\cos nt}{2n^2}\right]_{\pi}^{2\pi}\right)\\
&= \frac{1}{\pi}\left(\frac{\pi}{2n}\sin\tfrac{1}{2}n\pi + \frac{1}{n^2}\cos\tfrac{1}{2}n\pi - \frac{1}{n^2} - \frac{\pi}{2n}\sin\tfrac{1}{2}n\pi - \frac{1}{2n^2} + \frac{1}{2n^2}\cos n\pi\right)\\
&= \frac{1}{2\pi n^2}(2\cos\tfrac{1}{2}n\pi - 3 + \cos n\pi)
\end{aligned}$$

that is,

$$a_n = \begin{cases} \dfrac{1}{\pi n^2}[(-1)^{n/2} - 1] & \text{(even } n\text{)}\\[2ex] -\dfrac{2}{\pi n^2} & \text{(odd } n\text{)}\end{cases}$$

From (4.16),

$$\begin{aligned}
b_n &= \frac{1}{\pi}\int_0^{2\pi} f(t)\sin nt\,dt \quad (n = 1, 2, 3, \dots)\\
&= \frac{1}{\pi}\left[\int_0^{\pi/2} t\sin nt\,dt + \int_{\pi/2}^{\pi} \tfrac{1}{2}\pi\sin nt\,dt + \int_{\pi}^{2\pi} \left(\pi - \frac{1}{2}t\right)\sin nt\,dt\right]\\
&= \frac{1}{\pi}\left(\left[-\frac{t}{n}\cos nt + \frac{1}{n^2}\sin nt\right]_0^{\pi/2} + \left[-\frac{\pi}{2n}\cos nt\right]_{\pi/2}^{\pi}\right.\\
&\quad \left. + \left[\frac{t - 2\pi}{2n}\cos nt - \frac{1}{2n^2}\sin nt\right]_{\pi}^{2\pi}\right)
\end{aligned}$$

$$= \frac{1}{\pi}\left(-\frac{\pi}{2n}\cos\tfrac{1}{2}n\pi + \frac{1}{n^2}\sin\tfrac{1}{2}n\pi - \frac{\pi}{2n}\cos n\pi + \frac{\pi}{2n}\cos\tfrac{1}{2}n\pi + \frac{\pi}{2n}\cos n\pi\right)$$

$$= \frac{1}{\pi n^2}\sin\tfrac{1}{2}n\pi$$

$$= \begin{cases} 0 & (\text{even } n) \\ \dfrac{(-1)^{(n-1)/2}}{\pi n^2} & (\text{odd } n) \end{cases}$$

Hence from (4.14) the Fourier series expansion of $f(t)$ is

$$f(t) = \tfrac{5}{16}\pi - \frac{2}{\pi}\left(\cos t + \frac{\cos 3t}{3^2} + \frac{\cos 5t}{5^2} + \ldots\right)$$

$$- \frac{2}{\pi}\left(\frac{\cos 2t}{2^2} + \frac{\cos 6t}{6^2} + \frac{\cos 10t}{10^2} + \ldots\right)$$

$$+ \frac{1}{\pi}\left(\sin t - \frac{\sin 3t}{3^2} + \frac{\sin 5t}{5^2} - \frac{\sin 7t}{7^2} + \ldots\right)$$

4.2.5 Even and odd functions

Noting that a particular function possesses certain symmetrical properties enables us both to tell which terms are absent from a Fourier series expansion of the function and to simplify the expressions determining the remaining coefficients. In this section we consider even and odd function symmetries, while in Section 4.2.6 we shall consider symmetry due to even and odd harmonics.

First we review the properties of even and odd functions that are useful for determining the Fourier coefficients. If $f(t)$ is an even function then $f(t) = f(-t)$ for all t, and the graph of the function is symmetrical about the vertical axis as illustrated in Figure 4.6(a). From the definition of integration, it follows that if $f(t)$ is an even function then

$$\int_{-a}^{a} f(t)\,dt = 2\int_{0}^{a} f(t)\,dt$$

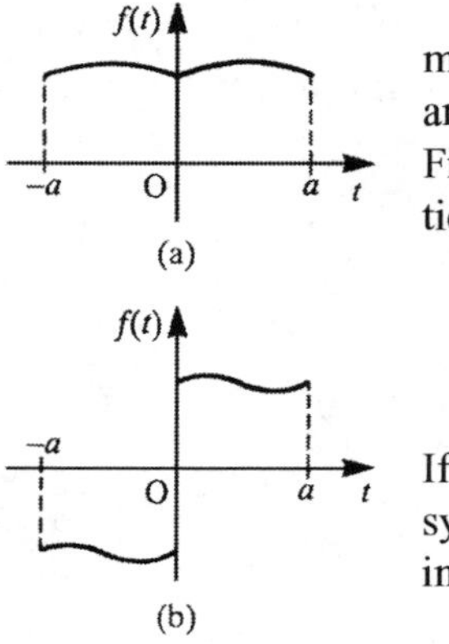

Figure 4.6 Graphs of (a) an even function and (b) an odd function.

If $f(t)$ is an odd function then $f(t) = -f(-t)$ for all t, and the graph of the function is symmetrical about the origin; that is, there is opposite-quadrant symmetry, as illustrated in Figure 4.6(b). It follows that if $f(t)$ is an odd function then

$$\int_{-a}^{a} f(t)\,dt = 0$$

The following properties of even and odd functions are also useful for our purposes:

(a) the *sum* of two (or more) *odd* functions is an *odd* function;

(b) the *product* of two *even* functions is an *even* function;

(c) the *product* of two *odd* functions is an *even* function;

(d) the *product* of an *odd* and an *even* function is an *odd* function;

(e) the *derivative* of an *even* function is an *odd* function;

(f) the *derivative* of an *odd* function is an *even* function.

(Noting that t^{even} is even and t^{odd} is odd helps one to remember (a)–(f).)

Using these properties, and taking $d = -\frac{1}{2}T$ in (4.11) and (4.12), we have the following:

(i) If $f(t)$ is an *even* periodic function of period T then

$$a_n = \frac{2}{T}\int_{-T/2}^{T/2} f(t)\cos n\omega t\,\mathrm{d}t = \frac{4}{T}\int_0^{T/2} f(t)\cos n\omega t\,\mathrm{d}t$$

using property (b), and

$$b_n = \frac{2}{T}\int_{-T/2}^{T/2} f(t)\sin n\omega t\,\mathrm{d}t = 0$$

using property (d).

Thus the Fourier series expansion of an even periodic function $f(t)$ with period T consists of cosine terms only and, from (4.3), is given by

$$f(t) = \tfrac{1}{2}a_0 + \sum_{n=1}^{\infty} a_n \cos n\omega t \qquad \textbf{(4.17)}$$

with

$$a_n = \frac{4}{T}\int_0^{T/2} f(t)\cos n\omega t \quad (n = 0, 1, 2, \dots) \qquad \textbf{(4.18)}$$

(ii) If $f(t)$ is an *odd* periodic function of period T then

$$a_n = \frac{2}{T}\int_{-T/2}^{T/2} f(t)\cos n\omega t\,\mathrm{d}t = 0$$

using property (d), and

$$b_n = \frac{2}{T}\int_{-T/2}^{T/2} f(t)\sin n\omega t\,\mathrm{d}t = \frac{4}{T}\int_0^{T/2} f(t)\sin n\omega t\,\mathrm{d}t$$

using property (c).

Thus the Fourier series expansion of an odd periodic function $f(t)$ with period T consists of sine terms only and, from (4.3), is given by

$$f(t) = \sum_{n=1}^{\infty} b_n \sin n\omega t \qquad \textbf{(4.19)}$$

with

$$b_n = \frac{4}{T}\int_0^{T/2} f(t)\sin n\omega t\,\mathrm{d}t \quad (n = 1, 2, 3, \dots) \qquad \textbf{(4.20)}$$

Example 4.4

A periodic function $f(t)$ with period 2π is defined within the period $-\pi < t < \pi$ by

$$f(t) = \begin{cases} -1 & (-\pi < t < 0) \\ 1 & (0 < t < \pi) \end{cases}$$

Find its Fourier series expansion.

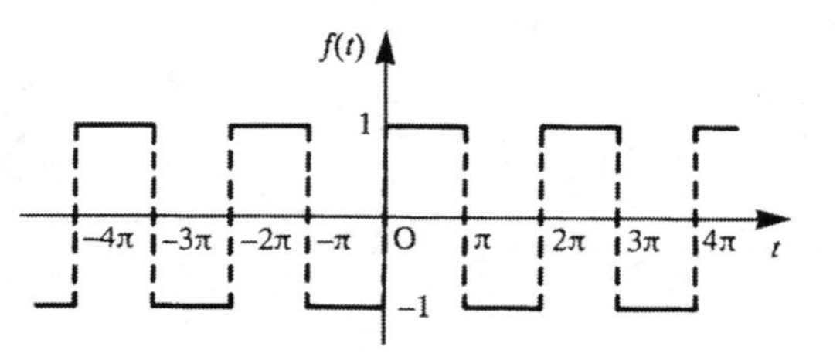

Figure 4.7 Square wave of Example 4.4.

Solution A sketch of the function $f(t)$ over the interval $-4\pi < t < 4\pi$ is shown in Figure 4.7. Clearly $f(t)$ is an odd function of t, so that its Fourier series expansion consists of sine terms only. Taking $T = 2\pi$, that is $\omega = 1$, in (4.19) and (4.20), the Fourier series expansion is given by

$$f(t) = \sum_{n=1}^{\infty} b_n \sin nt$$

with

$$\begin{aligned} b_n &= \frac{2}{\pi}\int_0^{\pi} f(t)\sin nt \, dt \quad (n = 1, 2, 3, \dots) \\ &= \frac{2}{\pi}\int_0^{\pi} 1 \sin nt \, dt = \frac{2}{\pi}\left[-\frac{1}{n}\cos nt\right]_0^{\pi} \\ &= \frac{2}{n\pi}(1 - \cos n\pi) = \frac{2}{n\pi}[1 - (-1)^n] \\ &= \begin{cases} 4/n\pi & (\text{odd } n) \\ 0 & (\text{even } n) \end{cases} \end{aligned}$$

Thus the Fourier series expansion of $f(t)$ is

$$f(t) = \frac{4}{\pi}\left(\sin t + \tfrac{1}{3}\sin 3t + \tfrac{1}{5}\sin 5t + \dots\right) = \frac{4}{\pi}\sum_{n=1}^{\infty}\frac{\sin(2n-1)t}{2n-1} \qquad (4.21)$$

Example 4.5

A periodic function $f(t)$ with period 2π is defined as

$$f(t) = t^2 \quad (-\pi < t < \pi), \qquad f(t) = f(t + 2\pi)$$

Obtain a Fourier series expansion for it.

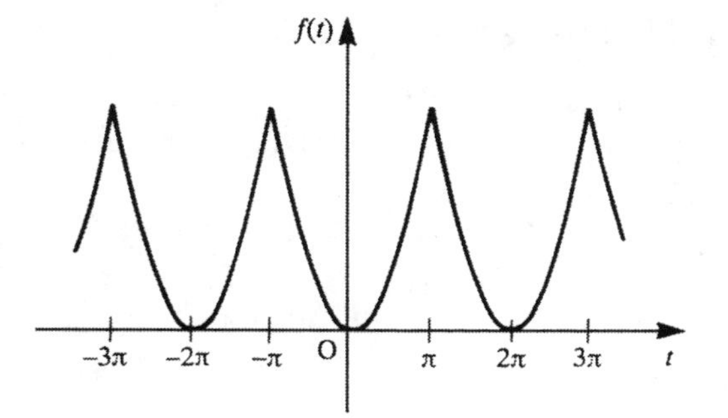

Figure 4.8 The function $f(t)$ of Example 4.5.

Solution A sketch of the function $f(t)$ over the interval $-3\pi < t < 3\pi$ is shown is Figure 4.8. Clearly, $f(t)$ is an even function of t, so that its Fourier series expansion consists of cosine terms only. Taking $T = 2\pi$, that is $\omega = 1$, in (4.17) and (4.18), the Fourier series expansion is given by

$$f(t) = \tfrac{1}{2}a_0 + \sum_{n=1}^{\infty} a_n \cos nt$$

with

$$a_0 = \frac{2}{\pi}\int_0^{\pi} f(t)\,\mathrm{d}t = \frac{2}{\pi}\int_0^{\pi} t^2\,\mathrm{d}t = \tfrac{2}{3}\pi^2$$

and

$$\begin{aligned} a_n &= \frac{2}{\pi}\int_0^{\pi} f(t)\cos nt\,\mathrm{d}t \quad (n = 1, 2, 3, \dots) \\ &= \frac{2}{\pi}\int_0^{\pi} t^2 \cos nt\,\mathrm{d}t \\ &= \frac{2}{\pi}\left[\frac{t^2}{n}\sin nt + \frac{2t}{n^2}\cos nt - \frac{2}{n^3}\sin nt\right]_0^{\pi} \\ &= \frac{2}{\pi}\left(\frac{2\pi}{n^2}\cos n\pi\right) = \frac{4}{n^2}(-1)^n \end{aligned}$$

since $\sin n\pi = 0$ and $\cos n\pi = (-1)^n$. Thus the Fourier series expansion of $f(t) = t^2$ is

$$f(t) = \tfrac{1}{3}\pi^2 + 4\sum_{n=1}^{\infty} \frac{(-1)^n}{n^2}\cos nt \tag{4.22}$$

or, writing out the first few terms,

$$f(t) = \tfrac{1}{3}\pi^2 - 4\cos t + \cos 2t - \tfrac{4}{9}\cos 3t + \dots$$

4.2.6 Even and odd harmonics

In this section we consider types of symmetry that can be identified in order to eliminate terms from the Fourier series expansion having even values of n (including $n = 0$) or odd values of n.

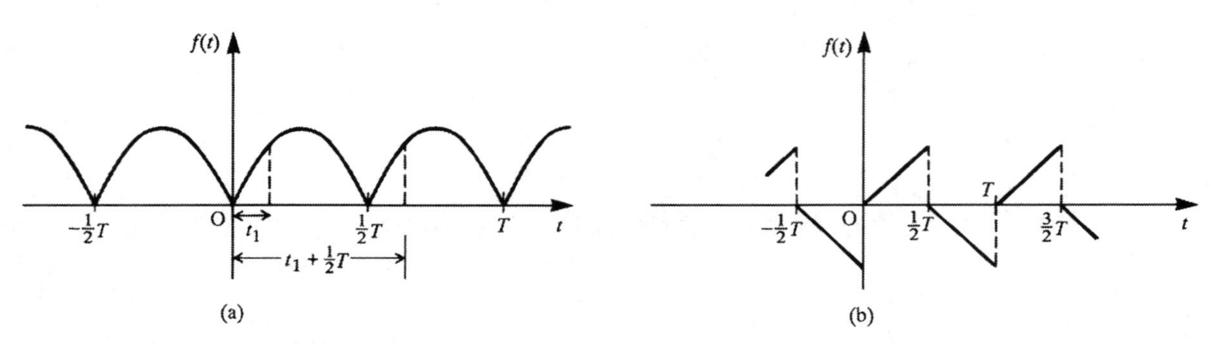

Figure 4.9 Functions having Fourier series with (a) only even harmonics and (b) only odd harmonics.

(a) If a periodic function $f(t)$ is such that

$$f(t + \tfrac{1}{2}T) = f(t)$$

then it has period $T/2$ and frequency $\omega = 2(2\pi/T)$ so only even harmonics are present in its Fourier series expansion. For even n we have

$$a_n = \frac{4}{T}\int_0^{T/2} f(t)\cos n\omega t\,dt \tag{4.23}$$

$$b_n = \frac{4}{T}\int_0^{T/2} f(t)\sin n\omega t\,dt \tag{4.24}$$

An example of such a function is given in Figure 4.9(a).

(b) If a periodic function $f(t)$ with period T is such that

$$f(t + \tfrac{1}{2}T) = -f(t)$$

then only odd harmonics are present in its Fourier series expansion. For odd n

$$a_n = \frac{4}{T}\int_0^{T/2} f(t)\cos n\omega t\,dt \tag{4.25}$$

$$b_n = \frac{4}{T}\int_0^{T/2} f(t)\sin n\omega t\,dt \tag{4.26}$$

An example of such a function is shown in Figure 4.9(b).

The square wave of Example 4.4 is such that $f(t + \pi) = -f(t)$, so that, from (b), its Fourier series expansion consists of only odd harmonics. Since it is also an odd function, it follows that its Fourier series expansion consists only of odd-harmonic sine terms, which is confirmed by the result (4.21).

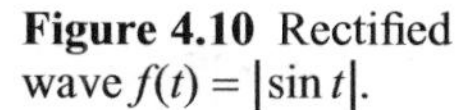

Example 4.6 Obtain the Fourier series expansion of the rectified sine wave

$$f(t) = |\sin t|$$

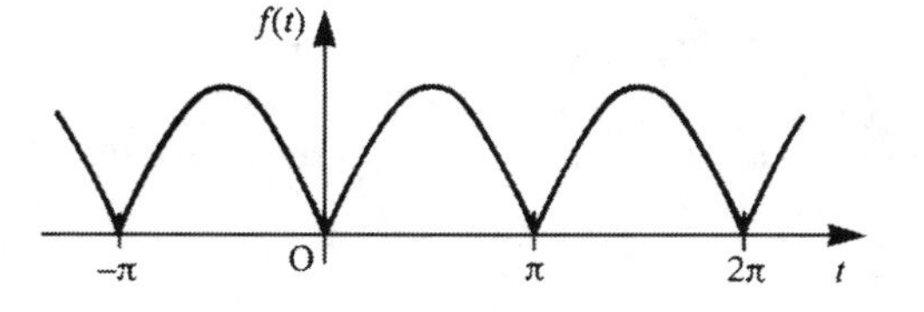

Figure 4.10 Rectified wave $f(t) = |\sin t|$.

Solution A sketch of the wave over the interval $-\pi < t < 2\pi$ is shown in Figure 4.10. Clearly, $f(t + \pi) = f(t)$ so that only even harmonics are present in the Fourier series expansion. Since the function is also an even function of t, it follows that the Fourier series expansion will consist only of even-harmonic cosine terms. Taking $T = 2\pi$, that is $\omega = 1$, in (4.23), the coefficients of the even harmonics are given by

$$a_n = \frac{2}{\pi}\int_0^{\pi} f(t)\cos nt \quad (\text{even } n) \quad = \frac{2}{\pi}\int_0^{\pi} \sin t \cos nt \, dt$$

$$= \frac{1}{\pi}\int_0^{\pi} [\sin(n+1)t - \sin(n-1)t]\, dt$$

$$= \frac{1}{\pi}\left[-\frac{\cos(n+1)t}{n+1} + \frac{\cos(n-1)t}{n-1}\right]_0^{\pi}$$

Since both $n + 1$ and $n - 1$ are odd when n is even,

$$\cos(n+1)\pi = \cos(n-1)\pi = -1$$

so that

$$a_n = \frac{1}{\pi}\left[\left(\frac{1}{n+1} - \frac{1}{n-1}\right) - \left(-\frac{1}{n+1} + \frac{1}{n-1}\right)\right] = -\frac{4}{\pi}\frac{1}{n^2 - 1}$$

Thus the Fourier series expansion of $f(t)$ is

$$f(t) = \tfrac{1}{2}a_0 + \sum_{\substack{n=2 \\ (n \text{ even})}}^{\infty} a_n \cos nt = \frac{2}{\pi} - \frac{4}{\pi}\sum_{\substack{n=2 \\ (n \text{ even})}}^{\infty} \frac{1}{n^2 - 1}\cos nt$$

$$= \frac{2}{\pi} - \frac{4}{\pi}\sum_{n=1}^{\infty} \frac{1}{4n^2 - 1}\cos 2nt$$

or, writing out the first few terms,

$$f(t) = \frac{2}{\pi} - \frac{4}{\pi}\left(\tfrac{1}{3}\cos 2t + \tfrac{1}{15}\cos 4t + \tfrac{1}{35}\cos 6t + \ldots\right)$$

4.2.7 Linearity property

The linearity property as applied to Fourier series may be stated in the form of the following theorem.

Theorem 4.1 If $f(t) = lg(t) + mh(t)$, where $g(t)$ and $h(t)$ are periodic functions of period T and l and m are arbitrary constants, then $f(t)$ has a Fourier series expansion in which the coefficients are the sums of the coefficients in the Fourier series expansions of $g(t)$ and $h(t)$ multiplied by l and m respectively.

Proof Clearly $f(t)$ is periodic with period T. If the Fourier series expansions of $g(t)$ and $h(t)$ are

$$g(t) = \tfrac{1}{2}a_0 + \sum_{n=1}^{\infty} a_n \cos n\omega t + \sum_{n=1}^{\infty} b_n \sin n\omega t$$

$$h(t) = \tfrac{1}{2}\alpha_0 + \sum_{n=1}^{\infty} \alpha_n \cos n\omega t + \sum_{n=1}^{\infty} \beta_n \sin n\omega t$$

then, using (4.11) and (4.12), the Fourier coefficients in the expansion of $f(t)$ are

$$A_n = \frac{2}{T}\int_d^{d+T} f(t)\cos n\omega t\,\mathrm{d}t = \frac{2}{T}\int_d^{d+T} [lg(t) + mh(t)]\cos n\omega t\,\mathrm{d}t$$

$$= \frac{2l}{T}\int_d^{d+T} g(t)\cos n\omega t\,\mathrm{d}t + \frac{2m}{T}\int_d^{d+T} h(t)\cos n\omega t\,\mathrm{d}t$$

$$= la_n + m\alpha_n$$

and

$$B_n = \frac{2}{T}\int_d^{d+T} f(t)\sin n\omega t\,\mathrm{d}t = \frac{2l}{T}\int_d^{d+T} g(t)\sin n\omega t\,\mathrm{d}t + \frac{2m}{T}\int_d^{d+T} h(t)\sin n\omega t\,\mathrm{d}t$$

$$= lb_n + m\beta_n$$

confirming that the Fourier series expansion of $f(t)$ is

$$f(t) = \tfrac{1}{2}(la_0 + m\alpha_0) + \sum_{n=1}^{\infty}(la_n + m\alpha_n)\cos n\omega t + \sum_{n=1}^{\infty}(lb_n + m\beta_n)\sin n\omega t$$

end of theorem

Example 4.7 Suppose that $g(t)$ and $h(t)$ are periodic functions of period 2π and are defined within the period $-\pi < t < \pi$ by

$$g(t) = t^2, \quad h(t) = t$$

Determine the Fourier series expansions of both $g(t)$ and $h(t)$ and use the linearity property to confirm the expansion obtained in Example 4.2 for the periodic function $f(t)$ defined within the period $-\pi < t < \pi$ by $f(t) = t^2 + t$.

Solution The Fourier series of $g(t)$ is given by (4.22) as

$$g(t) = \tfrac{1}{3}\pi^2 + 4\sum_{n=1}^{\infty} \frac{(-1)^n}{n^2} \cos nt$$

Recognizing that $h(t) = t$ is an odd function of t, we find, taking $T = 2\pi$ and $\omega = 1$ in (4.19) and (4.20), that its Fourier series expansion is

$$h(t) = \sum_{n=1}^{\infty} b_n \sin nt$$

where

$$b_n = \frac{2}{\pi}\int_0^{\pi} h(t) \sin nt \, dt \quad (n = 1, 2, 3, \dots)$$

$$= \frac{2}{\pi}\int_0^{\pi} t \sin nt \, dt = \frac{2}{\pi}\left[-\frac{t}{n}\cos nt + \frac{\sin nt}{n^2}\right]_0^{\pi}$$

$$= -\frac{2}{n}(-1)^n$$

recognizing again that $\cos n\pi = (-1)^n$ and $\sin n\pi = 0$. Thus the Fourier series expansion of $h(t) = t$ is

$$h(t) = -2\sum_{n=1}^{\infty} \frac{(-1)^n}{n} \sin nt \tag{4.27}$$

Using the linearity property, we find, by combining (4.12) and (4.27), that the Fourier series expansion of $f(t) = g(t) + h(t) = t^2 + t$ is

$$f(t) = \tfrac{1}{3}\pi^2 + 4\sum_{n=1}^{\infty} \frac{(-1)^n}{n^2} \cos nt - 2\sum_{n=1}^{\infty} \frac{(-1)^n}{n} \sin nt$$

which conforms to the series obtained in Example 4.2.

4.2.8 Convergence of the Fourier series

So far we have concentrated our attention on determining the Fourier series expansion corresponding to a given periodic function $f(t)$. In reality, this is an exercise in integration, since we merely have to compute the coefficients a_n and b_n using Euler's formulae (4.11) and (4.12) and then substitute these values into (4.3). We have not yet considered the question of whether or not the Fourier series thus obtained is a valid representation of the periodic function $f(t)$. It should not be assumed that the existence of the coefficients a_n and b_n in itself implies that the associated series converges to the function $f(t)$.

A full discussion of the convergence of a Fourier series is beyond the scope of this book and we shall confine ourselves to simply stating a set of conditions which ensures that $f(t)$ has a convergent Fourier series expansion. These conditions, known as **Dirichlet's conditions**, may be stated in the form of Theorem 4.2.

Theorem 4.2 **Dirichlet's conditions**

If $f(t)$ is a bounded periodic function that in any period has

(a) a finite number of isolated maxima and minima, and

(b) a finite number of points of finite discontinuity

then the Fourier series expansion of $f(t)$ converges to $f(t)$ at all points where $f(t)$ is continuous and to the average of the right- and left-hand limits of $f(t)$ at points where $f(t)$ is discontinuous (that is, to the mean of the discontinuity).

end of theorem

Example 4.8 Give reasons why the functions

(a) $\dfrac{1}{3-t}$ (b) $\sin\left(\dfrac{1}{t-2}\right)$

do not satisfy Dirichlet's conditions in the interval $0 < t < 2\pi$.

Solution (a) The function $f(t) = 1/(3 - t)$ has an infinite discontinuity at $t = 3$, which is within the interval, and therefore does not satisfy the condition that $f(t)$ must only have *finite* discontinuities within a period (that is, it is bounded).

(b) The function $f(t) = \sin[1/(t - 2)]$ has an infinite number of maxima and minima in the neighbourbood of $t = 2$, which is within the interval, and therefore does not satisfy the requirement that $f(t)$ must have only a finite number of isolated maxima and minima within one period.

The conditions of Theorem 4.2 are sufficient to ensure that a representative Fourier series expansion of $f(t)$ exists. However, they are not necessary conditions for convergence, and it does not follow that a representative Fourier series does not exist if they are not satisfied. Indeed, necessary conditions on $f(t)$ for the existence of a convergent Fourier series are not yet known. In practice, this does not cause any problems, since for almost all conceivable practical applications the functions that are encountered satisfy the conditions of Theorem 4.2 and therefore have representative Fourier series.

Another issue of importance in practical applications is the rate of convergence of a Fourier series, since this is an indication of how many terms must be taken in the expansion in order to obtain a realistic approximation to the function $f(t)$ it represents. Obviously, this is determined by the coefficients a_n and b_n of the Fourier series and the manner in which these decrease as n increases.

In an example, such as Example 4.1, in which the function $f(t)$ is only piecewise-continuous, exhibiting jump discontinuities, the Fourier coefficients decrease as $1/n$, and it may be necessary to include a large number of terms to obtain an adequate approximation to $f(t)$. In an example, such as Example 4.3, in which the function is a continuous function but has discontinuous first derivatives (owing to the sharp corners), the Fourier coefficients decrease as $1/n^2$, and so one would expect the series to converge more rapidly. Indeed, this argument applies in general, and we may summarize as follows:

(a) if $f(t)$ is only piecewise-continuous then the coefficients in its Fourier series representation decrease as $1/n$;

(b) if $f(t)$ is continuous everywhere but has discontinuous first derivatives then the coefficients in its Fourier series representation decrease as $1/n^2$;

(c) if $f(t)$ and all its derivatives up to that of the rth order are continuous but the $(r + 1)$th derivative is discontinuous then the coefficients in its Fourier series representation decrease as $1/n^{r+2}$.

These observations are not surprising, since they simply tell us that the smoother the function $f(t)$, the more rapidly will its Fourier series representation converge.

To illustrate some of these issues related to convergence we return to Example 4.4, in which the Fourier series (4.21) was obtained as a representation of the square wave of Figure 4.7.

Since (4.21) is an infinite series, it is clearly not possible to plot a graph of the result. However, by considering finite partial sums, it is possible to plot graphs of approximations to the series. Denoting the sum of the first N terms in the infinite series by $f_N(t)$, that is

$$f_N(t) = \frac{4}{\pi}\sum_{n=1}^{N}\frac{\sin(2n-1)t}{2n-1} \tag{4.28}$$

the graphs of $f_N(t)$ for $N = 1, 2, 3$ and 20 are as shown in Figure 4.11. It can be seen that at points where $f(t)$ is continuous the approximation of $f(t)$ by $f_N(t)$ improves as N increases, confirming that the series converges to $f(t)$ at all such points. It can also be seen that at points of discontinuity of $f(t)$, which occur at $t = \pm n\pi$ ($n = 0, 1, 2, \dots$), the series converges to the mean value of the discontinuity, which in this particular example is $\frac{1}{2}(-1 + 1) = 0$. As a consequence, the equality sign in (4.21) needs to be interpreted carefully. Although such use may be acceptable, in the sense that the series

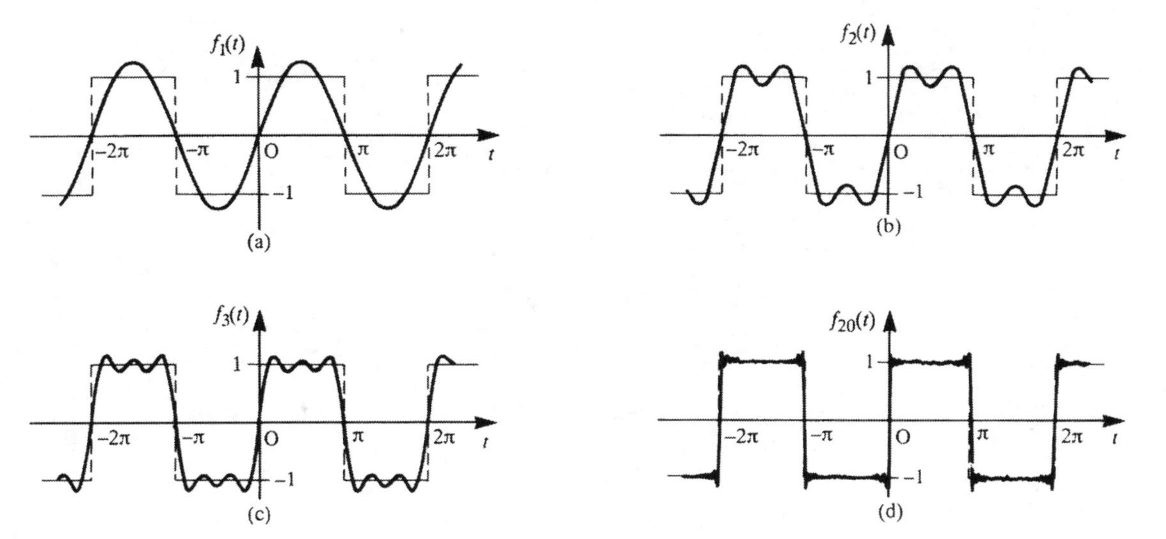

Figure 4.11 Plots of $f_N(t)$ for a square wave: (a) $N = 1$; (b) 2; (c) 3; (d) 20.

converges to $f(t)$ for values of t where $f(t)$ is continuous, this is not so at points of discontinuity. To overcome this problem, the symbol ~ (read as 'behaves as' or 'represented by') rather than = is frequently used in the Fourier series representation of a function $f(t)$, so that (4.21) is often written as

$$f(t) \sim \frac{4}{\pi} \sum_{n=1}^{\infty} \frac{\sin(2n-1)t}{2n-1}$$

In Section 4.7.3 it is shown that the Fourier series converges to $f(t)$ in the sense that the integral of the square of the difference between $f(t)$ and $f_N(t)$ is minimized and tends to zero as $N \to \infty$.

We note that convergence of the Fourier series is slowest near a point of discontinuity, such as the one that occurs at $t = 0$. Although the series does converge to the mean value of the discontinuity (namely zero) at $t = 0$, there is, as indicated in Figure 4.11(d), an undershoot at $t = 0^-$ (that is, just to the left of $t = 0$) and an overshoot at $t = 0^+$ (that is, just to the right of $t = 0$). This non-smooth convergence of the Fourier series leading to the occurrence of an undershoot and an overshoot at points of discontinuity of $f(t)$ is a characteristic of all Fourier series representing discontinuous functions, not only that of the square wave of Example 4.4, and is known as **Gibbs' phenomenon** after the American physicist J. W. Gibbs (1839–1903). The magnitude of the undershoot/overshoot does not diminish as $N \to \infty$ in (4.28), but simply gets 'sharper' and 'sharper', tending to a spike. In general, the magnitude of the undershoot and overshoot together amount to about 18% of the magnitude of the discontinuity (that is, the difference in the values of the function $f(t)$ to the left and right of the discontinuity). It is important that the existence of this phenomenon be recognized, since in certain practical applications these spikes at discontinuities have to be suppressed by using appropriate smoothing factors.

To reproduce the plots of Figure 4.11 and see how the series converges as N increases use the following MATLAB commands:

```
t=pi/100*[300:300];
f=0;
T=[-3*pi -2*pi -2*pi -pi -pi 0 0 pi pi 2*pi 2*pi 3*pi];
y=[-1 -1 1 1 -1 -1 1 1 -1 -1 1 1];
for n=1:20
f=f+4/pi*sin((2*n-1)*t)/(2*n-1);
plot(T,y,t,f,[-3*pi 3*pi],[0,0],'k-',[0,0],[-1.3 1.3],'k-')
axis([-3*pi,3*pi,-inf,inf]),pause
end
```

The `pause` command has been included to give you an opportunity to view the plots at the end of each step. Press any key to proceed.

Theoretically, we can use the series (4.21) to obtain an approximation to π. This is achieved by taking $t = \frac{1}{2}\pi$, when $f(t) = 1$; (4.21) then gives

$$1 = \frac{4}{\pi} \sum_{n=1}^{\infty} \frac{\sin \frac{1}{2}(2n-1)\pi}{2n-1}$$

leading to

$$\pi = 4(1 - \tfrac{1}{3} + \tfrac{1}{5} - \tfrac{1}{7} + \dots) = 4\sum_{n=1}^{\infty} \frac{(-1)^{n+1}}{2n-1}$$

For practical purposes, however, this is not a good way of obtaining an approximation to π, because of the slow rate of convergence of the series.

4.2.9 Exercises

1 In each of the following a periodic function $f(t)$ of period 2π is specified over one period. In each case sketch a graph of the function for $-4\pi \leqslant t \leqslant 4\pi$ and obtain a Fourier series representation of the function.

(a) $f(t) = \begin{cases} -\pi & (-\pi < t < 0) \\ t & (0 < t < \pi) \end{cases}$

(b) $f(t) = \begin{cases} t + \pi & (-\pi < t < 0) \\ 0 & (0 < t < \pi) \end{cases}$

(c) $f(t) = 1 - \dfrac{t}{\pi} \quad (0 \leqslant t \leqslant 2\pi)$

(d) $f(t) = \begin{cases} 0 & (-\pi \leqslant t \leqslant -\frac{1}{2}\pi) \\ 2\cos t & (-\frac{1}{2}\pi \leqslant t \leqslant \frac{1}{2}\pi) \\ 0 & (\frac{1}{2}\pi \leqslant t \leqslant \pi) \end{cases}$

(e) $f(t) = \cos\frac{1}{2}t \quad (-\pi < t < \pi)$

(f) $f(t) = |t| \quad (-\pi < t < \pi)$

(g) $f(t) = \begin{cases} 0 & (-\pi \leqslant t \leqslant 0) \\ 2t - \pi & (0 < t \leqslant \pi) \end{cases}$

(h) $f(t) = \begin{cases} -t + e^t & (-\pi \leqslant t < 0) \\ t + e^t & (0 \leqslant t < \pi) \end{cases}$

2 Obtain the Fourier series expansion of the periodic function $f(t)$ of period 2π defined over the period $0 \leqslant t \leqslant 2\pi$ by

$$f(t) = (\pi - t)^2 \quad (0 \leqslant t \leqslant 2\pi)$$

Use the Fourier series to show that

$$\tfrac{1}{12}\pi^2 = \sum_{n=1}^{\infty} \frac{(-1)^{n+1}}{n^2}$$

3 The charge $q(t)$ on the plates of a capacitor at time t is as shown in Figure 4.12. Express $q(t)$ as a Fourier series expansion.

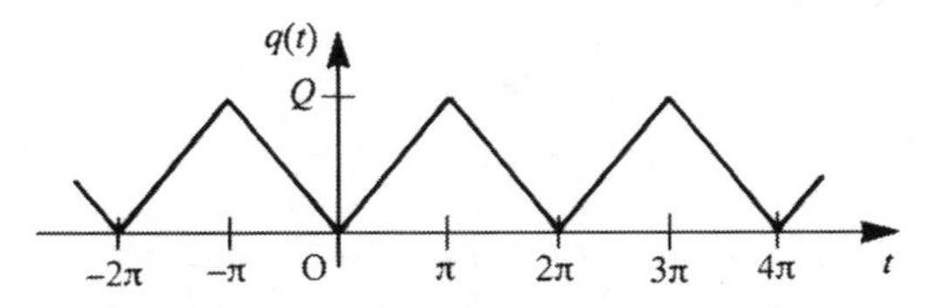

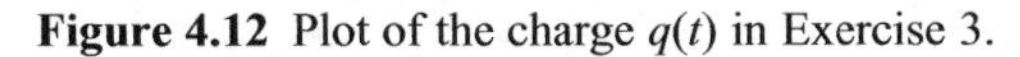

Figure 4.12 Plot of the charge $q(t)$ in Exercise 3.

4 The clipped response of a half-wave rectifier is the periodic function $f(t)$ of period 2π defined over the period $0 \leqslant t \leqslant 2\pi$ by

$$f(t) = \begin{cases} 5\sin t & (0 \leqslant t \leqslant \pi) \\ 0 & (\pi \leqslant t \leqslant 2\pi) \end{cases}$$

Express $f(t)$ as a Fourier series expansion.

5 Show that the Fourier series representing the periodic function $f(t)$, where

$$f(t) = \begin{cases} \pi^2 & (-\pi < t < 0) \\ (t - \pi)^2 & (0 < t < \pi) \end{cases}$$

$$f(t + 2\pi) = f(t)$$

is

$$f(t) = \tfrac{2}{3}\pi^2 + \sum_{n=1}^{\infty}\left[\frac{2}{n^2}\cos nt + \frac{(-1)^n}{n}\pi\sin nt\right] - \frac{4}{\pi}\sum_{n=1}^{\infty}\frac{\sin(2n-1)t}{(2n-1)^3}$$

Use this result to show that

(a) $\displaystyle\sum_{n=1}^{\infty}\frac{1}{n^2} = \tfrac{1}{6}\pi^2$ (b) $\displaystyle\sum_{n=1}^{\infty}\frac{(-1)^{n+1}}{n^2} = \tfrac{1}{12}\pi^2$

6 A periodic function $f(t)$ of period 2π is defined within the domain $0 \leqslant t \leqslant \pi$ by

$$f(t) = \begin{cases} t & (0 \leqslant t \leqslant \frac{1}{2}\pi) \\ \pi - t & (\frac{1}{2}\pi \leqslant t \leqslant \pi) \end{cases}$$

Sketch a graph of $f(t)$ for $-2\pi < t < 4\pi$ for the two cases where

(a) $f(t)$ is an even function
(b) $f(t)$ is an odd function

Find the Fourier series expansion that represents the even function for all values of t, and use it to show that

$$\tfrac{1}{8}\pi^2 = \sum_{n=1}^{\infty} \frac{1}{(2n-1)^2}$$

7 A periodic function $f(t)$ of period 2π is defined within the period $0 \leqslant t \leqslant 2\pi$ by

$$f(t) = \begin{cases} 2 - t/\pi & (0 \leqslant t \leqslant \pi) \\ t/\pi & (\pi \leqslant t \leqslant 2\pi) \end{cases}$$

Draw a graph of the function for $-4\pi \leqslant t \leqslant 4\pi$ and obtain its Fourier series expansion.

By replacing t by $t - \tfrac{1}{2}\pi$ in your answer, show that the periodic function $f(t - \tfrac{1}{2}\pi) - \tfrac{3}{2}$ is represented by a sine series of odd harmonics.

4.2.10 Functions of period T

Although all the results have been related to periodic functions having period T, all the examples we have considered so far have involved periodic functions of period 2π. This was done primarily for ease of manipulation in determining the Fourier coefficients while becoming acquainted with Fourier series. As mentioned in Section 4.2.4, functions having unit frequency (that is, of period 2π) are rarely encountered in practice, and in this section we consider examples of periodic functions having periods other than 2π.

Example 4.9 A periodic function $f(t)$ of period 4 (that is, $f(t + 4) = f(t)$) is defined in the range $-2 < t < 2$ by

$$f(t) = \begin{cases} 0 & (-2 < t < 0) \\ 1 & (0 < t < 2) \end{cases}$$

Sketch a graph of $f(t)$ for $-6 \leqslant t \leqslant 6$ and obtain a Fourier series expansion for the function.

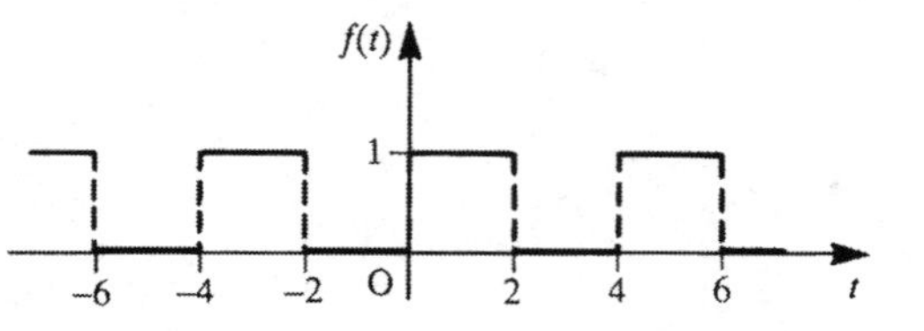

Figure 4.13 The function $f(t)$ of Example 4.9.

Solution A graph of $f(t)$ for $-6 \leqslant t \leqslant 6$ is shown in Figure 4.13. Taking $T = 4$ in (4.11) and (4.12), we have

$$a_0 = \tfrac{1}{2}\int_{-2}^{2} f(t)\,\mathrm{d}t = \tfrac{1}{2}\left(\int_{-2}^{0} 0\,\mathrm{d}t + \int_{0}^{2} 1\,\mathrm{d}t\right) = 1$$

$$a_n = \tfrac{1}{2}\int_{-2}^{2} f(t)\cos\tfrac{1}{2}n\pi t\,\mathrm{d}t \quad (n = 1, 2, 3, \dots)$$

$$= \tfrac{1}{2}\left(\int_{-2}^{0} 0\,\mathrm{d}t + \int_{0}^{2} \cos\tfrac{1}{2}n\pi t\,\mathrm{d}t\right) = 0$$

and

$$b_n = \tfrac{1}{2}\int_{-2}^{2} f(t)\sin \tfrac{1}{2}n\pi t\,dt \quad (n = 1, 2, 3, \dots)$$

$$= \tfrac{1}{2}\left(\int_{-2}^{0} 0\,dt + \int_{0}^{2} \sin \tfrac{1}{2}n\pi t\,dt\right) = \frac{1}{n\pi}(1 - \cos n\pi) = \frac{1}{n\pi}[1 - (-1)^n]$$

$$= \begin{cases} 0 & (\text{even } n) \\ 2/n\pi & (\text{odd } n) \end{cases}$$

Thus, from (4.10), the Fourier series expansion of $f(t)$ is

$$f(t) = \tfrac{1}{2} + \frac{2}{\pi}(\sin \tfrac{1}{2}\pi t + \tfrac{1}{3}\sin \tfrac{3}{2}\pi t + \tfrac{1}{5}\sin \tfrac{5}{2}\pi t + \dots)$$

$$= \tfrac{1}{2} + \frac{2}{\pi}\sum_{n=1}^{\infty} \frac{1}{2n-1}\sin \tfrac{1}{2}(2n-1)\pi t$$

Example 4.10

A periodic function $f(t)$ of period 2 is defined by

$$f(t) = \begin{cases} 3t & (0 < t < 1) \\ 3 & (1 < t < 2) \end{cases}$$

$$f(t + 2) = f(t)$$

Sketch a graph of $f(t)$ for $-4 \leqslant t \leqslant 4$ and determine a Fourier series expansion for the function.

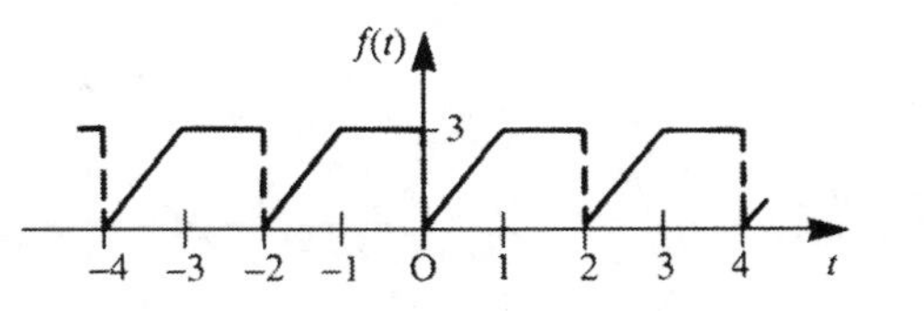

Figure 4.14 The function $f(t)$ of Example 4.10.

Solution A graph of $f(t)$ for $-4 \leqslant t \leqslant 4$ is shown in Figure 4.14. Taking $T = 2$ in (4.11) and (4.12), we have

$$a_0 = \tfrac{2}{2}\int_{0}^{2} f(t)\,dt = \int_{0}^{1} 3t\,dt + \int_{1}^{2} 3\,dt = \tfrac{9}{2}$$

$$a_n = \tfrac{2}{2}\int_{0}^{2} f(t)\cos\frac{n\pi t}{1}\,dt \quad (n = 1, 2, 3, \dots)$$

$$= \int_{0}^{1} 3t\cos n\pi t\,dt + \int_{1}^{2} 3\cos n\pi t\,dt$$

$$= \left[\frac{3t\sin n\pi t}{n\pi} + \frac{3\cos n\pi t}{(n\pi)^2}\right]_0^1 + \left[\frac{3\sin n\pi t}{n\pi}\right]_1^2$$

$$= \frac{3}{(n\pi)^2}(\cos n\pi - 1) = \begin{cases} 0 & (\text{even } n) \\ -6/(n\pi)^2 & (\text{odd } n) \end{cases}$$

and

$$\begin{aligned} b_n &= \tfrac{2}{2}\int_0^2 f(t)\sin\frac{n\pi t}{1}\,dt \quad (n = 1, 2, 3, \dots) \\ &= \int_0^1 3t\sin n\pi t\,dt + \int_1^2 3\sin n\pi t\,dt \\ &= \left[-\frac{3\cos n\pi t}{n\pi} + \frac{3\sin n\pi t}{(n\pi)^2}\right]_0^1 + \left[-\frac{3\cos n\pi t}{n\pi}\right]_1^2 = -\frac{3}{n\pi}\cos 2n\pi = -\frac{3}{n\pi} \end{aligned}$$

Thus, from (4.10), the Fourier series expansion of $f(t)$ is

$$\begin{aligned} f(t) &= \tfrac{9}{4} - \frac{6}{\pi^2}(\cos \pi t + \tfrac{1}{9}\cos 3\pi t + \tfrac{1}{25}\cos 5\pi t + \dots) \\ &\quad - \frac{3}{\pi}(\sin \pi t + \tfrac{1}{2}\sin 2\pi t + \tfrac{1}{3}\sin 3\pi t + \dots) \\ &= \tfrac{9}{4} - \frac{6}{\pi^2}\sum_{n=1}^{\infty}\frac{\cos(2n-1)\pi t}{(2n-1)^2} - \frac{3}{\pi}\sum_{n=1}^{\infty}\frac{\sin n\pi t}{n} \end{aligned}$$

4.2.11 Exercises

8 Find a Fourier series expansion of the periodic function

$$f(t) = t \quad (-l < t < l)$$
$$f(t + 2l) = f(t)$$

9 A periodic function $f(t)$ of period $2l$ is defined over one period by

$$f(t) = \begin{cases} -\dfrac{K}{l}(l + t) & (-l < t < 0) \\ \dfrac{K}{l}(l - t) & (0 < t < l) \end{cases}$$

Determine its Fourier series expansion and illustrate graphically for $-3l < t < 3l$.

10 A periodic function of period 10 is defined within the period $-5 < t < 5$ by

$$f(t) = \begin{cases} 0 & (-5 < t < 0) \\ 3 & (0 < t < 5) \end{cases}$$

Determine its Fourier series expansion and illustrate graphically for $-12 < t < 12$.

11 Passing a sinusoidal voltage $A \sin \omega t$ through a half-wave rectifier produces the clipped sine wave shown in Figure 4.15. Determine a Fourier series expansion of the rectified wave.

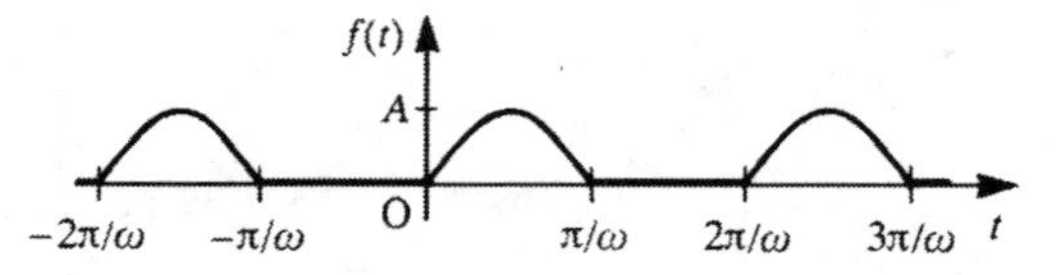

Figure 4.15 Rectified sine wave of Exercise 11.

12 Obtain a Fourier series expansion of the periodic function

$$f(t) = t^2 \quad (-T < t < T)$$
$$f(t + 2T) = f(t)$$

and illustrate graphically for $-3T < t < 3T$.

13 Determine a Fourier series representation of the periodic voltage $e(t)$ shown in Figure 4.16.

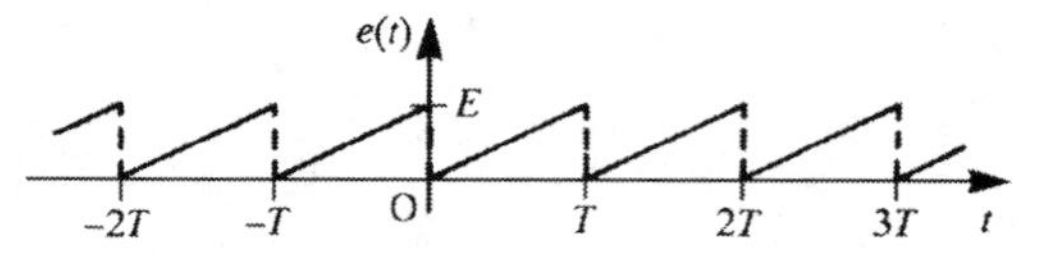

Figure 4.16 Voltage $e(t)$ of Exercise 13.

4.3 Functions defined over a finite interval

One of the requirements of Fourier's theorem is that the function to be expanded be periodic. Therefore a function $f(t)$ that is not periodic cannot have a Fourier series representation that converges to it *for all values* of t. However, we can obtain a Fourier series expansion that represents a *non-periodic* function $f(t)$ that is defined only over a finite time interval $0 \leqslant t \leqslant \tau$. This is a facility that is frequently used to solve problems in practice, particularly boundary-value problems involving partial differential equations, such as the consideration of heat flow along a bar or the vibrations of a string. Various forms of Fourier series representations of $f(t)$, valid only in the interval $0 \leqslant t \leqslant \tau$, are possible, including series consisting of cosine terms only or series consisting of sine terms only. To obtain these, various periodic extensions of $f(t)$ are formulated.

4.3.1 Full-range series

Suppose the given function $f(t)$ is defined only over the finite time interval $0 \leqslant t \leqslant \tau$. Then, to obtain a full-range Fourier series representation of $f(t)$ (that is, a series consisting of both cosine and sine terms), we define the **periodic extension** $\phi(t)$ of $f(t)$ by

$$\phi(t) = f(t) \quad (0 < t < \tau)$$

$$\phi(t + \tau) = \phi(t)$$

The graphs of a possible $f(t)$ and its periodic extension $\phi(t)$ are shown in Figures 4.17(a) and (b) respectively.

Provided that $f(t)$ satisfies Dirichlet's conditions in the interval $0 \leqslant t \leqslant \tau$, the new function $\phi(t)$, of period τ, will have a convergent Fourier series expansion. Since, within the particular period $0 < t < \tau$, $\phi(t)$ is identical with $f(t)$, it follows that this Fourier series expansion of $\phi(t)$ will be representative of $f(t)$ within this interval.

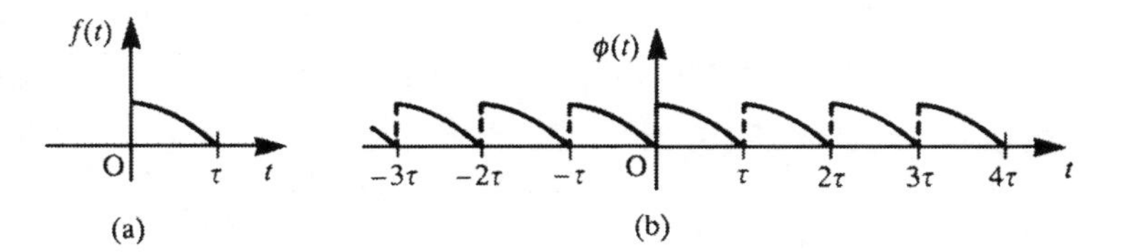

Figure 4.17 Graphs of a function defined only over (a) a finite interval $0 \leqslant t \leqslant \tau$ and (b) its periodic extension.

Example 4.11

Find a full-range Fourier series expansion of $f(t) = t$ valid in the finite interval $0 < t < 4$. Draw graphs of both $f(t)$ and the periodic function represented by the Fourier series obtained.

Solution Define the periodic function $\phi(t)$ by

$$\phi(t) = f(t) = t \quad (0 < t < 4)$$

$$\phi(t + 4) = \phi(t)$$

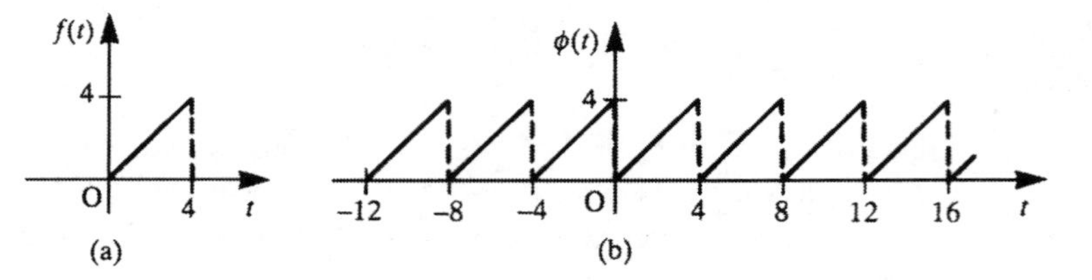

Figure 4.18 The functions $f(t)$ and $\phi(t)$ of Example 4.11.

Then the graphs of $f(t)$ and its periodic extension $\phi(t)$ are as shown in Figures 4.18(a) and (b) respectively. Since $\phi(t)$ is a periodic function with period 4, it has a convergent Fourier series expansion. Taking $T = 4$ in (4.11) and (4.12), the Fourier coefficients are determined as

$$a_0 = \tfrac{1}{2}\int_0^4 f(t)\,\mathrm{d}t = \tfrac{1}{2}\int_0^4 t\,\mathrm{d}t = 4$$

$$a_n = \tfrac{1}{2}\int_0^4 f(t)\cos\tfrac{1}{2}n\pi t\,\mathrm{d}t \quad (n = 1, 2, 3, \dots)$$

$$= \tfrac{1}{2}\int_0^4 t\cos\tfrac{1}{2}n\pi t\,\mathrm{d}t = \tfrac{1}{2}\left[\frac{2t}{n\pi}\sin\tfrac{1}{2}n\pi t + \frac{4}{(n\pi)^2}\cos\tfrac{1}{2}n\pi t\right]_0^4 = 0$$

and

$$b_n = \tfrac{1}{2}\int_0^4 f(t)\sin\tfrac{1}{2}n\pi t\,\mathrm{d}t \quad (n = 1, 2, 3, \dots)$$

$$= \tfrac{1}{2}\int_0^4 t\sin\tfrac{1}{2}n\pi t\,\mathrm{d}t = \tfrac{1}{2}\left[-\frac{2t}{n\pi}\cos\tfrac{1}{2}n\pi t + \frac{4}{(n\pi)^2}\sin\tfrac{1}{2}n\pi t\right]_0^4 = -\frac{4}{n\pi}$$

Thus, by (4.10), the Fourier series expansion of $\phi(t)$ is

$$\phi(t) = 2 - \frac{4}{\pi}(\sin\tfrac{1}{2}\pi t + \tfrac{1}{2}\sin\pi t + \tfrac{1}{3}\sin\tfrac{3}{2}\pi t + \tfrac{1}{4}\sin 2t + \tfrac{1}{5}\sin\tfrac{5}{2}\pi t + \dots)$$

$$= 2 - \frac{4}{\pi}\sum_{n=1}^{\infty}\frac{1}{n}\sin\tfrac{1}{2}n\pi t$$

Since $\phi(t) = f(t)$ for $0 < t < 4$, it follows that this Fourier series is representative of $f(t)$ within this interval, so that

$$f(t) = t = 2 - \frac{4}{\pi}\sum_{n=1}^{\infty}\frac{1}{n}\sin\tfrac{1}{2}n\pi t \quad (0 < t < 4) \tag{4.29}$$

It is important to appreciate that this series converges to t only within the interval $0 < t < 4$. For values of t outside this interval it converges to the periodic extended function $\phi(t)$. Again convergence is to be interpreted in the sense of Theorem 4.2, so that at the end points $t = 0$ and $t = 4$ the series does not converge to t but to the mean of the discontinuity in $\phi(t)$, namely the value 2.

4.3.2 Half-range cosine and sine series

Rather than develop the periodic extension $\phi(t)$ of $f(t)$ as in Section 4.3.1, it is possible to formulate periodic extensions that are either even or odd functions, so that the resulting Fourier series of the extended periodic functions consist either of cosine terms only or sine terms only.

For a function $f(t)$ defined only over the finite interval $0 \leq t \leq \tau$ its **even periodic extension** $F(t)$ is the even periodic function defined by

$$F(t) = \begin{cases} f(t) & (0 < t < \tau) \\ f(-t) & (-\tau < t < 0) \end{cases}$$

$$F(t + 2\tau) = f(t)$$

As an illustration, the even periodic extension $F(t)$ of the function $f(t)$ shown in Figure 4.17(a) (redrawn in Figure 4.19a) is shown in Figure 4.19(b).

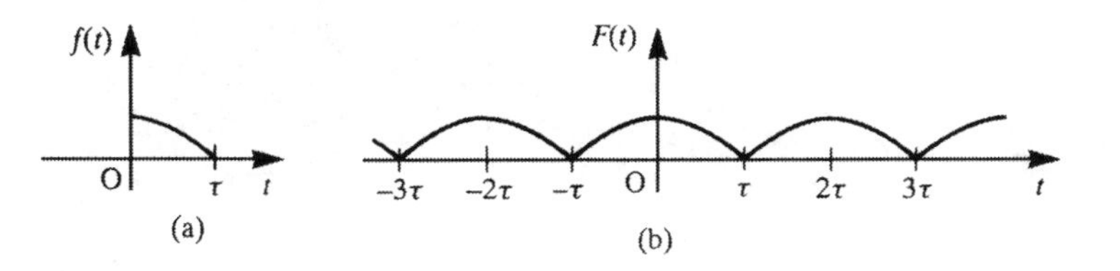

Figure 4.19
(a) A function $f(t)$;
(b) its even periodic extension $F(t)$.

Provided that $f(t)$ satisfies Dirichlet's conditions in the interval $0 < t < \tau$, since it is an even function of period 2τ, it follows from Section 4.2.5 that the even periodic extension $F(t)$ will have a convergent Fourier series representation consisting of cosine terms only and given by

$$F(t) = \tfrac{1}{2}a_0 + \sum_{n=1}^{\infty} a_n \cos \frac{n\pi t}{\tau} \tag{4.30}$$

where

$$a_n = \frac{2}{\tau}\int_0^{\tau} f(t) \cos \frac{n\pi t}{\tau}\,\mathrm{d}t \quad (n = 0, 1, 2, \ldots) \tag{4.31}$$

Since, within the particular interval $0 < t < \tau$, $F(t)$ is identical with $f(t)$, it follows that the series (4.30) also converges to $f(t)$ within this interval.

For a function $f(t)$ defined only over the finite interval $0 \leq t \leq \tau$, its **odd periodic extension** $G(t)$ is the odd periodic function defined by

$$G(t) = \begin{cases} f(t) & (0 < t < \tau) \\ -f(-t) & (-\tau < t < 0) \end{cases}$$

$$G(t + 2\tau) = G(t)$$

Again, as an illustration, the odd periodic extension $G(t)$ of the function $f(t)$ shown in Figure 4.17(a) (redrawn in Figure 4.20a) is shown in Figure 4.20(b).

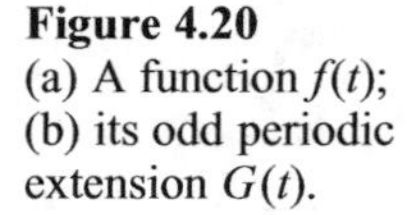

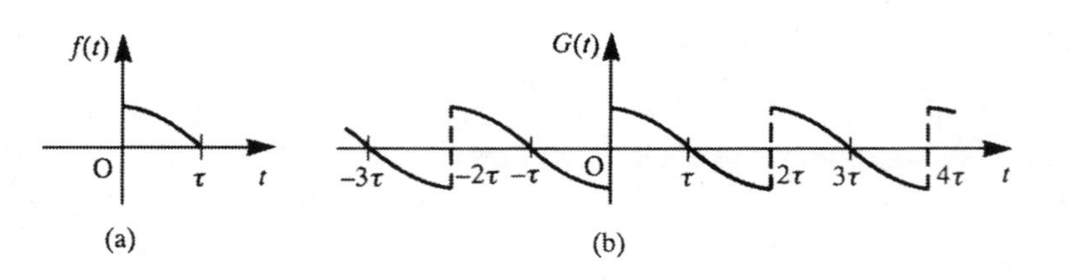

Figure 4.20
(a) A function $f(t)$;
(b) its odd periodic extension $G(t)$.

Provided that $f(t)$ satisfies Dirichlet's conditions in the interval $0 < t < \tau$, since it is an odd function of period 2τ, it follows from Section 4.2.5 that the odd periodic extension $G(t)$ will have a convergent Fourier series representation consisting of sine terms only and given by

$$G(t) = \sum_{n=1}^{\infty} b_n \sin \frac{n\pi t}{\tau} \tag{4.32}$$

where

$$b_n = \frac{2}{\tau}\int_0^{\tau} f(t) \sin \frac{n\pi t}{\tau}\,dt \quad (n = 1, 2, 3, \dots) \tag{4.33}$$

Again, since, within the particular interval $0 < t < \tau$, $G(t)$ is identical with $f(t)$, it follows that the series (4.32) also converges to $f(t)$ within this interval.

We note that both the even and odd periodic extensions $F(t)$ and $G(t)$ are of period 2τ, which is twice the length of the interval over which $f(t)$ is defined. However, the resulting Fourier series (4.30) and (4.32) are based only on the function $f(t)$, and for this reason are called the **half-range Fourier series expansions** of $f(t)$. In particular, the even half-range expansion $F(t)$, (4.30), is called the **half-range cosine series expansion** of $f(t)$, while the odd half-range expansion $G(t)$, (4.32), is called the **half-range sine series expansion** of $f(t)$.

Example 4.12

For the function $f(t) = t$ defined only in the interval $0 < t < 4$, and considered in Example 4.11, obtain

(a) a half-range cosine series expansion

(b) a half-range sine series expansion.

Draw graphs of $f(t)$ and of the periodic functions represented by the two series obtained for $-20 < t < 20$.

Solution (a) *Half-range cosine series.* Define the periodic function $F(t)$ by

$$F(t) = \begin{cases} f(t) = t & (0 < t < 4) \\ f(-t) = -t & (-4 < t < 0) \end{cases}$$

$$F(t + 8) = F(t)$$

Then, since $F(t)$ is an even periodic function with period 8, it has a convergent Fourier series expansion given by (4.30). Taking $\tau = 4$ in (4.31), we have

$$a_0 = \tfrac{2}{4}\int_0^4 f(t)\,dt = \tfrac{1}{2}\int_0^4 t\,dt = 4$$

$$a_n = \tfrac{2}{4}\int_0^4 f(t)\cos\tfrac{1}{4}n\pi t\,dt \quad (n = 1, 2, 3, \dots)$$

$$= \tfrac{1}{2}\int_0^4 t\cos\tfrac{1}{4}n\pi t\,dt = \tfrac{1}{2}\left[\frac{4t}{n\pi}\sin\tfrac{1}{4}n\pi t + \frac{16}{(n\pi)^2}\cos\tfrac{1}{4}n\pi t\right]_0^4$$

$$= \frac{8}{(n\pi)^2}(\cos n\pi - 1) = \begin{cases} 0 & (\text{even } n) \\ -16/(n\pi)^2 & (\text{odd } n) \end{cases}$$

Then, by (4.30), the Fourier series expansion of $F(t)$ is

$$F(t) = 2 - \frac{16}{\pi^2}\left(\cos\tfrac{1}{4}\pi t + \tfrac{1}{3^2}\cos\tfrac{3}{4}\pi t + \tfrac{1}{5^2}\cos\tfrac{5}{4}\pi t + \dots\right)$$

or

$$F(t) = 2 - \frac{16}{\pi^2}\sum_{n=1}^{\infty}\frac{1}{(2n-1)^2}\cos\tfrac{1}{4}(2n-1)\pi t$$

Since $F(t) = f(t)$ for $0 < t < 4$, it follows that this Fourier series is representative of $f(t)$ within this interval. Thus the half-range cosine series expansion of $f(t)$ is

$$f(t) = t = 2 - \frac{16}{\pi^2}\sum_{n=1}^{\infty}\frac{1}{(2n-1)^2}\cos\tfrac{1}{4}(2n-1)\pi t \quad (0 < t < 4) \tag{4.34}$$

(b) *Half-range sine series.* Define the periodic function $G(t)$ by

$$G(t) = \begin{cases} f(t) = t & (0 < t < 4) \\ -f(-t) = t & (-4 < t < 0) \end{cases}$$

$$G(t + 8) = G(t)$$

Then, since $G(t)$ is an odd periodic function with period 8, it has a convergent Fourier series expansion given by (4.32). Taking $\tau = 4$ in (4.33), we have

$$b_n = \tfrac{2}{4}\int_0^4 f(t)\sin\tfrac{1}{4}n\pi t\,dt \quad (n = 1, 2, 3, \dots)$$

$$= \tfrac{1}{2}\int_0^4 t\sin\tfrac{1}{4}n\pi t\,dt = \tfrac{1}{2}\left[-\frac{4t}{n\pi}\cos\tfrac{1}{4}n\pi t + \frac{16}{(n\pi)^2}\sin\tfrac{1}{4}n\pi t\right]_0^4$$

$$= -\frac{8}{n\pi}\cos n\pi = -\frac{8}{n\pi}(-1)^n$$

Thus, by (4.32), the Fourier series expansion of $G(t)$ is

$$G(t) = \frac{8}{\pi}(\sin \tfrac{1}{4}\pi t - \tfrac{1}{2}\sin \tfrac{1}{2}\pi t + \tfrac{1}{3}\sin \tfrac{3}{4}\pi t - \dots)$$

or

$$G(t) = \frac{8}{\pi}\sum_{n=1}^{\infty}\frac{(-1)^{n+1}}{n}\sin \tfrac{1}{4}n\pi t$$

Since $G(t) = f(t)$ for $0 < t < 4$, it follows that this Fourier series is representative of $f(t)$ within this interval. Thus the half-range sine series expansion of $f(t)$ is

$$f(t) = t = \frac{8}{\pi}\sum_{n=1}^{\infty}\frac{(-1)^{n+1}}{n}\sin \tfrac{1}{4}n\pi t \quad (0 < t < 4) \qquad \textbf{(4.35)}$$

Graphs of the given function $f(t)$ and of the even and odd periodic expansions $F(t)$ and $G(t)$ are given in Figures 4.21(a), (b) and (c) respectively.

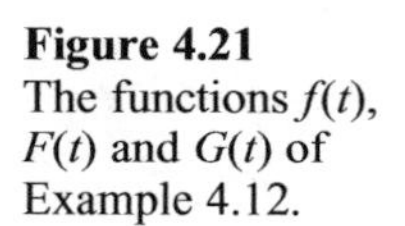

Figure 4.21 The functions $f(t)$, $F(t)$ and $G(t)$ of Example 4.12.

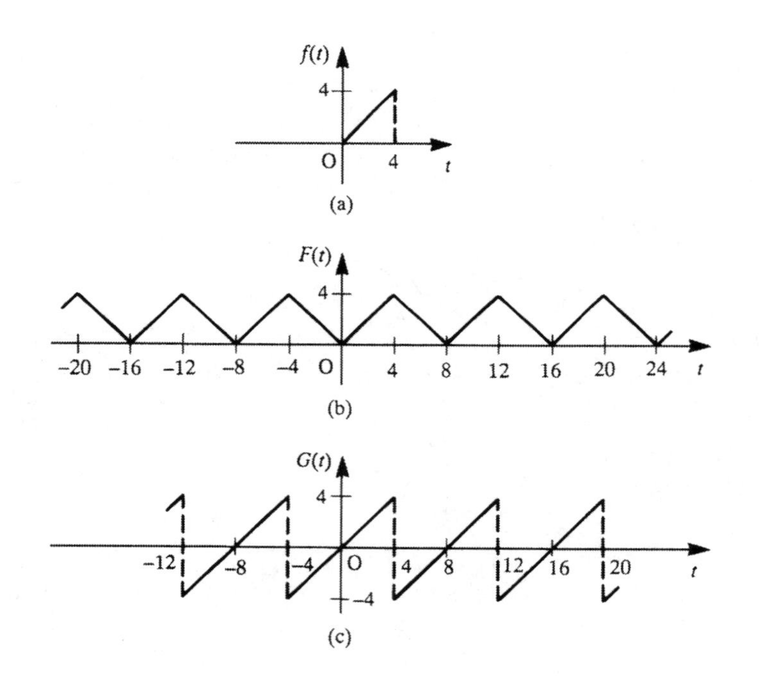

It is important to realize that the three different Fourier series representations (4.29), (4.34) and (4.35) are representative of the function $f(t) = t$ only within the defined interval $0 < t < 4$. Outside this interval the three Fourier series converge to the three different functions $\phi(t)$, $F(t)$ and $G(t)$, illustrated in Figures 4.18(b), 4.21(b) and 4.21(c) respectively.

4.4.3 Exercises

14 Show that the half-range Fourier sine series expansion of the function $f(t) = 1$, valid for $0 < t < \pi$, is

$$f(t) = \frac{4}{\pi}\sum_{n=1}^{\infty}\frac{\sin(2n-1)t}{2n-1} \quad (0 < t < \pi)$$

Sketch the graphs of both $f(t)$ and the periodic function represented by the series expansion for $-3\pi < t < 3\pi$.

15 Determine the half-range cosine series expansion of the function $f(t) = 2t - 1$, valid for $0 < t < 1$. Sketch the graphs of both $f(t)$ and the periodic function represented by the series expansion for $-2 < t < 2$.

16 The function $f(t) = 1 - t^2$ is to be represented by a Fourier series expansion over the finite interval $0 < t < 1$. Obtain a suitable

(a) full-range series expansion,
(b) half-range sine series expansion,
(c) half-range cosine series expansion.

Draw graphs of $f(t)$ and of the periodic functions represented by each of the three series for $-4 < t < 4$.

17 A function $f(t)$ is defined by

$$f(t) = \pi t - t^2 \quad (0 \leqslant t \leqslant \pi)$$

and is to be represented by either a half-range Fourier sine series or a half-range Fourier cosine series. Find both of these series and sketch the graphs of the functions represented by them for $-2\pi < t < 2\pi$.

18 A tightly stretched flexible uniform string has its ends fixed at the points $x = 0$ and $x = l$. The midpoint of the string is displaced a distance a, as shown in Figure 4.22. If $f(x)$ denotes the displaced profile of the string, express $f(x)$ as a Fourier series expansion consisting only of sine terms.

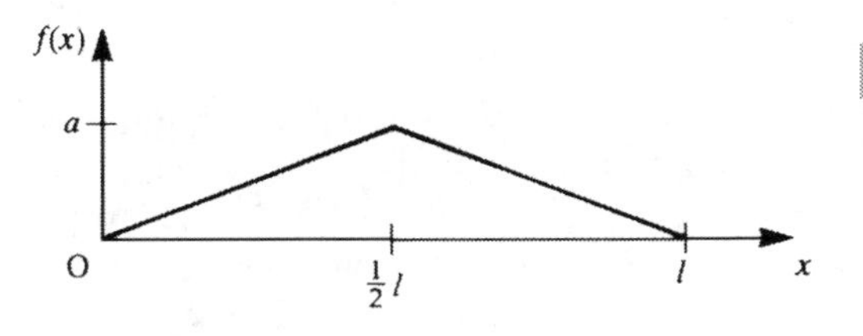

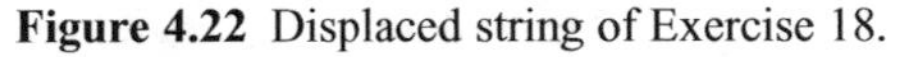

Figure 4.22 Displaced string of Exercise 18.

19 Repeat Exercise 18 for the case where the displaced profile of the string is as shown in Figure 4.23.

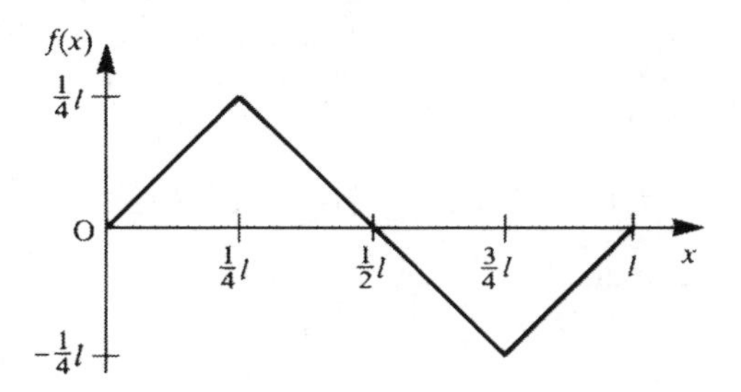

Figure 4.23 Displaced string of Exercise 19.

20 A function $f(t)$ is defined on $0 \leqslant t \leqslant \pi$ by

$$f(t) = \begin{cases} \sin t & (0 \leqslant t < \frac{1}{2}\pi) \\ 0 & (\frac{1}{2}\pi \leqslant t \leqslant \pi) \end{cases}$$

Find a half-range Fourier series expansion of $f(t)$ on this interval. Sketch a graph of the function represented by the series for $-2\pi \leqslant t \leqslant 2\pi$.

21 A function $f(t)$ is defined on the interval $-l \leqslant x \leqslant l$ by

$$f(x) = \frac{A}{l}(|x| - l)$$

Obtain a Fourier series expansion of $f(x)$ and sketch a graph of the function represented by the series for $-3l \leqslant x \leqslant 3l$.

22 The temperature distribution $T(x)$ at a distance x, measured from one end, along a bar of length L is given by

$$T(x) = Kx(L - x) \quad (0 \leqslant x \leqslant L), \quad K = \text{constant}$$

Express $T(x)$ as a Fourier series expansion consisting of sine terms only.

23 Find the Fourier series expansion of the function $f(t)$ valid for $-1 < t < 1$, where

$$f(t) = \begin{cases} 1 & (-1 < t < 0) \\ \cos \pi t & (0 < t < 1) \end{cases}$$

To what value does this series converge when $t = 1$?

4.4 Differentiation and integration of Fourier series

It is inevitable that the desire to obtain the derivative or the integral of a Fourier series will arise in some applications. Since the smoothing effects of the integration process tend to eliminate discontinuities, whereas the process of differentiation has the opposite effect, it is not surprising that the integration of a Fourier series is more likely to be possible than its differentiation. We shall not pursue the theory in depth here; rather we shall state, without proof, two theorems concerned with the term-by-term integration and differentiation of Fourier series, and make some observations on their use.

4.4.1 Integration of a Fourier series

Theorem 4.3 A Fourier series expansion of a periodic function $f(t)$ that satisfies Dirichlet's conditions may be integrated term by term, and the integrated series converges to the integral of the function $f(t)$.

end of theorem

According to this theorem, if $f(t)$ satisfies Dirichlet's conditions in the interval $-\pi \leqslant t \leqslant \pi$ and has a Fourier series expansion

$$f(t) = \tfrac{1}{2}a_0 + \sum_{n=1}^{\infty} (a_n \cos nt + b_n \sin nt)$$

then for $-\pi \leqslant t_1 < t \leqslant \pi$

$$\int_{t_1}^{t} f(t)\,\mathrm{d}t = \int_{t_1}^{t} \tfrac{1}{2}a_0\,\mathrm{d}t + \sum_{n=1}^{\infty} \int_{t_1}^{t} (a_n \cos nt + b_n \sin nt)\,\mathrm{d}t$$

$$= \tfrac{1}{2}a_0(t - t_1) + \sum_{n=1}^{\infty} \left[\frac{b_n}{n}(\cos nt_1 - \cos nt) + \frac{a_n}{n}(\sin nt - \sin nt_1)\right]$$

Because of the presence of the term $\tfrac{1}{2}a_0 t$ on the right-hand side, this is clearly not a Fourier series expansion of the integral on the left-hand side. However, the result can be rearranged to be a Fourier series expansion of the function

$$g(t) = \int_{t_1}^{t} f(t)\,\mathrm{d}t - \tfrac{1}{2}a_0 t$$

Example 4.13 serves to illustrate this process. Note also that the Fourier coefficients in the new Fourier series are $-b_n/n$ and a_n/n, so, from the observations made in Section 4.2.8, the integrated series converges faster than the original series for $f(t)$. If the given function $f(t)$ is piecewise-continuous, rather than continuous, over the interval $-\pi \leqslant t \leqslant \pi$ then care must be taken to ensure that the integration process is carried out properly over the various subintervals. Again, Example 4.14 serves to illustrate this point.

Example 4.13

From Example 4.5, the Fourier series expansion of the function

$$f(t) = t^2 \quad (-\pi \leqslant t \leqslant \pi), \qquad f(t + 2\pi) = f(\pi)$$

is

$$t^2 = \tfrac{1}{3}\pi^2 + 4\sum_{n=1}^{\infty} \frac{(-1)^n \cos nt}{n^2} \quad (-\pi \leqslant t \leqslant \pi)$$

Integrating this result between the limits $-\pi$ and t gives

$$\int_{-\pi}^{t} t^2 \,\mathrm{d}t = \int_{-\pi}^{t} \tfrac{1}{3}\pi^2 \,\mathrm{d}t + 4\sum_{n=1}^{\infty} \int_{-\pi}^{t} \frac{(-1)^n \cos nt}{n^2} \,\mathrm{d}t$$

that is,

$$\tfrac{1}{3}t^3 = \tfrac{1}{3}\pi^2 t + 4\sum_{n=1}^{\infty} \frac{(-1)^n \sin nt}{n^3} \quad (-\pi \leqslant t \leqslant \pi)$$

Because of the term $\frac{1}{3}\pi^2 t$ on the right-hand side, this is clearly not a Fourier series expansion. However, rearranging, we have

$$t^3 - \pi^2 t = 12\sum_{n=1}^{\infty} \frac{(-1)^n \sin nt}{n^2}$$

and now the right-hand side may be taken to be the Fourier series expansion of the function

$$g(t) = t^3 - \pi^2 t \quad (-\pi \leqslant t \leqslant \pi)$$

$$g(t + 2\pi) = g(t)$$

Example 4.14

Integrate term by term the Fourier series expansion obtained in Example 4.4 for the square wave

$$f(t) = \begin{cases} -1 & (-\pi < t < 0) \\ 1 & (0 < t < \pi) \end{cases}$$

$$f(t + 2\pi) = f(t)$$

illustrated in Figure 4.7.

Solution

From (4.21), the Fourier series expansion for $f(t)$ is

$$f(t) = \frac{4}{\pi} \frac{\sin(2n - 1)t}{2n - 1}$$

We now need to integrate between the limits $-\pi$ and t and, owing to the discontinuity in $f(t)$ at $t = 0$, we must consider separately values of t in the intervals $-\pi < t < 0$ and $0 < t < \pi$.

Case (*i*), *interval* $-\pi < t < 0$. Integrating (4.21) term by term, we have

$$\int_{-\pi}^{t} (-1)\,\mathrm{d}t = \frac{4}{\pi}\sum_{n=1}^{\infty}\int_{-\pi}^{t} \frac{\sin(2n-1)t}{(2n-1)}\,\mathrm{d}t$$

that is,

$$-(t+\pi) = -\frac{4}{\pi}\sum_{n=1}^{\infty}\left[\frac{\cos(2n-1)t}{(2n-1)^2}\right]_{-\pi}^{t}$$

$$= -\frac{4}{\pi}\left[\sum_{n=1}^{\infty}\frac{\cos(2n-1)t}{(2n-1)^2} + \sum_{n=1}^{\infty}\frac{1}{(2n-1)^2}\right]$$

It can be shown that

$$\sum_{n=1}^{\infty}\frac{2}{(2n-1)^2} = \tfrac{1}{8}\pi^2$$

(see Exercise 6), so that the above simplifies to

$$-t = \tfrac{1}{2}\pi - \frac{4}{\pi}\sum_{n=1}^{\infty}\frac{\cos(2n-1)t}{(2n-1)^2} \quad (-\pi < t < 0) \tag{4.36}$$

Case (*ii*), *interval* $0 < t < \pi$. Integrating (4.21) term by term, we have

$$\int_{-\pi}^{0} (-1)\,\mathrm{d}t + \int_{0}^{t} 1\,\mathrm{d}t = \frac{4}{\pi}\sum_{n=1}^{\infty}\int_{-\pi}^{t} \frac{\sin(2n-1)t}{(2n-1)}\,\mathrm{d}t$$

giving

$$t = \tfrac{1}{2}\pi - \frac{4}{\pi}\sum_{n=1}^{\infty}\frac{\cos(2n-1)t}{(2n-1)^2} \quad (0 < t < \pi) \tag{4.37}$$

Taking (4.36) and (4.37) together, we find that the function

$$g(t) = |t| = \begin{cases} -t & (-\pi < t < 0) \\ t & (0 < t < \pi) \end{cases}$$

$$g(t + 2\pi) = g(t)$$

has a Fourier series expansion

$$g(t) = |t| = \tfrac{1}{2}\pi - \frac{4}{\pi}\sum_{n=1}^{\infty}\frac{\cos(2n-1)t}{(2n-1)^2}$$

4.4.2 Differentiation of a Fourier series

Theorem 4.4

If $f(t)$ is a periodic function that satisfies Dirichlet's conditions then its derivative $f'(t)$, wherever it exists, may be found by term-by-term differentiation of the Fourier series of $f(t)$ if and only if the function $f(t)$ is continuous everywhere and the function $f'(t)$ has a Fourier series expansion (that is, $f'(t)$ satisfies Dirichlet's conditions).

end of theorem

It follows from Theorem 4.4 that if the Fourier series expansion of $f(t)$ is differentiable term by term then $f(t)$ must be periodic at the end points of a period (owing to the condition that $f(t)$ must be continuous everywhere). Thus, for example, if we are dealing with a function $f(t)$ of period 2π and defined in the range $-\pi < t < \pi$ then we must have $f(-\pi) = f(\pi)$. To illustrate this point, consider the Fourier series expansion of the function

$$f(t) = t \quad (-\pi < t < \pi)$$

$$f(t + 2\pi) = f(t)$$

which, from Example 4.7, is given by

$$f(t) = 2(\sin t - \tfrac{1}{2}\sin 2t + \tfrac{1}{3}\sin 3t - \tfrac{1}{4}\sin 4t + \dots)$$

Differentiating term by term, we have

$$f'(t) = 2(\cos t - \cos 2t + \cos 3t - \cos 4t + \dots)$$

If this differentiation process is valid then $f'(t)$ must be equal to unity for $-\pi < t < \pi$. Clearly this is not the case, since the series on the right-hand side does not converge for any value of t. This follows since the nth term of the series is $2(-1)^{n+1}\cos nt$ and does not tend to zero as $n \to \infty$.

If $f(t)$ is continuous everywhere and has a Fourier series expansion

$$f(t) = \tfrac{1}{2}a_0 + \sum_{n=1}^{\infty}(a_n \cos nt + b_n \sin nt)$$

then, from Theorem 4.4, provided that $f'(t)$ satisfies the required conditions, its Fourier series expansion is

$$f'(t) = \sum_{n=1}^{\infty}(nb_n \cos nt - na_n \sin nt)$$

In this case the Fourier coefficients of the derived expansion are nb_n and na_n, so, in contrast to the integrated series, the derived series will converge more slowly than the original series expansion for $f(t)$.

Example 4.15

Consider the process of differentiating term by term the Fourier series expansion of the function

$$f(t) = t^2 \quad (-\pi \leqslant t \leqslant \pi), \qquad f(t + 2\pi) = f(t)$$

Solution From Example 4.5, the Fourier series expansion of $f(t)$ is

$$t^2 = \tfrac{1}{3}\pi^2 + 4\sum_{n=1}^{\infty}\frac{(-1)^n \cos nt}{n^2} \quad (-\pi \leqslant t \leqslant \pi)$$

Since $f(t)$ is continuous within and at the end points of the interval $-\pi \leqslant t \leqslant \pi$, we may apply Theorem 4.4 to obtain

$$t = 2\sum_{n=1}^{\infty}\frac{(-1)^{n+1} \sin nt}{n} \quad (-\pi \leqslant t \leqslant \pi)$$

which conforms with the Fourier series expansion obtained for the function

$$f(t) = t \quad (-\pi < t < \pi), \qquad f(t + 2\pi) = f(t)$$

in Example 4.7.

4.4.3 Coefficients in terms of jumps at discontinuities

For periodic functions that, within a period, are piecewise polynomials and exhibit jump discontinuities, the Fourier coefficients may be determined in terms of the magnitude of the jumps and those of derived functions. This method is useful for determining describing functions (see Section 4.8) for nonlinear characteristics in control engineering, where only the fundamental component of the Fourier series is important; this applies particularly to the case of multivalued nonlinearities.

Consider a periodic function $f(t)$, of period T, having within the time interval $-\frac{1}{2}T \leqslant t \leqslant \frac{1}{2}T$ a finite number $(m + 1)$ of jump discontinuities $d_0, d_1, \ldots, d_m$ at times $t_0, t_1, \ldots t_m$, with $t_0 = \frac{1}{2}T$ and $t_m = \frac{1}{2}T$. Furthermore, within the interval $t_{s-1} < t < t_s$ $(s = 1, 2, \ldots, m)$ let $f(t)$ be represented by polynomial functions $P_s(t)$ $(s = 1, 2, \ldots, m)$, as illustrated in Figure 4.24. If $f(t)$ is to be represented in terms of the Fourier series

$$f(t) = \tfrac{1}{2}a_0 + \sum_{n=1}^{\infty} a_n \cos n\omega t + \sum_{n=1}^{\infty} b_n \sin n\omega t$$

then, from (4.11),

$$a_n = \frac{2}{T}\sum_{s=1}^{m}\int_{t_{s-1}}^{t_s} P_s(t) \cos n\omega t \, dt$$

Defining the magnitude of the jump discontinuities as in Section 2.5.11, namely

$$d_i = f(t_i + 0) - f(t_i - 0)$$

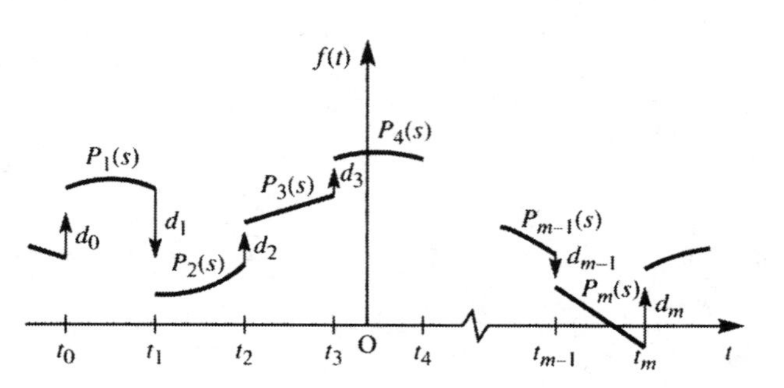

Figure 4.24 Piecewise polynomial periodic function exhibiting jump discontinuities.

and noting that $t_0 = -\frac{1}{2}T$ and $t_m = \frac{1}{2}T$, integration by parts and summation gives

$$a_n = -\frac{1}{n\pi}\sum_{s=1}^{m}\left[d_s \sin n\omega t_s + \int_{t_{s-1}}^{t_s} P_s^{(1)}(t)\sin n\omega t\,\mathrm{d}t\right] \tag{4.38}$$

where $P_s^{(1)}(t)$ denotes the piecewise components of the derivative $f^{(1)}(t) \equiv f'(t)$ in the generalized sense of (2.59).

In a similar manner the integral terms of (4.38) may be expressed as

$$\sum_{s=1}^{m}\int_{t_{s-1}}^{t_s} P_s^{(1)} \sin n\omega t\,\mathrm{d}t = \frac{1}{n\omega}\sum_{s=1}^{m}\left[d_s^{(1)}\cos n\omega t + \int_{t_{s-1}}^{t_s} P_s^{(2)}(t)\cos n\omega t\,\mathrm{d}t\right]$$

where $d_s^{(1)}$ $(s = 1, 2, \dots, m)$ denotes the magnitude of the jump discontinuities in the derivative $f^{(1)}(t)$.

Continuing in this fashion, integrals involving higher derivatives may be obtained. However, since all $P_s(t)$ $(s = 1, 2, \dots, m)$ are polynomials, a stage is reached when all the integrals vanish. If the degree of $P_s(t)$ is less than or equal to N for $s = 1, 2, \dots, m$ then

$$a_n = \frac{1}{n\pi}\sum_{s=1}^{m}\sum_{r=0}^{N}(-1)^{r+1}(n\omega)^{-2r}[d_s^{(2r)}\sin n\omega t_s + (n\omega)^{-1}d_s^{(2r+1)}\cos n\omega t_s] \quad (n \neq 0) \tag{4.39}$$

where $d_s^{(r)}$ denotes the magnitudes of the jump discontinuities in the rth derivative of $f(t)$ according to (2.59).

Similarly, it may be shown that

$$b_n = \frac{1}{n\pi}\sum_{s=1}^{m}\sum_{r=0}^{N}(-1)^{r}(n\omega)^{-2r}[d_s^{(2r)}\cos n\omega t_s - (n\omega)^{-1}d_s^{(2r+1)}\sin n\omega t_s] \tag{4.40}$$

and the coefficient a_0 is found by direct integration of the corresponding Euler formula

$$a_0 = \frac{2}{T}\int_{-T/2}^{T/2} f(t)\,\mathrm{d}t \tag{4.41}$$

Example 4.16

Using (4.39)–(4.41), obtain the Fourier series expansion of the periodic function $f(t)$ defined by

$$f(t) = \begin{cases} t^2 & (-\pi < t < 0) \\ -2 & (0 < t < \pi) \end{cases}$$

$$f(t + 2\pi) = f(t)$$

Solution

In this case $N = 2$, and the graphs of $f(t)$ together with those of its first two derivatives are shown in Figure 4.25.

Jump discontinuities occur at $t = -\pi$, 0 and π, so that $m = 2$. The piecewise polynomials involved and the corresponding jump discontinuities are

(a) $P_1(t) = t^2, \quad P_2(t) = -2$
$\quad d_1 = -2, \quad d_2 = \pi^2 + 2$

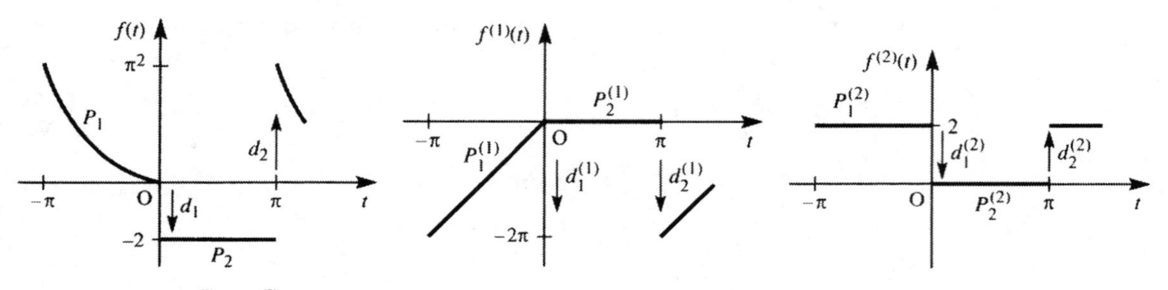

Figure 4.25 $f(t), f^{(1)}(t), f^{(2)}(t)$ of Example 4.16.

(b) $P_1^{(1)}(t) = 2t \quad P_2^{(1)}(t) = 0$
$\quad d_1^{(1)} = 0 \quad d_2^{(1)} = -2\pi$

(c) $P_1^{(2)}(t) = 2, \quad P_2^{(2)}(t) = 0$
$\quad d_1^{(2)} = -2 \quad d_2^{(2)} = 2$

with $d_1^{(r)} = d_2^{(r)} = 0$ for $r > 2$.

Taking $\omega = 1$ (since $T = 2\pi$) in (4.39) gives

$$a_n = \frac{1}{n\pi}\left(-\sum_{s=1}^{2} d_s \sin nt_s - \frac{1}{n}\sum_{s=1}^{2} d_s^{(1)} \cos nt_s + \frac{1}{n^2}\sum_{s=1}^{2} d_s^{(2)} \sin nt_s\right)$$

Since $t_1 = 0$, $t_2 = \pi$, $\sin 0 = \sin n\pi = 0$, $\cos 0 = 1$ and $\cos n\pi = (-1)^n$, we have

$$a_n = \frac{2}{n^2}(-1)^n \quad (n = 1, 2, 3, \ldots)$$

Likewise, from (4.40),

$$\begin{aligned} b_n &= \frac{1}{n\pi}\left(\sum_{s=1}^{2} d_s \cos nt_s - \frac{1}{n}\sum_{s=1}^{2} d_s^{(1)} \sin nt_s - \frac{1}{n^2}\sum_{s=1}^{2} d_s^{(2)} \cos nt_s\right) \\ &= \frac{1}{n\pi}\left\{-2 + (\pi^2 + 2)(-1)^n - \frac{1}{n^2}[-2 + 2(-1)^n]\right\} \\ &= \frac{1}{n\pi}\left\{\left(\frac{2}{n^2} - 2\right)[1 - (-1)^n] + \pi^2(-1)^n\right\} \quad (n = 1, 2, 3, \ldots) \end{aligned}$$

and, from (4.41),

$$a_0 = \frac{1}{\pi}\left[\int_{-\pi}^{0} t^2\,\mathrm{d}t + \int_{0}^{\pi} (-2)\,\mathrm{d}t\right] = \tfrac{1}{3}\pi^2 - 2$$

Thus the Fourier expansion for $f(t)$ is

$$\begin{aligned} f(t) = {} & (\tfrac{1}{6}\pi^2 - 1) + \sum_{n=1}^{\infty} \frac{2}{n^2}(-1)^n \cos nt \\ & + \sum_{n=1}^{\infty} \frac{1}{n\pi}\left\{\left(\frac{2}{n^2} - 2\right)[1 - (-1)^n] + \pi^2(-1)^n\right\} \sin nt \end{aligned}$$

4.4.4 Exercises

24 Show that the periodic function

$$f(t) = t \quad (-T < t < T)$$
$$f(t + 2T) = f(t)$$

has a Fourier series expansion

$$f(t) = \frac{2T}{\pi}\left(\sin\frac{\pi t}{T} - \tfrac{1}{2}\sin\frac{2\pi t}{T} + \tfrac{1}{3}\sin\frac{3\pi t}{T} - \tfrac{1}{4}\sin\frac{4\pi t}{T} + \ldots\right)$$

By term-by-term integration of this series, show that the periodic function

$$g(t) = t^2 \quad (-T < t < T)$$
$$g(t + 2T) = g(t)$$

has a Fourier series expansion

$$g(t) = \tfrac{1}{3}T^2 - \frac{4T^2}{\pi^2}\left(\cos\frac{\pi t}{T} - \frac{1}{2^2}\cos\frac{2\pi t}{T} + \frac{1}{3^2}\cos\frac{3\pi t}{T} - \frac{1}{4^2}\cos\frac{4\pi t}{T} + \ldots\right)$$

(*Hint*: A constant of integration must be introduced; it may be evaluated as the mean value over a period.)

25 The periodic function

$$h(t) = \pi^2 - t^2 \quad (-\pi < t < \pi)$$
$$h(t + 2\pi) = h(t)$$

has a Fourier series expansion

$$h(t) = \tfrac{2}{3}\pi^2 + 4\left(\cos t - \frac{1}{2^2}\cos 2t + \frac{1}{3^2}\cos 3t \ldots\right)$$

By term-by-term differentiation of this series, confirm the series obtained for $f(t)$ in Exercise 24 for the case when $T = \pi$.

26 (a) Suppose that the derivative $f'(t)$ of a periodic function $f(t)$ of period 2π has a Fourier series expansion

$$f'(t) = \tfrac{1}{2}A_0 + \sum_{n=1}^{\infty} A_n \cos nt + \sum_{n=1}^{\infty} B_n \sin nt$$

Show that

$$A_0 = \frac{1}{n}[f(\pi^-) - f(-\pi^+)]$$
$$A_n = (-1)^n A_0 + nb_n$$
$$B_n = -na_n$$

where a_0, a_n and b_n are the Fourier coefficients of the function $f(t)$.

(b) In Example 4.7 we saw that the periodic function

$$f(t) = t^2 + t \quad (-\pi < t < \pi)$$
$$f(t + 2\pi) = f(t)$$

has a Fourier series expansion

$$f(t) = \tfrac{1}{3}\pi^2 + \sum_{n=1}^{\infty} \frac{4}{n^2}(-1)^n \cos nt - \sum_{n=1}^{\infty} \frac{2}{n}(-1)^n \sin nt$$

Differentiate this series term by term, and explain why it is not a Fourier expansion of the periodic function

$$g(t) = 2t + 1 \quad (-\pi < t < \pi)$$
$$g(t + 2\pi) = g(t)$$

(c) Use the results of (a) to obtain the Fourier series expansion of $g(t)$ and confirm your solution by direct evaluation of the coefficients using Euler's formulae.

27 Using (4.39)–(4.41), confirm the following Fourier series expansions:

(a) (4.21) for the square wave of Example 4.4;
(b) the expansion obtained in Example 4.1 for the sawtooth wave;
(c) the expansion obtained for the piecewise-continuous function $f(t)$ of Example 4.3.

28 Consider the periodic function

$$f(t) = \begin{cases} 0 & (-\pi < t < -\tfrac{1}{2}\pi) \\ \pi + 2t & (-\tfrac{1}{2}\pi < t < 0) \\ \pi - 2t & (0 < t < \tfrac{1}{2}\pi) \\ 0 & (\tfrac{1}{2}\pi < t < \pi) \end{cases}$$

$$f(t + 2\pi) = f(t)$$

(a) Sketch a graph of the function for $-4\pi < t < 4\pi$.
(b) Use (4.39)–(4.41) to obtain the Fourier series expansion

$$f(t) = \tfrac{1}{4}\pi - \frac{4}{\pi}\sum_{n=1}^{\infty}\frac{1}{n^2}(\cos\tfrac{1}{2}n\pi - 1)\cos nt$$

and write out the first 10 terms of this series. (*Note*: Although the function $f(t)$ itself has no jump discontinuities, the method may be used since the derivative does have jump discontinuities.)

29 Use the method of Section 4.4.3 to obtain the Fourier series expansions for the following periodic functions:

(a) $f(t) = \begin{cases} 0 & (-\pi < t < 0) \\ t^2 & (0 < t < \pi) \end{cases}$

$f(t + 2\pi) = f(t)$

(b) $f(t) = \begin{cases} 2 & (-\pi < t < -\tfrac{1}{2}\pi) \\ t^3 & (-\tfrac{1}{2}\pi < t < \tfrac{1}{2}\pi) \\ -2 & (\tfrac{1}{2}\pi < t < \pi) \end{cases}$

$f(t + 2\pi) = f(t)$

(c) $f(t) = \begin{cases} t & (0 < t < 1) \\ 1 - t & (1 < t < 2) \end{cases}$

$f(t + 2) = f(t)$

(d) $f(t) = \begin{cases} \tfrac{1}{2} + t & (-\tfrac{1}{2} < t < 0) \\ \tfrac{1}{2} - t & (0 < t < \tfrac{1}{2}) \end{cases}$

$f(t + 1) = f(t)$

4.5 Engineering application: frequency response and oscillating systems

4.5.1 Response to periodic input

In Section 2.7 we showed that the frequency response, defined as the steady-state response to a sinusoidal input $A \sin \omega t$, of a stable linear system having a transfer function $G(s)$ is given by (2.86) as

$$x_{ss}(t) = A|G(j\omega)|\sin[\omega t + \arg G(j\omega)] \tag{4.42}$$

By employing a Fourier series expansion, we can use this result to determine the steady-state response of a stable linear system to a non-sinusoidal periodic input. For a stable linear system having a transfer function $G(s)$, let the input be a periodic function $P(t)$ of period $2T$ (that is, one having frequency $\omega = \pi/T$ in rad s^{-1}). From (4.21), $P(t)$ may be expressed in the form of the Fourier series expansion

$$P(t) = \tfrac{1}{2}a_0 + \sum_{n=1}^{\infty} A_n \sin(n\omega t + \phi_n) \tag{4.43}$$

where A_n and ϕ_n are defined as in Section 4.2.1. The steady-state response to each term in the series expansion (4.43) may be obtained using (4.42). Since the system is linear, the principle of superposition holds, so that the steady-state response to the periodic input $P(t)$ may be obtained as the sum of the steady-state responses to the individual sinusoids comprising the sum in (4.43). Thus the steady-state response to the input $P(t)$ is

$$x_{ss}(t) = \tfrac{1}{2}a_0 G(0) + \sum_{n=1}^{\infty} A_n|G(jn\omega)|\sin[n\omega t + \phi_n + \arg G(jn\omega)] \tag{4.44}$$

There are two issues related to this steady-state response that are worthy of note.

(a) For practical systems $|G(j\omega)| \to 0$ as $\omega \to \infty$, so that $|G(jn\omega)| \to 0$ as $n \to \infty$ in (4.44). As a consequence, the Fourier series representation of the steady-state response $x_{ss}(t)$ converges more rapidly than the Fourier series representation of the periodic input $P(t)$. From a practical point of view, this is not surprising, since it is a consequence of the smoothing action of the system (that is, as indicated in Section 4.4, integration is a 'smoothing' operation).

(b) There is a significant difference between the steady-state response (4.44) to a non-sinusoidal periodic input of frequency ω and the steady-state response (4.41) to a pure sinusoid at the same frequency. As indicated in (4.42), in the case of a sinusoidal input at frequency ω the steady-state response is also a sinusoid at the same frequency ω. However, for a non-sinusoidal periodic input $P(t)$ at frequency ω the steady-state response (4.44) is no longer at the same frequency; rather it comprises an infinite sum of sinusoids having frequencies $n\omega$ that are integer multiples of the input frequency ω. This clearly has important practical implications, particularly when considering the responses of oscillating or vibrating systems. If the frequency $n\omega$ of one of the harmonics in (4.44) is close to the natural oscillating frequency of an underdamped system then the phenomenon of **resonance** will arise.

To someone unfamiliar with the theory, it may seem surprising that a practical system may resonate at a frequency much higher than that of the input. As indicated in Example 2.30, the phenomenon of resonance is important in practice, and it is therefore important that engineers have some knowledge of the theory associated with Fourier series, so that the possible dominance of a system response by one of the higher harmonics, rather than the fundamental, may be properly interpreted.

Example 4.17

The mass–spring–damper system of Figure 4.26(a) is initially at rest in a position of equilibrium. Determine the steady-state response of the system when the mass is subjected to an externally applied periodic force $P(t)$ having the form of the square wave shown in Figure 4.26(b).

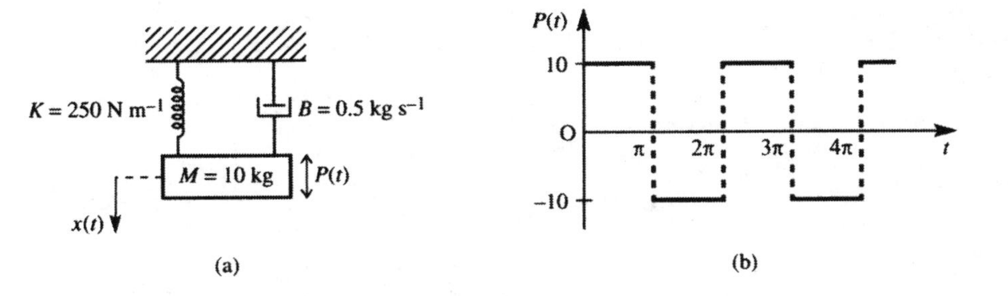

Figure 4.26 (a) System and (b) input for Example 4.17.

Solution From Newton's law, the displacement $x(t)$ of the mass at time t is given by

$$M\frac{d^2x}{dt^2} + B\frac{dx}{dt} + Kx = P(t) \tag{4.45}$$

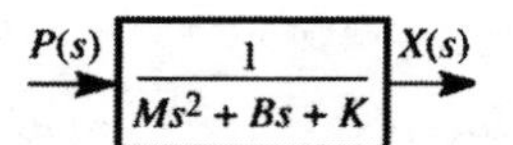

Figure 4.27 Block diagram for the system of Figure 4.26.

so that the system may be represented by the block diagram of Figure 4.27. Thus the system transfer function is

$$G(s) = \frac{1}{Ms^2 + Bs + K} \tag{4.46}$$

From Example 4.4, the Fourier series expansion for the square wave $P(t)$ is

$$P(t) = \frac{40}{\pi}\left[\sin t + \frac{\sin 3t}{3} + \frac{\sin 5t}{5} + \ldots + \frac{\sin(2n-1)t}{2n-1} + \ldots\right]$$

that is,

$$P(t) = u_1(t) + u_2(t) + u_3(t) + \ldots + u_n(t) + \ldots \tag{4.47}$$

where

$$u_n(t) = \frac{40}{\pi}\frac{\sin(2n-1)t}{2n-1} \tag{4.48}$$

Substituting the given values for M, B and K, the transfer function (4.46) becomes

$$G(s) = \frac{1}{10s^2 + 0.5s + 250}$$

Thus

$$G(j\omega) = \frac{1}{-10\omega^2 + 0.5j\omega + 250} = \frac{250 - 10\omega^2}{D} - j\frac{0.5\omega}{D}$$

where $D = (250 - 10\omega^2)^2 + 0.25\omega^2$, so that

$$|G(j\omega)| = \sqrt{\left[\frac{(250 - 10\omega^2)^2 + 0.25\omega^2}{D^2}\right]}$$

$$= \frac{1}{\sqrt{D}} = \frac{1}{\sqrt{[(250 - 10\omega^2)^2 + 0.25\omega^2]}} \tag{4.49}$$

$$\arg G(j\omega) = -\tan^{-1}\left(\frac{0.5\omega}{250 - 10\omega^2}\right) \tag{4.50}$$

Using (4.42), the steady-state response of the system to the nth harmonic $u_n(t)$ given by (4.48) is

$$x_{ssn}(t) = \frac{40}{\pi(2n-1)}|G(j(2n-1))|\sin[(2n-1)t + \arg G(j(2n-1))] \tag{4.51}$$

where $|G(j\omega)|$ and $\arg G(j\omega)$ are given by (4.49) and (4.50) respectively. The steady-state response $x_{ss}(t)$ of the system to the square-wave input $P(t)$ is then determined as the sum of the steady-state responses due to the individual harmonics in (4.47); that is,

$$x_{ss}(t) = \sum_{n=1}^{\infty} x_{ssn}(t) \tag{4.52}$$

where $x_{ssn}(t)$ is given by (4.51).

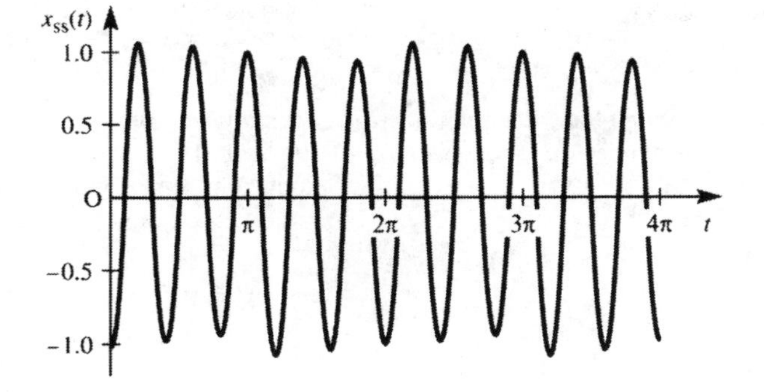

Figure 4.28 Steady-state response of system of Figure 4.26.

Evaluating the first few terms of the response (4.52), we have

$$x_{ss1}(t) = \frac{40}{\pi}\frac{1}{\sqrt{[(250-10)^2+0.25]}}\sin\left[t-\tan^{-1}\left(\frac{0.5}{240}\right)\right]$$

$$= 0.053\sin(t-0.003)$$

$$x_{ss2}(t) = \frac{40}{3\pi}\frac{1}{\sqrt{[(250-90)^2+2.25]}}\sin\left[3t-\tan^{-1}\left(\frac{1.5}{160}\right)\right]$$

$$= 0.027\sin(3t-0.009)$$

$$x_{ss3}(t) = \frac{40}{5\pi}\frac{1}{\sqrt{(6.25)}}\sin\left[5t-\tan^{-1}\left(\frac{2.5}{0}\right)\right]$$

$$= 1.02\sin(5t-\tfrac{1}{2}\pi)$$

$$x_{ss4}(t) = \frac{40}{7\pi}\frac{1}{\sqrt{[(250-490)^2+12.25]}}\sin\left[7t-\tan^{-1}\left(\frac{3.5}{-240}\right)\right]$$

$$= 0.0076\sin(7t-3.127)$$

Thus a good approximation to the steady-state response (4.52) is

$$x_{ss}(t) \simeq 0.053\sin(t-0.003) + 0.027\sin(3t-0.54) + 1.02\sin(5t-\tfrac{1}{2}\pi) + 0.0076\sin(7t-3.127) \tag{4.53}$$

The graph of this displacement is shown in Figure 4.28, and it appears from this that the response has a frequency about five times that of the input. This is because the term $1.02\sin(5t-\frac{1}{2}\pi)$ dominates in the response (4.53); this is a consequence of the fact that the natural frequency of oscillation of the system is $\sqrt{(K/M)} = 5\text{ rad s}^{-1}$, so that it is in resonance with this particular harmonic.

In conclusion, it should be noted that it was not essential to introduce transfer functions to solve this problem. Alternatively, by determining the particular integral of the differential equation (4.45), the steady-state response to an input $A\sin\omega t$ is determined as

$$x_{ss}(t) = \frac{A\sin(\omega t-\alpha)}{\sqrt{[(K-M\omega^2)^2+B^2\omega^2]}}, \qquad \tan\alpha = \frac{\omega B}{K-M\omega^2}$$

giving $x_{ssn}(t)$ as in (4.52). The solution then proceeds as before.

4.5.2 Exercises

30 Determine the steady-state current in the circuit of Figure 4.29(a) as a result of the applied periodic voltage shown in Figure 4.29(b).

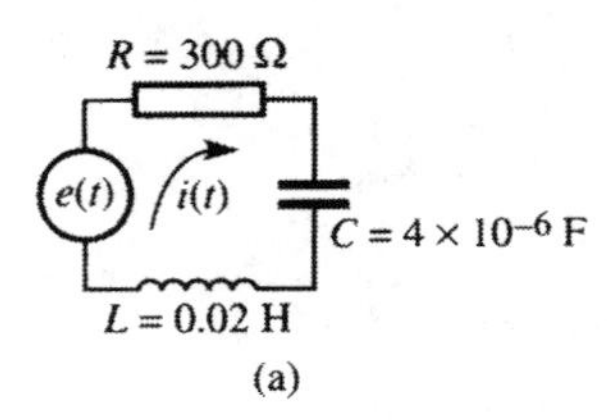

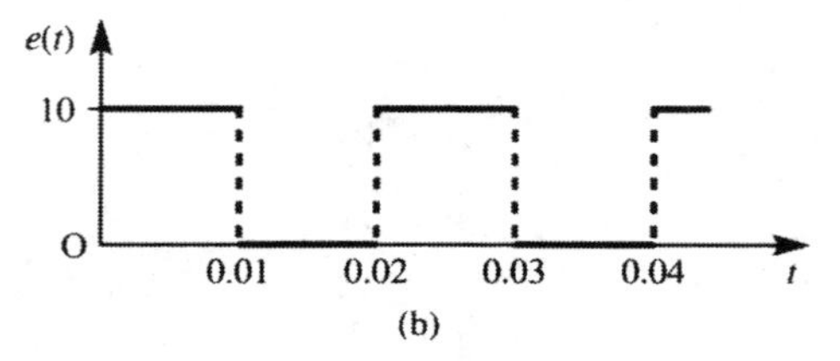

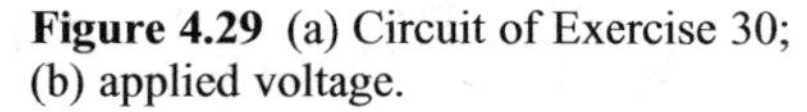

Figure 4.29 (a) Circuit of Exercise 30; (b) applied voltage.

31 Determine the steady-state response of the mass–spring–damper system of Figure 4.30(a) when the mass is subjected to the externally applied periodic force $f(t)$ shown in Figure 4.30(b).

What frequency dominates the response, and why?

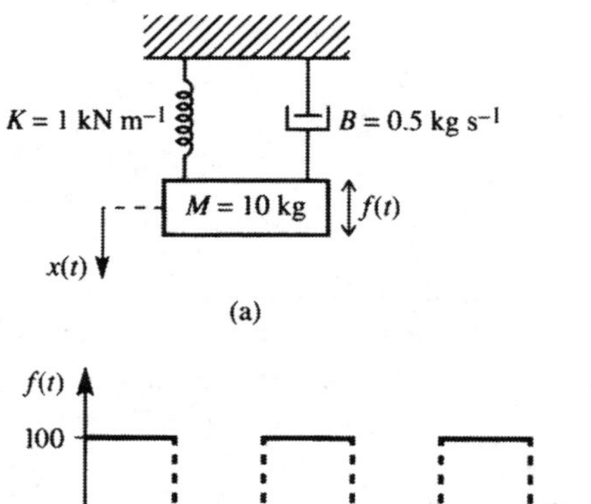

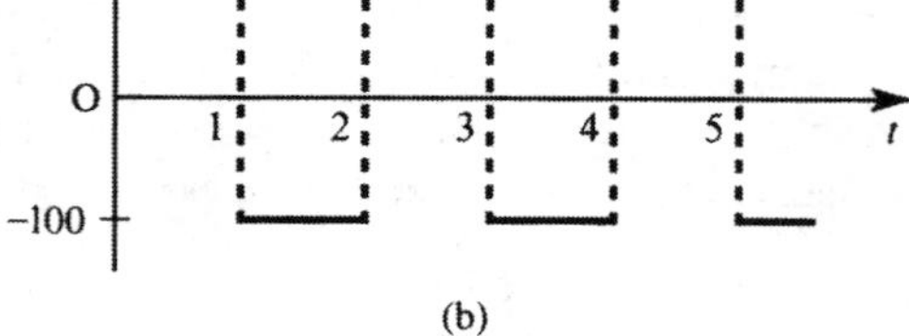

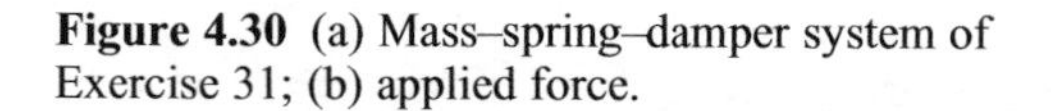

Figure 4.30 (a) Mass–spring–damper system of Exercise 31; (b) applied force.

32 Determine the steady-state motion of the mass of Figure 4.31(a) when it is subjected to the externally applied force of Figure 4.31(b).

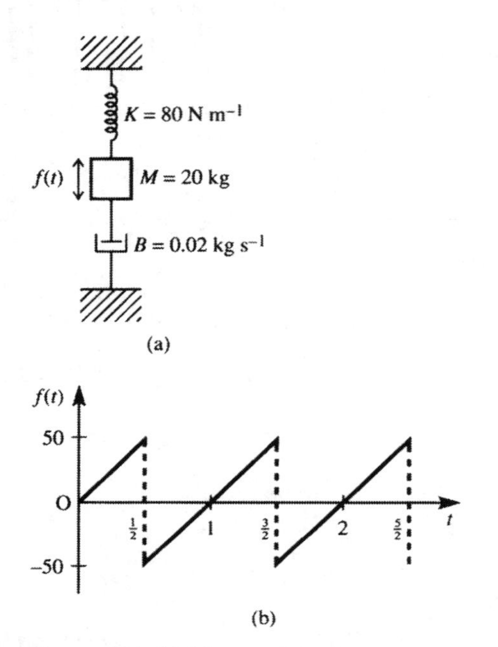

Figure 4.31 (a) Mass–spring–damper system of Exercise 32; (b) applied force.

33 Determine the steady-state current in the circuit shown in Figure 4.32(a) when the applied voltage is of the form shown in Figure 4.32(b).

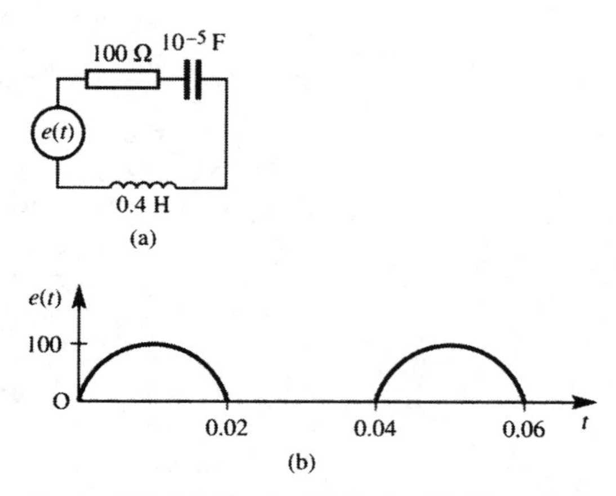

Figure 4.32 (a) Circuit of Exercise 33; (b) applied voltage.

4.6 Complex form of Fourier series

An alternative to the trigonometric form of the Fourier series considered so far is the complex or exponential form. As a result of the properties of the exponential function, this form is easily manipulated mathematically. It is widely used by engineers in practice, particularly in work involving signal analysis, and provides a smoother transition from the consideration of Fourier series for dealing with periodic signals to the consideration of Fourier transforms for dealing with aperiodic signals, which will be dealt with in Chapter 5.

4.6.1 Complex representation

To develop the complex form of the Fourier series

$$f(t) = \tfrac{1}{2}a_0 + \sum_{n=1}^{\infty} a_n \cos n\omega t + \sum_{n=1}^{\infty} b_n \sin n\omega t \tag{4.54}$$

representing a periodic function $f(t)$ of period T, we proceed as follows. Substituting the results

$$\sin n\omega t = \frac{1}{2\mathrm{j}}(\mathrm{e}^{\mathrm{j}n\omega t} - \mathrm{e}^{-\mathrm{j}n\omega t})$$

$$\cos n\omega t = \tfrac{1}{2}(\mathrm{e}^{\mathrm{j}n\omega t} + \mathrm{e}^{-\mathrm{j}n\omega t})$$

into (4.54) gives

$$f(t) = \tfrac{1}{2}a_0 + \sum_{n=1}^{\infty} a_n \frac{\mathrm{e}^{\mathrm{j}n\omega t} + \mathrm{e}^{-\mathrm{j}n\omega t}}{2} + \sum_{n=1}^{\infty} b_n \frac{\mathrm{e}^{\mathrm{j}n\omega t} - \mathrm{e}^{-\mathrm{j}n\omega t}}{2\mathrm{j}}$$

$$= \tfrac{1}{2}a_0 + \sum_{n=1}^{\infty} \tfrac{1}{2}a_n(\mathrm{e}^{\mathrm{j}n\omega t} + \mathrm{e}^{-\mathrm{j}n\omega t}) + \sum_{n=1}^{\infty} -\tfrac{1}{2}\mathrm{j}b_n(\mathrm{e}^{\mathrm{j}n\omega t} - \mathrm{e}^{-\mathrm{j}n\omega t})$$

$$= \tfrac{1}{2}a_0 + \sum_{n=1}^{\infty} [\tfrac{1}{2}(a_n - \mathrm{j}b_n)\,\mathrm{e}^{\mathrm{j}n\omega t} + \tfrac{1}{2}(a_n + \mathrm{j}b_n)\,\mathrm{e}^{-\mathrm{j}n\omega t}] \tag{4.55}$$

Writing

$$c_0 = \tfrac{1}{2}a_0, \qquad c_n = \tfrac{1}{2}(a_n - \mathrm{j}b_n), \qquad c_{-n} = c_n^* = \tfrac{1}{2}(a_n + \mathrm{j}b_n) \tag{4.56}$$

(4.55) becomes

$$f(t) = c_0 + \sum_{n=1}^{\infty} c_n\,\mathrm{e}^{\mathrm{j}n\omega t} + \sum_{n=1}^{\infty} c_{-n}\,\mathrm{e}^{-\mathrm{j}n\omega t}$$

$$= c_0 + \sum_{n=1}^{\infty} c_n\,\mathrm{e}^{\mathrm{j}n\omega t} + \sum_{n=-1}^{-\infty} c_n\,\mathrm{e}^{\mathrm{j}n\omega t}$$

$$= \sum_{n=-\infty}^{\infty} c_n\,\mathrm{e}^{\mathrm{j}n\omega t}, \quad \text{since} \quad c_0\,\mathrm{e}^0 = c_0$$

Thus the Fourier series (4.54) becomes simply

$$f(t) = \sum_{n=-\infty}^{\infty} c_n \mathrm{e}^{\mathrm{j}n\omega t} \tag{4.57}$$

which is referred to as the **complex** or **exponential form** of the Fourier series expansion of the function $f(t)$.

In order that we can apply this result directly, it is necessary to obtain a formula for calculating the complex coefficients c_n. To do this, we incorporate the Euler formulae (4.11) and (4.12) into the definitions given in (4.56), leading to

$$c_0 = \tfrac{1}{2}a_0 = \frac{1}{T}\int_d^{d+T} f(t)\,\mathrm{d}t \tag{4.58}$$

$$c_n = \tfrac{1}{2}(a_n - \mathrm{j}b_n) = \frac{1}{T}\left[\int_d^{d+T} f(t)\cos n\omega t\,\mathrm{d}t - \mathrm{j}\int_d^{d+T} f(t)\sin n\omega t\,\mathrm{d}t\right]$$

$$= \frac{1}{T}\int_d^{d+T} f(t)(\cos n\omega t - \mathrm{j}\sin n\omega t)\,\mathrm{d}t$$

$$= \frac{1}{T}\int_d^{d+T} f(t)\,\mathrm{e}^{-\mathrm{j}n\omega t}\,\mathrm{d}t \tag{4.59}$$

$$c_{-n} = \tfrac{1}{2}(a_n + \mathrm{j}b_n) = \frac{1}{T}\int_d^{d+T} f(t)(\cos n\omega t + \mathrm{j}\sin n\omega t)\,\mathrm{d}t$$

$$= \frac{1}{T}\int_d^{d+T} f(t)\,\mathrm{e}^{\mathrm{j}n\omega t}\,\mathrm{d}t \tag{4.60}$$

From (4.58)–(4.60), it is readily seen that for all values of n

$$c_n = \frac{1}{T}\int_d^{d+T} f(t)\,\mathrm{e}^{-\mathrm{j}n\omega t}\,\mathrm{d}t \tag{4.61}$$

In summary, the complex form of the Fourier series expansion of a periodic function $f(t)$, of period T, is

$$f(t) = \sum_{n=-\infty}^{\infty} c_n \mathrm{e}^{\mathrm{j}n\omega t} \tag{4.57}$$

where

$$c_n = \frac{1}{T}\int_d^{d+T} f(t)\,\mathrm{e}^{-\mathrm{j}n\omega t}\,\mathrm{d}t \quad (n = 0, \pm 1, \pm 2, \dots) \tag{4.61}$$

In general the coefficients c_n ($n = 0, \pm 1, \pm 2, \dots$) are complex, and may be expressed in the form

$$c_n = |c_n|\,\mathrm{e}^{\mathrm{j}\phi_n}$$

where $|c_n|$, the magnitude of c_n, is given from the definitions (4.56) by

$$|c_n| = \sqrt{[(\tfrac{1}{2}a_n)^2 + (\tfrac{1}{2}b_n)^2]} = \tfrac{1}{2}\sqrt{(a_n^2 + b_n^2)}$$

so that $2|c_n|$ is the amplitude of the nth harmonic. The argument ϕ_n of c_n is related to the phase of the nth harmonic.

Example 4.18

Find the complex form of the Fourier series expansion of the periodic function $f(t)$ defined by

$$f(t) = \cos \tfrac{1}{2}t \quad (-\pi < t < \pi), \qquad f(t + 2\pi) = f(t)$$

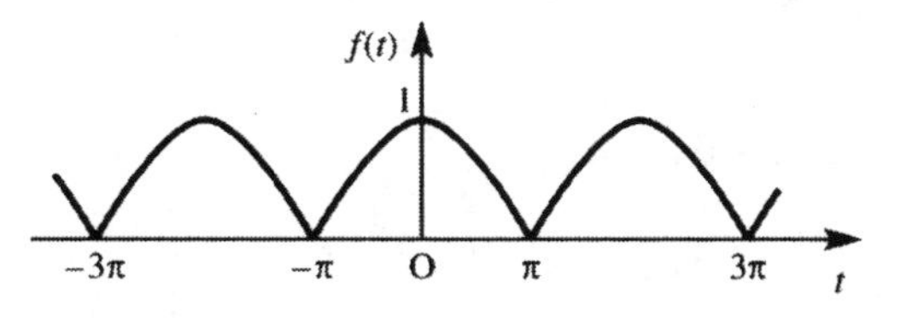

Figure 4.33 Function $f(t)$ of Example 4.18.

Solution A graph of the function $f(t)$ over the interval $-3\pi \leqslant t \leqslant 3\pi$ is shown in Figure 4.33. Here the period T is 2π, so from (4.61) the complex coefficients c_n are given by

$$c_n = \frac{1}{2\pi}\int_{-\pi}^{\pi} \cos \tfrac{1}{2}t\, e^{-jnt}\, dt = \frac{1}{4\pi}\int_{-\pi}^{\pi} (e^{jt/2} + e^{-jt/2})\, e^{-jnt}\, dt$$

$$= \frac{1}{4\pi}\int_{-\pi}^{\pi} (e^{-j(n-1/2)t} + e^{-j(n+1/2)t})\, dt$$

$$= \frac{1}{4\pi}\left[\frac{-2\, e^{-j(2n-1)t/2}}{j(2n-1)} - \frac{2\, e^{-j(2n+1)t/2}}{j(2n+1)}\right]_{-\pi}^{\pi}$$

$$= \frac{j}{2\pi}\left[\left(\frac{e^{-jn\pi}\, e^{j\pi/2}}{2n-1} + \frac{e^{-jn\pi}\, e^{-j\pi/2}}{2n+1}\right) - \left(\frac{e^{jn\pi}\, e^{-j\pi/2}}{2n-1} + \frac{e^{jn\pi}\, e^{j\pi/2}}{2n+1}\right)\right]$$

Now $e^{j\pi/2} = \cos \tfrac{1}{2}\pi + j \sin \tfrac{1}{2}\pi = j$, $e^{-j\pi/2} = -j$ and $e^{jn\pi} = e^{-jn\pi} = \cos n\pi = (-1)^n$, so that

$$c_n = \frac{j}{2\pi}\left(\frac{j}{2n-1} - \frac{j}{2n+1} + \frac{j}{2n-1} - \frac{j}{2n+1}\right)(-1)^n$$

$$= \frac{(-1)^n}{\pi}\left(\frac{1}{2n+1} - \frac{1}{2n-1}\right) = \frac{-2(-1)^n}{(4n^2-1)\pi}$$

Note that in this case c_n is real, which is as expected, since the function $f(t)$ is an even function of t.

From (4.57), the complex Fourier series expansion for $f(t)$ is

$$f(t) = \sum_{n=-\infty}^{\infty} \frac{2(-1)^{n+1}}{(4n^2-1)\pi}\, e^{jnt}$$

This may readily be converted back to the trigonometric form, since, from the definitions (4.56),

$$a_0 = 2c_0, \qquad a_n = c_n + c_n^*, \qquad b_n = \mathrm{j}(c_n - c_n^*)$$

so that in this particular case

$$a_0 = \frac{4}{\pi}, \qquad a_n = 2\left[\frac{2}{\pi}\frac{(-2)^{n+1}}{4n^2+1}\right] = \frac{4}{\pi}\frac{(-1)^{n+1}}{4n^2-1}, \qquad b_n = 0$$

Thus the trigonometric form of the Fourier series is

$$f(t) = \frac{2}{\pi} + \frac{4}{\pi}\sum_{n=1}^{\infty}\frac{(-1)^{n+1}}{4n^2-1}\cos nt$$

which corresponds to the solution to Exercise 1(e).

Example 4.19 Obtain the complex form of the Fourier series of the sawtooth function $f(t)$ defined by

$$f(t) = \frac{2t}{T} \quad (0 < t < 2T), \qquad f(t + 2T) = f(t)$$

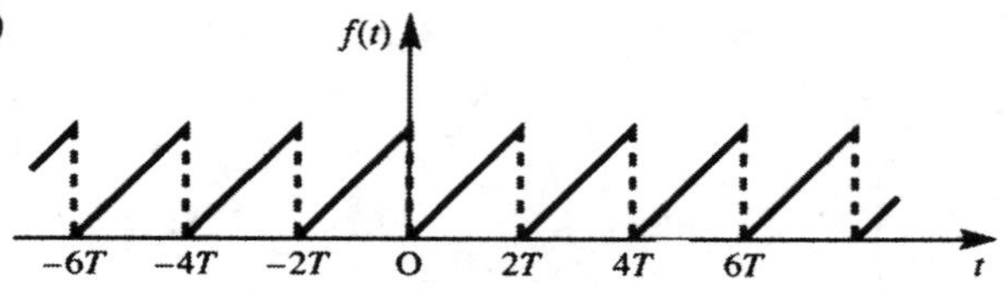

Figure 4.34 Function $f(t)$ of Example 4.19.

Solution A graph of the function $f(t)$ over the interval $-6T < t < 6T$ is shown in Figure 4.34. Here the period is $2T$, that is $\omega = \pi/T$, so from (4.61) the complex coefficients c_n are given by

$$c_n = \frac{1}{2T}\int_0^{2T} f(t)\,\mathrm{e}^{-\mathrm{j}n\pi t/T}\,\mathrm{d}t = \frac{1}{2T}\int_0^{2T}\frac{2}{T}t\,\mathrm{e}^{-\mathrm{j}n\pi t/T}\,\mathrm{d}t$$

$$= \frac{1}{T^2}\left[\frac{Tt}{-\mathrm{j}n\pi}\mathrm{e}^{-\mathrm{j}n\pi t/T} - \frac{T^2}{(\mathrm{j}n\pi)^2}\mathrm{e}^{-\mathrm{j}n\pi t/T}\right]_0^{2T} \quad (n \neq 0)$$

Now $\mathrm{e}^{-\mathrm{j}n2\pi} = \mathrm{e}^{-\mathrm{j}0} = 1$, so

$$c_n = \frac{1}{T^2}\left[\frac{2T^2}{-\mathrm{j}n\pi} + \frac{T^2}{(n\pi)^2} - \frac{T^2}{(n\pi)^2}\right] = \frac{\mathrm{j}2}{n\pi} \quad (n \neq 0)$$

In the particular case $n = 0$

$$c_0 = \frac{1}{2T}\int_0^{2T} f(t)\,\mathrm{d}t = \frac{1}{2T}\int_0^{2T}\frac{2t}{T}\,\mathrm{d}t = \frac{1}{T^2}\left[\tfrac{1}{2}t^2\right]_0^{2T} = 2$$

Thus from (4.57) the complex form of the Fourier series expansion of $f(t)$ is

$$f(t) = 2 + \sum_{n=-\infty}^{-1}\frac{\mathrm{j}2}{n\pi}\mathrm{e}^{\mathrm{j}n\pi t/T} + \sum_{n=1}^{\infty}\frac{\mathrm{j}2}{n\pi}\mathrm{e}^{\mathrm{j}n\pi t/T} = 2 + \sum_{\substack{n=-\infty \\ n\neq 0}}^{\infty}\frac{\mathrm{j}2}{n\pi}\mathrm{e}^{\mathrm{j}n\pi t/T}$$

Noting that $\mathrm{j} = \mathrm{e}^{\mathrm{j}\pi/2}$, this result may also be written in the form

$$f(t) = 2 + \frac{2}{\pi} \sum_{\substack{n=-\infty \\ n\neq 0}}^{\infty} \frac{1}{n} \mathrm{e}^{\mathrm{j}(n\pi t/T+\pi/2)}$$

As in Example 4.18, the Euler coefficients in the corresponding trigonometric series are

$$a_0 = 2c_0 = 4, \qquad a_n = c_n + c_n^* = 0, \qquad b_n = \mathrm{j}(c_n + c_n^*) = \mathrm{j}\left(\frac{2\mathrm{j}}{n\pi} + \frac{2\mathrm{j}}{n\pi}\right) = -\frac{4}{n\pi}$$

so that the corresponding trigonometric Fourier series expansion of $f(t)$ is

$$f(t) = 2 - \frac{4}{\pi} \sum_{n=1}^{\infty} \frac{1}{n} \sin \frac{n\pi t}{T}$$

which corresponds to the solution of Example 4.11 when $T = 2$.

4.6.2 The multiplication theorem and Parseval's theorem

Two useful results, particularly in the application of Fourier series to signal analysis, are the **multiplication theorem** and **Parseval's theorem**. The multiplication theorem enables us to write down the mean value of the product of two periodic functions over a period in terms of the coefficients of their Fourier series expansions, while Parseval's theorem enables us to write down the mean square value of a periodic function, which, as we will see in Section 4.6.4, determines the power spectrum of the function.

Theorem 4.5 **The multiplication theorem**

If $f(t)$ and $g(t)$ are two periodic functions having the same period T then

$$\frac{1}{T}\int_c^{c+T} f(t)g(t)\,\mathrm{d}t = \sum_{n=-\infty}^{\infty} c_n d_n^* \tag{4.62}$$

where the c_n and d_n are the coefficients in the complex Fourier series expansions of $f(t)$ and $g(t)$ respectively.

Proof Let $f(t)$ and $g(t)$ have complex Fourier series given by

$$f(t) = \sum_{n=-\infty}^{\infty} c_n \, \mathrm{e}^{\mathrm{j}n2\pi t/T} \tag{4.63a}$$

with

$$c_n = \frac{1}{T}\int_c^{c+T} f(t)\,\mathrm{e}^{-\mathrm{j}n2\pi t/T}\,\mathrm{d}T \tag{4.63b}$$

and

$$g(t) = \sum_{n=-\infty}^{\infty} d_n \, \mathrm{e}^{\mathrm{j}n2\pi t/T} \qquad \textbf{(4.64a)}$$

with

$$d_n = \frac{1}{T}\int_c^{c+T} g(t)\,\mathrm{e}^{-\mathrm{j}n2\pi t/T}\,\mathrm{d}t \qquad \textbf{(4.64b)}$$

Then

$$\frac{1}{T}\int_c^{c+T} f(t)g(t)\,\mathrm{d}t = \frac{1}{T}\int_c^{c+T}\left(\sum_{n=-\infty}^{\infty} c_n \,\mathrm{e}^{\mathrm{j}n2\pi t/T}\right)g(t)\,\mathrm{d}t \qquad \text{using (4.63a)}$$

$$= \sum_{n=-\infty}^{\infty} c_n \left[\frac{1}{T}\int_c^{c+T} g(t)\,\mathrm{e}^{\mathrm{j}n2\pi t/T}\,\mathrm{d}t\right] \qquad \text{assuming term-by-term integration is possible}$$

$$= \sum_{n=-\infty}^{\infty} c_n d_{-n} \qquad \text{using (4.64b)}$$

Since $d_{-n} = d_n^*$, the complex conjugate of d_n, this reduces to the required result:

$$\frac{1}{T}\int_c^{c+T} f(t)g(t)\,\mathrm{d}t = \sum_{n=-\infty}^{\infty} c_n d_n^*$$

end of theorem

In terms of the real coefficients a_n, b_n and α_n, β_n of the corresponding trigonometric Fourier series expansions of $f(t)$ and $g(t)$,

$$f(t) = \tfrac{1}{2}a_0 + \sum_{n=1}^{\infty} a_n \cos\left(\frac{n2\pi t}{T}\right) + \sum_{n=1}^{\infty} b_n \sin\left(\frac{n2\pi t}{T}\right)$$

$$g(t) = \tfrac{1}{2}\alpha_0 + \sum_{n=1}^{\infty} \alpha_n \cos\left(\frac{n2\pi t}{T}\right) + \sum_{n=1}^{\infty} \beta_n \sin\left(\frac{n2\pi t}{T}\right)$$

and using the definitions (4.56), the multiplication theorem result (4.62) reduces to

$$\frac{1}{T}\int_c^{c+T} f(t)g(t)\,\mathrm{d}t = \sum_{n=1}^{\infty} c_{-n}d_n + c_0 d_0 + \sum_{n=1}^{\infty} c_n d_{-n}$$

$$= \tfrac{1}{4}\alpha_0 a_0 + \tfrac{1}{4}\sum_{n=1}^{\infty}[(a_n - \mathrm{j}b_n)(\alpha_n + \mathrm{j}\beta_n) + (a_n + \mathrm{j}b_n)(\alpha_n - \mathrm{j}\beta_n)]$$

giving

$$\frac{1}{T}\int_c^{c+T} f(t)g(t)\,\mathrm{d}t = \tfrac{1}{4}\alpha_0 a_0 + \tfrac{1}{2}\sum_{n=1}^{\infty}(a_n\alpha_n + b_n\beta_n)$$

Theorem 4.6 **Parseval's theorem**

If $f(t)$ is a periodic function with period T then

$$\frac{1}{T}\int_{c}^{c+T}[f(t)]^2\,\mathrm{d}t=\sum_{n=-\infty}^{\infty}c_nc_n^*=\sum_{n=-\infty}^{\infty}|c_n|^2 \tag{4.65}$$

where the c_n are the coefficients in the complex Fourier series expansion of $f(t)$.

Proof This result follows from the multiplication theorem, since, taking $g(t) = f(t)$ in (4.62), we obtain

$$\frac{1}{T}\int_{c}^{c+T}[f(t)]^2\,\mathrm{d}t=\sum_{n=-\infty}^{\infty}c_nc_n^*=\sum_{n=-\infty}^{\infty}|c_n|^2$$

end of theorem

Using (4.60), Parseval's theorem may be written in terms of the real coefficients a_n and b_n of the trigonometric Fourier series expansion of the function $f(t)$ as

$$\frac{1}{T}\int_{c}^{c+T}[f(t)]^2\,\mathrm{d}t=\tfrac{1}{4}a_0^2+\tfrac{1}{2}\sum_{n=1}^{\infty}(a_n^2+b_n^2) \tag{4.66}$$

The **root mean square (RMS)** value f_{RMS} of a periodic function $f(t)$ of period T, defined by

$$f^2_{\mathrm{RMS}}=\frac{1}{T}\int_{c}^{c+T}[f(t)]^2\,\mathrm{d}t$$

may therefore be expressed in terms of the Fourier coefficients using (4.65) or (4.66).

Example 4.20 By applying Parseval's theorem to the function

$$f(t)=\frac{2t}{T}\quad(0<t<T),\qquad f(t+2T)=f(t)$$

considered in Example 4.19, show that

$$\tfrac{1}{6}\pi^2=\sum_{n=1}^{\infty}\frac{1}{n^2}$$

Solution From Example 4.19, the coefficients of the complex Fourier series expansion of $f(t)$ are

$$c_0=2,\ c_n=\frac{\mathrm{j}2}{n\pi}\quad(n\neq 0)$$

Thus, applying the Parseval's theorem result (4.65), noting that the period in this case is $2T$, we obtain

$$\frac{1}{2T}\int_0^{2T}[f(t)]^2\,dt = c_0^2 + \sum_{n=-\infty}^{-1}|c_n|^2 + \sum_{n=1}^{\infty}|c_n|^2$$

giving

$$\frac{1}{2T}\int_0^{2T}\frac{4t^2}{T^2}\,dt = 4 + 2\sum_{n=1}^{\infty}\left(\frac{2}{n\pi}\right)^2$$

which reduces to

$$\tfrac{16}{3} = 4 + \sum_{n=1}^{\infty}\frac{8}{n^2\pi^2}$$

leading to the required result

$$\tfrac{1}{6}\pi^2 = \sum_{n=1}^{\infty}\frac{1}{n^2}$$

4.6.3 Discrete frequency spectra

In expressing a periodic function $f(t)$ by its Fourier series expansion, we are decomposing the function into its **harmonic** or **frequency components**. We have seen that if $f(t)$ is of period T then it has frequency components at frequencies

$$\omega_n = \frac{2n\pi}{T} = n\omega_0 \quad (n = 1, 2, 3, \dots) \tag{4.67}$$

where ω_0 is the frequency of the parent function $f(t)$. (All frequencies here are measured in rad s^{-1}.)

A Fourier series may therefore be interpreted as constituting a **frequency spectrum** of the periodic function $f(t)$, and provides an alternative representation of the function to its time-domain waveform. This frequency spectrum is often displayed by plotting graphs of both the amplitudes and phases of the various harmonic components against angular frequency ω_n. A plot of amplitude against angular frequency is called the **amplitude spectrum**, while that of phase against angular frequency is called the **phase spectrum**. For a periodic function $f(t)$, of period T, harmonic components only occur at discrete frequencies ω_n, given by (4.63), so that these spectra are referred to as **discrete frequency spectra** or **line spectra**. In Chapter 5 Fourier transforms will be used to define continuous spectra for aperiodic functions. With the growing ability to process signals digitally, the representation of signals by their corresponding spectra is an approach widely used in almost all branches of engineering, especially electrical engineering, when considering topics such as filtering and modulation. An example of the use of a discrete spectral representation of a periodic function is in distortion measurements on amplifiers, where the harmonic content of the output, measured digitally, to a sinusoidal input provides a measure of the distortion.

If the Fourier series expansion of a periodic function $f(t)$, with period T, has been obtained in the trigonometric form

$$f(t) = \tfrac{1}{2}a_0 + \sum_{n=1}^{\infty} a_n \cos\left(\frac{2n\pi t}{T}\right) + \sum_{n=1}^{\infty} b_n \sin\left(\frac{2n\pi t}{T}\right)$$

then, as indicated in Section 4.2.2, this may be expressed in terms of the various harmonic components as

$$f(t) = A_0 + \sum_{n=1}^{\infty} A_n \sin\left(\frac{2n\pi t}{T} + \phi_n\right) \tag{4.68}$$

where

$$A_0 = \tfrac{1}{2}a_0, \quad A_n = \sqrt{(a_n^2 + b_n^2)}$$

and the ϕ_n are determined by

$$\sin\phi_n = \frac{b_n}{A_n}, \quad \cos\phi_n = \frac{a_n}{A_n}$$

In this case a plot of A_n against angular frequency ω_n will constitute the amplitude spectrum and that of ϕ_n against ω_n the phase spectrum. These may be incorporated in the same graph by indicating the various phases on the amplitude spectrum as illustrated in Figure 4.35. It can be seen that the amplitude spectrum consists of a series of equally spaced vertical lines whose lengths are proportional to the amplitudes of the various harmonic components making up the function $f(t)$. Clearly the trigonometric form of the Fourier series does not in general lend itself to the plotting of the discrete frequency spectrum, and the amplitudes A_n and phases ϕ_n must first be determined from the values of a_n and b_n previously determined.

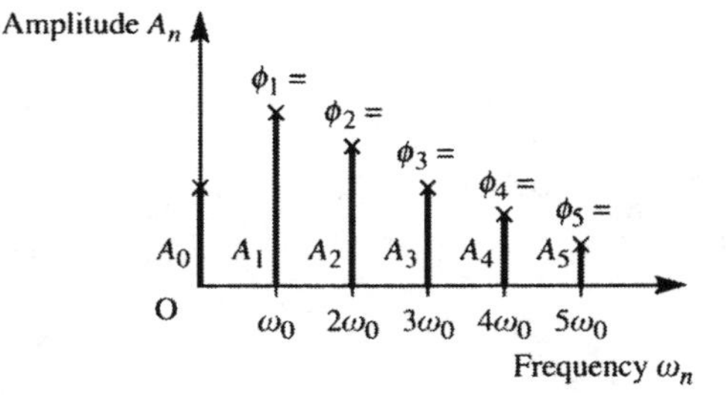

Figure 4.35 Real discrete frequency spectrum.

In work on signal analysis it is much more common to use the complex form of the Fourier series. For a periodic function $f(t)$, of period T, this is given by (4.57), with the complex coefficients being given by

$$c_n = |c_n| e^{j\phi_n} \quad (n = 0, \pm 1, \pm 2, \dots)$$

in which $|c_n|$ and ϕ_n denote the magnitude and argument of c_n respectively. Since in general c_n is a complex quantity, we need two line spectra to determine the discrete frequency spectrum; the amplitude spectrum being a plot of $|c_n|$ against ω_n and the phase spectrum that of ϕ_n against ω_n. In cases where c_n is real a single spectrum may be used to represent the function $f(t)$. Since $|c_{-n}| = |c_n^*| = |c_n|$, the amplitude spectrum will be symmetrical about the vertical axis, as illustrated in Figure 4.36.

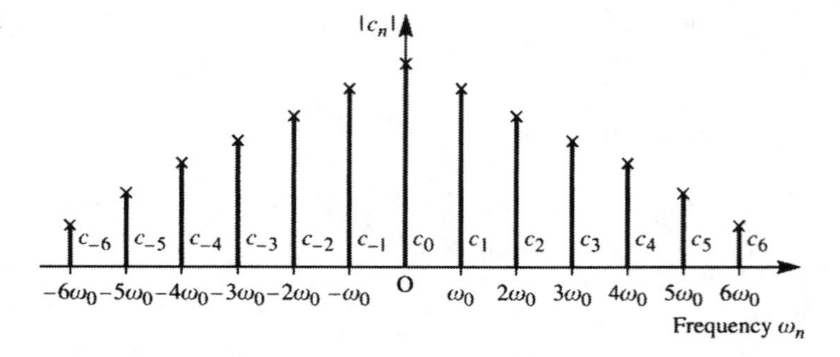

Figure 4.36 Complex form of the amplitude spectrum.

Note that in the complex form of the discrete frequency spectrum we have components at the discrete frequencies $0, \pm\omega_0, \pm 2\omega_0, \pm 3\omega_0, \ldots$; that is, both positive and negative discrete frequencies are involved. Clearly signals having negative frequencies are not physically realizable, and have been introduced for mathematical convenience. At frequency $n\omega_0$ we have the component $e^{jn\omega_0 t}$, which in itself is not a physical signal; to obtain a physical signal, we must consider this alongside the corresponding component $e^{-jn\omega_0 t}$ at the frequency $-n\omega_0$, since then we have

$$e^{jn\omega_0 t} + e^{-jn\omega_0 t} = 2\cos n\omega_0 t \tag{4.69}$$

Example 4.21 Plot the discrete amplitude and phase spectra for the periodic function

$$f(t) = \frac{2t}{T} \quad (0 < t < 2T), \qquad f(t + 2T) = f(t)$$

of Example 4.19. Consider both complex and real forms.

Solution In Example 4.19 the complex coefficients were determined as

$$c_0 = 2, \qquad c_n = \frac{j2}{n\pi} \quad (n = \pm 1, \pm 2, \pm 3, \ldots)$$

Thus

$$|c_n| = \begin{cases} 2/n\pi & (n = 1, 2, 3, \ldots) \\ -2/n\pi & (n = -1, -2, -3, \ldots) \end{cases}$$

$$\phi_n = \arg c_n = \begin{cases} \frac{1}{2}\pi & (n = 1, 2, 3, \ldots) \\ -\frac{1}{2}\pi & (n = -1, -2, -3, \ldots) \end{cases}$$

The corresponding amplitude and phase spectra are shown in Figures 4.37(a) and (b) respectively.

In Example 4.19 we saw that the coefficients in the trigonometric form of the Fourier series expansion of $f(t)$ are

$$a_0 = 4, \quad a_n = 0, \quad b_n = -\frac{4}{n\pi}$$

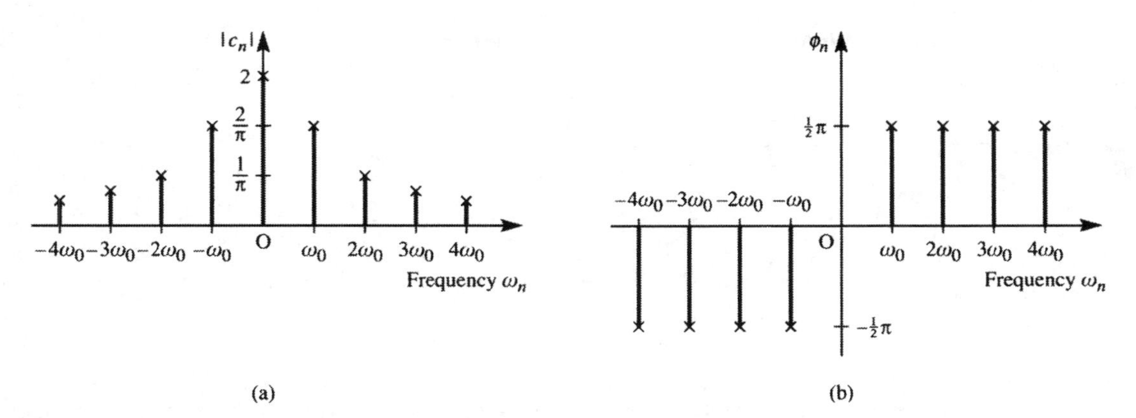

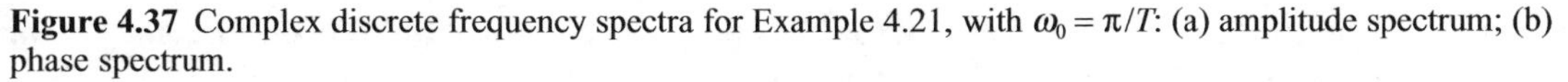

Figure 4.37 Complex discrete frequency spectra for Example 4.21, with $\omega_0 = \pi/T$: (a) amplitude spectrum; (b) phase spectrum.

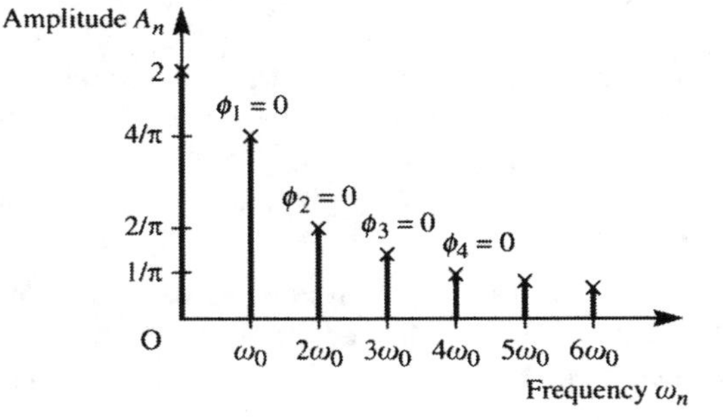

Figure 4.38 Real discrete frequency spectrum for Example 4.21 (corresponding to sinusoidal expansion).

so that the amplitude coefficients in (4.67) are

$$A_0 = 2, \quad A_n = \frac{4}{n\pi} \quad (n = 1, 2, 3, \ldots)$$

leading to the real discrete frequency spectrum of Figure 4.38.

Since $|c_n| = \frac{1}{2}\sqrt{(a_n^2 + b_n^2)} = \frac{1}{2}A_n$, the amplitude spectrum lines in the complex form (Figure 4.37) are, as expected, halved in amplitude relative to those in the real representation (Figure 4.38), the other half-value being allocated to the corresponding negative frequency. In the complex representation the phases at negative frequencies (Figure 4.37b) are the negatives of those at the corresponding positive frequencies. In our particular representation (4.68) of the real form the phases at positive frequencies differ by $\frac{1}{2}\pi$ between the real and complex form. Again this is not surprising, since from (4.69) we see that combining positive and negative frequencies in the complex form leads to a cosinusoid at that frequency rather than a sinusoid. In order to maintain equality of the phases at positive frequencies between the complex and real representations, a cosinusoidal expansion

$$f(t) = A_0 + \sum_{n=1}^{\infty} A_n \cos\left(\frac{n\pi t}{T} + \phi_n\right) \tag{4.70}$$

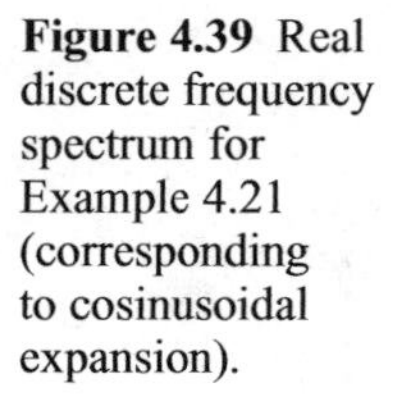

Figure 4.39 Real discrete frequency spectrum for Example 4.21 (corresponding to cosinusoidal expansion).

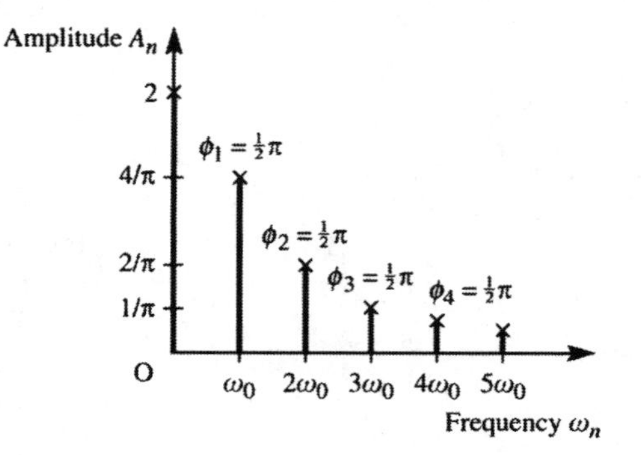

of the real Fourier series is frequently adopted as an alternative to the sinusoidal series expansion (4.68). Taking (4.70), the amplitude spectrum will remain the same as for (4.68), but the phase spectrum will be determined by

$$\sin \phi_n = -\frac{b_n}{A_n}, \quad \cos \phi_n = \frac{a_n}{A_n}$$

showing a phase shift of $\frac{1}{2}\pi$ from that of (4.68). Adopting the real representation (4.70), the corresponding real discrete frequency spectrum for the function $f(t)$ of Example 4.21 is as illustrated in Figure 4.39.

Example 4.22

Determine the complex form of the Fourier series expansion of the periodic (period $2T$) infinite train of identical rectangular pulses of magnitude A and duration $2d$ illustrated in Figure 4.40. Draw the discrete frequency spectrum in the particular case when $d = \frac{1}{10}$ and $T = \frac{1}{2}$.

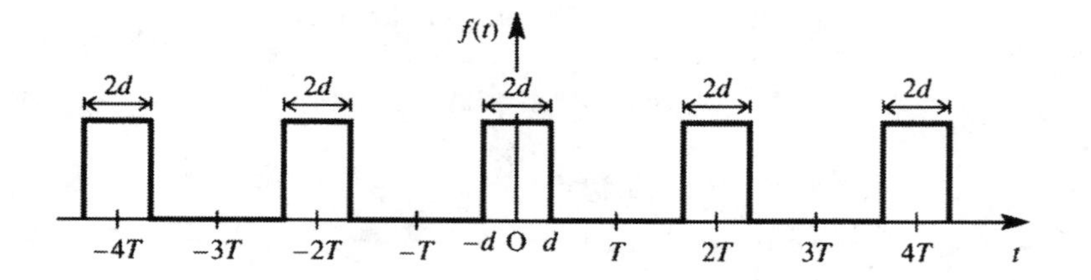

Figure 4.40 Infinite train of rectangular pulses of Example 4.22.

Solution Over one period $-T < t < T$ the function $f(t)$ representing the train is expressed as

$$f(t) = \begin{cases} 0 & (-T < t < -d) \\ A & (-d < t < d) \\ 0 & (d < t < T) \end{cases}$$

From (4.61), the complex coefficients c_n are given by

$$c_n = \frac{1}{2T}\int_{-T}^{T} f(t)\,\mathrm{e}^{-\mathrm{j}n\pi t/T}\,\mathrm{d}t = \frac{1}{2T}\int_{-d}^{d} A\,\mathrm{e}^{-\mathrm{j}n\pi t/T}\,\mathrm{d}t = \frac{A}{2T}\left[\frac{-T}{\mathrm{j}n\pi}\mathrm{e}^{-\mathrm{j}n\pi t/T}\right]_{-d}^{d} \quad (n \neq 0)$$

$$= \frac{A}{n\pi}\frac{\mathrm{e}^{\mathrm{j}n\pi d/T} - \mathrm{e}^{-\mathrm{j}n\pi d/T}}{\mathrm{j}2} = \frac{A}{n\pi}\sin\left(\frac{n\pi d}{T}\right) = \frac{Ad}{T}\frac{\sin(n\pi d/T)}{n\pi d/T} \quad (n = \pm 1, \pm 2, \ldots)$$

In the particular case when $n = 0$

$$c_0 = \frac{1}{2T}\int_{-T}^{T} f(t)\,\mathrm{d}t = \frac{1}{2T}\int_{-d}^{d} A\,\mathrm{d}t = \frac{Ad}{T}$$

so that

$$c_n = \frac{Ad}{T}\,\mathrm{sinc}\left(\frac{n\pi d}{T}\right) \quad (n = 0, \pm 1, \pm 2, \dots)$$

where the **sinc function** is defined by

$$\mathrm{sinc}\,t = \begin{cases} \dfrac{\sin t}{t} & (t \neq 0) \\ 1 & (t = 0) \end{cases}$$

Thus from (4.57) the complex Fourier series expansion for the infinite train of pulses $f(t)$ is

$$f(t) = \sum_{n=-\infty}^{\infty} \frac{Ad}{T}\,\mathrm{sinc}\left(\frac{n\pi d}{T}\right)\mathrm{e}^{\mathrm{j}n\pi t/T}$$

As expected, since $f(t)$ is an even function, c_n is real, so we need only plot the discrete amplitude spectrum to represent $f(t)$. Since the amplitude spectrum is a plot of $|c_n|$ against frequency $n\omega_0$, with $\omega_0 = \pi/T$, it will only take values at the discrete frequency values

$$0, \pm\frac{\pi}{T}, \pm\frac{2\pi}{7}, \pm\frac{3\pi}{7}, \dots$$

In the particular case $d = \frac{1}{10}$, $T = \frac{1}{2}$, $\omega_0 = 2\pi$ the amplitude spectrum will only exist at frequency values

$$0, \pm 2\pi, \pm 4\pi, \dots$$

Since in this case

$$c_n = \tfrac{1}{5}A\,\mathrm{sinc}\,\tfrac{1}{5}n\pi \quad (n = 0, \pm 1, \pm 2, \dots)$$

noting that $\mathrm{sinc}\,\frac{1}{5}n\pi = 0$ when $\frac{1}{5}n\pi = m\pi$ or $n = 5m$ $(m = \pm 1, \pm 2, \dots)$, the spectrum is as shown in Figure 4.41.

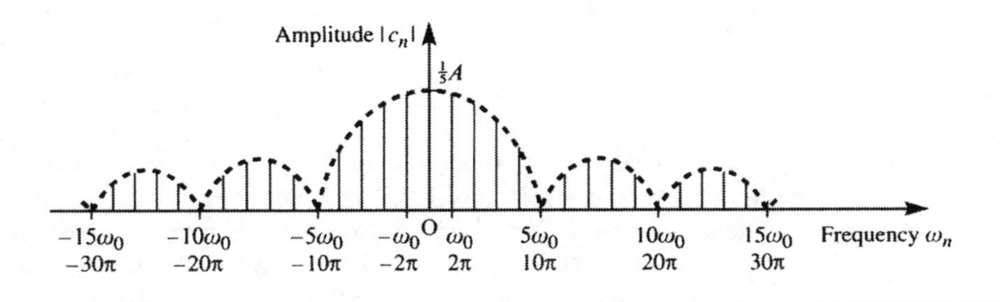

Figure 4.41 Discrete amplitude spectrum for an infinite train of pulses when $d = \frac{1}{10}$ and $T = \frac{1}{2}$.

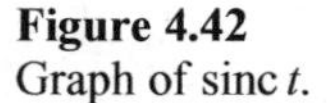
Figure 4.42
Graph of sinc t.

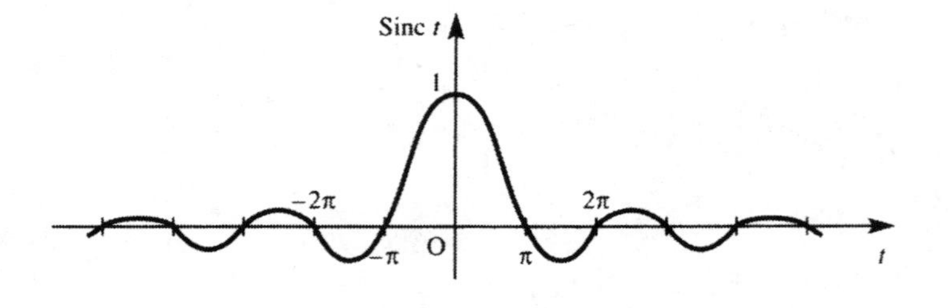

As we will see in Chapter 5, the sinc function sinc $t = (\sin t)/t$ plays an important role in signal analysis, and it is sometimes referred to as the **sampling function**. A graph of sinc t is shown in Figure 4.42, and it is clear that the function oscillates over intervals of length 2π and decreases in amplitude with increasing t. Note also that the function has zeros at $t = \pm n\pi$ $(n = 1, 2, 3, \ldots)$.

4.6.4 Power spectrum

The **average power** P associated with a periodic signal $f(t)$, of period T, is defined as the mean square value; that is,

$$P = \frac{1}{T}\int_{d}^{d+T} [f(t)]^2\,\mathrm{d}t \tag{4.71}$$

For example, if $f(t)$ represents a voltage waveform applied to a resistor then P represents the average power, measured in watts, dissipated by a $1\,\Omega$ resistor.

By Parseval's theorem (Theorem 4.6),

$$P = \tfrac{1}{4}a_0^2 + \tfrac{1}{2}\sum_{n=1}^{\infty}(a_n^2 + b_n^2) \tag{4.72}$$

Since

$$\frac{1}{T}\int_{d}^{d+T}\left[a_n \cos\left(\frac{2n\pi t}{T}\right)\right]^2 \mathrm{d}t = \tfrac{1}{2}a_n^2, \qquad \frac{1}{T}\int_{d}^{d+T}\left[b_n \sin\left(\frac{2n\pi t}{T}\right)\right]^2 \mathrm{d}t = \tfrac{1}{2}b_n^2$$

the power in the nth harmonic is

$$P_n = \tfrac{1}{2}(a_n^2 + b_n^2) \tag{4.73}$$

and it follows from (4.72) that the power of the periodic function $f(t)$ is the sum of the power of the individual harmonic components contained in $f(t)$.

In terms of the complex Fourier coefficients, Parseval's theorem gives

$$P = \sum_{n=-\infty}^{\infty} |c_n|^2 \tag{4.74}$$

As discussed in Section 4.6.3, the component $\mathrm{e}^{\mathrm{j}n\omega_0 t}$ at frequency $\omega_n = n\omega_0$, $\omega_0 = 2\pi/T$, must be considered alongside the component $\mathrm{e}^{-\mathrm{j}n\omega_0 t}$ at the corresponding negative frequency $-\omega_n$ in order to form the actual nth harmonic component of the function $f(t)$. Since $|c_{-n}|^2 = |c_n^*|^2 = |c_n|^2$, it follows that the power associated with the nth harmonic is the sum of the power associated with $\mathrm{e}^{\mathrm{j}n\omega_0 t}$ and $\mathrm{e}^{-\mathrm{j}n\omega_0 t}$; that is,

$$P_n = 2|c_n|^2 \tag{4.75}$$

which, since $|c_n| = \frac{1}{2}\sqrt{(a_n^2 + b_n^2)}$, corresponds to (4.73). Thus in the complex form half the power of the nth harmonic is associated with the positive frequency and half with the negative frequency.

Since the total power of a periodic signal is the sum of the power associated with each of the harmonics of which the signal is composed, it is again useful to consider a spectral representation, and a plot of $|c_n|^2$ against angular frequency ω_n is called the **power spectrum** of the function $f(t)$. Clearly such a spectrum is readily deduced from the discrete amplitude spectrum of $|c_n|$ against angular frequency ω_n.

Example 4.23

For the spectrum of the infinite train of rectangular pulses shown in Figure 4.40, determine the percentage of the total power contained within the frequency band up to the first zero value (called the **zero crossing** of the spectrum) at 10π rad s^{-1}.

Solution

From (4.71), the total power associated with the infinite train of rectangular pulses $f(t)$ is

$$P = \frac{1}{2T}\int_{-T}^{T} [f(t)]^2 \, dt = \frac{1}{2T}\int_{-d}^{d} A^2 \, dt$$

which in the particular case when $d = \frac{1}{10}$ and $T = \frac{1}{2}$ becomes

$$P = \int_{-1/10}^{1/10} A^2 \, dt = \tfrac{1}{5}A^2$$

The power contained in the frequency band up to the first zero crossing at 10π rad s^{-1} is

$$P_1 = c_0^2 + 2(c_1^2 + c_2^2 + c_3^2 + c_4^2)$$

where

$$c_n = \tfrac{1}{5}A \operatorname{sinc} \tfrac{1}{5}n\pi$$

That is,

$$\begin{aligned} P_1 &= \tfrac{1}{25}A^2 + \tfrac{2}{25}A^2(\operatorname{sinc}^2 \tfrac{1}{5}\pi + \operatorname{sinc}^2 \tfrac{2}{5}\pi + \operatorname{sinc}^2 \tfrac{3}{5}\pi + \operatorname{sinc}^2 \tfrac{4}{5}\pi) \\ &= \tfrac{1}{25}A^2[1 + 2(0.875 + 0.756 + 0.255 + 0.055)] = \tfrac{1}{5}A^2(0.976) \end{aligned}$$

Thus $P_1 = 0.976P$, so that approximately 97.6% of the total power associated with $f(t)$ is contained in the frequency band up to the first zero crossing at 10π rad s^{-1}.

Suppose that a periodic voltage $v(t)$, of period T, applied to a linear circuit, results in a corresponding current $i(t)$, having the same period T. Then, given the Fourier series representation of both the voltage and current at a pair of terminals, we can use the multiplication theorem (Theorem 4.5) to obtain an expression for the average power P at the terminals. Thus, given

$$v(t) = \sum_{n=-\infty}^{\infty} c_n e^{j2n\pi t/T}, \qquad i(t) = \sum_{n=-\infty}^{\infty} d_n e^{j2n\pi t/T}$$

the instantaneous power at the terminals is vi and the average power is

$$P = \frac{1}{T}\int_d^{d+T} vi\,\mathrm{d}t = \sum_{n=-\infty}^{\infty} c_n d_n^*$$

or, in terms of the corresponding trigonometric Fourier series coefficients a_n, b_n and α_n, β_n,

$$P = \tfrac{1}{4}\alpha_0\beta_0 + \tfrac{1}{2}\sum_{n=1}^{\infty}(a_n\alpha_n + b_n\beta_n)$$

4.6.5 Exercises

34 Show that the complex form of the Fourier series expansion of the periodic function

$$f(t) = t^2 \quad (-\pi < t < \pi)$$

$$f(t + 2\pi) = f(t)$$

is

$$f(t) = \frac{\pi^2}{6} + \sum_{n=0}^{\infty} \frac{2}{n^2}(-1)^n \mathrm{e}^{\mathrm{j}nt}$$

Using (4.56), obtain the corresponding trigonometric series and check with the series obtained in Example 4.5.

35 Obtain the complex form of the Fourier series expansion of the square wave

$$f(t) = \begin{cases} 0 & (-2 < t < 0) \\ 1 & (0 < t < 2) \end{cases}$$

$$f(t + 4) = f(t)$$

Using (4.56), obtain the corresponding trigonometric series and check with the series obtained in Example 4.9.

36 Obtain the complex form of the Fourier series expansion of the following periodic functions.

(a) $f(t) = \begin{cases} \pi & (-\pi < t < 0) \\ t & (0 < t < \pi) \end{cases}$

$f(t + 2\pi) = f(t)$

(b) $f(t) = \begin{cases} a \sin \omega t & (0 < t < \tfrac{1}{2}T) \\ 0 & (\tfrac{1}{2}T < t < T) \end{cases}$

$f(t + T) = f(t), \quad T = 2\pi/\omega$

(c) $f(t) = \begin{cases} 2 & (-\pi < t < 0) \\ 1 & (0 < t < \pi) \end{cases}$

$f(t + 2\pi) = f(t)$

(d) $f(t) = |\sin t| \quad (-\pi < t < \pi)$

$f(t + 2\pi) = f(t)$

37 A periodic function $f(t)$, of period 2π, is defined within the period $-\pi < t < \pi$ by

$$f(t) = \begin{cases} 0 & (-\pi < t < 0) \\ 1 & (0 < t < \pi) \end{cases}$$

Using the Fourier coefficients of $f(t)$, together with Parseval's theorem, show that

$$\sum_{n=1}^{\infty} \frac{1}{(2n-1)^2} = \tfrac{1}{8}\pi^2$$

(*Note*: The Fourier coefficients may be deduced from Example 4.9 or Exercise 35.)

38 (a) Show that the Fourier series expansion of the periodic function

$$f(t) = 500\pi t \quad (0 < t < \tfrac{1}{50})$$

$$f(t + \tfrac{1}{50}) = f(t)$$

may be expressed as

$$f(t) = 5\pi - 10\sum_{n=1}^{\infty} \frac{1}{n} \sin 100n\pi t$$

(b) Using (4.66), estimate the RMS value of $f(t)$ by

(i) using the first four terms of the Fourier series;

(ii) using the first eight terms of the Fourier series.

(c) Obtain the true RMS value of $f(t)$, and hence determine the percentage errors in the estimated values obtained in (b).

39 A periodic voltage $v(t)$ (in V) of period 5 ms and specified by

$$v(t) = \begin{cases} 60 & (0 < t < 1.25 \text{ ms}) \\ 0 & (1.25 \text{ ms} < t < 5 \text{ ms}) \end{cases}$$

$$v(t + 5 \text{ ms}) = v(t)$$

is applied across the terminals of a 15 Ω resistor.

(a) Obtain expressions for the coefficients c_n of the complex Fourier series representation of $v(t)$, and write down the values of the first five non-zero terms.
(b) Calculate the power associated with each of the first five non-zero terms of the Fourier expansion.
(c) Calculate the total power delivered to the 15 Ω resistor.
(d) What is the percentage of the total power delivered to the resistor by the first five non-zero terms of the Fourier series?

4.7 Orthogonal functions

As was noted in Section 4.2.3, the fact that the set of functions $\{1, \cos \omega t, \sin \omega t, \dots, \cos n\omega t, \sin n\omega t, \dots\}$ is an orthogonal set of functions on the interval $d \leq t \leq d + T$ was crucial in the evaluation of the coefficients in the Fourier series expansion of a function $f(t)$. It is natural to ask whether it is possible to express the function $f(t)$ as a series expansion in other sets of functions. In the case of periodic functions $f(t)$ there is no natural alternative, but if we are concerned with representing a function $f(t)$ only in a finite interval $t_1 \leq t \leq t_2$ then a variety of other possibilities exist. These possibilities are drawn from a class of functions called **orthogonal functions**, of which the trigonometric set $\{1, \cos \omega t, \sin \omega t, \dots, \cos n\omega t, \sin n\omega t\}$ is a particular example.

4.7.1 Definitions

Two real functions $f(t)$ and $g(t)$ that are piecewise-continuous in the interval $t_1 \leq t \leq t_2$ are said to be **orthogonal** in this interval if

$$\int_{t_1}^{t_2} f(t)g(t)\,dt = 0$$

A set of real functions $\phi_1(t), \phi_2(t), \dots \equiv \{\phi_n(t)\}$, each of which is piecewise-continuous on $t_1 \leq t \leq t_2$, is said to be an **orthogonal set** on this interval if $\phi_n(t)$ and $\phi_m(t)$ are orthogonal for each pair of distinct indices n, m; that is, if

$$\int_{t_1}^{t_2} \phi_n(t)\phi_m(t)\,dt = 0 \quad (n \neq m) \tag{4.76}$$

We shall also assume that no member of the set $\{\phi_n(t)\}$ is identically zero except at a finite number of points, so that

$$\int_{t_1}^{t_2} \phi_m^2(t)\,dt = \gamma_m \quad (m = 1, 2, 3, \dots) \tag{4.77}$$

where γ_m $(m = 1, 2, \dots)$ are all non-zero constants.

An orthogonal set $\{\phi_n(t)\}$ is said to be **orthonormal** if each of its components is also normalized; that is, $\gamma_m = 1$ $(m = 1, 2, 3, \ldots)$. We note that any orthogonal set $\{\phi_n(t)\}$ can be converted into an orthonormal set by dividing each member $\phi_m(t)$ of the set by $\sqrt{\gamma_m}$.

Example 4.24 Since (4.4)–(4.8) hold,

$$\{1, \cos t, \sin t, \cos 2t, \sin 2t, \ldots, \cos nt, \sin nt\}$$

is an orthogonal set on the interval $d \leqslant t \leqslant d + 2\pi$, while the set

$$\left\{\frac{1}{\sqrt{(2\pi)}}, \frac{\cos t}{\sqrt{\pi}}, \frac{\sin t}{\sqrt{\pi}}, \ldots, \frac{\cos nt}{\sqrt{\pi}}, \frac{\sin nt}{\sqrt{\pi}}\right\}$$

forms an orthonormal set on the same interval.

The latter follows since

$$\int_d^{d+2\pi} \left[\frac{1}{\sqrt{(2\pi)}}\right]^2 \mathrm{d}t = 1$$

$$\int_d^{d+2\pi} \left(\frac{\cos nt}{\sqrt{\pi}}\right)^2 \mathrm{d}t = \int_d^{d+2\pi} \left(\frac{\sin nt}{\sqrt{\pi}}\right)^2 \mathrm{d}t = 1 \quad (n = 1, 2, 3, \ldots)$$

The definition of orthogonality considered so far applies to real functions, and has to be amended somewhat if members of the set $\{\phi_n(t)\}$ are complex functions of the real variable t. In such a case the set $\{\phi_n(t)\}$ is said to be an orthogonal set on the interval $t_1 \leqslant t \leqslant t_2$ if

$$\int_{t_1}^{t_2} \phi_n(t)\phi_m^*(t)\,\mathrm{d}t = \begin{cases} 0 & (n \neq m) \\ \gamma & (n = m) \end{cases} \tag{4.78}$$

where $\phi_m^*(t)$ denotes the complex conjugate of $\phi_m(t)$.

Example 4.25 Verify that the set of complex exponential functions

$$\{\mathrm{e}^{\mathrm{j}n\pi t/T}\} \quad (n = 0, \pm1, \pm2, \pm3, \ldots)$$

used in the complex representation of the Fourier series is an orthogonal set on the interval $0 \leqslant t \leqslant 2T$.

Solution First,

$$\int_0^{2T} \mathrm{e}^{\mathrm{j}n\pi t/T}\,1\,\mathrm{d}t = \left[\frac{T}{\mathrm{j}n\pi}\mathrm{e}^{\mathrm{j}n\pi t/T}\right]_0^{2T} = 0 \quad (n \neq 0)$$

since $\mathrm{e}^{\mathrm{j}2n\pi} = \mathrm{e}^0 = 1$. Secondly,

$$\int_0^{2T} \mathrm{e}^{\mathrm{j}n\pi t/T}(\mathrm{e}^{\mathrm{j}m\pi t/T})^*\,\mathrm{d}t = \int_0^{2T} \mathrm{e}^{\mathrm{j}(n-m)\pi t/T}\,\mathrm{d}t = \left[\frac{T}{\mathrm{j}(n-m)\pi}\mathrm{e}^{\mathrm{j}(n-m)\pi t/T}\right]_0^{2T} = 0 \quad (n \neq m)$$

and, when $n = m$,

$$\int_0^{2T} e^{jn\pi t/T}(e^{jn\pi t/T})^* \, dt = \int_0^{2T} 1 \, dt = 2T$$

Thus

$$\int_0^{2T} e^{jn\pi t/T} 1 \, dt = 0 \quad (n \neq 0)$$

$$\int_0^{2T} e^{jn\pi t/T}(e^{jm\pi t/T})^* \, dt = \begin{cases} 0 & (n \neq m) \\ 2T & (n = m) \end{cases}$$

and, from (4.78), the set is an orthogonal set on the interval $0 \leqslant t \leqslant 2T$.

The trigonometric and exponential sets are examples of orthogonal sets that we have already used in developing the work on Fourier series. Examples of other sets of orthogonal functions that are widely used in practice are Legendre polynomials, Bessel functions, Hermite polynomials, Laguerre polynomials, Jacobi polynomials, Tchebyshev (sometimes written as Chebyshev) polynomials and Walsh functions. Over recent years wavelets are another set of orthogonal functions that have been widely used, particularly in applications such as signal processing and data compression.

4.7.2 Generalized Fourier series

Let $\{\phi_n(t)\}$ be an orthogonal set on the interval $t_1 \leqslant t \leqslant t_2$ and suppose that we wish to represent the piecewise-continuous function $f(t)$ in terms of this set within this interval. Following the Fourier series development, suppose that it is possible to express $f(t)$ as a series expansion of the form

$$f(t) = \sum_{n=1}^{\infty} c_n \phi_n(t) \qquad \textbf{(4.79)}$$

We now wish to determine the coefficients c_n, and to do so we again follow the Fourier series development. Multiplying (4.79) throughout by $\phi_m(t)$ and integrating term by term, we obtain

$$\int_{t_1}^{t_2} f(t)\phi_m(t) \, dt = \sum_{n=1}^{\infty} c_n \int_{t_1}^{t_2} \phi_m(t)\phi_n(t) \, dt$$

which, on using (4.76) and (4.77), reduces to

$$\int_{t_1}^{t_2} f(t)\phi_n(t) \, dt = c_n \gamma_n$$

giving

$$c_n = \frac{1}{\gamma_n} \int_{t_1}^{t_2} f(t)\phi_n(t) \, dt \quad (n = 1, 2, 3, \dots) \qquad \textbf{(4.80)}$$

Summarizing, if $f(t)$ is a piecewise-continuous function on the interval $t_1 \leqslant t \leqslant t_2$ and $\{\phi_n(t)\}$ is an orthogonal set on this interval then the series

$$f(t) = \sum_{n=1}^{\infty} c_n\phi_n(t)$$

is called the **generalized Fourier series** of $f(t)$ with respect to the basis set $\{\phi_n(t)\}$, and the coefficients c_n, given by (4.80), are called the **generalized Fourier coefficients** with respect to the same basis set.

A parallel can be drawn between a generalized Fourier series expansion of a function $f(t)$ with respect to an orthogonal basis set of functions $\{\phi_n(t)\}$ and the representation of a vector $\boldsymbol{f}$ in terms of an orthogonal basis set of vectors $\boldsymbol{v}_1, \boldsymbol{v}_2, \dots, \boldsymbol{v}_n$ as

$$\boldsymbol{f} = \alpha_1\boldsymbol{v}_1 + \dots + \alpha_n\boldsymbol{v}_n$$

where

$$\alpha_i = \frac{\boldsymbol{f}\cdot\boldsymbol{v}_i}{\boldsymbol{v}_i\cdot\boldsymbol{v}_i} = \frac{\boldsymbol{f}\cdot\boldsymbol{v}_i}{|\boldsymbol{v}_i|^2}$$

There is clearly a similarity between this pair of results and the pair (4.79)–(4.80).

4.7.3 Convergence of generalized Fourier series

As in the case of a Fourier series expansion, partial sums of the form

$$F_N(t) = \sum_{n=1}^{N} c_n\phi_n(t) \tag{4.81}$$

can be considered, and we wish this representation to be, in some sense, a 'close approximation' to the parent function $f(t)$. The question arises when considering such a partial sum as to whether choosing the coefficients c_n as the generalized Fourier coefficients (4.80) leads to the 'best' approximation. Defining the **mean square error** E_N between the actual value of $f(t)$ and the approximation $F_N(t)$ as

$$E_N = \frac{1}{t_2 - t_1}\int_{t_1}^{t_2} [f(t) - F_N(t)]^2\,\mathrm{d}t$$

it can be shown that E_N is minimized, for all N, when the coefficients c_n are chosen according to (4.80). Thus in this sense the finite generalized Fourier series gives the best approximation.

To verify this result, assume, for convenience, that the set $\{\phi_n(t)\}$ is orthonormal, and consider the Nth partial sum

$$F_N(t) = \sum_{n=1}^{N} \tilde{c}_n\phi_n(t)$$

where the $\tilde{c}_n$ are to be chosen in order to minimize the mean square error E_N. Now

$$(t_2 - t_1)E_N = \int_{t_1}^{t_2} \left[f(t) - \sum_{n=1}^{N} \tilde{c}_n \phi_n(t) \right]^2 \mathrm{d}t$$

$$= \int_{t_1}^{t_2} f^2(t)\,\mathrm{d}t - 2\sum_{n=1}^{N} \tilde{c}_n \int_{t_1}^{t_2} f(t)\phi_n(t)\,\mathrm{d}t + \sum_{n=1}^{N} \tilde{c}_n^2 \int_{t_1}^{t_2} \phi_n^2(t)\,\mathrm{d}t$$

$$= \int_{t_1}^{t_2} f^2(t)\,\mathrm{d}t - 2\sum_{n=1}^{N} \tilde{c}_n c_n + \sum_{n=1}^{N} \tilde{c}_n^2$$

since $\{\phi_n(t)\}$ is an orthonormal set. That is,

$$(t_2 - t_1)E_n = \int_{t_1}^{t_2} f^2(t)\,\mathrm{d}t - \sum_{n=1}^{N} c_n^2 + \sum_{n=1}^{N} (\tilde{c}_n - c_n)^2 \qquad \textbf{(4.82)}$$

which is clearly minimized when $\tilde{c}_n = c_n$.

Taking $\tilde{c}_n = c_n$ in (4.82), the mean square error E_N in approximating $f(t)$ by $F_N(t)$ of (4.77) is given by

$$E_N = \frac{1}{t_2 - t_1}\left[\int_{t_1}^{t_2} f^2(t)\,\mathrm{d}t - \sum_{n=1}^{N} c_n^2\right]$$

if the set $\{\phi_n(t)\}$ is orthonormal, and is given by

$$E_N = \frac{1}{t_2 - t_1}\left[\int_{t_1}^{t_2} f^2(t)\,\mathrm{d}t - \sum_{n=1}^{N} \gamma_n c_n^2\right] \qquad \textbf{(4.83)}$$

if the set $\{\phi_n(t)\}$ is orthogonal.

Since, by definition, E_N is non-negative, it follows from (4.83) that

$$\int_{t_1}^{t_2} f^2(t)\,\mathrm{d}t \geqslant \sum_{n=1}^{N} \gamma_n c_n^2 \qquad \textbf{(4.84)}$$

a result known as **Bessel's inequality**. The question that arises in practice is whether or not $E_N \to 0$ as $N \to \infty$, indicating that the sum

$$\sum_{n=1}^{N} c_n \phi_n(t)$$

converges to the function $f(t)$. If this were the case then, from (4.83),

$$\int_{t_1}^{t_2} f^2(t)\,\mathrm{d}t = \sum_{n=1}^{\infty} \gamma_n c_n^2 \qquad \textbf{(4.85)}$$

which is the **generalized form of Parseval's theorem**, and the set $\{\phi_n(t)\}$ is said to be complete. Strictly speaking, the fact that Parseval's theorem holds ensures that the partial sum $F_N(t)$ converges in the mean to the parent function $f(t)$ as $N \to \infty$, and this does not necessarily guarantee convergence at any particular point. In engineering applications, however, this distinction may be overlooked, since for the functions met in practice convergence in the mean also ensures pointwise convergence at points where $f(t)$ is convergent, and convergence to the mean of the discontinuity at points where $f(t)$ is discontinuous.

Example 4.26

The set $\{1, \cos t, \sin t, \ldots, \cos nt, \sin nt\}$ is a complete orthogonal set in the interval $d \leqslant t \leqslant d + 2\pi$. Following the same argument as above, it is readily shown that for a function $f(t)$ that is piecewise-continuous on $d \leqslant t \leqslant d + 2\pi$ the mean square error between $f(t)$ and the finite Fourier series

$$F_N(t) = \tfrac{1}{2}\tilde{a}_0 + \sum_{n=1}^{N} \tilde{a}_n \cos nt + \sum_{n=1}^{N} \tilde{b}_n \sin nt$$

is minimized when $\tilde{a}_0$, $\tilde{a}_n$ and $\tilde{b}_n$ $(n = 1, 2, 3, \ldots)$ are equal to the corresponding Fourier coefficients a_0, a_n and b_n $(n = 1, 2, 3, \ldots)$ determined using (4.11) and (4.12). In this case the mean square error E_N is given by

$$E_N = \frac{1}{2\pi}\left[\int_d^{d+2\pi} f^2(t)\,\mathrm{d}t - \pi\left[\tfrac{1}{2}a_0^2 + \sum_{n=1}^{N}(a_n^2 + b_n^2)\right]\right]$$

Bessel's inequality (4.84) becomes

$$\int_d^{d+2\pi} f^2(t)\,\mathrm{d}t \geqslant \pi\left[\tfrac{1}{2}a_0^2 + \sum_{n=1}^{N}(a_n^2 + b_n^2)\right]$$

and Parseval's theorem (4.85) reduces to

$$\frac{1}{2\pi}\int_d^{d+2\pi} f^2(t) = \tfrac{1}{4}a_0^2 + \tfrac{1}{2}\sum_{n=1}^{\infty}(a_n^2 + b_n^2)$$

which conforms with (4.66). Since, in this case, the basis set is complete, Parseval's theorem holds, and the Fourier series converges to $f(t)$ in the sense discussed above.

4.7.4 Exercises

40 The Fourier series expansion for the periodic square wave

$$f(t) = \begin{cases} -1 & (-\pi < t < 0) \\ 1 & (0 < t < \pi) \end{cases}$$

$$f(t + 2\pi) = f(t)$$

is

$$f(t) = \sum_{n=1}^{\infty} \frac{4}{\pi(2n-1)} \sin(2n-1)t$$

Determine the mean square error corresponding to approximations to $f(t)$ based on the use of one term, two terms and three terms respectively in the series expansion.

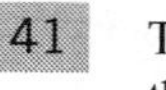

41 The Legendre polynomials $P_n(t)$ are generated by the formula

$$P_n(t) = \frac{1}{2^n n!}\frac{\mathrm{d}^n}{\mathrm{d}t^n}(t^2 - 1)^n \quad (n = 0, 1, 2, \ldots)$$

and satisfy the recurrence relationship

$$nP_n(t) = (2n - 1)tP_{n-1}(t) - (n - 1)P_{n-2}(t)$$

(a) Deduce that

$$P_0(t) = 1, \quad P_1(t) = t$$

$$P_2(t) = \tfrac{1}{2}(3t^2 - 1), \quad P_3(t) = \tfrac{1}{2}(5t^3 - 3t)$$

(b) Show that the polynomials form an orthogonal set on the interval $(-1, 1)$ and, in particular, that

$$\int_{-1}^{1} P_m(t)P_n(t)\,\mathrm{d}t = \begin{cases} 0 & (n \neq m) \\ 2/(2n+1) & (n = m;\ m = 0, 1, 2, \dots) \end{cases}$$

(c) Given that the function

$$f(t) = \begin{cases} -1 & (-1 < t < 0) \\ 0 & (t = 0) \\ 1 & (0 < t < 1) \end{cases}$$

is expressed as a Fourier–Legendre series expansion

$$f(t) = \sum_{r=0}^{\infty} c_r P_r(t)$$

determine the values of c_0, c_1, c_2 and c_3.

(d) Plot graphs to illustrate convergence of the series obtained in (c), and compare the mean square error with that of the corresponding Fourier series expansion.

42 Repeat parts (c) and (d) of Exercise 41 for the function

$$f(x) = \begin{cases} 0 & (-1 < x < 0) \\ x & (0 < x < 1) \end{cases}$$

43 Laguerre polynomials $L_n(t)$ are generated by the formula

$$L_n(t) = \mathrm{e}^t \frac{\mathrm{d}^n}{\mathrm{d}t^n}(t^n \mathrm{e}^{-t}) \quad (n = 0, 1, 2, \dots)$$

and satisfy the recurrence relation

$$L_n(t) = (2n - 1 - t)L_{n-1}(t) - (n-1)^2 L_{n-2}(t) \quad (n = 2, 3, \dots)$$

These polynomials are orthogonal on the interval $0 \leqslant t < \infty$ with respect to the weighting function e^{-t}, so that

$$\int_0^{\infty} \mathrm{e}^{-t} L_n(t) L_m(t)\,\mathrm{d}t = \begin{cases} 0 & (n \neq m) \\ (n!)^2 & (n = m) \end{cases}$$

(a) Deduce that

$$L_0(t) = 1, \quad L_1(t) = 1 - t$$

$$L_2(t) = 2 - 4t + t^2$$

$$L_3(t) = 6 - 18t + 9t^2 - t^3$$

(b) Confirm the above orthogonality result in the case of L_0, L_1, L_2 and L_3.

(c) Given that the function $f(t)$ is to be approximated over the interval $0 \leqslant t < \infty$ by

$$f(t) = \sum_{r=0}^{\infty} c_r L_r(t)$$

show that

$$c_r = \frac{1}{(r!)^2} \int_0^{\infty} f(t)\,\mathrm{e}^{-t} L_r(t)\,\mathrm{d}t \quad (r = 0, 1, 2, \dots)$$

(*Note*: Laguerre polynomials are of particular importance to engineers, since they can be generated as the impulse responses of relatively simple networks.)

44 Hermite polynomials $H_n(t)$ are generated by the formula

$$H_n(t) = (-1)^n \mathrm{e}^{t^2/2} \frac{\mathrm{d}^n}{\mathrm{d}t^n} \mathrm{e}^{-t^2/2} \quad (n = 0, 1, 2, \dots)$$

and satisfy the recurrence relationship

$$H_n(t) = tH_{n-1}(t) - (n-1)H_{n-2}(t) \quad (n = 2, 3, \dots)$$

The polynomials are orthogonal on the interval $-\infty < t < \infty$ with respect to the weighting function $\mathrm{e}^{-t^2/2}$, so that

$$\int_{-\infty}^{\infty} \mathrm{e}^{-t^2/2} H_n(t) H_m(t)\,\mathrm{d}t = \begin{cases} 0 & (n \neq m) \\ \sqrt{(2\pi)}\,n! & (n = m) \end{cases}$$

(a) Deduce that

$$H_0(t) = 1, \quad H_1(t) = t$$

$$H_2(t) = t^2 - 1, \quad H_3(t) = t^3 - 3t$$

$$H_4(t) = t^4 - 6t^2 + 3$$

(b) Confirm the above orthogonality result for H_0, H_1, H_2 and H_3.

(c) Given that the function $f(t)$ is to be approximated over the interval $-\infty < t < \infty$ by

$$f(t) = \sum_{r=0}^{\infty} c_r H_r(t)$$

show that

$$c_r = \frac{1}{r!\sqrt{\pi}} \int_{-\infty}^{\infty} e^{-t^2/2} f(t) H_r(t)\, dt$$

$$(r = 0, 1, \dots)$$

45 Tchebyshev polynomials $T_n(t)$ are generated by the formula

$$T_n(t) = \cos(n \cos^{-1} t) \quad (n = 0, 1, 2, \dots)$$

or

$$T_n(t) = \sum_{r=0}^{[n/2]} (-1)^r \frac{n!}{(2r)!(n-2r)!} (1-t^2)^r t^{n-2r}$$

$$(n = 0, 1, 2, \dots)$$

where

$$[n/2] = \begin{cases} n/2 & (\text{even } n) \\ (n-1)/2 & (\text{odd } n) \end{cases}$$

They also satisfy the recurrence relationship

$$T_n(t) = 2tT_{n-1}(t) - T_{n-2}(t) \quad (n = 2, 3, \dots)$$

and are orthogonal on the interval $-1 \leq t \leq 1$ with respect to the weighting function $1/\sqrt{(1-t^2)}$, so that

$$\int_{-1}^{1} \frac{T_n(t)T_m(t)}{\sqrt{(1-t^2)}}\, dt = \begin{cases} 0 & (m \neq n) \\ \frac{1}{2}\pi & (m = n \neq 0) \\ \pi & (m = n = 0) \end{cases}$$

(a) Deduce that

$$T_0(t) = 1, \quad T_1(t) = t$$

$$T_2(t) = 2t^2 - 1, \quad T_3(t) = 4t^3 - 3t$$

$$T_4(t) = 8t^4 - 8t^2 + 1$$

$$T_5(t) = 16t^5 - 20t^3 + 5t$$

(b) Confirm the above orthogonality result for T_0, T_1, T_2 and T_3.

(c) Given that the function $f(t)$ is to be approximated over the interval $-1 \leq t \leq 1$ by

$$f(t) = \sum_{r=0}^{\infty} c_r T_r(t)$$

show that

$$c_0 = \frac{1}{\pi} \int_{-1}^{1} \frac{f(t)T_0(t)}{\sqrt{(1-t^2)}}\, dt$$

$$c_r = \frac{2}{\pi} \int_{-1}^{1} \frac{f(t)T_r(t)}{\sqrt{(1-t^2)}}\, dt \quad (r = 1, 2, \dots)$$

46 With developments in digital techniques, Walsh functions $W_n(t)$ have become of considerable importance in practice, since they are so easily generated by digital logic circuitry. The first four Walsh functions may be defined on the interval $0 \leq t \leq T$ by

$$W_0(t) = \frac{1}{\sqrt{T}} \quad (0 \leq t \leq T)$$

$$W_1(t) = \begin{cases} 1/\sqrt{T} & (0 \leq t < \frac{1}{2}T) \\ -1/\sqrt{T} & (\frac{1}{2}T < t \leq T) \end{cases}$$

$$W_2(t) = \begin{cases} 1/\sqrt{T} & (0 \leq t < \frac{1}{4}T, \frac{3}{4}T < t \leq T) \\ -1/\sqrt{T} & (\frac{1}{4}T < t < \frac{3}{4}T) \end{cases}$$

$$W_3(t) =$$

$$\begin{cases} 1/\sqrt{T} & (0 \leq t < \frac{1}{8}T, \frac{3}{8}T < t < \frac{5}{8}T, \frac{7}{8}T < t \leq T) \\ -1/\sqrt{T} & (\frac{1}{8}T < t < \frac{3}{8}T, \frac{5}{8}T < t < \frac{7}{8}T) \end{cases}$$

(a) Plot graphs of the functions $W_0(t)$, $W_1(t)$, $W_2(t)$ and $W_3(t)$, and show that they are orthonormal on the interval $0 \leq t \leq T$. Write down an expression for $W_n(t)$.

(b) The Walsh functions may be used to obtain a Fourier–Walsh series expansion for a function $f(t)$, over the interval $0 \leq t \leq T$, in the form

$$f(t) = \sum_{r=0}^{\infty} c_r W_r(t)$$

Illustrate this for the square wave of Exercise 40. What is the corresponding mean square error? Comment on your answer.

4.8 Engineering application: describing functions

Many control systems containing a nonlinear element may be represented by the block diagram of Figure 4.43. In practice, describing function techniques are used to analyse and design such control systems. Essentially the method involves replacing the nonlinearity by an equivalent gain N and then using the techniques developed for linear systems, such as the frequency response methods of Section 2.7. If the nonlinear element is subjected to a sinusoidal input $e(t) = X \sin \omega t$ then its output $z(t)$ may be represented by the Fourier series expansion

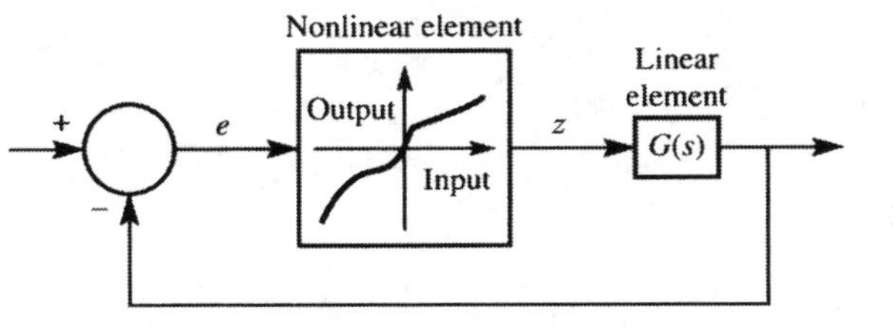

Figure 4.43 Nonlinear control system.

$$z(t) = \tfrac{1}{2}a_0 + \sum_{n=1}^{\infty} a_n \cos n\omega t + \sum_{n=1}^{\infty} b_n \sin n\omega t$$

$$= \tfrac{1}{2}a_0 + \sum_{n=1}^{\infty} A_n \sin(n\omega t + \phi_n)$$

with $A_n = \sqrt{(a_n^2 + b_n^2)}$ and $\phi_n = \tan^{-1}(a_n/b_n)$.

The **describing function** $N(X)$ of the nonlinear element is then defined to be the complex ratio of the fundamental component of the output to the input; that is,

$$N(X) = \frac{A_1}{X} e^{j\phi_1}$$

with $N(X)$ being independent of the input frequency ω if the nonlinear element is memory-free.

Having determined the describing function, the behaviour of the closed-loop system is then determined by the characteristic equation

$$1 + N(X)G(j\omega) = 0$$

If a combination of X and ω can be found to satisfy this equation then the system is capable of sustained oscillations at that frequency and magnitude; that is, the system exhibits **limit-cycle behaviour**. In general, more than one combination can be found, and the resulting oscillations can be a stable or unstable limit cycle.

Normally the characteristic equation is investigated graphically by plotting $G(j\omega)$ and $-1/N(X)$, for all values of X, on the same polar diagram. Limit cycles then occur at frequencies and amplitudes corresponding to points of intersection of the curves. Sometimes plotting can be avoided by calculating the maximum value of $N(X)$ and hence the value of the gain associated with $G(s)$ that will just cause limit cycling to occur.

Using this background information, the following investigation is left as an exercise for the reader to develop.

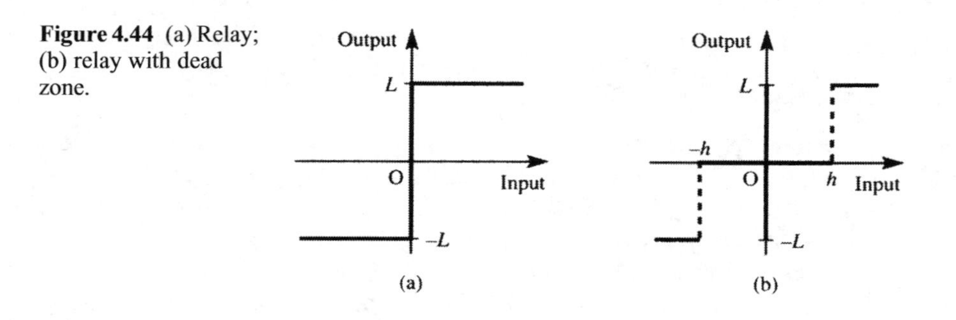

Figure 4.44 (a) Relay; (b) relay with dead zone.

Figure 4.45 Nonlinear system of exercise.

+
–
NL
$\dfrac{10}{s(s+1)(s+2)}$

(a) Show that the describing functions $N_1(X)$ and $N_2(X)$ corresponding respectively to the relay (on–off nonlinearity) of Figure 4.44(a) and the relay with dead zone of Figure 4.44(b) are

$$N_1(X) = \frac{4L}{\pi X}, \qquad N_2(X) = \frac{4L}{\pi X}\sqrt{\left[1-\left(\frac{h}{X}\right)^2\right]}$$

(b) For the system of Figure 4.45 show that a limit cycle exists when the nonlinearity is the relay of Figure 4.44(a) with $L = 1$. Determine the amplitude and frequency of this limit cycle.

In an attempt to eliminate the limit-cycle oscillation, the relay is replaced by the relay with dead zone illustrated in Figure 4.44(b), again with $L = 1$. Show that this allows our objective to be achieved provided that $h > 10/3\pi$.

4.9 Review exercises (1–20)

1 A periodic function $f(t)$ is defined by

$$f(t) = \begin{cases} t^2 & (0 \leqslant t < \pi) \\ 0 & (\pi < t \leqslant 2\pi) \end{cases}$$

$$f(t + 2\pi) = f(t)$$

Obtain a Fourier series expansion of $f(t)$ and deduce that

$$\tfrac{1}{6}\pi^2 = \sum_{r=1}^{\infty} \frac{1}{r^2}$$

2 Determine the full-range Fourier series expansion of the even function $f(t)$ of period 2π defined by

$$f(t) = \begin{cases} \tfrac{2}{3}t & (0 \leqslant t \leqslant \tfrac{1}{3}\pi) \\ \tfrac{1}{3}(\pi - t) & (\tfrac{1}{3}\pi \leqslant t \leqslant \pi) \end{cases}$$

To what value does the series converge at $t = \tfrac{1}{3}\pi$?

3 A function $f(t)$ is defined for $0 \leqslant t \leqslant \tfrac{1}{2}T$ by

$$f(t) = \begin{cases} t & (0 \leqslant t \leqslant \tfrac{1}{4}T) \\ \tfrac{1}{2}T - t & (\tfrac{1}{4}T \leqslant t \leqslant \tfrac{1}{2}T) \end{cases}$$

Sketch odd and even functions that have a period T and are equal to $f(t)$ for $0 \leqslant t \leqslant \frac{1}{2}T$.

(a) Find the half-range Fourier sine series of $f(t)$.
(b) To what value will the series converge for $t = -\frac{1}{4}T$?
(c) What is the sum of the following series?

$$S = \sum_{r=1}^{\infty} \frac{1}{(2r-1)^2}$$

4 Prove that if $g(x)$ is an odd function and $f(x)$ an even function of x, the product $g(x)[c + f(x)]$ is an odd function if c is a constant.

A periodic function with period 2π is defined by

$$F(\theta) = \tfrac{1}{12}\theta(\pi^2 - \theta^2)$$

in the interval $-\pi \leqslant \theta \leqslant \pi$. Show that the Fourier series representation of the function is

$$F(\theta) = \sum_{n=1}^{\infty} \frac{(-1)^{n+1}}{n^3} \sin n\theta$$

5 A repeating waveform of period 2π is described by

$$f(t) = \begin{cases} \pi + t & (-\pi \leqslant t \leqslant -\frac{1}{2}\pi) \\ -t & (-\frac{1}{2}\pi \leqslant t \leqslant \frac{1}{2}\pi) \\ t - \pi & (\frac{1}{2}\pi \leqslant t \leqslant \pi) \end{cases}$$

Sketch the waveform over the range $t = -2\pi$ to $t = 2\pi$ and find the Fourier series representation of $f(t)$, making use of any properties of the waveform that you can identify before any integration is performed.

6 A function $f(x)$ is defined in the interval $-1 \leqslant x \leqslant 1$ by

$$f(x) = \begin{cases} 1/2\varepsilon & (-\varepsilon < x < \varepsilon) \\ 0 & (-1 \leqslant x < -\varepsilon;\ \varepsilon < x \leqslant 1) \end{cases}$$

Sketch a graph of $f(x)$ and show that a Fourier series expansion of $f(x)$ valid in the interval $-1 \leqslant x \leqslant 1$ is given by

$$f(x) = \tfrac{1}{2} + \sum_{n=1}^{\infty} \frac{\sin n\pi\varepsilon}{n\pi\varepsilon} \cos n\pi x$$

7 Show that the half-range Fourier sine series for the function

$$f(t) = \left(1 - \frac{t}{\pi}\right)^2 \quad (0 \leqslant t \leqslant \pi)$$

is

$$f(t) = \sum_{n=1}^{\infty} \frac{2}{n\pi}\left\{1 - \frac{2}{n^2\pi^2}[1 - (-1)^n]\right\} \sin nt$$

8 Find a half-range Fourier sine and Fourier cosine series for $f(x)$ valid in the interval $0 < x < \pi$ when $f(x)$ is defined by

$$f(x) = \begin{cases} x & (0 \leqslant x \leqslant \frac{1}{2}\pi) \\ \pi - x & (\frac{1}{2}\pi \leqslant x \leqslant \pi) \end{cases}$$

Sketch the graph of the Fourier series obtained for $-2\pi < x \leqslant 2\pi$.

9 A function $f(x)$ is periodic of period 2π and is defined by $f(x) = e^x$ $(-\pi < x < \pi)$. Sketch the graph of $f(x)$ from $x = -2\pi$ to $x = 2\pi$ and prove that

$$f(x) = \frac{2 \sinh \pi}{\pi}\left[\frac{1}{2} + \sum_{n=1}^{\infty} \frac{(-1)^n}{1+n^2}(\cos nx - n \sin nx)\right]$$

10 A function $f(t)$ is defined on $0 < t < \pi$ by

$$f(t) = \pi - t$$

Find

(a) a half-range Fourier sine series, and
(b) a half-range Fourier cosine series for $f(t)$ valid for $0 < t < \pi$.

Sketch the graphs of the functions represented by each series for $-2\pi < t < 2\pi$.

11 Show that the Fourier series

$$\tfrac{1}{2}\pi - \frac{4}{\pi}\sum_{n=1}^{\infty} \frac{\cos(2n-1)t}{(2n-1)^2}$$

represents the function $f(t)$, of period 2π, given by

$$f(t) = \begin{cases} t & (0 \leqslant t \leqslant \pi) \\ -t & (-\pi \leqslant t \leqslant 0) \end{cases}$$

Deduce that, apart from a transient component (that is, a complementary function that dies away as $t \to \infty$), the differential equation

$$\frac{dx}{dt} + x = f(t)$$

has the solution

$$x = \tfrac{1}{2}\pi - \frac{4}{\pi}\sum_{n=1}^{\infty}\frac{\cos(2n-1)t + (2n-1)\sin(2n-1)t}{(2n-1)^2[1+(2n-1)^2]}$$

12 Show that if $f(t)$ is a periodic function of period 2π and

$$f(t) = \begin{cases} t/\pi & (0 < t < \pi) \\ (2\pi - t)/\pi & (\pi < t < 2\pi) \end{cases}$$

then

$$f(t) = \tfrac{1}{2} - \frac{4}{\pi^2}\sum_{n=0}^{\infty}\frac{\cos(2n+1)t}{(2n+1)^2}$$

Show also that, when ω is not an integer,

$$y = \frac{1}{2\omega^2}(1 - \cos\omega t) - \frac{4}{\pi^2}\sum_{n=1}^{\infty}\frac{\cos(2n+1)t - \cos\omega t}{(2n+1)^2[\omega^2 - (2n+1)^2]}$$

satisfies the differential equation

$$\frac{d^2y}{dt^2} + \omega^2 y = f(t)$$

subject to the initial conditions $y = dy/dt = 0$ at $t = 0$.

13 (a) A periodic function $f(t)$, of period 2π, is defined in $-\pi \leqslant t \leqslant \pi$ by

$$f(t) = \begin{cases} -t & (-\pi \leqslant t \leqslant 0) \\ t & (0 \leqslant t \leqslant \pi) \end{cases}$$

Obtain a Fourier series expansion for $f(t)$, and from it, using Parseval's theorem, deduce that

$$\tfrac{1}{96}\pi^4 = \sum_{n=1}^{\infty}\frac{1}{(2n-1)^4}$$

(b) By formally differentiating the series obtained in (a), obtain the Fourier series expansion of the periodic square wave

$$g(t) = \begin{cases} -1 & (-\pi < t < 0) \\ 0 & (t = 0) \\ 1 & (0 < t < \pi) \end{cases}$$

$$g(t + 2\pi) = g(t)$$

Check the validity of your result by determining directly the Fourier series expansion of $g(t)$.

14 A periodic function $f(t)$, of period 2π, is defined in the range $-\pi < t < \pi$ by

$$f(t) = \sin\tfrac{1}{2}t$$

Show that the complex form of the Fourier series expansion for $f(t)$ is

$$f(t) = \sum_{n=-\infty}^{\infty}\frac{j4n(-1)^n}{\pi(4n^2-1)}e^{jnt}$$

15 (a) Find the Fourier series expansion of the voltage $v(t)$ represented by the half-wave rectified sine wave

$$v(t) = \begin{cases} 10\sin(2\pi t/T) & (0 < t < \tfrac{1}{2}T) \\ 0 & (\tfrac{1}{2}T < t < T) \end{cases}$$

$$v(t + T) = v(t)$$

(b) If the voltage $v(t)$ in (a) is applied to a $10\,\Omega$ resistor, what is the total average power delivered to the resistor? What percentage of the total power is carried by the second-harmonic component of the voltage?

16 The periodic waveform $f(t)$ shown in Figure 4.46 may be written as

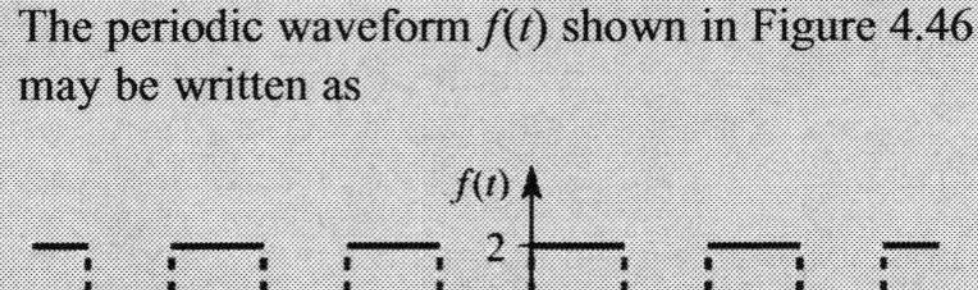
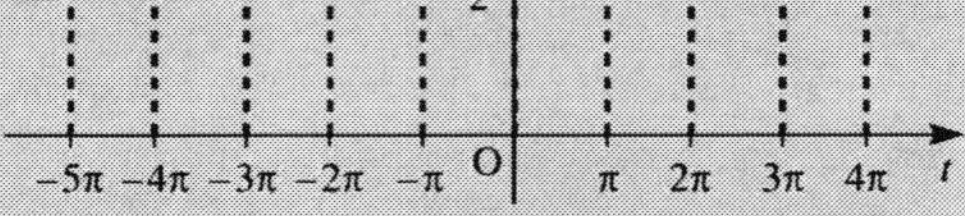

Figure 4.46 Waveform $f(t)$ of Review exercise 16.

$$f(t) = 1 + g(t)$$

where $g(t)$ represents an odd function.

(a) Sketch the graph of $g(t)$.

(b) Obtain the Fourier series expansion for $g(t)$, and hence write down the Fourier series expansion for $f(t)$.

17 Show that the complex Fourier series expansion for the periodic function

$$f(t) = t \quad (0 < t < 2\pi)$$

$$f(t + 2\pi) = f(t)$$

is

$$f(t) = \pi + \sum_{\substack{n=-\infty \\ n\neq 0}}^{\infty} \frac{\mathrm{j}\,\mathrm{e}^{\mathrm{j}nt}}{n}$$

18 (a) A square-wave voltage $v(t)$ of period T is defined by

$$v(t) = \begin{cases} -1 & (-\frac{1}{2}T < t < 0) \\ 1 & (0 < t < \frac{1}{2}T) \end{cases}$$

$$v(t + T) = v(t)$$

Show that its Fourier series expansion is given by

$$v(t) = \frac{4}{\pi} \sum_{n=1}^{\infty} \frac{\sin[(4n-2)\pi t/T]}{2n-1}$$

(b) Find the steady-state response of the circuit shown in Figure 4.47 to the sinusoidal input voltage

$$v_\omega(t) = \sin \omega t$$

and hence write down the Fourier series expansion of the circuit's steady-state response to the square-wave voltage $v(t)$ in (a).

Figure 4.47 Circuit of Review exercise 18.

19 (a) Defining the nth Tchebyshev polynomial by

$$T_n(t) = \cos(n \cos^{-1} t)$$

use Euler's formula $\cos\theta = \frac{1}{2}(\mathrm{e}^{\mathrm{j}\theta} + \mathrm{e}^{-\mathrm{j}\theta})$ to obtain the expansions of t^{2k} and t^{2k+1} in Tchebyshev polynomials, where k is a positive integer.

(b) Establish the recurrence relation

$$T_n(t) = 2tT_{n-1}(t) - T_{n-2}(t)$$

(c) Write down the values of $T_0(t)$ and $T_1(t)$ from the definition, and then use (b) to find $T_2(t)$ and $T_3(t)$.

(d) Express $t^5 - 5t^4 + 7t^3 + 6t - 8$ in Tchebyshev polynomials.

(e) Find the cubic polynomial that approximates to

$$t^5 - 5t^4 + 7t^3 + 6t - 8$$

over the interval $(-1, 1)$ with the smallest maximum error. Give an upper bound for this error. Is there a value of t for which this upper bound is attained?

20 The relationship between the input and output of a relay with a dead zone Δ and no hysteresis is shown in Figure 4.48. Show that the describing function is

$$N(x_\mathrm{i}) = \frac{4M}{\pi x_\mathrm{i}}\left[1 - \left(\frac{\Delta}{2x_\mathrm{i}}\right)^2\right]^{1/2}$$

for an input amplitude x_i.

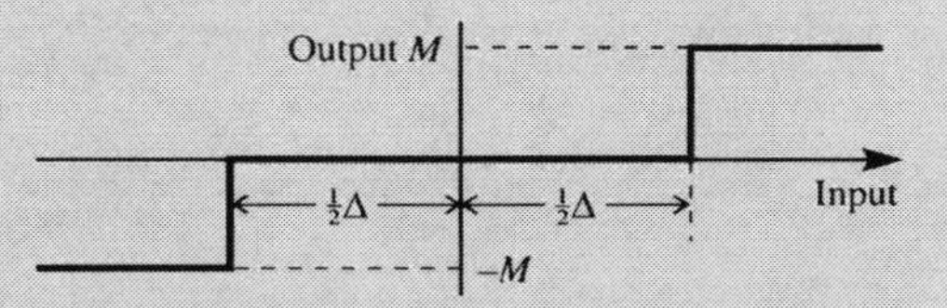

Figure 4.48 Relay with dead zone of Review exercise 20.

If this relay is used in the forward path of the on–off positional control system shown in Figure 4.49, where the transfer function

$$\frac{K}{s(T_1 s + 1)(T_2 s + 1)}$$

characterizes the time constant of the servo-motor, and the inertia and viscous damping of the load, show that a limit-cycle oscillation will not occur provided that the dead zone in the relay is such that

$$\Delta > \frac{4MK}{\pi} \frac{T_1 T_2}{T_1 + T_2}$$

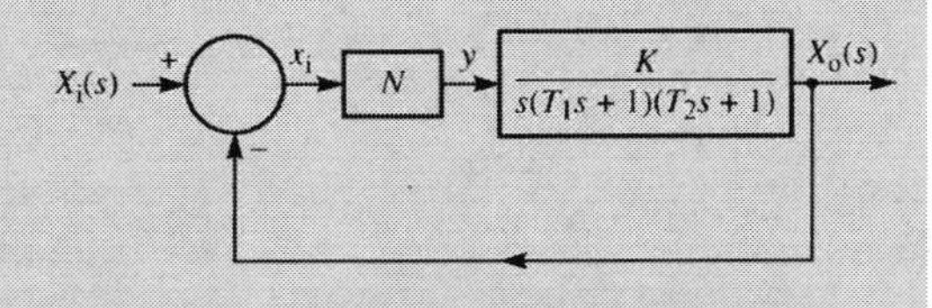

Figure 4.49 Positional control system of Review exercise 20.

5 The Fourier Transform

Chapter 5	Contents	

5.1 Introduction

In Chapter 4 we saw how Fourier series provided an ideal framework for analysing the steady-state response of systems to a periodic input signal. In this chapter we extend the ideas of Fourier analysis to deal with non-periodic functions. We do this through the introduction of the Fourier transform. As the theory develops, we shall see how the complex exponential form of the Fourier series representation of a periodic function emerges as a special case of the Fourier transform. Similarities between the transform and the Laplace transform, discussed in Chapter 2, will also be highlighted.

While Fourier transforms first found most application in the solution of partial differential equations, it is probably true to say that today Fourier transform methods are most heavily used in the analysis of signals and systems. This chapter is therefore developed with such applications in mind, and its main aim is to develop an understanding of the underlying mathematics as a preparation for a specialist study of application areas in various branches of engineering.

Throughout this book we draw attention to the impact of digital computers on engineering and thus on the mathematics required to understand engineering concepts. While much of the early work on signal analysis was implemented using analogue devices, the bulk of modern equipment exploits digital technology. In Chapter 2 we developed the Laplace transform as an aid to the analysis and design of continuous-time systems while in Chapter 3 we introduced the z and $\mathscr{D}$ transforms to assist with the analysis and design of discrete-time systems. In this chapter the frequency-domain analysis introduced in Chapter 2 for continuous-time systems is consolidated and then extended to provide a framework for the frequency-domain description of discrete-time systems through the introduction of discrete Fourier transforms. These discrete transforms provide one of the most advanced methods for discrete signal analysis, and are widely used in such fields as communications theory and speech and image processing. In practice, the computational aspects of the work assume great importance, and the use of appropriate computational algorithms for the calculation of the discrete Fourier transform is essential. For this reason we have included an introduction to the fast Fourier transform algorithm, based on the pioneering work of J. W. Cooley and J. W. Tukey published in 1965, which it is hoped will serve the reader with the necessary understanding for progression to the understanding of specialist engineering applications.

5.2 The Fourier transform

5.2.1 The Fourier integral

In Chapter 4 we saw how Fourier series methods provided a technique for the frequency-domain representation of periodic functions. As indicated in Section 4.6.3, in expressing a function as its Fourier series expansion we are decomposing the function into its harmonic or frequency components. Thus a periodic function $f(t)$, of period T', has frequency components at discrete frequencies

$$\omega_n = \frac{2\pi n}{T'} = n\omega_0 \quad (n = 0, 1, 2, 3, \dots)$$

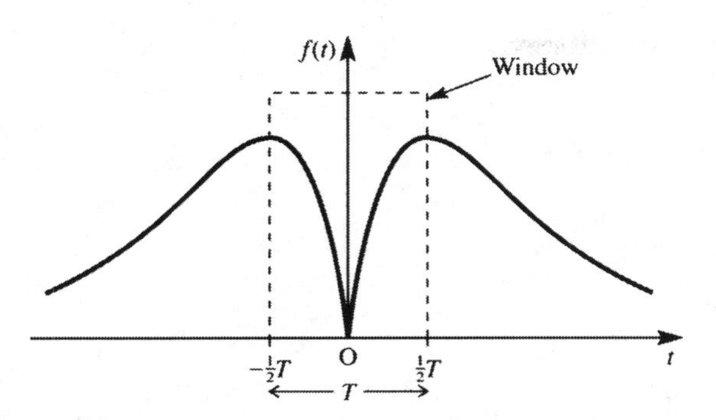

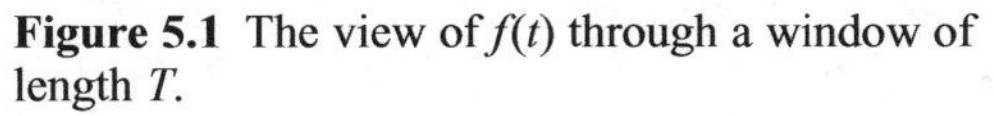

Figure 5.1 The view of $f(t)$ through a window of length T.

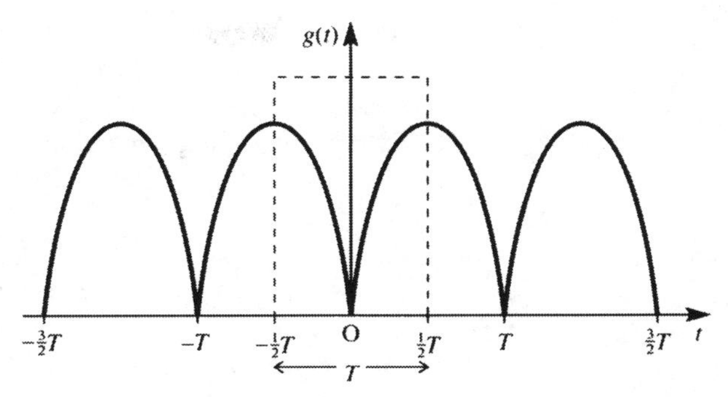

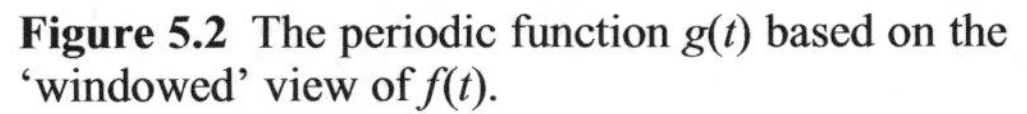

Figure 5.2 The periodic function $g(t)$ based on the 'windowed' view of $f(t)$.

where ω_0 is the fundamental frequency, that is the frequency of the parent function $f(t)$. Consequently we were able to interpret a Fourier series as constituting a **discrete frequency spectrum** of the periodic function $f(t)$, thus providing an alternative frequency-domain representation of the function to its time-domain waveform. However, not all functions are periodic and so we need to develop an approach that will give a similar representation for non-periodic functions, defined on $-\infty < t < \infty$. One way of achieving this is to look at a portion of a non-periodic function $f(t)$ over an interval T, by imagining that we are looking at a graph of $f(t)$ through a 'window' of length T, and then to consider what happens as T gets larger.

Figure 5.1 depicts this situation, with the window placed symmetrically about the origin. We could now concentrate only on the 'view through the window' and carry out a Fourier series development based on that portion of $f(t)$ alone. Whatever the behaviour of $f(t)$ outside the window, the Fourier series thus generated would represent the periodic function defined by

$$g(t) = \begin{cases} f(t) & (|t| < \frac{1}{2}T) \\ f(t - nT) & (\frac{1}{2}(2n-1)T < |t| < \frac{1}{2}(2n+1)T) \end{cases}$$

Figure 5.2 illustrates $g(t)$, and we can see that the graphs of $f(t)$ and $g(t)$ agree on the interval $(-\frac{1}{2}T, \frac{1}{2}T)$. Note that this approach corresponds to the one adopted in Section 4.3 to obtain the Fourier series expansion of functions defined over a finite interval.

Using the complex or exponential form of the Fourier series expansion, we have from (4.57) and (4.61) that

$$g(t) = \sum_{n=-\infty}^{\infty} G_n \, e^{jn\omega_0 t} \tag{5.1}$$

with

$$G_n = \frac{1}{T}\int_{-T/2}^{T/2} g(t)\, e^{-jn\omega_0 t}\, dt \tag{5.2}$$

and where

$$\omega_0 = 2\pi/T \tag{5.3}$$

Equation (5.2) in effect *transforms* the time-domain function $g(t)$ into the associated frequency-domain components G_n, where n is any integer (positive, negative or zero). Equation (5.1) can also be viewed as transforming the discrete components G_n in the frequency-domain representation to the time-domain form $g(t)$. Substituting for G_n in (5.1), using (5.2), we obtain

$$g(t) = \sum_{n=-\infty}^{\infty} \left[\frac{1}{T} \int_{-T/2}^{T/2} g(\tau)\, e^{-jn\omega_0 \tau}\, d\tau \right] e^{jn\omega_0 t} \tag{5.4}$$

The frequency of the general term in the expansion (5.4) is

$$\frac{2\pi n}{T} = n\omega_0 = \omega_n$$

and so the difference in frequency between successive terms is

$$\frac{2\pi}{T}[(n+1) - n] = \frac{2\pi}{T} = \Delta\omega$$

Since $\Delta\omega = \omega_0$, we can express (5.4) as

$$g(t) = \sum_{n=-\infty}^{\infty} \left[\frac{1}{2\pi} \int_{-T/2}^{T/2} g(\tau)\, e^{-j\omega_n \tau}\, d\tau \right] e^{j\omega_n t} \Delta\omega \tag{5.5}$$

Defining $G(j\omega)$ as

$$G(j\omega) = \int_{-T/2}^{T/2} g(\tau)\, e^{-j\omega t}\, d\tau \tag{5.6}$$

we have

$$g(t) = \frac{1}{2\pi} \sum_{n=-\infty}^{\infty} e^{-j\omega_n t} G(j\omega_n) \Delta\omega \tag{5.7}$$

As $T \to \infty$, our window widens, so that $g(t) = f(t)$ everywhere and $\Delta\omega \to 0$. Since we also have

$$\lim_{\Delta\omega \to 0} \frac{1}{2\pi} \sum_{n=-\infty}^{\infty} e^{j\omega_n t} G(j\omega_n) \Delta\omega = \frac{1}{2\pi} \int_{-\infty}^{\infty} e^{j\omega t} G(j\omega)\, d\omega$$

it follows from (5.7) and (5.6) that

$$f(t) = \int_{-\infty}^{\infty} \left[\frac{1}{2\pi} e^{j\omega t} \int_{-\infty}^{\infty} f(\tau)\, e^{-j\omega \tau}\, d\tau \right] d\omega \tag{5.8}$$

The result (5.8) is known as the **Fourier integral representation** of $f(t)$. A set of conditions that are sufficient for the existence of the Fourier integral is a revised form of Dirichlet's conditions for Fourier series, contained in Theorem 4.2. These conditions may be stated in the form of Theorem 5.1.

Theorem 5.1 **Dirichlet's conditions for the Fourier integral**

If the function $f(t)$ is such that

(a) it is absolutely integrable, so that

$$\int_{-\infty}^{\infty} |f(t)|\,dt < \infty$$

(that is, the integral is finite), and

(b) it has at most a finite number of maxima and minima and a finite number of discontinuities in any finite interval

then the Fourier integral representation of $f(t)$, given in (5.8), converges to $f(t)$ at all points where $f(t)$ is continuous and to the average of the right- and left-hand limits of $f(t)$ where $f(t)$ is discontinuous (that is, to the mean of the discontinuity).

end of theorem

As was indicated in Section 4.2.8 for Fourier series, the use of the equality sign in (5.8) must be interpreted carefully because of the non-convergence to $f(t)$ at points of discontinuity. Again the symbol ~ (read as 'behaves as' or 'represented by') rather than = is frequently used.

The absolute integrable condition (a) of Theorem 5.1 implies that the absolute area under the graph of $y = f(t)$ is finite. Clearly this is so if $f(t)$ decays sufficiently fast with time. However, in general the condition seems to imply a very tight constraint on the nature of $f(t)$, since clearly functions of the form $f(t) = \text{constant}$, $f(t) = e^{at}$, $f(t) = e^{-at}$, $f(t) = \sin \omega t$, and so on, defined for $-\infty < t < \infty$, do not meet the requirement. In practice, however, signals are usually causal and do not last for ever (that is, they only exist for a finite time). Also, in practice no signal amplitude goes to infinity, so consequently no **practical signal** $f(t)$ can have an infinite area under its graph $y = f(t)$. Thus for practical signals the integral in (5.8) exists.

To obtain the trigonometric (or real) form of the Fourier integral, we substitute

$$e^{-j\omega(\tau - t)} = \cos \omega(\tau - t) - j \sin \omega(\tau - t)$$

in (5.8) to give

$$f(t) = \frac{1}{2\pi}\int_{-\infty}^{\infty}\int_{-\infty}^{\infty} f(\tau)[\cos \omega(\tau - t) - j \sin \omega(\tau - t)]\,d\tau\,d\omega$$

Since $\sin \omega(\tau - t)$ is an odd function of ω, this reduces to

$$f(t) = \frac{1}{2\pi}\int_{-\infty}^{\infty}\int_{-\infty}^{\infty} f(\tau) \cos \omega(\tau - t)\,d\tau\,d\omega$$

which, on noting that the integrand is an even function of ω, reduces further to

$$f(t) = \frac{1}{\pi}\int_{0}^{\infty} d\omega \int_{-\infty}^{\infty} f(\tau) \cos \omega(\tau - t)\,d\tau \tag{5.9}$$

The representation (5.9) is then the required trigonometric form of the Fourier integral.

If $f(t)$ is either an odd function or an even function then further simplifications of (5.9) are possible. Detailed calculations are left as an exercise for the reader, and we shall simply quote the results.

(a) If $f(t)$ is an even function then (5.9) reduces to

$$f(t) = \frac{2}{\pi}\int_0^\infty\int_0^\infty f(\tau)\cos\omega\tau\cos\omega t\,d\tau\,d\omega \tag{5.10}$$

which is referred to as the **Fourier cosine integral**.

(b) If $f(t)$ is an odd function then (5.9) reduces to

$$f(t) = \frac{2}{\pi}\int_0^\infty\int_0^\infty f(\tau)\sin\omega\tau\sin\omega t\,d\tau\,d\omega \tag{5.11}$$

which is referred to as the **Fourier sine integral**.

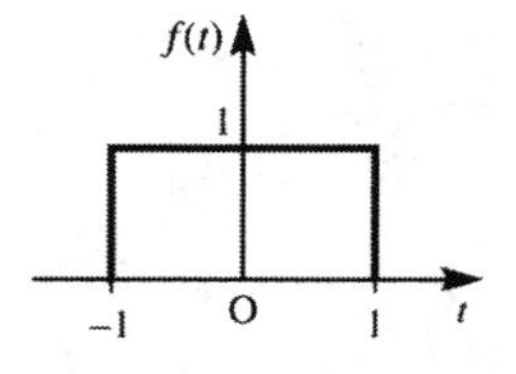

Figure 5.3 Rectangular pulse

$$f(t) = \begin{cases} 1 & (|t| \leq 1) \\ 0 & (|t| > 1) \end{cases}.$$

In the case of the Fourier series representation of a periodic function it was a matter of some interest to determine how well the first few terms of the expansion represented the function. The corresponding problem in the non-periodic case is to investigate how well the Fourier integral represents a function when only the components in the lower part of the (continuous) frequency range are taken into account. To illustrate, consider the rectangular pulse of Figure 5.3 given by

$$f(t) = \begin{cases} 1 & (|t| \leq 1) \\ 0 & (|t| > 1) \end{cases}$$

This is clearly an even function, so from (5.10) its Fourier integral is

$$f(t) = \frac{2}{\pi}\int_0^\infty\int_0^1 1\cos\omega\tau\cos\omega t\,d\tau\,d\omega = \frac{2}{\pi}\int_0^\infty \frac{\cos\omega t\sin\omega}{\omega}\,d\omega$$

An elementary evaluation of this integral is not possible, so we consider frequencies $\omega < \omega_0$, when

$$\begin{aligned} f(t) &\simeq \frac{2}{\pi}\int_0^{\omega_0}\frac{\cos\omega t\sin\omega}{\omega}\,d\omega \\ &= \frac{1}{\pi}\int_0^{\omega_0}\frac{\sin\omega(t+1)}{\omega}\,d\omega - \frac{1}{\pi}\int_0^{\omega_0}\frac{\sin\omega(t-1)}{\omega}\,d\omega \\ &= \frac{1}{\pi}\int_0^{\omega_0(t+1)}\frac{\sin u}{u}\,du - \frac{1}{\pi}\int_0^{\omega_0(t-1)}\frac{\sin u}{u}\,du \end{aligned}$$

The integral

$$\text{Si}(x) = \int_0^x \frac{\sin u}{u}\,\text{d}u \quad (x \geqslant 0)$$

occurs frequently, and it can be shown that

$$\text{Si}(x) = \sum_{n=0}^{\infty} \frac{(-1)^n x^{2n+1}}{(2n+1)(2n+1)!}$$

Its values have been tabulated (see for example L. Rade and B. Westergren, *Beta Mathematics Handbook*, Chartwell-Bratt Ltd, 1990). Thus

$$f(t) \simeq \text{Si}(\omega_0(t+1)) - \text{Si}(\omega_0(t-1)) \tag{5.12}$$

This has been plotted for $\omega_0 = 4$, 8 and 16, and the responses are shown in Figures 5.4(a), (b) and (c) respectively. Physically, these responses describe the output of an ideal low-pass filter, cutting out all frequencies $\omega > \omega_0$, when the input signal is the rectangular pulse of Figure 5.3. The reader will no doubt note the similarities with the Fourier series discussion of Section 4.2.8 and the continuing existence of the Gibbs phenomenon.

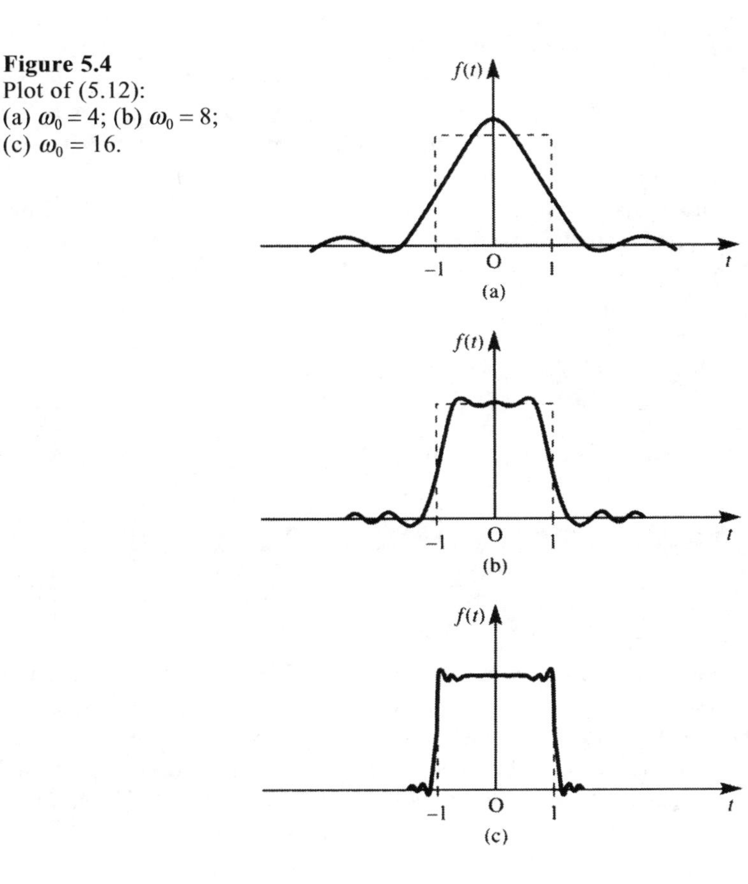

Figure 5.4
Plot of (5.12):
(a) $\omega_0 = 4$; (b) $\omega_0 = 8$;
(c) $\omega_0 = 16$.

5.2.2 The Fourier transform pair

We note from (5.6) and (5.7) that the Fourier integral (5.8) may be written in the form of the pair of equations

$$F(j\omega) = \int_{-\infty}^{\infty} f(t)\,e^{-j\omega t}\,dt \tag{5.13}$$

$$f(t) = \frac{1}{2\pi}\int_{-\infty}^{\infty} F(j\omega)\,e^{j\omega t}\,d\omega \tag{5.14}$$

$F(j\omega)$ as defined by (5.13) is called the **Fourier transform** of $f(t)$, and it provides a frequency-domain representation of the non-periodic function $f(t)$, whenever the integral in (5.13) exists. Note that we have used the notation $F(j\omega)$ for the Fourier transform of $f(t)$ rather than the alternative $F(\omega)$, which is also in common use. The reason for this choice is a consequence of the relationship between the Fourier and Laplace transforms, which will emerge later in Section 5.4.1. We stress that this is a *choice* that we have made, but the reader should have no difficulty in using either form, provided that once the choice has been made it is then adhered to. Equation (5.14) then provides us with a way of reconstructing $f(t)$ if we know its Fourier transform $F(j\omega)$.

A word of caution is in order here regarding the scaling factor $1/2\pi$ in (5.14). Although the convention that we have adopted here is fairly standard, some authors associate the factor $1/2\pi$ with (5.13) rather than (5.14), while others associate a factor of $(2\pi)^{-1/2}$ with each of (5.13) and (5.14). In all cases the pair combine to give the Fourier integral (5.8). We could overcome this possible confusion by measuring the frequency in cycles per second or hertz rather than in radians per second, this being achieved using the substitution $f = \omega/2\pi$, where f is in hertz and ω is in radians per second. We have not adopted this approach, since ω is so widely used by engineers.

In line with our notation for Laplace transforms in Chapter 2, we introduce the symbol $\mathcal{F}$ to denote the Fourier transform operator. Then from (5.13) the Fourier transform $\mathcal{F}\{f(t)\}$ of a function $f(t)$ is defined by

$$\mathcal{F}\{f(t)\} = F(j\omega) = \int_{-\infty}^{\infty} f(t)\,e^{-j\omega t}\,dt \tag{5.15}$$

whenever the integral exists. Similarly, using (5.14), we define the inverse Fourier transform of $G(j\omega)$ as

$$\mathcal{F}^{-1}\{G(j\omega)\} = g(t) = \frac{1}{2\pi}\int_{-\infty}^{\infty} G(j\omega)\,e^{j\omega t}\,d\omega \tag{5.16}$$

whenever the integral exists. The relations (5.15) and (5.16) together constitute the **Fourier transform pair**, and they provide a pathway between the time- and frequency-domain representations of a function. Equation (5.15) expresses $f(t)$ in the frequency domain, and is analogous to resolving it into harmonic components with a continuously varying frequency ω. This contrasts with a Fourier series representation of a periodic function, where the resolved frequencies take discrete values.

The conditions for the existence of the Fourier transform $F(j\omega)$ of the function $f(t)$ are Dirichlet's conditions (Theorem 5.1). Corresponding trigonometric forms of the Fourier transform pair may be readily written down from (5.9), (5.10) and (5.11).

Example 5.1

Does the function

$$f(t) = 1 \quad (-\infty < t < \infty)$$

have a Fourier transform representation?

Solution

Since the area under the curve of $y = f(t)$ $(-\infty < t < \infty)$ is infinite, it follows that $\int_{-\infty}^{\infty} |f(t)| \mathrm{d}t$ is unbounded, so the conditions of Theorem 5.1 are not satisfied. We can confirm that the Fourier transform does not exist from the definition (5.15). We have

$$\int_{-\infty}^{\infty} 1\,\mathrm{e}^{-j\omega t}\,\mathrm{d}t = \lim_{\alpha\to\infty} \int_{-\alpha}^{\alpha} \mathrm{e}^{-j\omega t}\,\mathrm{d}t$$

$$= \lim_{\alpha\to\infty} \left[-\frac{1}{j\omega}(\mathrm{e}^{-j\omega\alpha} - \mathrm{e}^{j\omega\alpha})\right]$$

$$= \lim_{\alpha\to\infty} \frac{2\sin\omega\alpha}{\omega}$$

Since this last limit does not exist, we conclude that $f(t) = 1$ $(-\infty < t < \infty)$ does not have a Fourier transform representation.

It is clear, using integration by parts, that $f(t) = t$ $(-\infty < t < \infty)$ does not have a Fourier transform, nor indeed does $f(t) = t^n$ ($n > 1$, an integer; $-\infty < t < \infty$). While neither e^{at} nor e^{-at} $(a > 0)$ has a Fourier transform, when we consider the causal signal $f(t) = H(t)\,\mathrm{e}^{-at}$ $(a > 0)$, we do obtain a transform.

Example 5.2

Find the Fourier transform of the one-sided exponential function

$$f(t) = H(t)\,\mathrm{e}^{-at} \quad (a > 0)$$

where $f(t)$ is the Heaviside unit step function.

Solution

The graph of $f(t)$ is shown in Figure 5.5, and we can show that the area under the graph is bounded. Hence, by Theorem 5.1, a Fourier transform exists. Using the definition (5.15), we have

$$\mathcal{F}\{f(t)\} = \int_{-\infty}^{\infty} H(t)\,\mathrm{e}^{-at}\,\mathrm{e}^{-j\omega t}\,\mathrm{d}t \quad (a > 0)$$

$$= \int_{0}^{\infty} \mathrm{e}^{-(a+j\omega)t}\,\mathrm{d}t = \left[-\frac{\mathrm{e}^{-(a+j\omega)t}}{a + j\omega}\right]_0^{\infty}$$

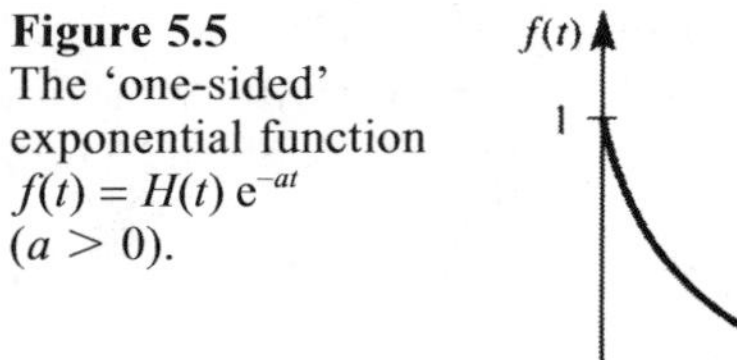

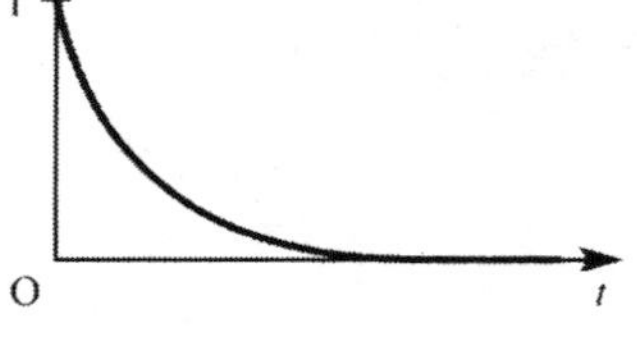

Figure 5.5 The 'one-sided' exponential function $f(t) = H(t)\,\mathrm{e}^{-at}$ $(a > 0)$.

so that

$$\mathscr{F}\{H(t)\,\mathrm{e}^{-at}\} = \frac{1}{a + \mathrm{j}\omega} \tag{5.17}$$

Example 5.3

Calculate the Fourier transform of the rectangular pulse

$$f(t) = \begin{cases} A & (|t| \leqslant T) \\ 0 & (|t| > T) \end{cases}$$

Solution

The graph of $f(t)$ is shown in Figure 5.6, and since the area under it is finite, a Fourier transform exists. From the definition (5.15), we have

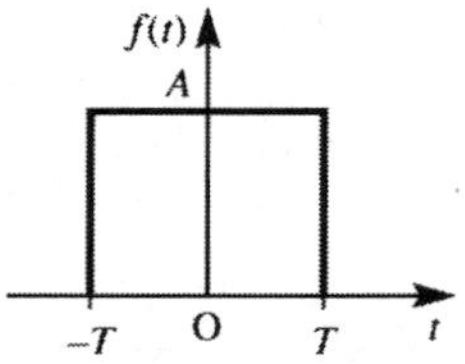

$$\mathscr{F}\{f(t)\} = \int_{-T}^{T} A\,\mathrm{e}^{-\mathrm{j}\omega t}\,\mathrm{d}t = \begin{cases} \left[-\dfrac{A}{\mathrm{j}\omega}\mathrm{e}^{-\mathrm{j}\omega t}\right]_{-T}^{T} & \omega \neq 0 \\ 2A & \omega = 0 \end{cases}$$

$$= 2AT \operatorname{sinc} \omega T$$

Figure 5.6 The rectangular pulse $f(t) = \begin{cases} A & (|t| \leqslant T) \\ 0 & (|t| > T) \end{cases}$.

where $\operatorname{sinc} x$ is defined, as in Example 4.22, by

$$\operatorname{sinc} x = \begin{cases} \dfrac{\sin x}{x} & (x \neq 0) \\ 1 & (x = 0) \end{cases}$$

Figure 5.7 A brief table of Fourier transforms.

$f(t)$	$\mathscr{F}\{f(t)\} = \int_{-\infty}^{\infty} f(t)\mathrm{e}^{-\mathrm{j}\omega t}\,\mathrm{d}t$
$\mathrm{e}^{-at}H(t)$ $(a > 0)$	$\dfrac{1}{a + \mathrm{j}\omega}$
$t\mathrm{e}^{-at}H(t)$ $(a > 0)$	$\dfrac{1}{(a + \mathrm{j}\omega)^2}$
$\begin{cases} A & (\lvert t\rvert \leqslant T) \\ 0 & (\lvert t\rvert > T) \end{cases}$	$2AT \operatorname{sinc} \omega T$
$\mathrm{e}^{-a\lvert t\rvert}$ $(a > 0)$	$\dfrac{2a}{a^2 + \omega^2}$

By direct use of the definition (5.15), we can, as in Examples 5.2 and 5.3, determine the Fourier transforms of some standard functions. A brief table of transforms in given in Figure 5.7.

In MATLAB, incorporating the Symbolic Math Toolbox, the Fourier transform $F(j\omega)$ of $f(t)$ is obtained using the commands

```
syms w t
F=fourier(f(t),t,w)
```

whilst the inverse Fourier transform $f(t)$ of $F(j\omega)$ is obtained using the command

```
f=ifourier(F(jw),w,t)
```

Corresponding commands in MAPLE are

```
with(intrans):
F=fourier(f(t),t,w);
f=infourier(F(jw),w,t);
```

Returning to Example 5.2, and considering the particular case of $a = 2$, the commands

```
syms w t
H=sym('Heaviside(t)');
F=fourier(H*exp(-2*t))
```

in MATLAB return

```
F=1/(2+i*w)
```

as expected. In MATLAB there is an `assume` command (as in MAPLE) to enable us to specify that $a > 0$. However, since abs(a) = a for $a > 0$, the following commands in MATLAB can be used to deal with the general case

```
syms w t a
H=sym('Heaviside(t)');
F=fourier(H*exp(-abs(a)*t),t,w)
```

As another illustration, consider the function $f(t) = e^{-a|t|}$, $a > 0$, given in the table of Figure 5.7. Considering the particular case $a = 2$ then the MATLAB commands

```
syms w t
F=fourier(exp(-2*abs(t),t,w)
```

return

```
F=4/(4+w^2)
```

as specified in the table. It is left as an exercise to consider the general case of a. To illustrate the use, in MATLAB, of the `ifourier` command this transform can be inverted using the commands

```
syms w t
f=ifourier(4/(4+w^2),w,t)
```

which return

```
f=Heaviside(t)*exp(-2*t)+exp(2*t)*Heaviside(-t)
```

which corresponds to the expected answer f = exp(–2*abs(t)).

As another illustration consider the Fourier transform $F(\omega) = 1/(a + j\omega)^2$ given in the second entry of the table in Figure 5.7. The MATLAB commands

```
syms w t a
f=ifourier(1/(a+i*w)^2,w,t)
```

return

```
f=t*exp(-a*t)*Heaviside(t)
```

as given in the table.

Considering the rectangular pulse $f(t)$ of Example 5.3, we first express the pulse in terms of Heaviside functions as

$$f(t) = A(H(t + T) - H(t - T))$$

and then use the MATLAB commands

```
syms w t T A
H=sym('Heaviside(t+T)-Heaviside(t-T)');
F=fourier(A*H,t,w);
F=simple(F)
```

which return

```
F=2*A*sin(T*w)/w
```

5.2.3 The continuous Fourier spectra

From Figure 5.7, it is clear that Fourier transforms are generally complex-valued functions of the real frequency variable ω. If $\mathcal{F}\{f(t)\} = F(j\omega)$ is the Fourier transform of the signal $f(t)$ then $F(j\omega)$ is also known as the **(complex) frequency spectrum** of $f(t)$. Writing $F(j\omega)$ in the exponential form

$$F(j\omega) = |F(j\omega)|\,e^{j\arg F(j\omega)}$$

plots of $|F(j\omega)|$ and $\arg F(j\omega)$, which are both real-valued functions of ω, are called the **amplitude** and **phase spectra** respectively of the signal $f(t)$. These two spectra represent the **frequency-domain portrait** of the signal $f(t)$. In contrast to the situation when $f(t)$ was periodic, where (as shown in Section 4.6.3) the amplitude and phase spectra were defined only at discrete values of ω, we now see that both spectra are defined for all values of the continuous variable ω.

Example 5.4 Determine the amplitude and phase spectra of the causal signal

$$f(t) = e^{-at}H(t) \quad (a > 0)$$

and plot their graphs.

Solution From (5.17),

$$\mathcal{F}\{f(t)\} = F(j\omega) = \frac{1}{a + j\omega}$$

Thus the amplitude and argument of $F(j\omega)$ are

$$|F(j\omega)| = \frac{1}{\sqrt{(a^2 + \omega^2)}} \tag{5.18}$$

$$\arg F(j\omega) = \tan^{-1}(1) - \tan^{-1}\left(\frac{\omega}{a}\right) = -\tan^{-1}\left(\frac{\omega}{a}\right) \tag{5.19}$$

These are the amplitude and phase spectra of $f(t)$, and are plotted in Figure 5.8.

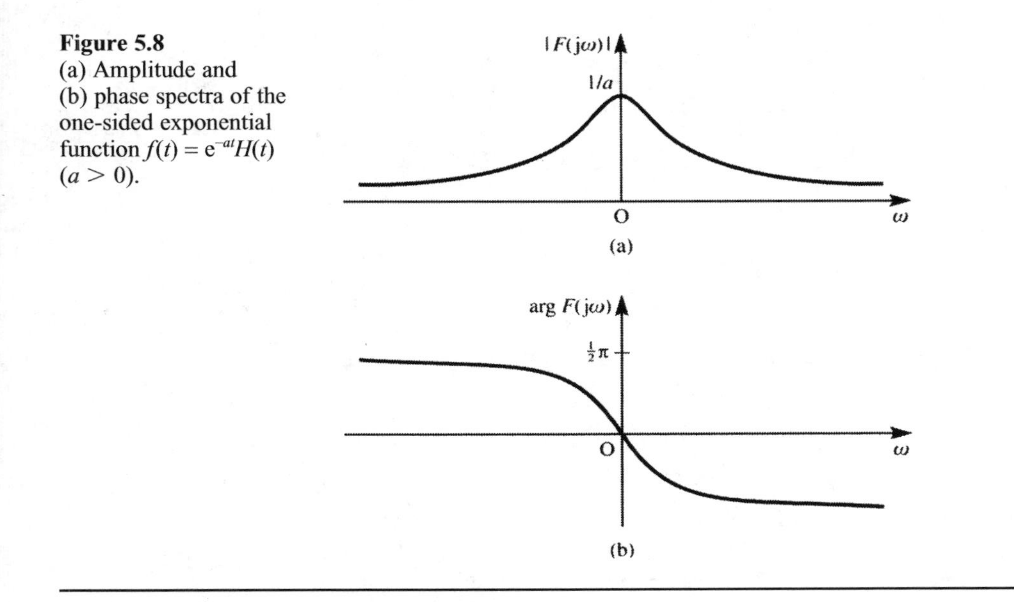

Figure 5.8
(a) Amplitude and (b) phase spectra of the one-sided exponential function $f(t) = e^{-at}H(t)$ $(a > 0)$.

Generally, as we have observed, the Fourier transform and thus the frequency spectrum are complex-valued quantities. In some cases, as for instance in Example 5.3, the spectrum is purely real. In Example 5.3 we found that the transform of the pulse illustrated in Figure 5.6 was

$$F(j\omega) = 2AT \operatorname{sinc} \omega T$$

where

$$\operatorname{sinc} \omega T = \begin{cases} \dfrac{\sin \omega T}{\omega T} & (\omega \neq 0) \\ 1 & (\omega = 0) \end{cases}$$

is an even function of ω, taking both positive and negative values. In this case the amplitude and phase spectra are given by

$$|F(j\omega)| = 2AT|\operatorname{sinc} \omega T| \tag{5.20}$$

$$\arg F(j\omega) = \begin{cases} 0 & (\operatorname{sinc} \omega T \geqslant 0) \\ \pi & (\operatorname{sinc} \omega T < 0) \end{cases} \tag{5.21}$$

with corresponding graphs shown in Figure 5.9.

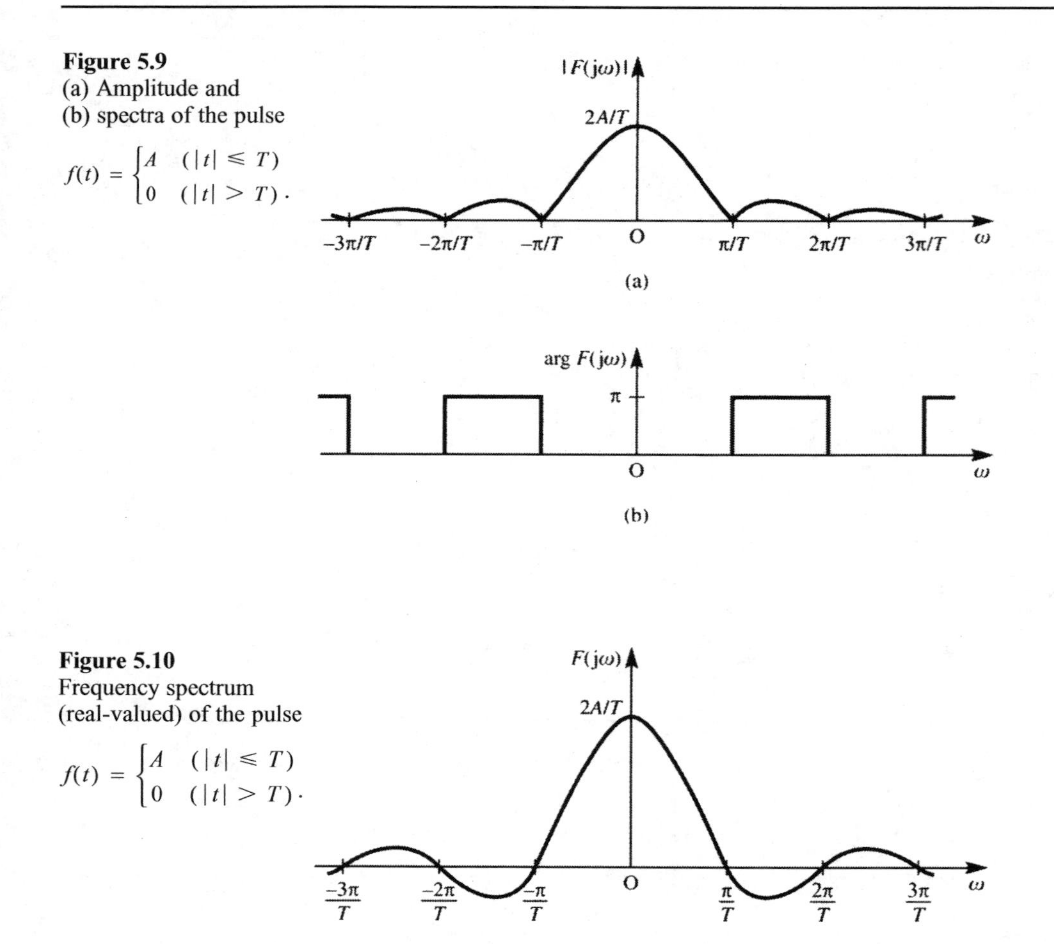

Figure 5.9
(a) Amplitude and
(b) spectra of the pulse

$$f(t) = \begin{cases} A & (|t| \leqslant T) \\ 0 & (|t| > T) \end{cases}.$$

Figure 5.10
Frequency spectrum
(real-valued) of the pulse

$$f(t) = \begin{cases} A & (|t| \leqslant T) \\ 0 & (|t| > T) \end{cases}.$$

In fact, when the Fourier transform is a purely real-valued function, we can plot all the information on a single frequency spectrum of $F(j\omega)$ versus ω. For the rectangular pulse of Figure 5.6 the resulting graph is shown in Figure 5.10.

From Figure 5.7, we can see that the Fourier transforms discussed so far have two properties in common. First, the amplitude spectra are even functions of the frequency variable ω. This is always the case when the time signal $f(t)$ is real; that is, loosely speaking, a consequence of the fact that we have decomposed, or analysed $f(t)$, relative to complex exponentials rather than real-valued sines and cosines. The second common feature is that all the amplitude spectra decrease rapidly as ω increases. This means that most of the information concerning the 'shape' of the signal $f(t)$ is contained in a fairly small interval of the frequency axis around $\omega = 0$. From another point of view, we see that a device capable of passing signals of frequencies up to about $\omega = 3\pi/T$ would pass a reasonably accurate version of the rectangular pulse of Example 5.3.

5.2.4 Exercises

1 Calculate the Fourier transform of the two-sided exponential pulse given by

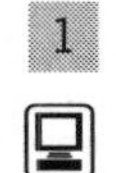

$$f(t) = \begin{cases} e^{at} & (t \leqslant 0) \\ e^{-at} & (t > 0) \end{cases} \quad (a > 0)$$

2 Determine the Fourier transform of the 'on–off' pulse shown in Figure 5.11.

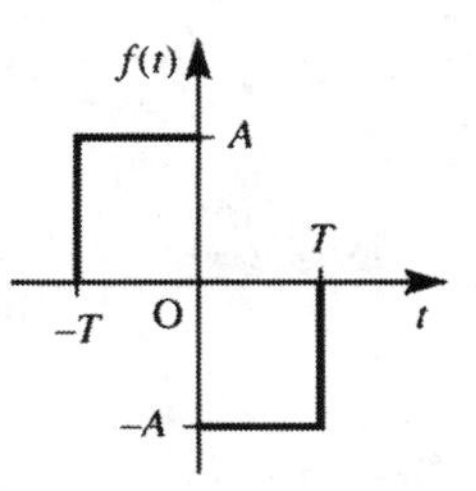

Figure 5.11 The 'on–off' pulse.

3 A triangular pulse is defined by

$$f(t) = \begin{cases} (A/T)t + A & (-T \leqslant t \leqslant 0) \\ (-A/T)t + A & (0 < t \leqslant T) \end{cases}$$

Sketch $f(t)$ and determine its Fourier transform. What is the relationship between this pulse and that of Exercise 2?

4 Determine the Fourier transforms of

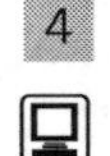

$$f(t) = \begin{cases} 2K & (|t| \leqslant 2) \\ 0 & (|t| > 2) \end{cases}$$

$$g(t) = \begin{cases} K & (|t| \leqslant 1) \\ 0 & (|t| > 1) \end{cases}$$

Sketch the function $h(t) = f(t) - g(t)$ and determine its Fourier transform.

5 Calculate the Fourier transform of the 'off–on–off' pulse $f(t)$ defined by

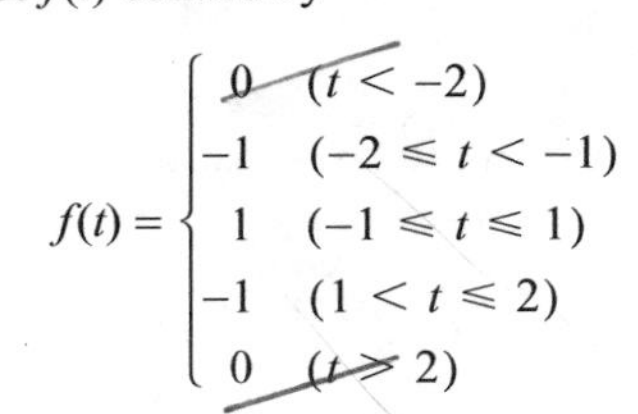

$$f(t) = \begin{cases} 0 & (t < -2) \\ -1 & (-2 \leqslant t < -1) \\ 1 & (-1 \leqslant t \leqslant 1) \\ -1 & (1 < t \leqslant 2) \\ 0 & (t > 2) \end{cases}$$

6 Show that the Fourier transform of

$$f(t) = \begin{cases} \sin at & (|t| \leqslant \pi/a) \\ 0 & (|t| > \pi/a) \end{cases}$$

is

$$\frac{j2a \sin(\pi\omega/a)}{\omega^2 - a^2}$$

7 Calculate the Fourier transform of

$$f(t) = e^{-at} \sin \omega_0 t \, H(t)$$

8 Based on (5.10) and (5.11), define the **Fourier sine transform** as

$$F_s(x) = \int_0^\infty f(t) \sin xt \, dt$$

and the **Fourier cosine transform** as

$$F_c(x) = \int_0^\infty f(t) \cos xt \, dt$$

Show that

$$f(t) = \begin{cases} 0 & (t < 0) \\ \cos at & (0 \leqslant t \leqslant a) \\ 0 & (t > a) \end{cases}$$

has Fourier cosine transform

$$\tfrac{1}{2}\left[\frac{\sin(1+x)a}{1+x} + \frac{\sin(1-x)a}{1-x}\right]$$

9 Show that the Fourier sine and cosine transforms of

$$f(t) = \begin{cases} 0 & (t < 0) \\ 1 & (0 \leqslant t \leqslant a) \\ 0 & (t > a) \end{cases}$$

are

$$\frac{1 - \cos xa}{x}, \quad \frac{\sin xa}{x}$$

respectively.

10 Find the sine and cosine transforms of $f(t) = e^{-at} H(t)$ $(a > 0)$.

5.3 Properties of the Fourier transform

In this section we establish some of the properties of the Fourier transform that allow its use as a practical tool in system analysis and design.

5.3.1 The linearity property

Linearity is a fundamental property of the Fourier transform, and may be stated as follows.

If $f(t)$ and $g(t)$ are functions having Fourier transforms $F(\mathrm{j}\omega)$ and $G(\mathrm{j}\omega)$ respectively, and if α and β are constants, then

$$\mathscr{F}\{\alpha f(t) + \beta g(t)\} = \alpha\mathscr{F}\{f(t)\} + \beta\mathscr{F}\{g(t)\} = \alpha F(\mathrm{j}\omega) + \beta G(\mathrm{j}\omega) \tag{5.22}$$

As a consequence of this, we say that the Fourier transform operator $\mathscr{F}$ is a **linear operator**. The proof of this property follows readily from the definition (5.15), since

$$\begin{aligned}\mathscr{F}\{\alpha f(t) + \beta g(t)\} &= \int_{-\infty}^{\infty} [\alpha f(t) + \beta g(t)]\,\mathrm{e}^{-\mathrm{j}\omega t}\,\mathrm{d}t \\ &= \alpha\int_{-\infty}^{\infty} f(t)\,\mathrm{e}^{-\mathrm{j}\omega t}\,\mathrm{d}t + \beta\int_{-\infty}^{\infty} g(t)\,\mathrm{e}^{-\mathrm{j}\omega t}\,\mathrm{d}t \\ &= \alpha F(\mathrm{j}\omega) + \beta G(\mathrm{j}\omega)\end{aligned}$$

Clearly the linearity property also applies to the inverse transform operator $\mathscr{F}^{-1}$.

5.3.2 Time-differentiation property

If the function $f(t)$ has a Fourier transform $F(\mathrm{j}\omega)$ then, by (5.16),

$$f(t) = \frac{1}{2\pi}\int_{-\infty}^{\infty} F(\mathrm{j}\omega)\,\mathrm{e}^{\mathrm{j}\omega t}\,\mathrm{d}\omega$$

Differentiating with respect to t gives

$$\frac{\mathrm{d}f}{\mathrm{d}t} = \frac{1}{2\pi}\int_{-\infty}^{\infty} \frac{\partial}{\partial t}[F(\mathrm{j}\omega)\,\mathrm{e}^{\mathrm{j}\omega t}]\,\mathrm{d}\omega = \frac{1}{2\pi}\int_{-\infty}^{\infty} (\mathrm{j}\omega)F(\mathrm{j}\omega)\,\mathrm{e}^{\mathrm{j}\omega t}\,\mathrm{d}\omega$$

implying that the time signal $\mathrm{d}f/\mathrm{d}t$ is the inverse Fourier transform of $(\mathrm{j}\omega)F(\mathrm{j}\omega)$. In other words

$$\mathscr{F}\left\{\frac{\mathrm{d}f}{\mathrm{d}t}\right\} = (\mathrm{j}\omega)F(\mathrm{j}\omega)$$

Repeating the argument n times, it follows that

$$\mathcal{F}\left\{\frac{d^n f}{dt^n}\right\} = (j\omega)^n F(j\omega) \tag{5.23}$$

The result (5.23) is referred to as the **time-differentiation property**, and may be used to obtain frequency-domain representations of differential equations.

Example 5.5

Show that if the time signals $y(t)$ and $u(t)$ have Fourier transforms $Y(j\omega)$ and $U(j\omega)$ respectively, and if

$$\frac{d^2y(t)}{dt^2} + 3\frac{dy(t)}{dt} + 7y(t) = 3\frac{du(t)}{dt} + 2u(t) \tag{5.24}$$

then $Y(j\omega) = G(j\omega)U(j\omega)$ for some function $G(j\omega)$.

Solution Taking Fourier transforms throughout in (5.24), we have

$$\mathcal{F}\left\{\frac{d^2y(t)}{dt^2} + 3\frac{dy(t)}{dt} + 7y(t)\right\} = \mathcal{F}\left\{3\frac{du(t)}{dt} + 2u(t)\right\}$$

which, on using the linearity property (5.22), reduces to

$$\mathcal{F}\left\{\frac{d^2y(t)}{dt^2}\right\} + 3\mathcal{F}\left\{\frac{dy(t)}{dt}\right\} + 7\mathcal{F}\{y(t)\} = 3\mathcal{F}\left\{\frac{du(t)}{dt}\right\} + 2\mathcal{F}\{u(t)\}$$

Then, from (5.23),

$$(j\omega)^2Y(j\omega) + 3(j\omega)Y(j\omega) + 7Y(j\omega) = 3(j\omega)U(j\omega) + 2U(j\omega)$$

that is,

$$(-\omega^2 + j3\omega + 7)Y(j\omega) = (j3\omega + 2)U(j\omega)$$

giving

$$Y(j\omega) = G(j\omega)U(j\omega)$$

where

$$G(j\omega) = \frac{2 + j3\omega}{7 - \omega^2 + j3\omega}$$

The reader may at this stage be fearing that we are about to propose yet *another* method for solving differential equations. This is not the idea! Rather, we shall show that the Fourier transform provides an essential tool for the analysis (and synthesis) of linear systems from the viewpoint of the frequency domain.

5.3.3 Time-shift property

If a function $f(t)$ has Fourier transform $F(j\omega)$ then what is the Fourier transform of the shifted version $g(t) = f(t - \tau)$, where τ is a constant? From the definition (5.15),

$$\mathscr{F}\{g(t)\} = \int_{-\infty}^{\infty} g(t)\,e^{-j\omega t}\,dt = \int_{-\infty}^{\infty} f(t-\tau)\,e^{-j\omega t}\,dt$$

Making the substitution $x = t - \tau$, we have

$$\mathscr{F}\{g(t)\} = \int_{-\infty}^{\infty} f(x)\,e^{-j\omega(x+\tau)}\,dx = e^{-j\omega\tau}\int_{-\infty}^{\infty} f(x)\,e^{-j\omega x}\,dx = e^{-j\omega\tau}F(j\omega)$$

that is,

$$\mathscr{F}\{f(t-\tau)\} = e^{-j\omega\tau}F(j\omega) \tag{5.25}$$

The result (5.25) is known as the **time-shift property**, and implies that delaying a signal by a time τ causes its Fourier transform to be multiplied by $e^{-j\omega\tau}$.

Since

$$|e^{-j\omega\tau}| = |\cos\omega\tau - j\sin\omega\tau| = |\sqrt{(\cos^2\omega\tau + \sin^2\omega\tau)}| = 1$$

we have

$$|e^{-j\omega\tau}F(j\omega)| = |F(j\omega)|$$

indicating that the amplitude spectrum of $f(t-\tau)$ is identical with that of $f(t)$. However,

$$\arg[e^{-j\omega t}F(j\omega)] = \arg F(j\omega) - \arg e^{j\omega\tau} = \arg F(j\omega) - \omega\tau$$

indicating that each frequency component is shifted by an amount proportional to its frequency ω.

Example 5.6 Determine the Fourier transform of the rectangular pulse $f(t)$ shown in Figure 5.12.

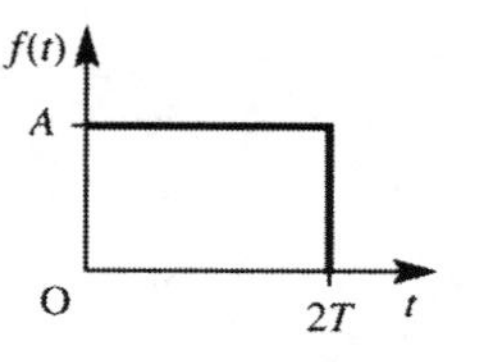

Figure 5.12 Rectangular pulse of Example 5.6.

Solution This is just the pulse of Example 5.3 (shown in Figure 5.6), delayed by T. The pulse of Example 5.3 had a Fourier transform $2AT\,\text{sinc}\,\omega T$, and so, using the shift property (5.25) with $\tau = T$, we have

$$\mathscr{F}\{f(t)\} = F(j\omega) = e^{-j\omega T}\,2AT\,\text{sinc}\,\omega T = 2AT\,e^{-j\omega T}\,\text{sinc}\,\omega T$$

5.3.4 Frequency-shift property

Suppose that a function $f(t)$ has Fourier transform $F(j\omega)$. Then, from the definition (5.15), the Fourier transform of the related function $g(t) = e^{j\omega_0 t}f(t)$ is

$$\mathscr{F}\{g(t)\} = \int_{-\infty}^{\infty} e^{j\omega_0 t} f(t) e^{-j\omega t}\, dt = \int_{-\infty}^{\infty} f(t) e^{-j(\omega-\omega_0)t}\, dt$$

$$= \int_{-\infty}^{\infty} f(t) e^{-j\tilde{\omega} t}\, dt, \quad \text{where } \tilde{\omega} = \omega - \omega_0$$

$$= F(j\tilde{\omega}), \quad \text{by definition}$$

Thus

$$\mathscr{F}\{e^{j\omega_0 t} f(t)\} = F(j(\omega - \omega_0)) \tag{5.26}$$

The result (5.26) is known as the **frequency-shift property**, and indicates that multiplication by $e^{j\omega_0 t}$ simply shifts the spectrum of $f(t)$ so that it is centred on the point $\omega = \omega_0$ in the frequency domain. This phenomenon is the mathematical foundation for the process of **modulation** in communication theory, illustrated in Example 5.7.

Example 5.7 Determine the frequency spectrum of the signal $g(t) = f(t) \cos \omega_c t$.

Solution Since $\cos \omega_c t = \frac{1}{2}(e^{j\omega_c t} + e^{-j\omega_c t})$, it follows, using the linearity property (5.22), that

$$\mathscr{F}\{g(t)\} = \mathscr{F}\{\tfrac{1}{2} f(t)(e^{j\omega_c t} + e^{-j\omega_c t})\}$$

$$= \tfrac{1}{2}\mathscr{F}\{f(t)\, e^{j\omega_c t}\} + \tfrac{1}{2}\mathscr{F}\{f(t)\, e^{-j\omega_c t}\}$$

If $\mathscr{F}\{f(t)\} = F(j\omega)$ then, using (5.26),

$$\mathscr{F}\{f(t) \cos \omega_c t\} = \mathscr{F}\{g(t)\} = \tfrac{1}{2} F(j(\omega - \omega_c)) + \tfrac{1}{2} F(j(\omega + \omega_c))$$

The effect of multiplying the signal $f(t)$ by the **carrier signal** $\cos \omega_c t$ is thus to produce a signal whose spectrum consists of two (scaled) versions of $F(j\omega)$, the spectrum of $f(t)$: one centred on $\omega = \omega_c$ and the other on $\omega = -\omega_c$. The carrier signal $\cos \omega_c t$ is said to be modulated by the signal $f(t)$.

Demodulation is considered in Exercise 5, Section 5.9, and the ideas of modulation and demodulation are developed in Section 5.8.

5.3.5 The symmetry property

From the definition of the transform pair (5.15) and (5.16) it is apparent that there is some symmetry of structure in relation to the variables t and ω. We can establish the exact form of this symmetry as follows. From (5.16),

$$f(t) = \frac{1}{2\pi} \int_{-\infty}^{\infty} F(j\omega)\, e^{j\omega t}\, d\omega$$

or, equivalently, by changing the 'dummy' variable in the integration,

$$2\pi f(t) = \int_{-\infty}^{\infty} F(jy)\, e^{jyt}\, dy$$

so that

$$2\pi f(-t) = \int_{-\infty}^{\infty} F(jy)\,e^{-jyt}\,dy$$

or, on replacing t by ω,

$$2\pi f(-\omega) = \int_{-\infty}^{\infty} F(jy)\,e^{-jy\omega}\,dy \tag{5.27}$$

The right-hand side of (5.27) is simply the definition (5.15) of the Fourier transform of $F(jt)$, with the integration variable t replaced by y. We therefore conclude that

$$\mathcal{F}\{F(jt)\} = 2\pi f(-\omega) \tag{5.28a}$$

given that

$$\mathcal{F}\{f(t)\} = F(j\omega) \tag{5.28b}$$

What (5.28) tells us is that if $f(t)$ and $F(j\omega)$ form a Fourier transform pair then $F(jt)$ and $2\pi f(-\omega)$ also form a Fourier transform pair. This property is referred to as the **symmetry property of Fourier transforms**. It is also sometimes referred to as the **duality property**.

Example 5.8

Determine the Fourier transform of the signal

$$g(t) = C\,\text{sinc}\,at = \begin{cases} \dfrac{C\sin at}{at} & (t \neq 0) \\ C & (t = 0) \end{cases} \tag{5.29}$$

Solution

From Example 5.3, we know that if

$$f(t) = \begin{cases} A & (|t| \leqslant T) \\ 0 & (|t| > T) \end{cases} \tag{5.30}$$

then

$$\mathcal{F}\{f(t)\} = F(j\omega) = 2AT\,\text{sinc}\,\omega T$$

Thus, by the symmetry property (5.28), $F(jt)$ and $2\pi f(-\omega)$ are also a Fourier transform pair. In this case

$$F(jt) = 2AT\,\text{sinc}\,tT$$

and so, choosing $T = a$ and $A = C/2a$ to correspond to (5.29), we see that

$$F(jt) = C\,\text{sinc}\,at = g(t)$$

has Fourier transform $2\pi f(-\omega)$. Rewriting (5.30), we find that, since $|\omega| = |-\omega|$,

$$\mathcal{F}\{C\,\text{sinc}\,at\} = \begin{cases} 2\pi C/2a & (|\omega| \leqslant a) \\ 0 & (|\omega| > a) \end{cases} = \begin{cases} \pi C/a & (|\omega| \leqslant a) \\ 0 & (|\omega| > a) \end{cases}$$

A graph of $g(t)$ and its Fourier transform $G(j\omega) = 2\pi f(-\omega)$ is shown in Figure 5.13.

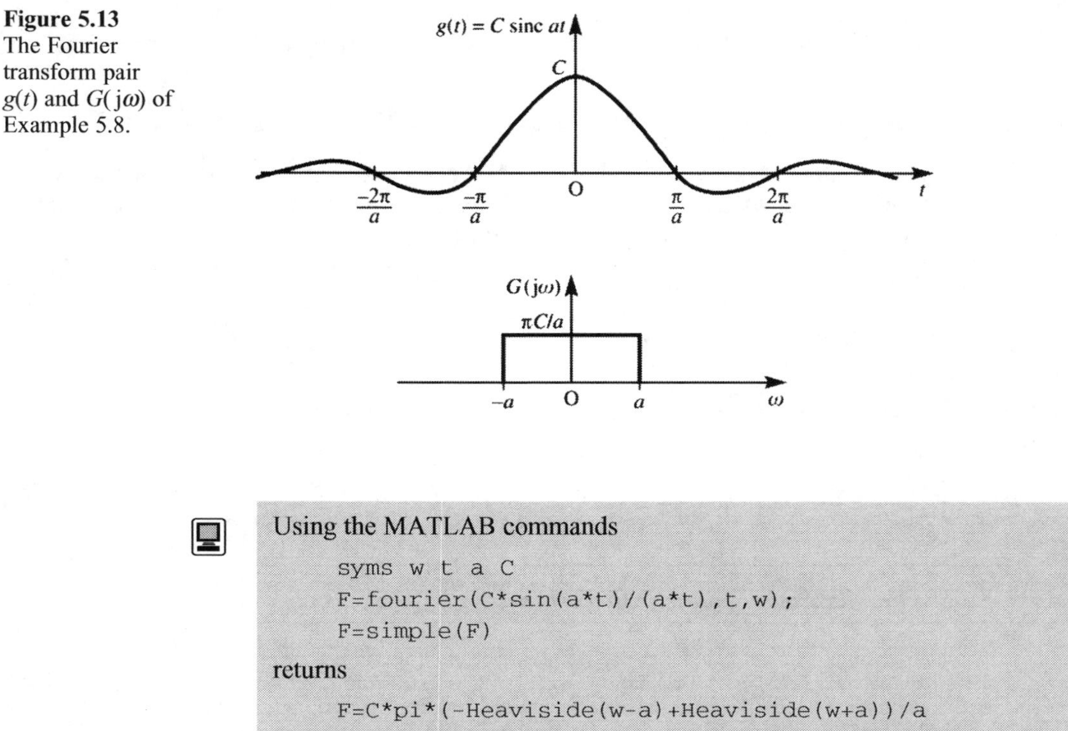

Figure 5.13 The Fourier transform pair $g(t)$ and $G(j\omega)$ of Example 5.8.

Using the MATLAB commands

```
syms w t a C
F=fourier(C*sin(a*t)/(a*t),t,w);
F=simple(F)
```

returns

```
F=C*pi*(-Heaviside(w-a)+Heaviside(w+a))/a
```

which is the answer given in the solution expressed in Heaviside functions.

5.3.6 Exercises

11 Use the linearity property to verify the result in Exercise 4.

12 If $y(t)$ and $u(t)$ are signals with Fourier transforms $Y(j\omega)$ and $U(j\omega)$ respectively, and

$$\frac{d^2y(t)}{dt^2} + 3\frac{dy(t)}{dt} + y(t) = u(t)$$

show that $Y(j\omega) = H(j\omega)U(j\omega)$ for some function $H(j\omega)$. What is $H(j\omega)$?

13 Use the time-shift property to calculate the Fourier transform of the double pulse defined by

$$f(t) = \begin{cases} 1 & (1 \leqslant |t| \leqslant 2) \\ 0 & (\text{otherwise}) \end{cases}$$

14 Calculate the Fourier transform of the windowed cosine function

$$f(t) = \cos \omega_0 t[H(t + \tfrac{1}{2}T) - H(t - \tfrac{1}{2}T)]$$

15 Find the Fourier transform of the shifted form of the windowed cosine function

$$g(t) = \cos \omega_0 t[H(t) - H(t - T)]$$

16 Calculate the Fourier transform of the windowed sine function

$$f(t) = \sin 2t[H(t + 1) - H(t - 1)]$$

5.4 The frequency response

In this section we first consider the relationship between the Fourier and Laplace transforms, and then proceed to consider the frequency response in terms of the Fourier transform.

5.4.1 Relationship between Fourier and Laplace transforms

The differences between the Fourier and Laplace transforms are quite subtle. At first glance it appears that to obtain the Fourier transform from the Laplace transform we merely write $j\omega$ for s, and that the difference ends there. This is true in some cases, but not in all. Strictly, the Fourier and Laplace transforms are distinct, and neither is a generalization of the other.

Writing down the defining integrals, we have

The Fourier transform

$$\mathcal{F}\{f(t)\} = \int_{-\infty}^{\infty} f(t)\,\mathrm{e}^{-j\omega t}\,\mathrm{d}t \tag{5.31}$$

The bilateral Laplace transform

$$\mathcal{L}_B\{f(t)\} = \int_{-\infty}^{\infty} f(t)\,\mathrm{e}^{-st}\,\mathrm{d}t \tag{5.32}$$

The unilateral Laplace transform

$$\mathcal{L}\{f(t)\} = \int_{0^-}^{\infty} f(t)\,\mathrm{e}^{-st}\,\mathrm{d}t \tag{5.33}$$

There is an obvious structural similarity between (5.31) and (5.32), while the connection with (5.33) is not so clear in view of the lower limit of integration. In the Laplace transform definitions recall that s is a complex variable, and may be written as

$$s = \sigma + j\omega \tag{5.34}$$

where σ and ω are real variables. We can then interpret (5.31), the Fourier transform of $f(t)$, as a special case of (5.32), when $\sigma = 0$, provided that the Laplace transform exists when $\sigma = 0$, or equivalently when $s = j\omega$ (that is, s describes the imaginary axis in the s plane). If we restrict our attention to causal functions, that is functions (or signals) that are zero whenever $t < 0$, the bilateral Laplace transform (5.32) is identical with the unilateral Laplace transform (5.33). The Fourier transform can thus be regarded as a special case of the unilateral Laplace transform for causal functions, provided again that the unilateral Laplace transform exists on the imaginary axis $s = j\omega$.

The next part of the story is concerned with a class of time signals $f(t)$ whose Laplace transforms do exist on the imaginary axis $s = j\omega$. Recall from (2.71) that a causal linear time-invariant system with Laplace transfer function $G(s)$ has an impulse response $h(t)$ given by

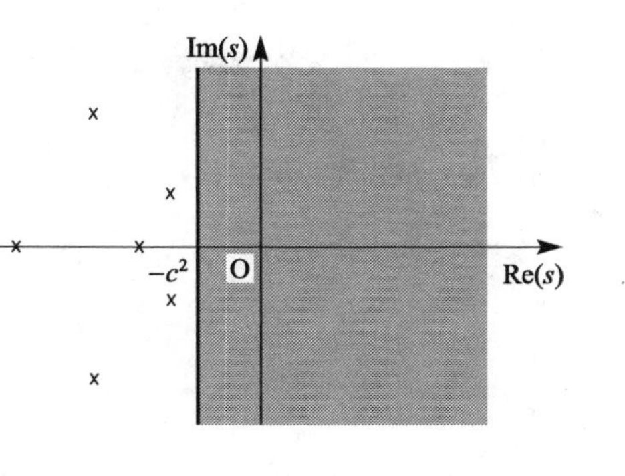

Figure 5.14 Pole locations for $G(s)$ and the region of existence of $G(s)$.

$$h(t) = \mathscr{L}^{-1}\{G(s)\} = g(t)H(t), \quad \text{say} \tag{5.35}$$

Furthermore, if the system is stable then all the poles of $G(s)$ are in the left half-plane, implying that $g(t)H(t) \to 0$ as $t \to \infty$. Let the pole locations of $G(s)$ be

$$p_1, p_2, \ldots, p_n$$

where

$$p_k = -a_k^2 + \mathrm{j}b_k$$

in which a_k, b_k are real and $a_k \neq 0$ for $k = 1, 2, \ldots, n$. Examples of such poles are illustrated in Figure 5.14, where we have assumed that $G(s)$ is the transfer function of a real system so that poles that do not lie on the real axis occur in conjugate pairs. As indicated in Section 2.2.3, the Laplace transfer function $G(s)$ will exist in the shaded region of Figure 5.14 defined by

$$\mathrm{Re}(s) > -c^2$$

where $-c^2$ is the abscissa of convergence and is such that

$$0 < c^2 < \min a_k^2$$

The important conclusion is that for such systems $G(s)$ always exists on the imaginary axis $s = \mathrm{j}\omega$, and so $h(t) = g(t)H(t)$ always has a Fourier transform. In other words, we have demonstrated that the impulse response function $h(t)$ of a *stable causal*, linear time-invariant system always has a Fourier transform. Moreover, we have shown that this can be found by evaluating the Laplace transform on the imaginary axis; that is, by putting $s = \mathrm{j}\omega$ in the Laplace transform. We have thus established that Fourier transforms exist for a significant class of useful signals; this knowledge will be used in Section 5.4.2.

Example 5.9

Which of the following causal time-invariant systems have impulse responses that possess Fourier transforms? Find the latter when they exist.

(a) $$\frac{\mathrm{d}^2y(t)}{\mathrm{d}t^2} + 3\frac{\mathrm{d}y(t)}{\mathrm{d}t} + 2y(t) = u(t)$$

(b) $$\frac{\mathrm{d}^2y(t)}{\mathrm{d}t^2} + \omega^2y(t) = u(t)$$

(c) $$\frac{\mathrm{d}^2y(t)}{\mathrm{d}t^2} + \frac{\mathrm{d}y(t)}{\mathrm{d}t} + y(t) = 2u(t) + \frac{\mathrm{d}u(t)}{\mathrm{d}t}$$

Solution Assuming that the systems are initially in a quiescent state when $t < 0$, taking Laplace transforms gives

(a) $Y(s) = \dfrac{1}{s^2 + 3s + 2}U(s) = G_1(s)U(s)$

(b) $Y(s) = \dfrac{1}{s^2 + \omega^2}U(s) = G_2(s)U(s)$

(c) $Y(s) = \dfrac{s + 2}{s^2 + s + 1}U(s) = G_3(s)U(s)$

In case (a) the poles of $G_1(s)$ are at $s = -1$ and $s = -2$, so the system is stable and the impulse response has a Fourier transform given by

$$G_1(\mathrm{j}\omega) = \left.\frac{1}{s^2 + 3s + 2}\right|_{s=\mathrm{j}\omega} = \frac{1}{2 - \omega^2 + \mathrm{j}3\omega}$$

$$= \frac{2 - \omega^2 - \mathrm{j}3\omega}{(2 - \omega^2)^2 + 9\omega^2} = \frac{(2 - \omega^2) - \mathrm{j}3\omega}{\omega^4 + 5\omega^2 + 4}$$

In case (b) we find that the poles of $G_2(s)$ are at $s = \mathrm{j}\omega$ and $s = -\mathrm{j}\omega$; that is, on the imaginary axis. The system is not stable (notice that the impulse response does not decay to zero), and the impulse response does not possess a Fourier transform.

In case (c) the poles of $G_3(s)$ are at $s = -\frac{1}{2} + \mathrm{j}\frac{1}{2}\sqrt{3}$ and $s = -\frac{1}{2} - \mathrm{j}\frac{1}{2}\sqrt{3}$. Since these are in the left half-plane, $\mathrm{Re}(s) < 0$, we conclude that the system is stable. The Fourier transform of the impulse response is then

$$G_3(\mathrm{j}\omega) = \frac{2 + \mathrm{j}\omega}{1 - \omega^2 + \mathrm{j}\omega}$$

5.4.2 The frequency response

For a linear time-invariant system, initially in a quiescent state, having a Laplace transfer function $G(s)$, the response $y(t)$ to an input $u(t)$ is given in (2.66) as

$$Y(s) = G(s)U(s) \tag{5.36}$$

where $Y(s)$ and $U(s)$ are the Laplace transforms of $y(t)$ and $u(t)$ respectively. In Section 2.7 we saw that, subject to the system being stable, the steady-state response $y_{ss}(t)$ to a sinusoidal input $u(t) = A \sin \omega t$ is given by (2.86) as

$$y_{ss}(t) = A|G(\mathrm{j}\omega)| \sin[\omega t + \arg G(\mathrm{j}\omega)] \tag{5.37}$$

That is, the steady-state response is also sinusoidal, with the same frequency as the input signal but having an amplitude gain $|G(\mathrm{j}\omega)|$ and a phase shift $\arg G(\mathrm{j}\omega)$.

More generally, we could have taken the input to be the complex sinusoidal signal

$$u(t) = A\,\mathrm{e}^{\mathrm{j}\omega t}$$

and, subject to the stability requirement, showed that the steady-state response is

$$y_{ss}(t) = AG(\mathrm{j}\omega)\,\mathrm{e}^{\mathrm{j}\omega t} \tag{5.38}$$

or

$$y_{ss}(t) = A|G(\mathrm{j}\omega)|\,\mathrm{e}^{\mathrm{j}[\omega t + \arg G(\mathrm{j}\omega)]} \tag{5.39}$$

As before, $|G(\mathrm{j}\omega)|$ and $\arg G(\mathrm{j}\omega)$ are called the amplitude gain and phase shift respectively. Both are functions of the real frequency variable ω, and their plots versus ω constitute the **system frequency response**, which, as we saw in Section 2.7, characterizes the behaviour of the system. Note that taking imaginary parts throughout in (5.39) leads to the sinusoidal response (5.37).

We note that the steady-state response (5.38) is simply the input signal $A\mathrm{e}^{\mathrm{j}\omega t}$ multiplied by the Fourier transform $G(\mathrm{j}\omega)$ of the system's impulse response. Consequently $G(\mathrm{j}\omega)$ is called the **frequency transfer function** of the system. Therefore if the system represented in (5.36) is stable, so that $G(\mathrm{j}\omega)$ exists as the Fourier transform of its impulse response, and the input $u(t) = \mathscr{L}^{-1}\{U(s)\}$ has a Fourier transform $U(\mathrm{j}\omega)$, then we may represent the system in terms of the frequency transfer function as

$$Y(\mathrm{j}\omega) = G(\mathrm{j}\omega)U(\mathrm{j}\omega) \tag{5.40}$$

Equation (5.40) thus determines the Fourier transform of the system output, and can be used to determine the frequency spectrum of the output from that of the input. This means that both the amplitude and phase spectra of the output are available, since

$$|Y(\mathrm{j}\omega)| = |G(\mathrm{j}\omega)|\,|U(\mathrm{j}\omega)| \tag{5.41a}$$

$$\arg Y(\mathrm{j}\omega) = \arg G(\mathrm{j}\omega) + \arg U(\mathrm{j}\omega) \tag{5.41b}$$

We shall now consider an example that will draw together both these and some earlier ideas which serve to illustrate the relevance of this material in the communications industry.

Example 5.10

A signal $f(t)$ consists of two components:

(a) a symmetric rectangular pulse of duration 2π (see Example 5.3) and

(b) a second pulse, also of duration 2π (that is, a copy of (a)), modulating a signal with carrier frequency $\omega_0 = 3$ (the process of modulation was introduced in Section 5.3.4).

Write down an expression for $f(t)$ and illustrate its amplitude spectrum. Describe the amplitude spectrum of the output signal if $f(t)$ is applied to a stable causal system with a Laplace transfer function

$$G(s) = \frac{1}{s^2 + \sqrt{2}s + 1}$$

Solution

Denoting the pulse of Example 5.3, with $T = \pi$, by $P_\pi(t)$, and noting the use of the term 'carrier signal' in Example 5.7, we have

$$f(t) = P_\pi(t) + (\cos 3t)P_\pi(t)$$

From Example 5.3,

$$\mathscr{F}\{P_\pi(t)\} = 2\pi \operatorname{sinc} \omega\pi$$

so, using the result of Example 5.7, we have

$$\mathscr{F}\{f(t)\} = F(\mathrm{j}\omega) = 2\pi \operatorname{sinc} \omega\pi + \tfrac{1}{2}[2\pi \operatorname{sinc}(\omega - 3)\pi + 2\pi \operatorname{sinc}(\omega + 3)\pi]$$

The corresponding amplitude spectrum obtained by plotting $|F(\mathrm{j}\omega)|$ versus ω is illustrated in Figure 5.15.

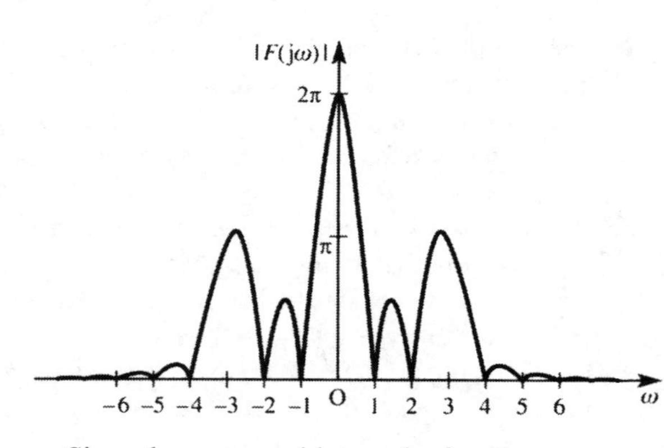

Figure 5.15 Amplitude spectrum of the signal $P_\pi(t) + (\cos 3t)P_\pi(t)$.

Since the system with transfer function

$$G(s) = \frac{1}{s^2 + \sqrt{2}s + 1}$$

is stable and causal, it has a frequency transfer function

$$G(j\omega) = \frac{1}{1 - \omega^2 + j\sqrt{2}\omega}$$

so that its amplitude gain is

$$|G(j\omega)| = \frac{1}{\sqrt{(\omega^4 + 1)}}$$

The amplitude spectrum of the output signal $|Y(j\omega)|$ when the input is $f(t)$ is then obtained from (5.41a) as the product of $|F(j\omega)|$ and $|G(j\omega)|$. Plots of both the amplitude gain spectrum $|G(j\omega)|$ and the output amplitude spectrum $|Y(j\omega)|$ are shown in Figures 5.16(a) and (b) respectively. Note from Figure 5.16(b) that we have a reasonably good copy of the amplitude spectrum of $P_\pi(t)$ (see Figure 5.9 with $A = \pi$, $T = 1$). However, the second element of $f(t)$ has effectively vanished. Our system has 'filtered out' this latter component while 'passing' an almost intact version of the first. Examination of the time-domain response would show that the first component does in fact experience some 'smoothing', which, roughly speaking, consists of rounding of the sharp edges. The system considered here is a second-order 'low-pass' Butterworth filter (introduced in Section 3.8.1).

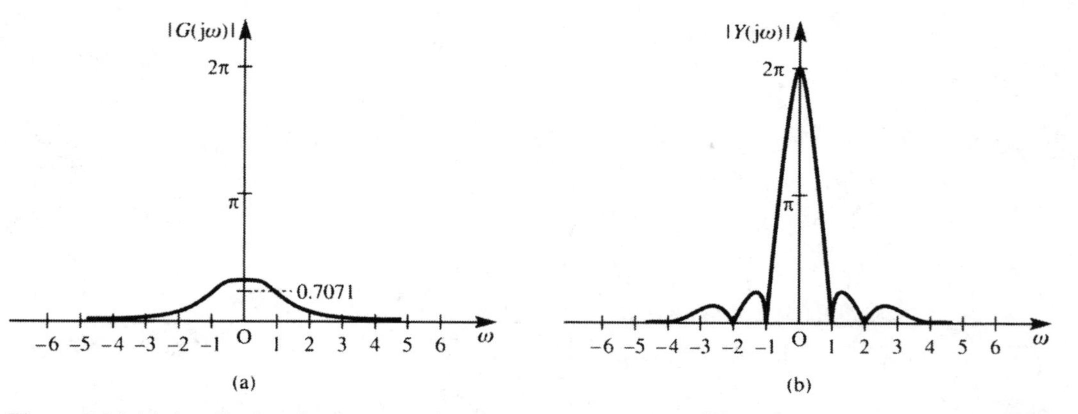

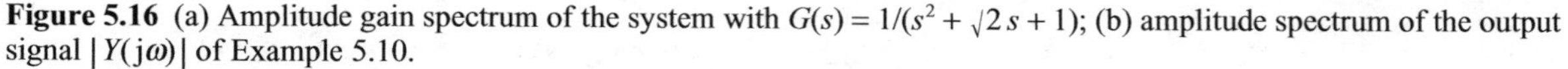
Figure 5.16 (a) Amplitude gain spectrum of the system with $G(s) = 1/(s^2 + \sqrt{2}s + 1)$; (b) amplitude spectrum of the output signal $|Y(j\omega)|$ of Example 5.10.

5.4.3 Exercises

17 Find the impulse response of systems (a) and (c) of Example 5.9. Calculate the Fourier transform of each using the definition (5.15), and verify the results given in Example 5.9.

18 Use the time-shift property to calculate the Fourier transform of the double rectangular pulse $f(t)$ illustrated in Figure 5.17.

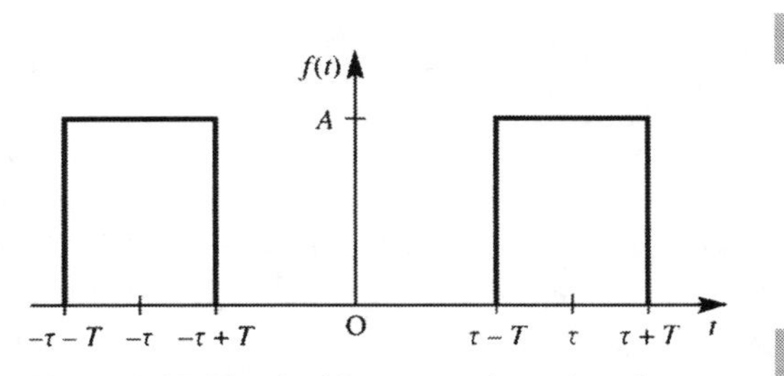

Figure 5.17 The double rectangular pulse of Exercise 18.

19 The system with transfer function

$$G(s) = \frac{1}{s^2 + \sqrt{2}s + 1}$$

was discussed in Example 5.10. Make a transformation

$$s \to \frac{1}{s'}$$

and write down $G(s')$. Examine the frequency response of a system with transfer function $G(s')$ and in particular find the amplitude response when $\omega = 0$ and as $\omega \to \infty$. How would you describe such a system?

20 Use the symmetry property, and the result of Exercise 1, to calculate the Fourier transform of

$$f(t) = \frac{1}{a^2 + t^2}$$

Sketch $f(t)$ and its transform (which is real).

21 Using the results of Examples 5.3 and 5.7, calculate the Fourier transform of the pulse-modulated signal

$$f(t) = P_T(t)\cos\omega_0 t$$

where

$$P_T(t) = \begin{cases} 1 & (|t| \leq T) \\ 0 & (|t| > T) \end{cases}$$

is the pulse of duration $2T$.

5.5 Transforms of the step and impulse functions

In this section we consider the application of Fourier transforms to the concepts of energy, power and convolution. In so doing, we shall introduce the Fourier transform of the Heaviside unit step function $H(t)$ and the impulse function $\delta(t)$.

5.5.1 Energy and power

In Section 4.6.4 we introduced the concept of the power spectrum of a periodic signal and found that it enabled us to deduce useful information relating to the latter. In this section we define two quantities associated with time signals $f(t)$, defined for $-\infty < t < \infty$, namely signal energy and signal power. Not only are these important quantities in themselves, but, as we shall see, they play an important role in characterizing signal types.

The total **energy** associated with the signal $f(t)$ is defined as

$$E = \int_{-\infty}^{\infty} [f(t)]^2 \, dt \tag{5.42}$$

If $f(t)$ has a Fourier transform $F(\mathrm{j}\omega)$, so that, from (5.16),

$$f(t) = \frac{1}{2\pi}\int_{-\infty}^{\infty} F(\mathrm{j}\omega)\,\mathrm{e}^{\mathrm{j}\omega t}\,\mathrm{d}\omega$$

then (5.42) may be expressed as

$$E = \int_{-\infty}^{\infty} f(t)f(t)\,\mathrm{d}t = \int_{-\infty}^{\infty} f(t)\left[\frac{1}{2\pi}\int_{-\infty}^{\infty} F(\mathrm{j}\omega)\,\mathrm{e}^{\mathrm{j}\omega t}\,\mathrm{d}\omega\right]\mathrm{d}t$$

On changing the order of integration, this becomes

$$E = \frac{1}{2\pi}\int_{-\infty}^{\infty} F(\mathrm{j}\omega)\left[\int_{-\infty}^{\infty} f(t)\,\mathrm{e}^{\mathrm{j}\omega t}\,\mathrm{d}t\right]\mathrm{d}\omega \tag{5.43}$$

From the defining integral (5.15) for $F(\mathrm{j}\omega)$, we recognize the part of the integrand within the square brackets as $F(-\mathrm{j}\omega)$, which, if $f(t)$ is real, is such that $F(-\mathrm{j}\omega) = F^*(\mathrm{j}\omega)$, where $F^*(\mathrm{j}\omega)$ is the complex conjugate of $F(\mathrm{j}\omega)$. Thus (5.43) becomes

$$E = \frac{1}{2\pi}\int_{-\infty}^{\infty} F(\mathrm{j}\omega)F^*(\mathrm{j}\omega)\,\mathrm{d}\omega$$

so that

$$E = \int_{-\infty}^{\infty} [f(t)]^2\,\mathrm{d}t = \frac{1}{2\pi}\int_{-\infty}^{\infty} |F(\mathrm{j}\omega)|^2\,\mathrm{d}\omega \tag{5.44}$$

Equation (5.44) relates the total energy of the signal $f(t)$ to the integral over all frequencies of $|F(\mathrm{j}\omega)|^2$. For this reason, $|F(\mathrm{j}\omega)|^2$ is called the **energy spectral density**, and a plot of $|F(\mathrm{j}\omega)|^2$ versus ω is called the **energy spectrum** of the signal $f(t)$. The result (5.44) is called **Parseval's theorem**, and is an extension of the result contained in Theorem 4.6 for periodic signals.

Example 5.11

Determine the energy spectral densities of

(a) the one-sided exponential function $f(t) = \mathrm{e}^{-at}H(t)$ $(a > 0)$,

(b) the rectangular pulse of Figure 5.6.

Solution

(a) From (5.17), the Fourier transform of $f(t)$ is

$$F(\mathrm{j}\omega) = \frac{a - \mathrm{j}\omega}{a^2 + \omega^2}$$

The energy spectral density of the function is therefore

$$|F(\mathrm{j}\omega)|^2 = F(\mathrm{j}\omega)F^*(\mathrm{j}\omega) = \frac{a - \mathrm{j}\omega}{a^2 + \omega^2}\,\frac{a + \mathrm{j}\omega}{a^2 + \omega^2}$$

that is,

$$|F(j\omega)|^2 = \frac{1}{a^2 + \omega^2}$$

(b) From Example 5.3, the Fourier transform $F(j\omega)$ of the rectangular pulse is

$$F(j\omega) = 2AT \text{ sinc } \omega T$$

Thus the energy spectral density of the pulse is

$$|F(j\omega)|^2 = 4A^2T^2 \text{ sinc}^2 \omega T$$

There are important signals $f(t)$, defined in general for $-\infty < t < \infty$, for which the integral $\int_{-\infty}^{\infty} [f(t)]^2 dt$ in (5.42) either is unbounded (that is, it becomes infinite) or does not converge to a finite limit; for example, $\sin t$. For such signals, instead of considering energy, we consider the average power P, frequently referred to as the **power** of the signal. This is defined by

$$P = \lim_{T \to \infty} \frac{1}{T} \int_{-T/2}^{T/2} [f(t)]^2 \, dt \tag{5.45}$$

Note that for signals that satisfy the Dirichlet conditions (Theorem 5.1) the integral in (5.42) exists and, since in (5.45) we divide by the signal duration, it follows that such signals have zero power associated with them.

We now pose the question: 'Are there other signals which possess Fourier transforms?' As you may expect, the answer is 'Yes', although the manner of obtaining the transforms will be different from our procedure so far. We shall see that the transforms so obtained, on using the inversion integral (5.16), yield some very 'ordinary' signals so far excluded from our discussion.

We begin by considering the Fourier transform of the generalized function $\delta(t)$, the Dirac delta function introduced in Section 2.5.8. Recall from (2.49) that $\delta(t)$ satisfies the sifting property; that is, for a continuous function $g(t)$,

$$\int_a^b g(t)\delta(t - c)\, dt = \begin{cases} g(c) & (a < c < b) \\ 0 & \text{otherwise} \end{cases}$$

Using the defining integral (5.15), we readily obtain the following two Fourier transforms:

$$\mathscr{F}\{\delta(t)\} = \int_{-\infty}^{\infty} \delta(t) e^{-j\omega t}\, dt = 1 \tag{5.46}$$

$$\mathscr{F}\{\delta(t - t_0)\} = \int_{-\infty}^{\infty} \delta(t - t_0) e^{-j\omega t}\, dt = e^{-j\omega t_0} \tag{5.47}$$

These two transforms are, by now, unremarkable, and, noting that $|e^{-j\omega t_0}| = 1$, we illustrate the signals and their spectra in Figure 5.18.

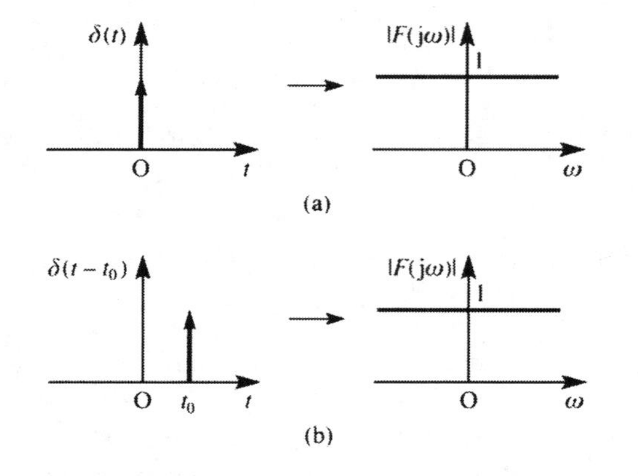

Figure 5.18 (a) $\delta(t)$ and its amplitude spectrum; (b) $\delta(t - t_0)$ and its amplitude spectrum.

These results may be confirmed in MATLAB. Using the commands

```
syms w t
D=sym('Dirac(t)');
F=fourier(D,t,w)
```

returns

```
F=1
```

in agreement with (5.46); whilst the commands

```
syms w t T
D1=sym('Dirac(t-T)');
F1=fourier(D1,t,w)
```

return

```
F1=exp(-i*T*w)
```

which confirms (5.47), with T replacing t_0.

We now depart from the definition of the Fourier transform given in (5.15) and seek new transform pairs based on (5.46) and (5.47). Using the symmetry (duality) property of Section 5.3.5, we deduce from (5.46) that

$$1 \quad \text{and} \quad 2\pi\delta(-\omega) = 2\pi\delta(\omega) \tag{5.48}$$

is another Fourier transform pair. Likewise, from (5.47), we deduce that

$$e^{-jt_0t} \quad \text{and} \quad 2\pi\delta(-\omega - t_0)$$

is also a Fourier transform pair. Substituting $t_0 = -\omega_0$ into the latter, we have

$$e^{j\omega_0 t} \quad \text{and} \quad 2\pi\delta(\omega_0 - \omega) = 2\pi\delta(\omega - \omega_0) \tag{5.49}$$

as another Fourier transform pair.

We are thus claiming that in (5.48) and (5.49) that $f_1(t) = 1$ and $f_2(t) = e^{j\omega_0 t}$, which do not have 'ordinary' Fourier transforms as defined by (5.15), actually do have **'generalized' Fourier transforms** given by

$$F_1(j\omega) = 2\pi\delta(\omega) \tag{5.50}$$

$$F_2(j\omega) = 2\pi\delta(\omega - \omega_0) \tag{5.51}$$

respectively.

The term 'generalized' has been used because the two transforms contain the generalized functions $\delta(\omega)$ and $\delta(\omega - \omega_0)$. Let us now test our conjecture that (5.50) and (5.51) are Fourier transforms of $f_1(t)$ and $f_2(t)$ respectively. If (5.50) and (5.51) really are Fourier transforms then their time-domain images $f_1(t)$ and $f_2(t)$ respectively should reappear via the inverse transform (5.16). Substituting $F_1(\mathrm{j}\omega)$ from (5.50) into (5.16), we have

$$\mathscr{F}^{-1}\{F_1(\mathrm{j}\omega)\} = \frac{1}{2\pi}\int_{-\infty}^{\infty} F_1(\mathrm{j}\omega)\,\mathrm{e}^{\mathrm{j}\omega t}\,\mathrm{d}\omega = \frac{1}{2\pi}\int_{-\infty}^{\infty} 2\pi\delta(\omega)\,\mathrm{e}^{\mathrm{j}\omega t}\,\mathrm{d}\omega = 1$$

so $f_1(t) = 1$ is recovered.

Similarly, using (5.51), we have

$$\mathscr{F}^{-1}\{F_2(\mathrm{j}\omega)\} = \frac{1}{2\pi}\int_{-\infty}^{\infty} 2\pi\delta(\omega - \omega_0)\,\mathrm{e}^{\mathrm{j}\omega t}\,\mathrm{d}\omega = \mathrm{e}^{\mathrm{j}\omega_0 t}$$

so that $f_2(t) = \mathrm{e}^{\mathrm{j}\omega_0 t}$ is also recovered.

Our approach has therefore been successful, and we do indeed have a way of generating new pairs of transforms. We shall therefore use the approach to find generalized Fourier transforms for the signals

$$f_3(t) = \cos\omega_0 t, \qquad f_4(t) = \sin\omega_0 t$$

Since

$$f_3(t) = \cos\omega_0 t = \tfrac{1}{2}(\mathrm{e}^{\mathrm{j}\omega_0 t} + \mathrm{e}^{-\mathrm{j}\omega_0 t})$$

the linearity property (5.22) gives

$$\mathscr{F}\{f_3(t)\} = \tfrac{1}{2}\mathscr{F}\{\mathrm{e}^{\mathrm{j}\omega_0 t}\} + \tfrac{1}{2}\mathscr{F}\{\mathrm{e}^{-\mathrm{j}\omega_0 t}\}$$

which, on using (5.49), leads to the generalized Fourier transform pair

$$\mathscr{F}\{\cos\omega_0 t\} = \pi[\delta(\omega - \omega_0) + \delta(\omega + \omega_0)] \tag{5.52}$$

Likewise, we deduce the generalized Fourier transform pair

$$\mathscr{F}\{\sin\omega_0 t\} = \mathrm{j}\pi[\delta(\omega + \omega_0) - \delta(\omega - \omega_0)] \tag{5.53}$$

The development of (5.53) and the verification that both (5.52) and (5.53) invert correctly using the inverse transform (5.16) is left as an exercise for the reader.

It is worth noting at this stage that defining the Fourier transform $\mathscr{F}\{f(t)\}$ of $f(t)$ in (5.15) as

$$\mathscr{F}\{f(t)\} = \int_{-\infty}^{\infty} f(t)\,\mathrm{e}^{-\mathrm{j}\omega t}\,\mathrm{d}t$$

whenever the integral exists does not preclude the existence of other Fourier transforms, such as the generalized one just introduced, defined by other means.

It is clear that the total energy

$$E = \int_{-\infty}^{\infty} \cos^2\omega_0 t\,\mathrm{d}t$$

associated with the signal $f_3(t) = \cos \omega_0 t$ is unbounded. However, from (5.45), we can calculate the power associated with the signal as

$$P = \lim_{T\to\infty} \frac{1}{T}\int_{-T/2}^{T/2} \cos^2\omega_0 t\,\mathrm{d}t = \lim_{T\to\infty}\frac{1}{T}\left[t + \frac{1}{2\omega_0}\sin 2\omega_0 t\right]_{-T/2}^{T/2} = \tfrac{1}{2}$$

Thus, while the signal $f_3(t) = \cos\omega_0 t$ has unbounded energy associated with it, its power content is $\frac{1}{2}$. Signals whose associated energy is finite, for example $f(t) = \mathrm{e}^{-at}H(t)$ $(a > 0)$, are sometimes called **energy signals**, while those whose associated energy is unbounded but whose total power is finite are known as **power signals**. The concepts of power signals and power spectral density are important in the analysis of random signals, and the interested reader should consult specialized texts.

Example 5.12

Suppose that a periodic function $f(t)$, defined on $-\infty < t < \infty$, may be expanded in a Fourier series having exponential form

$$f(t) = \sum_{n=-\infty}^{\infty} F_n \mathrm{e}^{\mathrm{j}n\omega_0 t}$$

What is the (generalized) Fourier transform of $f(t)$?

Solution From the definition,

$$\mathscr{F}\{f(t)\} = \mathscr{F}\left\{\sum_{n=-\infty}^{\infty} F_n \mathrm{e}^{\mathrm{j}n\omega_0 t}\right\} = \sum_{n=-\infty}^{\infty} F_n \mathscr{F}\{\mathrm{e}^{\mathrm{j}n\omega_0 t}\}$$

which, on using (5.49), gives

$$\mathscr{F}\{f(t)\} = \sum_{n=-\infty}^{\infty} F_n 2\pi\delta(\omega - n\omega_0)$$

That is,

$$\mathscr{F}\{f(t)\} = 2\pi\sum_{n=-\infty}^{\infty} F_n \delta(\omega - n\omega_0)$$

where F_n $(-\infty < n < \infty)$ are the coefficients of the exponential form of the Fourier series representation of $f(t)$.

Example 5.13

Use the result of Example 5.12 to verify the Fourier transform of $f(t) = \cos\omega_0 t$ given in (5.52).

Solution Since

$$f(t) = \cos\omega_0 t = \tfrac{1}{2}\mathrm{e}^{\mathrm{j}\omega_0 t} + \tfrac{1}{2}\mathrm{e}^{-\mathrm{j}\omega_0 t}$$

the F_n of Example 5.12 are

$$F_{-1} = F_1 = \tfrac{1}{2}$$

$$F_n = 0 \quad (n \neq \pm 1)$$

Thus, using the result

$$\mathscr{F}\{f(t)\} = 2\pi \sum_{n=-\infty}^{\infty} F_n \delta(\omega - \omega_0)$$

we have

$$\begin{aligned}\mathscr{F}\{\cos \omega_0 t\} &= 2\pi F_{-1}\delta(\omega + \omega_0) + 2\pi F_1 \delta(\omega - \omega_0) \\ &= \pi[\delta(\omega + \omega_0) + \delta(\omega - \omega_0)]\end{aligned}$$

in agreement with (5.52).

Confirm this answer using the MATLAB commands

```
syms w t a
F=fourier(cos(a*t),t,w)
```

where a has been used to represent ω_0.

Example 5.14

Determine the (generalized) Fourier transform of the periodic 'sawtooth' function, defined by

$$f(t) = \frac{2t}{T} \quad (0 < t < 2T)$$

$$f(t + 2T) = f(t)$$

Solution In Example 4.19 we saw that the exponential form of the Fourier series representation of $f(t)$ is

$$f(t) = \sum_{n=-\infty}^{\infty} F_n \mathrm{e}^{\mathrm{j}n\omega_0 t}$$

with

$$\omega_0 = \frac{2\pi}{2T} = \frac{\pi}{T}$$

$$F_0 = 2$$

$$F_n = \frac{\mathrm{j}2}{n\pi} \quad (n \neq 0)$$

It follows from Example 5.12 that the Fourier transform $\mathscr{F}\{f(t)\}$ is

$$\begin{aligned}\mathscr{F}\{f(t)\} = F(\mathrm{j}\omega) &= 4\pi\delta(\omega) + \sum_{\substack{n=-\infty \\ n\neq 0}}^{\infty} \mathrm{j}\frac{4}{n}\delta(\omega - n\omega_0) \\ &= 4\pi\delta(\omega) + \mathrm{j}4\sum_{\substack{n=-\infty \\ n\neq 0}}^{\infty} \frac{1}{n}\delta\left(\omega - \frac{n\pi}{T}\right)\end{aligned}$$

Thus we see that the amplitude spectrum simply consists of pulses located at integer multiples of the fundamental frequency $\omega_0 = \pi/T$. The discrete line spectra obtained via the exponential form of the Fourier series for this periodic function is thus reproduced, now with a scaling factor of 2π.

Example 5.15

Determine the (generalized) Fourier transform of the unit impulse train $f(t) = \sum_{n=-\infty}^{\infty} \delta(t - nT)$ shown symbolically in Figure 5.19.

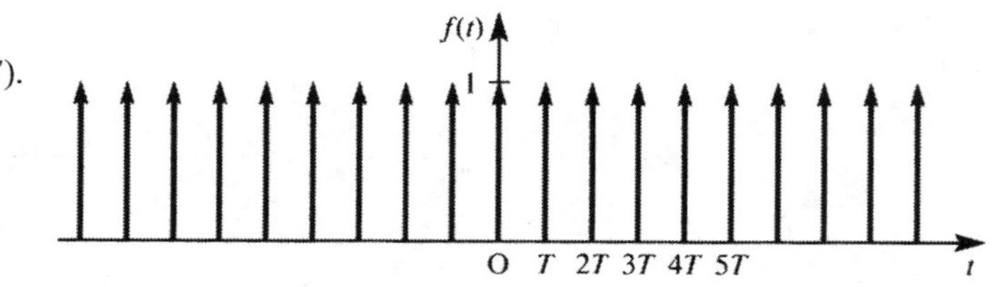

Figure 5.19 Unit impulse train $f(t) = \sum_{n=-\infty}^{\infty} \delta(t - nT)$.

Solution Although $f(t)$ is a generalized function, and not a function in the ordinary sense, it follows that since

$$f(t + kT) = \sum_{n=-\infty}^{\infty} \delta(t + (k - n)T) \quad (k \text{ an integer})$$

$$= \sum_{m=-\infty}^{\infty} \delta(t - mT) \quad (m = n - k)$$

$$= f(t)$$

it is periodic, with period T. Moreover, we can formally expand $f(t)$ as a Fourier series

$$f(t) = \sum_{n=-\infty}^{\infty} F_n \mathrm{e}^{\mathrm{j}n\omega_0 t} \quad \left(\omega_0 = \frac{2\pi}{T}\right)$$

with

$$F_n = \frac{1}{T}\int_{-T/2}^{T/2} f(t)\mathrm{e}^{-\mathrm{j}n\omega_0 t}\,\mathrm{d}t = \frac{1}{T}\int_{-T/2}^{T/2} \delta(t)\mathrm{e}^{-\mathrm{j}n\omega_0 t}\,\mathrm{d}t = \frac{1}{T} \quad \text{for all } n$$

It follows from Example 5.12 that

$$\mathscr{F}\{f(t)\} = 2\pi \sum_{n=-\infty}^{\infty} \frac{1}{T}\delta(\omega - n\omega_0) = \omega_0 \sum_{n=-\infty}^{\infty} \delta(\omega - n\omega_0)$$

Thus we have shown that

$$\mathscr{F}\left\{\sum_{n=-\infty}^{\infty} \delta(t - nT)\right\} = \omega_0 \sum_{n=-\infty}^{\infty} \delta(\omega - n\omega_0) \tag{5.54}$$

where $\omega_0 = 2\pi/T$. That is, the time-domain impulse train has another impulse train as its transform. We shall see in Section 5.6.4 that this result is of particular importance in dealing with sampled time signals.

Following our successful hunt for generalized Fourier transforms, we are led to consider the possibility that the Heaviside unit step function $H(t)$ defined in Section 2.5.1 may have a transform in this sense. Recall from (2.56) that if

$$f(t) = H(t)$$

then

$$\frac{\mathrm{d}f(t)}{\mathrm{d}t} = \delta(t)$$

From the time-differentiation property (5.23), we might expect that if

$$\mathscr{F}\{H(t)\} = \bar{H}(\mathrm{j}\omega)$$

then

$$(\mathrm{j}\omega)\bar{H}(\mathrm{j}\omega) = \mathscr{F}\{\delta(t)\} = 1 \tag{5.55}$$

Equation (5.55) suggests that a candidate for $\bar{H}(\mathrm{j}\omega)$ might be $1/\mathrm{j}\omega$, but this is not the case, since inversion using (5.16) does not give $H(t)$ back. Using (5.16) and complex variable techniques, it can be shown that

$$\mathscr{F}^{-1}\left\{\frac{1}{\mathrm{j}\omega}\right\} = \frac{1}{2\pi}\int_{-\infty}^{\infty}\frac{\mathrm{e}^{\mathrm{j}\omega t}}{\mathrm{j}\omega}\,\mathrm{d}\omega = \left\{\begin{array}{cc} \frac{1}{2} & (t > 0) \\ 0 & (t = 0) \\ -\frac{1}{2} & (t < 0) \end{array}\right\} = \tfrac{1}{2}\operatorname{sgn}(t)$$

where $\operatorname{sgn}(t)$ is the **signum function**, defined by

$$\operatorname{sgn}(t) = \begin{cases} 1 & (t > 0) \\ 0 & (t = 0) \\ -1 & (t < 0) \end{cases}$$

(*Note*: This last result may be obtained in terms of Heaviside functions using the MATLAB commands

```
syms w t
f=ifourier(1/(i*w))
```

However, we note that (5.55) is also satisfied by

$$\bar{H}(\mathrm{j}\omega) = \frac{1}{\mathrm{j}\omega} + c\delta(\omega) \tag{5.56}$$

where c is a constant. This follows from the equivalence property (see Definition 2.2, Section 2.5.11) $f(\omega)\delta(\omega) = f(0)\delta(\omega)$ with $f(\omega) = \mathrm{j}\omega$, which gives

$$(\mathrm{j}\omega)\bar{H}(\mathrm{j}\omega) = 1 + (\mathrm{j}\omega)c\delta(\omega) = 1$$

Inverting (5.56) using (5.16), we have

$$g(t) = \mathscr{F}^{-1}\left\{\frac{1}{j\omega} + c\delta(\omega)\right\} = \frac{1}{2\pi}\int_{-\infty}^{\infty}\left[\frac{1}{j\omega} + c\delta(\omega)\right]e^{j\omega t}\,d\omega$$

$$= \begin{cases} c/2\pi + \frac{1}{2} & (t > 0) \\ c/2\pi & (t = 0) \\ c/2\pi - \frac{1}{2} & (t < 0) \end{cases}$$

and, choosing $c = \pi$, we have

$$g(t) = \begin{cases} 1 & (t > 0) \\ \frac{1}{2} & (t = 0) \\ 0 & (t < 0) \end{cases}$$

Thus we have (almost) recovered the step function $H(t)$. Here $g(t)$ takes the value $\frac{1}{2}$ at $t = 0$, but this is not surprising in view of the convergence of the Fourier integral at points of discontinuity as given in Theorem 5.1. With this proviso, we have shown that

$$\bar{H}(j\omega) = \mathscr{F}\{H(t)\} = \frac{1}{j\omega} + \pi\delta(\omega) \qquad \textbf{(5.57)}$$

We must confess to having made an informed guess as to what additional term to add in (5.56) to produce the Fourier transform (5.57). We could instead have chosen $c\delta(k\omega)$ with k a constant as an additional term. While it is possible to show that this would not lead to a different result, proving uniqueness is not trivial and is beyond the scope of this book.

Using the MATLAB commands

```
syms w t
H=sym('Heaviside(t)');
F=fourier(h,t,w)
```

returns

```
F=pi*Dirac(w)-i/w
```

which, noting that $-i = 1/i$, confirms result (5.57).

Likewise the MATLAB commands

```
syms w t T
H=sym('Heaviside(t-T)');
F=fourier(H,t,w)
```

return

```
F=exp(-i*T*w)*(pi*Dirac(w)-i/w)
```

which gives us another Fourier transform

$$\mathscr{F}\{H(t-T)\} = e^{-j\omega T}(\pi\delta(\omega) + 1/j\omega)$$

5.5.2 Convolution

In Section 2.6.6 we saw that the convolution integral, in conjunction with the Laplace transform, provided a useful tool for *discussing* the nature of the solution of a differential equation, although it was not perhaps the most efficient way of evaluating the solution to a particular problem. As the reader may now have come to expect, in view of the duality between time and frequency domains, there are two convolution results involving the Fourier transform.

Convolution in time

Suppose that

$$\mathscr{F}\{u(t)\} = U(\mathrm{j}\omega) = \int_{-\infty}^{\infty} u(t)\,\mathrm{e}^{-\mathrm{j}\omega t}\,\mathrm{d}t$$

$$\mathscr{F}\{v(t)\} = V(\mathrm{j}\omega) = \int_{-\infty}^{\infty} v(t)\,\mathrm{e}^{-\mathrm{j}\omega t}\,\mathrm{d}t$$

then the Fourier transform of the convolution

$$y(t) = \int_{-\infty}^{\infty} u(\tau)v(t-\tau)\,\mathrm{d}\tau = u(t) * v(t) \tag{5.58}$$

is

$$\mathscr{F}\{y(t)\} = Y(\mathrm{j}\omega) = \int_{-\infty}^{\infty} \mathrm{e}^{-\mathrm{j}\omega t}\left[\int_{-\infty}^{\infty} u(\tau)v(t-\tau)\,\mathrm{d}\tau\right]\mathrm{d}t$$

$$= \int_{-\infty}^{\infty} u(\tau)\left[\int_{-\infty}^{\infty} \mathrm{e}^{-\mathrm{j}\omega t}v(t-\tau)\,\mathrm{d}t\right]\mathrm{d}\tau$$

Introducing the change of variables $z \to t - \tau$, $\tau \to \tau$ and following the procedure for change of variable from Section 2.6.6, the transform can be expressed as

$$Y(\mathrm{j}\omega) = \int_{-\infty}^{\infty} u(\tau)\left[\int_{-\infty}^{\infty} v(z)\,\mathrm{e}^{-\mathrm{j}\omega(z+\tau)}\,\mathrm{d}z\right]\mathrm{d}\tau$$

$$= \int_{-\infty}^{\infty} u(\tau)\,\mathrm{e}^{-\mathrm{j}\omega\tau}\,\mathrm{d}\tau \int_{-\infty}^{\infty} v(z)\,\mathrm{e}^{-\mathrm{j}\omega z}\,\mathrm{d}z$$

so that

$$Y(\mathrm{j}\omega) = U(\mathrm{j}\omega)V(\mathrm{j}\omega) \tag{5.59}$$

That is,

$$\mathscr{F}\{u(t) * v(t)\} = \mathscr{F}\{v(t) * u(t)\} = U(\mathrm{j}\omega)V(\mathrm{j}\omega) \tag{5.60}$$

indicating that a convolution in the time domain is transformed into a product in the frequency domain.

Convolution in frequency

If

$$\mathscr{F}\{u(t)\} = U(j\omega), \qquad \text{with} \quad u(t) = \frac{1}{2\pi}\int_{-\infty}^{\infty} U(j\omega)\,e^{j\omega t}\,d\omega$$

$$\mathscr{F}\{v(t)\} = V(j\omega), \qquad \text{with} \quad v(t) = \frac{1}{2\pi}\int_{-\infty}^{\infty} V(j\omega)\,e^{j\omega t}\,d\omega$$

then the inverse transform of the convolution

$$U(j\omega) * V(j\omega) = \int_{-\infty}^{\infty} U(jy)V(j(\omega - y))\,dy$$

is given by

$$\mathscr{F}^{-1}\{U(j\omega) * V(j\omega)\} = \frac{1}{2\pi}\int_{-\infty}^{\infty} e^{j\omega t}\left[\int_{-\infty}^{\infty} U(jy)V(j(\omega - y))\,dy\right]d\omega$$

$$= \frac{1}{2\pi}\int_{-\infty}^{\infty} U(jy)\left[\int_{-\infty}^{\infty} V(j(\omega - y))\,e^{j\omega t}\,d\omega\right]dy$$

A change of variable $z \rightarrow \omega - y$, $\omega \rightarrow \omega$ leads to

$$\mathscr{F}^{-1}\{U(j\omega) * V(j\omega)\} = \frac{1}{2\pi}\int_{-\infty}^{\infty} U(jy)\left[\int_{-\infty}^{\infty} V(jz)\,e^{j(z+y)t}\,dz\right]dy$$

$$= \frac{1}{2\pi}\int_{-\infty}^{\infty} U(jy)\,e^{jyt}\,dy\int_{-\infty}^{\infty} V(jz)\,e^{jzt}\,dz$$

$$= 2\pi\,u(t)v(t)$$

That is,

$$\mathscr{F}\{u(t)v(t)\} = \frac{1}{2\pi}\,U(j\omega) * V(j\omega) \tag{5.61}$$

and thus multiplication in the time domain corresponds to convolution in the frequency domain (subject to the scaling factor $1/(2\pi)$).

Example 5.16

Suppose that $f(t)$ has a Fourier transform $F(j\omega)$. Find an expression for the Fourier transform of $g(t)$, where

$$g(t) = \int_{-\infty}^{t} f(\tau)\,d\tau$$

Solution Since

$$H(t-\tau) = \begin{cases} 1 & (\tau \leqslant t) \\ 0 & (\tau > t) \end{cases}$$

we can write

$$g(t) = \int_{-\infty}^{\infty} f(\tau)H(t-\tau)\,\mathrm{d}\tau = f(t) * H(t)$$

the convolution of $g(t)$ and $H(t)$. Then, using (5.60),

$$\mathscr{F}\{g(t)\} = G(\mathrm{j}\omega) = F(\mathrm{j}\omega)\bar{H}(\mathrm{j}\omega)$$

which, on using the expression for $\bar{H}(\mathrm{j}\omega)$ from (5.57), gives

$$G(\mathrm{j}\omega) = \frac{F(\mathrm{j}\omega)}{\mathrm{j}\omega} + \pi F(\mathrm{j}\omega)\delta(\omega)$$

so that

$$G(\mathrm{j}\omega) = \frac{F(\mathrm{j}\omega)}{\mathrm{j}\omega} + \pi F(0)\delta(\omega) \tag{5.62}$$

5.5.3 Exercises

22 Verify that $\mathscr{F}^{-1}\{\pi[\delta(\omega-\omega_0)+\delta(\omega+\omega_0)]\} = \cos\omega_0 t$.

23 Show that $\mathscr{F}\{\sin\omega_0 t\} = \mathrm{j}\pi[\delta(\omega+\omega_0)-\delta(\omega-\omega_0)]$. Use (5.16) to verify that

$$\mathscr{F}^{-1}\{\mathrm{j}\pi[\delta(\omega+\omega_0)-\delta(\omega-\omega_0)]\} = \sin\omega_0 t$$

24 Suppose that $f(t)$ and $g(t)$ have Fourier transforms $F(\mathrm{j}\omega)$ and $G(\mathrm{j}\omega)$ respectively, defined in the 'ordinary' sense (that is, using (5.15)), and show that

$$\int_{-\infty}^{\infty} f(t)G(\mathrm{j}t)\,\mathrm{d}t = \int_{-\infty}^{\infty} F(\mathrm{j}t)g(t)\,\mathrm{d}t$$

This result is known as **Parseval's formula**.

25 Use the results of Exercise 24 and the symmetry property to show that

$$\int_{-\infty}^{\infty} f(t)g(t)\,\mathrm{d}t = \frac{1}{2\pi}\int_{-\infty}^{\infty} F(\mathrm{j}\omega)G(-\mathrm{j}\omega)\,\mathrm{d}\omega$$

26 Use the convolution result in the frequency domain to obtain $\mathscr{F}\{H(t)\sin\omega_0 t\}$.

27 Calculate the exponential form of the Fourier series for the periodic pulse train shown in Figure 5.20. Hence show that

$$\mathscr{F}\{f(t)\} = \frac{2\pi A d}{T}\sum_{n=-\infty}^{\infty}\operatorname{sinc}\left(\frac{n\pi d}{T}\right)\delta(\omega - n\omega_0)$$

($\omega_0 = 2\pi/T$), and A is the height of the pulse.

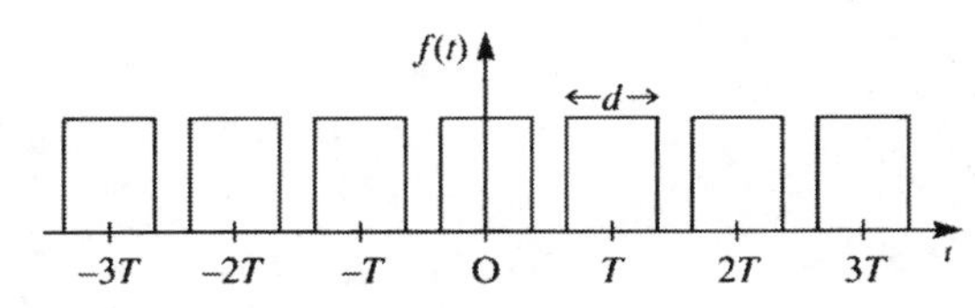

Figure 5.20 Periodic pulse train of Exercise 27.

5.6 The Fourier transform in discrete time

5.6.1 Introduction

The earlier sections of this chapter have discussed the Fourier transform of signals defined as functions of the continuous-time variable t. We have seen that a major area of application is in the analysis of signals in the frequency domain, leading to the concept of the frequency response of a linear system. In Chapter 4 we considered signals defined at discrete-time instants, together with linear systems modelled by difference equations. There we found that in system analysis the z transform plays a role similar to that of the Laplace transform for continuous-time systems. We now attempt to develop a theory of Fourier analysis to complement that for continuous-time systems, and then consider the problem of estimating the continuous-time Fourier transform in a form suitable for computer execution.

5.6.2 A Fourier transform for sequences

First we return to our work on Fourier series and write down the exponential form of the Fourier series representation for the periodic function $F(e^{j\theta})$ of period 2π. Writing $\theta = \omega t$, we infer from (4.57) and (4.61) that

$$F(e^{j\theta}) = \sum_{n=-\infty}^{\infty} f_n e^{jn\theta} \tag{5.63}$$

where

$$f_n = \frac{1}{2\pi}\int_{-\pi}^{\pi} F(e^{j\theta})e^{-jn\theta}\,d\theta \tag{5.64}$$

Thus the operation has generated a sequence of numbers $\{f_n\}$ from the periodic function $F(e^{j\theta})$ of the continuous variable θ. Let us reverse the process and imagine that we *start* with a sequence $\{g_k\}$ and use (5.63) to *define* a periodic function $\tilde{G}'(e^{j\theta})$ such that

$$\tilde{G}'(e^{j\theta}) = \sum_{n=-\infty}^{\infty} g_n e^{jn\theta} \tag{5.65}$$

We have thus defined a transformation from the sequence $\{g_k\}$ to $\tilde{G}'(e^{j\theta})$. This transformation can be inverted, since, from (5.64),

$$g_k = \frac{1}{2\pi}\int_{-\pi}^{\pi} \tilde{G}'(e^{j\theta})e^{-jk\theta}\,d\theta \tag{5.66}$$

and we recover the terms of the sequence $\{g_k\}$ from $\tilde{G}'(e^{j\theta})$.

It is convenient for our later work if we modify the definition slightly, defining the Fourier transform of the sequence $\{g_k\}$ as

$$\mathcal{F}\{g_k\} = G(e^{j\theta}) = \sum_{n=-\infty}^{\infty} g_n e^{-jn\theta} \tag{5.67}$$

whenever the series converges. The inverse transform is then given from (5.66), by

$$g_k = \frac{1}{2\pi}\int_{-\pi}^{\pi} G(e^{j\theta})\,e^{jk\theta}\,d\theta \tag{5.68}$$

The results (5.67) and (5.68) thus constitute the Fourier transform pair for the sequence $\{g_k\}$. Note that $G(e^{j\theta})$ is a function of the continuous variable θ, and since it is a function of $e^{j\theta}$ it is periodic (with a period of at most 2π), irrespective of whether or not the sequence $\{g_k\}$ is periodic.

Note that we have adopted the notation $G(e^{j\theta})$ rather than $G(\theta)$ for the Fourier transform, similar to our use of $F(j\omega)$ rather than $F(\omega)$ in the case of continuous-time signals. In the present case we shall be concerned with the relationship with the z transform of Chapter 3, where $z = r\,e^{j\theta}$, and the significance of our choice will soon emerge.

Example 5.17

Find the transform of the sequence $\{g_k\}_{-\infty}^{\infty}$, where $g_0 = 2$, $g_2 = g_{-2} = 1$ and $g_k = g_{-k} = 0$ for $k \neq 0$ or 2.

Solution

From the definition (5.67),

$$\mathscr{F}\{g_k\} = G(e^{j\theta}) = \sum_{n=-\infty}^{\infty} g_n\,e^{-jn\theta}$$

$$= g_{-2}\,e^{j2\theta} + g_0 1 + g_2\,e^{-j2\theta} = e^{j2\theta} + 2 + e^{-j2\theta}$$

$$= 2(1 + \cos 2\theta) = 4\cos^2\theta$$

In this particular case the transform is periodic of period π, rather than 2π. This is because $g_1 = g_{-1} = 0$, so that $\cos\theta$ does not appear in the transform. Since $G(e^{j\theta})$ is purely real, we may plot the transform as in Figure 5.21.

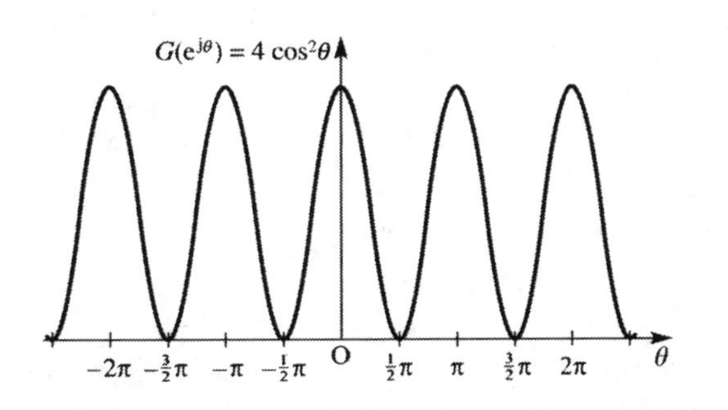

Figure 5.21 Transform of the sequence of Example 5.17.

Having defined a Fourier transform for sequences, we now wish to link it to the frequency response of discrete-time systems. In Section 5.4.2 the link between frequency responses and the Fourier transforms of continuous-time systems was established using the Laplace transform. We suspect therefore that the z transform should yield the necessary link for discrete-time systems. Indeed, the argument follows closely that of Section 5.4.2.

For a causal linear time-invariant discrete-time system with z transfer function $G(z)$ the relationship between the input sequence $\{u_k\}$ and output sequence $\{y_k\}$ in the transform domain is given from Section 3.6.1 by

$$Y(z) = G(z)U(z) \tag{5.69}$$

where $U(z) = \mathscr{Z}\{u_k\}$ and $Y(z) = \mathscr{Z}\{y_k\}$.

To investigate the system frequency response, we seek the output sequence corresponding to an input sequence

$$\{u_k\} = \{A\,\mathrm{e}^{\mathrm{j}\omega kT}\} = \{A\,\mathrm{e}^{\mathrm{j}k\theta}\}, \quad \theta = \omega T \tag{5.70}$$

which represents samples drawn, at equal intervals T, from the continuous-time complex sinusoidal signal $\mathrm{e}^{\mathrm{j}\omega t}$.

The frequency response of the discrete-time system is then its steady-state response to the sequence $\{u_k\}$ given in (5.70). As for the continuous-time case (Section 5.4.2), the complex form $\mathrm{e}^{\mathrm{j}\omega t}$ is used in order to simplify the algebra, and the steady-state sinusoidal response is easily recovered by taking imaginary parts, if necessary.

From Figure 3.3, we see that

$$\mathscr{Z}\{A\,\mathrm{e}^{\mathrm{j}k\theta}\} = \mathscr{Z}\{A(\mathrm{e}^{\mathrm{j}\theta})^k\} = \frac{Az}{z - \mathrm{e}^{\mathrm{j}\theta}}$$

so, from (5.69), the response of the system to the input sequence (5.70) is determined by

$$Y(z) = G(z)\frac{Az}{z - \mathrm{e}^{\mathrm{j}\theta}} \tag{5.71}$$

Taking the system to be of order n, and under the assumption that the n poles p_r $(r = 1, 2, \dots, n)$ of $G(z)$ are distinct and none is equal to $\mathrm{e}^{\mathrm{j}\theta}$, we can expand $Y(z)/z$ in terms of partial fractions to give

$$\frac{Y(z)}{z} = \frac{c}{z - \mathrm{e}^{\mathrm{j}\theta}} + \sum_{r=1}^{n} \frac{c_r}{z - p_r} \tag{5.72}$$

where, in general, the constants c_r $(r = 1, 2, \dots, n)$ are complex. Taking inverse z transforms throughout in (5.72) then gives the response sequence as

$$\{y_k\} = \mathscr{Z}^{-1}\{Y(z)\} = \mathscr{Z}^{-1}\left\{\frac{zc}{z - \mathrm{e}^{\mathrm{j}\theta}}\right\} + \sum_{r=1}^{n} \mathscr{Z}^{-1}\left\{\frac{zc_r}{z - p_r}\right\}$$

that is,

$$\{y_k\} = c\{\mathrm{e}^{\mathrm{j}k\theta}\} + \sum_{r=1}^{n} c_r\{p_r^k\} \tag{5.73}$$

If the transfer function $G(z)$ corresponds to a stable discrete-time system then all its poles p_r $(r = 1, 2, \dots, n)$ lie within the unit circle $|z| < 1$, so that all the terms under the summation sign in (5.73) tend to zero as $k \to \infty$. This is clearly seen by expressing p_r in the form $p_r = |p_r|\,\mathrm{e}^{\mathrm{j}\phi_r}$ and noting that if $|p_r| < 1$ then $|p_r|^k \to 0$ as $k \to \infty$. Consequently, for stable systems the steady-state response corresponding to (5.73) is

$$\{y_{k_{\mathrm{ss}}}\} = c\{\mathrm{e}^{\mathrm{j}k\theta}\}$$

Using the 'cover-up' rule for partial fractions, the constant c is readily determined from (5.71) as

$$c = AG(e^{j\theta})$$

so that the steady-state response becomes

$$\{y_{k_{ss}}\} = AG(e^{j\theta})\{e^{jk\theta}\} \tag{5.74}$$

We have assumed that the poles of $G(z)$ are distinct in order to simplify the algebra. Extending the development to accommodate multiple poles is readily accomplished, leading to the same steady-state response as given in (5.74).

The result (5.74) corresponds to (5.38) for continuous-time systems, and indicates that the steady-state response sequence is simply the input sequence with each term multiplied by $G(e^{j\theta})$. Consequently $G(e^{j\theta})$ is called the **frequency transfer function** of the discrete-time system and, as for the continuous case, it characterizes the system's frequency response. Clearly $G(e^{j\theta})$ is simply $G(z)$, the z transfer function, with $z = e^{j\theta}$, and so we are simply evaluating the z transfer function around the unit circle $|z| = 1$. The z transfer function $G(z)$ will exist on $|z| = 1$ if and only if the system is stable, and thus the result is the exact analogue of the result for continuous-time systems in Section 5.4.2, where the Laplace transfer function was evaluated along the imaginary axis to yield the frequency response of a stable linear continuous-time system.

To complete the analogy with continuous-time systems, we need one further result. From Section 3.6.2, the impulse response of the linear causal discrete-time system with z transfer function $G(z)$ is

$$\{y_{k_\delta}\} = \mathscr{Z}^{-1}\{G(z)\} = \{g_k\}_{k=0}^{\infty}, \quad \text{say}$$

Taking inverse transforms then gives

$$G(z) = \sum_{k=0}^{\infty} g_k z^{-k} = \sum_{k=-\infty}^{\infty} g_k z^{-k}$$

since $g_k = 0$ $(k < 0)$ for a causal system. Thus

$$G(e^{j\theta}) = \sum_{k=-\infty}^{\infty} g_k e^{-jk\theta}$$

and we conclude from (5.67) that $G(e^{j\theta})$ is simply the Fourier transform of the sequence $\{g_k\}$. Therefore the discrete-time frequency transfer function $G(e^{j\theta})$ is the Fourier transform of the impulse response sequence.

Example 5.18

Determine the frequency transfer function of the causal discrete-time system shown in Figure 5.22 and plot its amplitude spectrum.

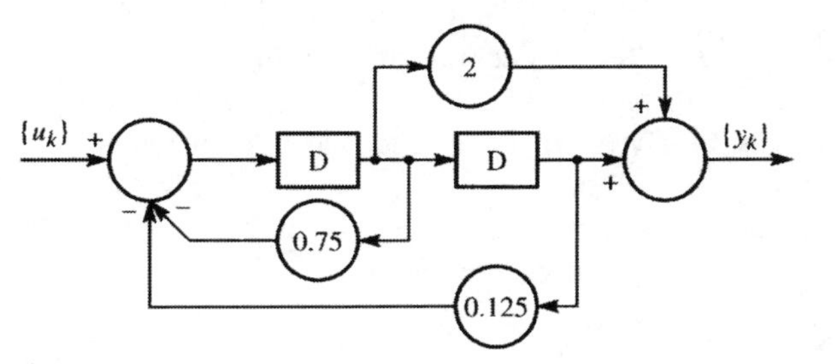

Figure 5.22 Discrete-time system of Example 5.18.

Solution Using the methods of Section 3.6.1, we readily obtain the z transfer function as

$$G(z) = \frac{2z + 1}{z^2 + 0.75z + 0.125}$$

Next we check for system stability. Since $z^2 + 0.75z + 0.125 = (z + 0.5)(z + 0.25)$, the poles of $G(z)$ are at $p_1 = -0.5$ and $p_2 = -0.25$, and since both are inside the unit circle $|z| = 1$, the system is stable. The frequency transfer function may then be obtained as $G(\mathrm{e}^{\mathrm{j}\theta})$, where

$$G(\mathrm{e}^{\mathrm{j}\theta}) = \frac{2\,\mathrm{e}^{\mathrm{j}\theta} + 1}{\mathrm{e}^{\mathrm{j}2\theta} + 0.75\,\mathrm{e}^{\mathrm{j}\theta} + 0.125}$$

To determine the amplitude spectrum, we evaluate $|G(\mathrm{e}^{\mathrm{j}\theta})|$ as

$$|G(\mathrm{e}^{\mathrm{j}\theta})| = \frac{|2\,\mathrm{e}^{\mathrm{j}\theta} + 1|}{|\mathrm{e}^{\mathrm{j}2\theta} + 0.75\,\mathrm{e}^{\mathrm{j}\theta} + 0.125|}$$

$$= \frac{\sqrt{(5 + 4\cos\theta)}}{\sqrt{(1.578 + 1.688\cos\theta + 0.25\cos 2\theta)}}$$

A plot of $|G(\mathrm{e}^{\mathrm{j}\theta})|$ versus θ then leads to the amplitude spectrum of Figure 5.23.

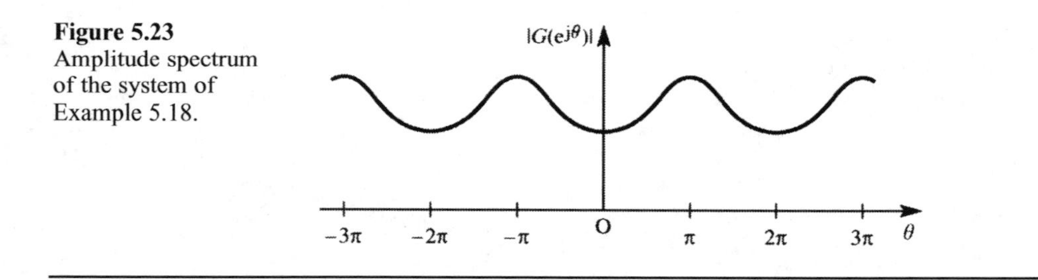

Figure 5.23 Amplitude spectrum of the system of Example 5.18.

In Example 5.18 we note the periodic behaviour of the amplitude spectrum, which is inescapable when discrete-time signals and systems are concerned. Note, however, that the periodicity is in the variable $\theta = \omega T$ and that we may have control over the choice of T, the time between samples of our input signal.

5.6.3 The discrete Fourier transform

The Fourier transform of sequences discussed in Section 5.6.2 transforms a sequence $\{g_k\}$ into a continuous function $G(\mathrm{e}^{\mathrm{j}\theta})$ of a frequency variable θ, where $\theta = \omega T$ and T is the time between signal samples. In this section, with an eye to computer requirements, we look at the implications of sampling $G(\mathrm{e}^{\mathrm{j}\theta})$. The overall operation will have commenced with samples of a time signal $\{g_k\}$ and proceeded via a Fourier transformation process, finally producing a sequence $\{G_k\}$ of samples drawn from the frequency-domain image $G(\mathrm{e}^{\mathrm{j}\theta})$ of $\{g_k\}$.

Suppose that we have a sequence $\{g_k\}$ of N samples drawn from a continuous-time signal $g(t)$, at equal intervals T; that is,

$$\{g_k\} = \{g(kT)\}_{k=0}^{N-1}$$

Using (5.67), the Fourier transform of this sequence is

$$\mathscr{F}\{g_k\} = G(e^{j\theta}) = \sum_{n=-\infty}^{\infty} g_n e^{-jn\theta} \tag{5.75}$$

where $g_k = 0$ ($k \notin [0, N-1]$). Then, with $\theta = \omega T$, we may write (5.75) as

$$G(e^{j\omega T}) = \sum_{n=0}^{N-1} g_n e^{-jn\omega T} \tag{5.76}$$

We now sample this transform $G(e^{j\omega T})$ at intervals $\Delta\omega$ in such a way as to create N samples spread equally over the interval $0 \leqslant \theta \leqslant 2\pi$; that is, over one period of the essentially periodic function $G(e^{j\theta})$. We then have

$$N\Delta\theta = 2\pi$$

where $\Delta\theta$ is the normalized frequency spacing. Since $\theta = \omega T$ and T is a constant such that $\Delta\theta = T\Delta\omega$, we deduce that

$$\Delta\omega = \frac{2\pi}{NT} \tag{5.77}$$

Sampling (5.76) at intervals $\Delta\omega$ produces the sequence

$$\{G_k\}_{k=0}^{N-1}, \quad \text{where} \quad G_k = \sum_{n=0}^{N-1} g_n e^{-jnk\Delta\omega T} \tag{5.78}$$

Since

$$\begin{aligned} G_{k+N} &= \sum_{n=0}^{N-1} g_n e^{-jn(k+N)\Delta\omega T} \\ &= \sum_{n=0}^{N-1} g_n e^{-jnk\Delta\omega T} e^{-jn2\pi}, \quad \text{using (5.77)} \\ &= \sum_{n=0}^{N-1} g_n e^{-jnk\Delta\omega T} = G_k \end{aligned}$$

it follows that the sequence $\{G_k\}_{-\infty}^{\infty}$ is periodic, with period N. We have therefore generated a sequence of samples in the frequency domain that in some sense represents the spectrum of the underlying continuous-time signal. We shall postpone the question of the exact nature of this representation for the moment, but as the reader will have guessed, it is crucial to the purpose of this section. First, we consider the question of whether, from knowledge of the sequence $\{G_k\}_{k=0}^{N-1}$ of (5.78), we can recover the original sequence $\{g_n\}_{n=0}^{N-1}$. To see how this can be achieved, consider a sum of the form

$$S_r = \sum_{k=0}^{N-1} G_k e^{-jkr\Delta\omega T}, \quad (N-1) \leqslant r \leqslant 0 \tag{5.79}$$

Substituting for G_k from (5.78), we have

$$S_r = \sum_{k=0}^{N-1}\left(\sum_{m=0}^{N-1} g_m e^{-jmk\Delta\omega T}\right)e^{-jkr\Delta\omega T} = \sum_{k=0}^{N-1}\sum_{m=0}^{N-1} g_m e^{-jk\Delta\omega(m+r)T}$$

That is, on interchanging the order of integration,

$$S_r = \sum_{m=0}^{N-1} g_m \sum_{k=0}^{N-1} e^{-jk\Delta\omega(m+r)T} \tag{5.80}$$

Now

$$\sum_{k=0}^{N-1} e^{-jk\Delta\omega(m+r)T}$$

is a geometric progression with first term $e^0 = 1$ and common ratio $e^{-j\Delta\omega(m+r)T}$, and so the sum to N terms is thus

$$\sum_{k=0}^{N-1} e^{-jk\Delta\omega(m+r)T} = \frac{1 - e^{-j\Delta\omega(m+r)NT}}{1 - e^{-j\Delta\omega(m+r)T}} = \frac{1 - e^{-j(m+r)2\pi}}{1 - e^{-j\Delta\omega(m+r)T}} = 0 \quad (m \neq -r + nN)$$

When $m = -r$

$$\sum_{k=0}^{N-1} e^{-jk\Delta\omega(m+r)T} = \sum_{k=0}^{N-1} 1 = N$$

Thus

$$\sum_{k=0}^{N-1} e^{-jk\Delta\omega(m+r)T} = N\delta_{m,-r} \tag{5.81}$$

where δ_{ij} is the Kronecker delta defined by

$$\delta_{ij} = \begin{cases} 1 & (i = j) \\ 0 & (i \neq j) \end{cases}$$

Substituting (5.81) into (5.80), we have

$$S_r = N\sum_{m=0}^{N-1} g_m \delta_{m,-r} = Ng_{-r}$$

Returning to (5.79) and substituting for S_r we see that

$$g_{-r} = \frac{1}{N}\sum_{k=0}^{N-1} G_k e^{-jkr\Delta\omega T}$$

which on taking $n = -r$ gives

$$g_n = \frac{1}{N}\sum_{k=0}^{N-1} G_k e^{jkn\Delta\omega T} \tag{5.82}$$

Thus (5.82) allows us to determine the members of the sequence

$$\{g_n\}_{n=0}^{N-1}$$

that is, it enables us to recover the time-domain samples from the frequency-domain samples *exactly*.

The relations

$$G_k = \sum_{n=0}^{N-1} g_n \mathrm{e}^{-\mathrm{j}nk\Delta\omega T} \quad \textbf{(5.78)}$$

$$g_n = \frac{1}{N}\sum_{k=0}^{N-1} G_k \mathrm{e}^{\mathrm{j}nk\Delta\omega T} \quad \textbf{(5.82)}$$

with $\Delta\omega = 2\pi/NT$, between the time- and frequency-domain sequences $\{g_n\}_{n=0}^{N-1}$ and $\{G_k\}_{k=0}^{N-1}$ define the **discrete Fourier transform (DFT)** pair. The pair provide pathways between time and frequency domains for discrete-time signals in exactly the same sense that (5.15) and (5.16) defined similar pathways for continuous-time signals. It should be stressed again that, whatever the properties of the sequences $\{g_n\}$ and $\{G_k\}$ on the right-hand sides of (5.78) and (5.82), the sequences generated on the left-hand sides will be periodic, with period N.

Example 5.19

The sequence $\{g_k\}_{k=0}^{2} = \{1, 2, 1\}$ is generated by sampling a time signal $g(t)$ at intervals with $T = 1$. Determine the discrete Fourier transform of the sequence, and verify that the sequence can be recovered exactly from its transform.

Solution

From (5.78), the discrete Fourier transform sequence $\{G_k\}_{k=0}^{2}$ is generated by

$$G_k = \sum_{n=0}^{2} g_n \mathrm{e}^{-\mathrm{j}kn\Delta\omega T} \quad (k = 0, 1, 2)$$

In this case $T = 1$ and, with $N = 3$, (5.77) gives

$$\Delta\omega = \frac{2\pi}{3\times 1} = \tfrac{2}{3}\pi$$

Thus

$$G_0 = \sum_{n=0}^{2} g_n \mathrm{e}^{-\mathrm{j}n\times 0\times 2\pi/3} = \sum_{n=0}^{2} g_n = g_0 + g_1 + g_2 = 1 + 2 + 1 = 4$$

$$G_1 = \sum_{n=0}^{2} g_n \mathrm{e}^{-\mathrm{j}n\times 1\times 2\pi/3} = g_0\mathrm{e}^0 + g_1\mathrm{e}^{-\mathrm{j}2\pi/3} + g_2\mathrm{e}^{-\mathrm{j}4\pi/3} = 1 + 2\mathrm{e}^{-\mathrm{j}2\pi/3} + 1\,\mathrm{e}^{-\mathrm{j}4\pi/3}$$

$$= \mathrm{e}^{-\mathrm{j}2\pi/3}(\mathrm{e}^{\mathrm{j}2\pi/3} + 2 + \mathrm{e}^{-\mathrm{j}2\pi/3}) = 2\,\mathrm{e}^{-\mathrm{j}2\pi/3}(1 + \cos\tfrac{2}{3}\pi) = \mathrm{e}^{-\mathrm{j}2\pi/3}$$

$$G_2 = \sum_{n=0}^{2} g_n \mathrm{e}^{-\mathrm{j}n\times 2\times 2\pi/3} = \sum_{n=0}^{2} g_n \mathrm{e}^{-\mathrm{j}n4\pi/3} = g_0\mathrm{e}^0 + g_1\mathrm{e}^{-\mathrm{j}4\pi/3} + g_2\mathrm{e}^{-\mathrm{j}8\pi/3}$$

$$= \mathrm{e}^{-\mathrm{j}4\pi/3}[\mathrm{e}^{\mathrm{j}4\pi/3} + 2 + \mathrm{e}^{-\mathrm{j}4\pi/3}] = 2\,\mathrm{e}^{-\mathrm{j}4\pi/3}(1 + \cos\tfrac{4}{3}\pi) = \mathrm{e}^{-\mathrm{j}4\pi/3}$$

Thus

$$\{G_k\}_{k=0}^{2} = \{4, \mathrm{e}^{-\mathrm{j}2\pi/3}, \mathrm{e}^{-\mathrm{j}4\pi/3}\}$$

We must now show that use of (5.82) will recover the original sequence $\{g_k\}_{k=0}^{2}$. From (5.82), the inverse transform of $\{G_k\}_{k=0}^{2}$ is given by

$$\tilde{g}_n = \frac{1}{N}\sum_{k=0}^{N-1} G_k \, e^{jkn\Delta\omega T}$$

again with $T = 1$, $\Delta\omega = \frac{2}{3}\pi$ and $N = 3$. Thus

$$\tilde{g}_0 = \tfrac{1}{3}\sum_{k=0}^{2} G_k \, e^{jk\times 0\times 2\pi/3} = \tfrac{1}{3}\sum_{k=0}^{2} G_k = \tfrac{1}{3}\,(4 + e^{-j2\pi/3} + e^{-j4\pi/3})$$

$$= \tfrac{1}{3}\,[4 + e^{-j\pi}(e^{j\pi/3} + e^{-j\pi/3})] = \tfrac{1}{3}\,(4 - 2\cos\tfrac{1}{3}\pi) = 1$$

$$\tilde{g}_1 = \tfrac{1}{3}\sum_{k=0}^{2} G_k \, e^{jk\times 1\times 2\pi/3} = \tfrac{1}{3}\,(G_0 + G_1 \, e^{j2\pi/3} + G_2 \, e^{j4\pi/3})$$

$$= \tfrac{1}{3}\,(4 + 1 + 1) = 2$$

$$\tilde{g}_2 = \tfrac{1}{3}\sum_{k=0}^{2} G_k \, e^{jk\times 2\times 2\pi/3} = \tfrac{1}{3}\,(G_0 + G_1 \, e^{j4\pi/3} + G_2 \, e^{j8\pi/3})$$

$$= \tfrac{1}{3}\,[4 + e^{j\pi}(e^{j\pi/3} + e^{-j\pi/3})] = \tfrac{1}{3}\,(4 - 2\cos\tfrac{1}{3}\pi) = 1$$

That is

$$\{\tilde{g}_n\}_{n=0}^{2} = \{1, 2, 1\} = \{g_k\}_{k=0}^{2}$$

and thus the original sequence has been recovered exactly from its transform.

We see from Example 5.19 that the operation of calculating N terms of the transformed sequence involved $N \times N = N^2$ multiplications and $N(N - 1)$ summations, all of which are operations involving complex numbers in general. The computation of the discrete Fourier transform in this direct manner is thus said to be a computation of complexity N^2. Such computations rapidly become impossible as N increases, owing to the time required for this execution.

5.6.4 Estimation of the continuous Fourier transform

We saw in Section 5.4.2 that the continuous Fourier transform provides a means of examining the frequency response of a stable linear time-invariant *continuous*-time system. Similarly, we saw in Section 5.6.2 how a discrete-time Fourier transform could be developed that allows examination of the frequency response of a stable linear time-invariant *discrete*-time system. By sampling this latter transform, we developed the discrete Fourier transform itself. Why did we do this? First we have found a way (at least in theory) of involving the computer in our efforts. Secondly, as we shall now show, we can use the discrete Fourier transform to estimate the continuous Fourier transform of a continuous-time signal. To see how this is done, let us first examine what happens when we sample a continuous-time signal.

Suppose that $f(t)$ is a non-periodic continuous-time signal, a portion of which is shown in Figure 5.24(a). Let us sample the signal at equal intervals T, to generate the sequence

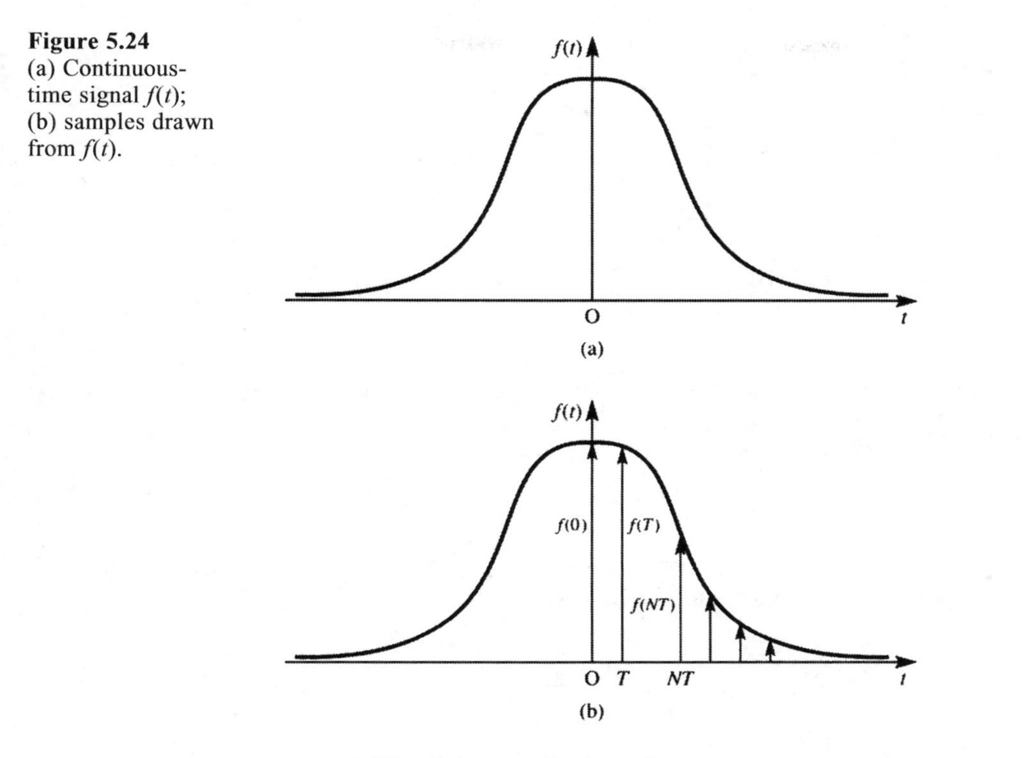

Figure 5.24
(a) Continuous-time signal $f(t)$;
(b) samples drawn from $f(t)$.

$$\{f(0), f(T), \dots, f(nT), \dots\}$$

as shown in Figure 5.24(b). Imagine now that each of these samples is presented in turn, at the appropriate instant, as the input to a continuous linear time-invariant system with impulse response $h(t)$. The output would then be, from Section 2.6.6,

$$\begin{aligned} y(t) &= \int_{-\infty}^{\infty} h(t-\tau)f(0)\delta(\tau)\,\mathrm{d}\tau + \int_{-\infty}^{\infty} h(t-\tau)f(\tau)\delta(\tau - T)\,\mathrm{d}\tau \\ &\quad + \dots + \int_{-\infty}^{\infty} h(t-\tau)f(nT)\delta(\tau - nT)\,\mathrm{d}\tau + \dots \\ &= \int_{-\infty}^{\infty} h(t-\tau)\sum_{k=0}^{\infty} f(kT)\delta(\tau - kT)\,\mathrm{d}\tau \end{aligned}$$

Thus

$$y(t) = \int_{-\infty}^{\infty} h(t-\tau)f_s(\tau)\,\mathrm{d}\tau \tag{5.83}$$

where

$$f_s(t) = \sum_{k=0}^{\infty} f(kT)\delta(t - kT) = f(t)\sum_{k=0}^{\infty}\delta(t - kT) \tag{5.84}$$

which we identify as a 'continuous-time' representation of the sampled version of $f(t)$. We are thus led to picture $f_s(t)$ as in Figure 5.25.

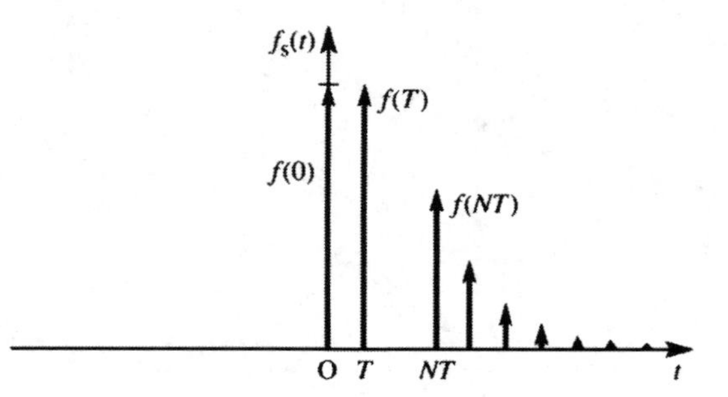

Figure 5.25
Visualization of $f_s(t)$ defined in (5.84).

In order to admit the possibility of signals that are non-zero for $t < 0$, we can generalize (5.84) slightly by allowing in general that

$$f_s(t) = f(t) \sum_{k=-\infty}^{\infty} \delta(t - kT) \tag{5.85}$$

We can now use convolution to find the Fourier transform $F_s(j\omega)$ of $f_s(t)$. Using the representation (5.85) for $f_s(t)$, we have

$$F_s(j\omega) = \mathscr{F}\{f_s(t)\} = \mathscr{F}\left\{f(t) \sum_{k=-\infty}^{\infty} \delta(t - kT)\right\}$$

which, on using (5.61), leads to

$$F_s(j\omega) = \frac{1}{2\pi} F(j\omega) * \mathscr{F}\left\{\sum_{k=-\infty}^{\infty} \delta(t - kT)\right\} \tag{5.86}$$

where

$$\mathscr{F}\{f(\mathrm{t})\} = F(j\omega)$$

From (5.54),

$$\mathscr{F}\left\{\sum_{k=-\infty}^{\infty} \delta(t - kT)\right\} = \frac{2\pi}{T} \sum_{k=-\infty}^{\infty} \delta\left(\omega - \frac{2\pi k}{T}\right)$$

so that, assuming the interchange of the order of integration and summation to be possible, (5.86) becomes

$$\begin{aligned}
F_s(j\omega) &= \frac{1}{2\pi} F(j\omega) * \frac{2\pi}{T} \sum_{k=-\infty}^{\infty} \delta\left(\omega - \frac{2\pi k}{T}\right) \\
&= \frac{1}{T} \int_{-\infty}^{\infty} F(j[\omega - \omega']) \sum_{k=-\infty}^{\infty} \delta\left(\omega' - \frac{2\pi k}{T}\right) d\omega' \\
&= \frac{1}{T} \sum_{k=-\infty}^{\infty} \int_{-\infty}^{\infty} F(j[\omega - \omega']) \delta\left(\omega' - \frac{2\pi k}{T}\right) d\omega' \\
&= \frac{1}{T} \sum_{k=-\infty}^{\infty} F\left(j\left(\omega - \frac{2\pi k}{T}\right)\right)
\end{aligned}$$

Thus

$$F_s(j\omega) = \frac{1}{T}\sum_{k=-\infty}^{\infty} F(j[\omega - k\omega_0]), \quad \omega_0 = \frac{2\pi}{T} \tag{5.87}$$

Examining (5.87), we see that the spectrum $F_s(j\omega)$ of the sampled version $f_s(t)$ of $f(t)$ consists of repeats of the spectrum $F(j\omega)$ of $f(t)$ scaled by a factor $1/T$, these repeats being spaced at intervals $\omega_0 = 2\pi/T$ apart. Figure 5.26(a) shows the amplitude spectrum

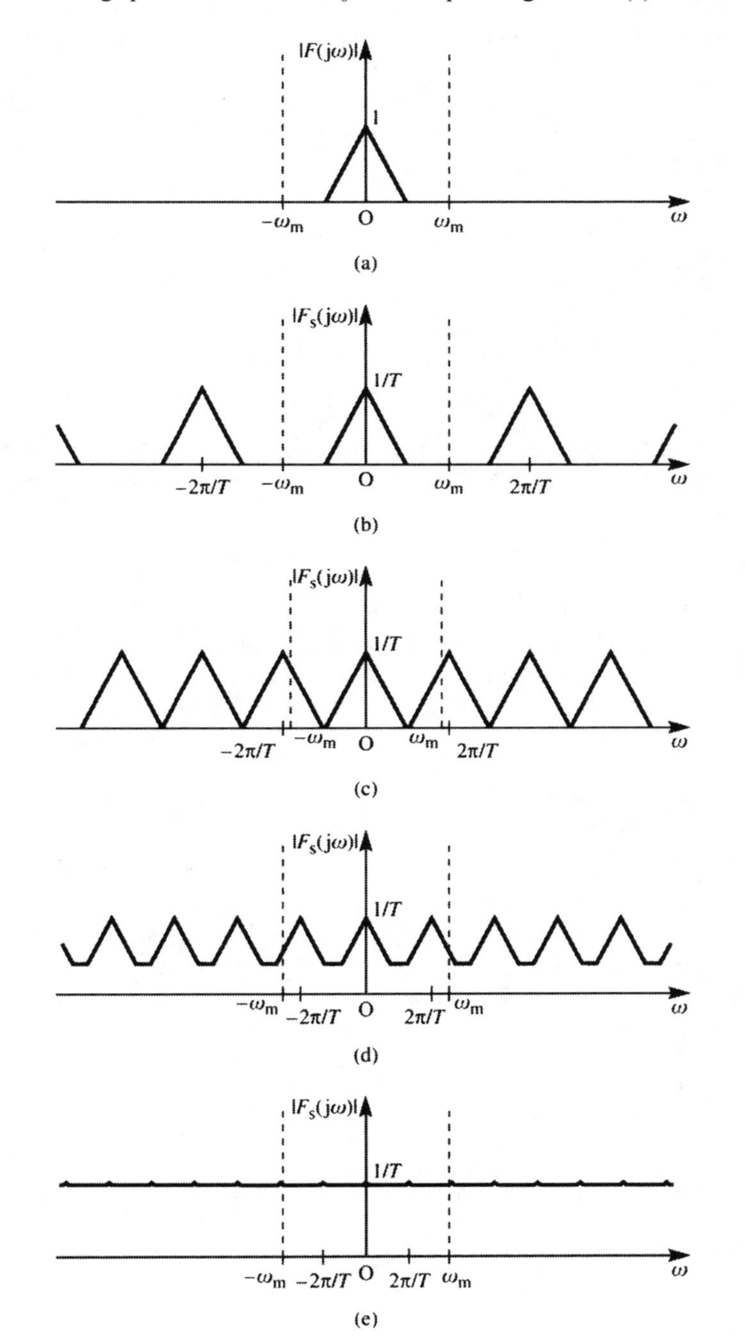

Figure 5.26 (a) Amplitude spectrum of a band-limited signal $f(t)$; (b)–(e) amplitude spectrum $|F_s(j\omega)|$ of $f_s(t)$, showing periodic repetition of $|F_s(j\omega)|$ and interaction effects as T increases.

$|F(j\omega)|$ of a band-limited signal $f(t)$; that is, a signal whose spectrum is zero for $|\omega| > \omega_m$. Figures 5.26(b–e) show the amplitude spectrum $|F_s(j\omega)|$ of the sampled version for increasing values of the sampling interval T. Clearly, as T increases, the spectrum of $F(j\omega)$, as observed using $|F_s(j\omega)|$ in $-\omega_m < \omega < \omega_m$, becomes more and more misleading because of 'interaction' from neighbouring copies.

As we saw in Section 5.6.2, the periodicity in the amplitude spectrum $|F_s(j\omega)|$ of $f_s(t)$ is inevitable as a consequence of the sampling process, and ways have to be found to minimize the problems it causes. The interaction observed in Figure 5.26 between the periodic repeats is known as **aliasing error**, and it is clearly essential to minimize this effect. This can be achieved in an obvious way if the original unsampled signal $f(t)$ is band-limited as in Figure 5.26(a). It is apparent that we must arrange that the periodic repeats of $|F(j\omega)|$ be far enough apart to prevent interaction between the copies. This implies that we have

$$\omega_0 \geqslant 2\omega_m$$

at an absolute (and impractical!) minimum. Since $\omega_0 = 2\pi/T$, the constraint implies that

$$T \leqslant \pi/\omega_m$$

where T is the interval between samples. The minimum time interval allowed is

$$T_{min} = \pi/\omega_m$$

which is known as the **Nyquist interval** and we have in fact deduced a form of the **Nyquist–Shannon sampling theorem**. If $T < T_{min}$ then the 'copies' of $F(j\omega)$ are isolated from each other, and we can focus on just one copy, either for the purpose of signal reconstruction, or for the purposes of the estimation of $F(j\omega)$ itself. Here we are concerned only with the latter problem. Basically, we have established a condition under which the spectrum of the samples of the band-limited signal $f(t)$, that is the spectrum of $f_s(t)$, can be used to estimate $F(j\omega)$.

Suppose we have drawn N samples from a continuous signal $f(t)$ at intervals T, in accordance with the Nyquist criterion, as in Figure 5.27. We then consider

$$f_s(t) = \sum_{k=0}^{N-1} f(kT)\delta(t - kT)$$

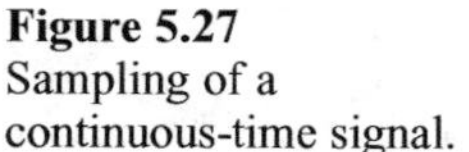

Figure 5.27
Sampling of a continuous-time signal.

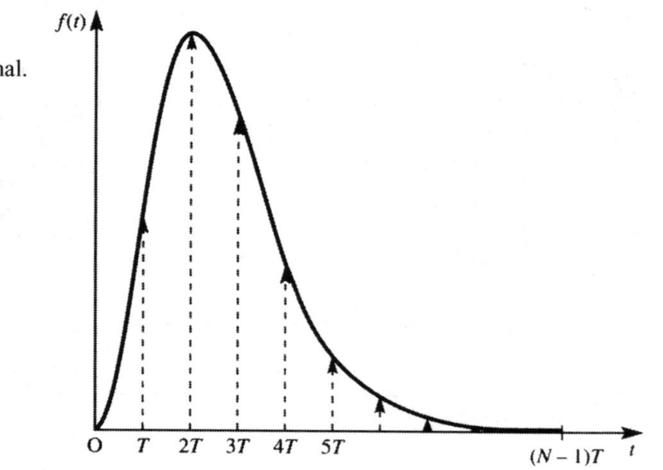

or equivalently, the sequence

$$\{f_k\}_{k=0}^{N-1}, \quad \text{where} \quad f_k = f(kT)$$

Note that

$$f_s(t) = 0 \quad (t > (N-1)T)$$

so that

$$f_k = 0 \quad (k > N-1)$$

The Fourier transform of $f_s(t)$ is

$$F_s(j\omega) = \int_{-\infty}^{\infty} f_s(t)\,e^{-j\omega t}\,dt = \int_{-\infty}^{\infty} \sum_{k=0}^{N-1} f(kT)\delta(t-kT)\,e^{-j\omega t}\,dt$$

$$= \sum_{k=0}^{N-1} \int_{-\infty}^{\infty} f(kT)\delta(t-kT)\,e^{-j\omega t}\,dt$$

$$= \sum_{k=0}^{N-1} f(kT)\,e^{-j\omega kT} = \sum_{k=0}^{N-1} f_k\,e^{-j\omega kT} \tag{5.88}$$

The transform in (5.88) is a function of the continuous variable ω, so, as in (5.78), we must now sample the continuous spectrum $F_s(j\omega)$ to permit computer evaluation.

We chose N samples to represent $f(t)$ in the time domain, and for this reason we also choose N samples in the frequency domain to represent $F(j\omega)$. Thus we sample (5.88) at intervals $\Delta\omega$, to generate the sequence

$$\{F_s(jn\,\Delta\omega)\}_{n=0}^{N-1} \tag{5.89a}$$

where

$$F_s(jn\,\Delta\omega) = \sum_{k=0}^{N-1} f_k\,e^{-jkn\,\Delta\omega\,T} \tag{5.89b}$$

We must now choose the frequency-domain sampling interval $\Delta\omega$. To see how to do this, recall that the sampled spectrum $F_s(j\omega)$ consisted of repeats of $F(j\omega)$, spaced at intervals $2\pi/T$ apart. Thus to sample just one copy in its entirety, we should choose

$$N\Delta\omega = 2\pi/T$$

or

$$\Delta\omega = 2\pi/NT \tag{5.90}$$

Note that the resulting sequence, defined outside $0 \leqslant n \leqslant N-1$, is periodic, as we should expect. However, note also that, following our discussion in Section 5.6, the process of recovering a time signal from samples of its spectrum will result in a periodic waveform, whatever the nature of the original time signal. We should not be surprised by this, since it is exactly in accordance with our introductory discussion in Section 5.1.

In view of the scaling factor $1/T$ in (5.87), our estimate of the Fourier transform $F(j\omega)$ of $f(t)$ over the interval

$$0 \leqslant t \leqslant (N-1)T$$

will, from (5.89), be the sequence of samples

$$\{TF_s(jn\Delta\omega)\}_{n=0}^{N-1}$$

where

$$TF_s(jn\Delta\omega) = T\sum_{k=0}^{N-1} f_k\, e^{-jkn\Delta\omega T}$$

which, from the definition of the discrete Fourier transform in (5.78), gives

$$TF_s(jn\Delta\omega) = T \times \text{DFT}\,\{f_k\}$$

where DFT $\{f_k\}$ is the discrete Fourier transform of the sequence $\{f_k\}$. We illustrate the use of this estimate in Example 5.20.

Example 5.20

The delayed triangular pulse $f(t)$ is as illustrated in Figure 5.28. Estimate its Fourier transform using 10 samples and compare with the exact values.

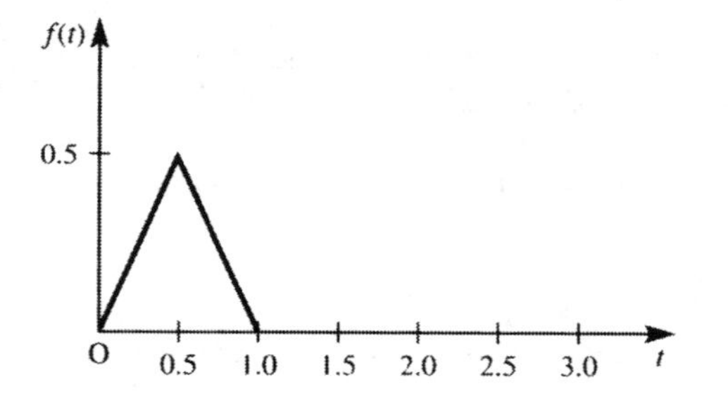

Figure 5.28 The delayed triangular pulse.

Solution

Using $N = 10$ samples at intervals $T = 0.2$ s, we generate the sequence

$$\{f_k\}_{k=0}^{9} = \{f(0), f(0.2), f(0.4), f(0.6), f(0.8), f(1.0), f(1.2), f(1.4), f(1.6), f(1.8)\}$$

Clearly, from Figure 5.28, we can express the continuous function $f(t)$ as

$$f(t) = \begin{cases} t & (0 \leqslant t \leqslant 0.5) \\ 1 - t & (0.5 < t < 1) \\ 0 & (t \geqslant 1) \end{cases}$$

and so

$$\{f_k\}_{k=0}^{9} = \{0, 0.2, 0.4, 0.4, 0.2, 0, 0, 0, 0, 0\}$$

Using (5.78), the discrete Fourier transform $\{F_n\}_{n=0}^{9}$ of the sequence $\{f_k\}_{k=0}^{9}$ is generated by

$$F_n = \sum_{k=0}^{9} f_k\, e^{-jkn\Delta\omega T}, \quad \text{where} \quad \Delta\omega = \frac{2\pi}{NT} = \frac{2\pi}{10 \times 0.2} = \pi$$

That is,

$$F_n = \sum_{k=0}^{9} f_k \, e^{-jkn(0.2\pi)}$$

or, since $f_0 = f_5 = f_6 = f_7 = f_8 = f_9 = 0$,

$$F_n = \sum_{k=1}^{4} f_k \, e^{-jnk(0.2\pi)}$$

The estimate of the Fourier transform, also based on $N = 10$ samples, is then the sequence

$$\{TF_n\}_{n=0}^{9} = \{0.2F_n\}_{n=0}^{9}$$

We thus have 10 values representing the Fourier transform at

$$\omega = n\Delta\omega \quad (n = 0, 1, 2, \dots, 9)$$

or since $\Delta\omega = 2\pi/NT$

$$\omega = 0, \pi, 2\pi, \dots, 9\pi$$

At $\omega = \pi$, corresponding to $n = 1$, our estimate is

$$\begin{aligned} 0.2F_1 &= 0.2 \sum_{k=1}^{4} f_k \, e^{-jk(0.2\pi)} \\ &= 0.2[0.2\,e^{-j(0.2\pi)} + 0.4(e^{-j(0.4\pi)} + e^{-j(0.6\pi)}) + 0.2\,e^{-j(0.8\pi)}] \\ &= -0.1992j \end{aligned}$$

At $\omega = 2\pi$, corresponding to $n = 2$, our estimate is

$$\begin{aligned} 0.2F_2 &= 0.2 \sum_{k=1}^{4} f_k \, e^{-jk(0.4\pi)} \\ &= 0.2[0.2\,e^{-j(0.4\pi)} + 0.4(e^{-j(0.8\pi)} + e^{-j(1.2\pi)}) + 0.2\,e^{-j(1.6\pi)}] \\ &= -0.1047 \end{aligned}$$

Continuing in this manner, we compute the sequence

$$\{0.2F_0, 0.2F_1, \dots, 0.2F_n\}$$

as

$$\{0.2400, -0.1992j, -0.1047, 0.0180j, -0.0153, 0, -0.0153, -0.0180j, \\ -0.1047, 0.1992j\}$$

This then represents the estimate of the Fourier transform of the continuous function $f(t)$. The exact value of the Fourier transform of $f(t)$ is easily computed by direct use of the definition (5.15) as

$$F(j\omega) = \mathscr{F}\{f(t)\} = \tfrac{1}{4}\,e^{-j\omega/2}\operatorname{sinc}^2 \tfrac{1}{4}\,\omega$$

which we can use to examine the validity of our result. The comparison is shown in Figure 5.29 and illustrated graphically in Figure 5.30.

Figure 5.29 Comparison of exact results and DFT estimate for the amplitude spectrum of the signal of Example 5.20.

ω	Exact $F(j\omega)$	DFT estimate	$\lvert F(j\omega)\rvert$	$\lvert$DFT estimate$\rvert$	% error
0	0.2500	0.2400	0.2500	0.2400	4%
π	−0.2026j	−0.1992j	0.2026	0.1992	1.7%
2π	−0.1013	−0.1047	0.1013	0.1047	3.2%
3π	0.0225j	0.0180j	0.0225	0.0180	20%
4π	0	−0.0153	0	0.0153	–
5π	−0.0081j	0	0.0081	0	–
6π	−0.0113	−0.0153	0.0113	0.0153	–
7π	0.0041	−0.0180j	0.0041	0.0180	–
8π	0	−0.1047	0	0.1047	–
9π	−0.0025j	0.1992j	0.0025	0.1992	–

Figure 5.30 Exact result $\lvert F(j\omega)\rvert$ ($*$) and DFT estimate TF_n ($\square$) of the Fourier transform in Example 5.20.

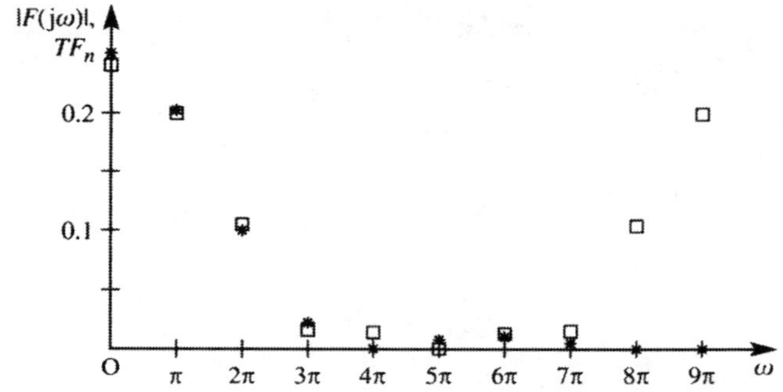

From the Nyquist–Shannon sampling theorem, with $T = 0.2$ s, we deduce that our results will be completely accurate if the original signal $f(t)$ is band-limited with a zero spectrum for $\lvert\omega\rvert > \lvert\omega_m\rvert = 5\pi$. Our signal is not strictly band-limited in this way, and we thus expect to observe some error in our results, particularly near $\omega = 5\pi$, because of the effects of aliasing. The estimate obtained is satisfactory at $\omega = 0, \pi, 2\pi$, but begins to lose accuracy at $\omega = 3\pi$. Results obtained above $\omega = 5\pi$ are seen to be images of those obtained for values below $\omega = 5\pi$, and this is to be expected owing to the periodicity of the DFT. In our calculation the DFT sequence will be periodic, with period $N = 10$; thus, for example,

$$\lvert TF_7\rvert = \lvert TF_{7-10}\rvert = \lvert TF_{-3}\rvert = T\lvert F_{-3}\rvert$$

As we have seen many times, for a real signal the amplitude spectrum is symmetric about $\omega = 0$. Thus $\lvert F_{-3}\rvert = \lvert F_3\rvert$, $\lvert F_{-5}\rvert = \lvert F_5\rvert$, and so on, and the effects of the symmetry are apparent in Figure 5.29. It is perhaps worth observing that if we had calculated (say) $\{TF_{-4}, TF_{-3}, \dots, TF_0, TF_1, \dots, TF_5\}$, we should have obtained a 'conventional' plot, with the right-hand portion, beyond $\omega = 5\pi$, translated to the left of the origin. However, using the plot of the amplitude spectrum in the chosen form does highlight the source of error due to aliasing.

In this section we have discussed a method by which Fourier transforms can be estimated numerically, at least in theory. It is apparent, though, that the amount of labour involved is significant, and as we observed in Section 5.6.3 an algorithm based on this approach is in general prohibitive in view of the amount of computing time required. The next section gives a brief introduction to a method of overcoming this problem.

5.6.5 The fast Fourier transform

The calculation of a discrete Fourier transform based on N sample values requires, as we have seen, N^2 complex multiplications and $N(N-1)$ summations. For real signals, symmetry can be exploited, but for large N, $\frac{1}{2}N^2$ does not represent a significant improvement over N^2 for the purposes of computation. In fact, a totally new approach to the problem was required before the discrete Fourier transform could become a practical engineering tool. In 1965 Cooley and Tukey introduced the **fast Fourier transform (FFT)** in order to reduce the computational complexity (J. W. Cooley and J. W. Tukey, An algorithm for the machine computation of complex Fourier series, *Mathematics of Computation* **19** (1965) 297–301). We shall briefly introduce their approach in this section: for a full discussion see E. E. Brigham, *The Fast Fourier Transform* (Prentice Hall, Englewood Cliffs, NJ, 1974), whose treatment is similar to that adopted here.

We shall restrict ourselves to the situation where $N = 2^\gamma$ for some integer γ, and, rather than examine the general case, we shall focus on a particular value of γ. In proceeding in this way, the idea should be clear and the extension to other values of γ appear credible. We can summarize the approach as being in three stages:

(a) matrix formulation;
(b) matrix factorization; and, finally,
(c) rearranging.

We first consider a matrix formulation of the DFT. From (5.78), the Fourier transform sequence $\{G_k\}_{k=0}^{N-1}$ of the sequence $\{g_n\}_{n=0}^{N-1}$ is generated by

$$G_k = \sum_{n=0}^{N-1} g_n \, e^{-j2\pi nk/N} \quad (k = 0, 1, \dots, N-1) \tag{5.91}$$

We shall consider the particular case when $\gamma = 2$ (that is, $N = 2^2 = 4$), and define

$$W = e^{-j2\pi/N} = e^{-j\pi/2}$$

so that (5.91) becomes

$$G_k = \sum_{n=0}^{N-1} g_n W^{nk} = \sum_{n=0}^{3} g_n W^{nk} \quad (k = 0, 1, 2, 3)$$

Writing out the terms of the transformed sequence, we have

$$G_0 = g_0W^0 + g_1W^0 + g_2W^0 + g_3W^0$$

$$G_1 = g_0W^0 + g_1W^1 + g_2W^2 + g_3W^3$$

$$G_2 = g_0W^0 + g_1W^2 + g_2W^4 + g_3W^6$$

$$G_3 = g_0W^0 + g_1W^3 + g_2W^6 + g_3W^9$$

which may be expressed in the vector–matrix form

$$\begin{bmatrix} G_0 \\ G_1 \\ G_2 \\ G_3 \end{bmatrix} = \begin{bmatrix} W^0 & W^0 & W^0 & W^0 \\ W^0 & W^1 & W^2 & W^3 \\ W^0 & W^2 & W^4 & W^6 \\ W^0 & W^3 & W^6 & W^9 \end{bmatrix} \begin{bmatrix} g_0 \\ g_1 \\ g_2 \\ g_3 \end{bmatrix} \tag{5.92}$$

or, more generally, as

$$\boldsymbol{G}_k = \boldsymbol{W}^{nk}\boldsymbol{g}_n$$

where the vectors $\boldsymbol{G}_k$ and $\boldsymbol{g}_n$ and the square matrix $\boldsymbol{W}^{nk}$ are defined as in (5.92). The next step relates to the special properties of the entries in the matrix $\boldsymbol{W}^{nk}$. Note that $W^{nk} = W^{nk+pN}$, where p is an integer, and so

$$W^4 = W^0 = 1$$

$$W^6 = W^2$$

$$W^9 = W^1$$

Thus (5.92) becomes

$$\begin{bmatrix} G_0 \\ G_1 \\ G_2 \\ G_3 \end{bmatrix} = \begin{bmatrix} 1 & 1 & 1 & 1 \\ 1 & W^1 & W^2 & W^3 \\ 1 & W^2 & W^0 & W^2 \\ 1 & W^3 & W^2 & W^1 \end{bmatrix} \begin{bmatrix} g_0 \\ g_1 \\ g_2 \\ g_3 \end{bmatrix} \tag{5.93}$$

Equation (5.93) is the end of the first stage of the development. In fact, we have so far only made use of the properties of the Nth roots of unity. Stage two involves the factorization of a matrix, the details of which will be explained later.

Note that

$$\begin{bmatrix} 1 & W^0 & 0 & 0 \\ 1 & W^2 & 0 & 0 \\ 0 & 0 & 1 & W^1 \\ 0 & 0 & 1 & W^3 \end{bmatrix} \begin{bmatrix} 1 & 0 & W^0 & 0 \\ 0 & 1 & 0 & W^0 \\ 1 & 0 & W^2 & 0 \\ 0 & 1 & 0 & W^2 \end{bmatrix} = \begin{bmatrix} 1 & 1 & 1 & 1 \\ 1 & W^2 & W^0 & W^2 \\ 1 & W^1 & W^2 & W^3 \\ 1 & W^3 & W^2 & W^1 \end{bmatrix} \tag{5.94}$$

where we have used $W^5 = W^1$ and $W^0 = 1$ (in the top row). The matrix on the right-hand side of (5.94) is the coefficient matrix of (5.93), *but with rows 2 and 3 interchanged.* Thus we can write (5.93) as

$$\begin{bmatrix} G_0 \\ G_2 \\ G_1 \\ G_3 \end{bmatrix} = \begin{bmatrix} 1 & W^0 & 0 & 0 \\ 1 & W^2 & 0 & 0 \\ 0 & 0 & 1 & W^1 \\ 0 & 0 & 1 & W^3 \end{bmatrix} \begin{bmatrix} 1 & 0 & W^0 & 0 \\ 0 & 1 & 0 & W^0 \\ 1 & 0 & W^2 & 0 \\ 0 & 1 & 0 & W^2 \end{bmatrix} \begin{bmatrix} g_0 \\ g_1 \\ g_2 \\ g_3 \end{bmatrix} \tag{5.95}$$

We now define a vector $\boldsymbol{g}'$ as

$$\boldsymbol{g}' = \begin{bmatrix} g_0' \\ g_1' \\ g_2' \\ g_3' \end{bmatrix} = \begin{bmatrix} 1 & 0 & W^0 & 0 \\ 0 & 1 & 0 & W^0 \\ 1 & 0 & W^2 & 0 \\ 0 & 1 & 0 & W^2 \end{bmatrix} \begin{bmatrix} g_0 \\ g_1 \\ g_2 \\ g_3 \end{bmatrix} \tag{5.96}$$

It then follows from (5.96) that

$$g_0' = g_0 + W^0 g_2$$

$$g_1' = g_1 + W^0 g_3$$

so that g'_0 and g'_1 are each calculated by one complex multiplication and one addition. Of course, in this special case, since $W^0 = 1$, the multiplication is unnecessary, but we are attempting to infer the general situation. For this reason, W^0 has not been replaced by 1.

Also, it follows from (5.96) that

$$g'_2 = g_0 + W^2 g_2$$

$$g'_3 = g_1 + W^2 g_3$$

and, since $W^2 = -W^0$, the computation of the pair g'_2 and g'_3 can make use of the computations of $W^0 g_2$ and $W^0 g_3$, with one further addition in each case. Thus the vector $\boldsymbol{g}'$ is determined by a total of four complex additions and two complex multiplications.

To complete the calculation of the transform, we return to (5.95), and rewrite it in the form

$$\begin{bmatrix} G_0 \\ G_2 \\ G_1 \\ G_3 \end{bmatrix} = \begin{bmatrix} 1 & W^0 & 0 & 0 \\ 1 & W^2 & 0 & 0 \\ 0 & 0 & 1 & W^1 \\ 0 & 0 & 1 & W^3 \end{bmatrix} \begin{bmatrix} g'_0 \\ g'_1 \\ g'_2 \\ g'_3 \end{bmatrix} \tag{5.97}$$

It then follows from (5.97) that

$$G_0 = g'_0 + W^0 g'_1$$

$$G_2 = g'_0 + W^2 g'_1$$

and we see that G_0 is determined by one complex multiplication and one complex addition. Furthermore, because $W^2 = -W^0$, G_2 follows after one further complex addition.

Similarly, it follows from (5.97) that

$$G_1 = g'_2 + W^1 g'_3$$

$$G_3 = g'_2 + W^3 g'_3$$

and, since $W^3 = -W^1$, a total of one further complex multiplication and two further additions are required to produce the re-ordered transform vector

$$[G_0 \quad G_2 \quad G_1 \quad G_3]^{\mathrm{T}}$$

Thus the total number of operations required to generate the (re-ordered) transform is four complex multiplications and eight complex additions. Direct calculation would have required $N^2 = 16$ complex multiplications and $N(N-1) = 12$ complex additions. Even with a small value of N, these savings are significant, and, interpreting computing time requirements as being proportional to the number of complex multiplications involved, it is easy to see why the FFT algorithm has become an essential tool for computational Fourier analysis. When $N = 2^\gamma$, the FFT algorithm is effectively a procedure for producing $\gamma N \times N$ matrices of the form (5.94). Extending our ideas, it is possible to see that generally the FFT algorithm, when $N = 2^\gamma$, will require $\frac{1}{2}N\gamma$ (four, when $N = 2^2 = 4$) complex multiplications and $N\gamma$ (eight, when $N = 4$) complex additions. Since

$$\gamma = \log_2 N$$

the demands of the FFT algorithm in terms of computing time, estimated on the basis of the number of complex multiplications, are often given as about $N \log_2 N$, as opposed to N^2 for the direct evaluation of the transform. This completes the second stage of our task, and we are only left with the problem of rearrangement of our transform vector into 'natural' order.

The means by which this is achieved is most elegant. Instead of indexing G_0, G_1, G_2, G_3 in decimal form, an alternative binary notation is used, and $[G_0 \quad G_1 \quad G_2 \quad G_3]^T$ becomes

$$[G_{00} \quad G_{01} \quad G_{10} \quad G_{11}]^T$$

The process of 'bit reversal' means rewriting a binary number with its bits or digits in reverse order. Applying this process to $[G_{00} \quad G_{01} \quad G_{10} \quad G_{11}]^T$ yields

$$[G_{00} \quad G_{10} \quad G_{01} \quad G_{11}]^T = [G_0 \quad G_2 \quad G_1 \quad G_3]^T$$

with decimal labelling. This latter form is exactly the one obtained at the end of the FFT calculation, and we see that the natural order can easily be recovered by rearranging the output on the basis of bit reversal of the binary indexed version.

We have now completed our introduction to the fast Fourier transform. We shall now consider an example to illustrate the ideas discussed here. We shall then conclude by considering in greater detail the matrix factorization process used in the second stage.

Example 5.21 Use the method of the FFT algorithm to compute the Fourier transform of the sequence

$$\{g_n\}_{n=0}^{3} = \{1, 2, 1, 0\}$$

Solution In this case $N = 4 = 2^2$, and we begin by computing the vector $\boldsymbol{g}'_n = [g'_0 \quad g'_1 \quad g'_2 \quad g'_3]^T$, which, from (5.96), is given by

$$\boldsymbol{g}'_n = \begin{bmatrix} 1 & 0 & W^0 & 0 \\ 0 & 1 & 0 & W^0 \\ 1 & 0 & W^2 & 0 \\ 0 & 1 & 0 & W^2 \end{bmatrix} \begin{bmatrix} g_0 \\ g_1 \\ g_2 \\ g_3 \end{bmatrix}$$

For $N = 4$

$$W^n = (e^{-j2\pi/4})^n = e^{-jn\pi/2}$$

and so

$$\boldsymbol{g}'_n = \begin{bmatrix} 1 & 0 & 1 & 0 \\ 0 & 1 & 0 & 1 \\ 1 & 0 & -1 & 0 \\ 0 & 1 & 0 & -1 \end{bmatrix} \begin{bmatrix} 1 \\ 2 \\ 1 \\ 0 \end{bmatrix} = \begin{bmatrix} 2 \\ 2 \\ 0 \\ 2 \end{bmatrix}$$

Next, we compute the 'bit-reversed' order transform vector $\boldsymbol{G}'$, say, which from (5.97) is given by

$$\boldsymbol{G}' = \begin{bmatrix} 1 & W^0 & 0 & 0 \\ 1 & W^2 & 0 & 0 \\ 0 & 0 & 1 & W^1 \\ 0 & 0 & 1 & W^3 \end{bmatrix} \begin{bmatrix} g'_0 \\ g'_1 \\ g'_2 \\ g'_3 \end{bmatrix}$$

or, in this particular case,

$$\boldsymbol{G}' = \begin{bmatrix} G_{00} \\ G_{10} \\ G_{01} \\ G_{11} \end{bmatrix} \begin{bmatrix} 1 & 1 & 0 & 0 \\ 1 & -1 & 0 & 0 \\ 0 & 0 & 1 & -j \\ 0 & 0 & 1 & j \end{bmatrix} \begin{bmatrix} 2 \\ 2 \\ 0 \\ 2 \end{bmatrix} = \begin{bmatrix} 4 \\ 0 \\ -2j \\ 2j \end{bmatrix} \tag{5.98}$$

Finally, we recover the transform vector $\boldsymbol{G} = [G_0 \quad G_1 \quad G_2 \quad G_3]^{\mathrm{T}}$ as

$$\boldsymbol{G} = \begin{bmatrix} 4 \\ -2j \\ 0 \\ 2j \end{bmatrix}$$

and we have thus established the Fourier transform of the sequence $\{1, 2, 1, 0\}$ as the sequence

$$\{4, -2j, 0, 2j\}$$

It is interesting to compare the labour involved in this calculation with that in Example 5.19.

To conclude this section, we reconsider the matrix factorization operation, which is at the core of the process of calculating the fast Fourier transform. In a book of this nature it is not appropriate to reproduce a proof of the validity of the algorithm for any N of the form $N = 2^\gamma$. Rather, we shall illustrate how the factorization we introduced in (5.94) was obtained. The factored form of the matrix will not be generated in any calculation: what actually happens is that the various summations are performed using their structural properties.

From (5.91), with $W = e^{-j2\pi/N}$, we wish to calculate the sums

$$G_k = \sum_{n=0}^{N-1} g_n W^{nk} \quad k = 0, 1, \dots, N-1 \tag{5.99}$$

In the case $N = 4$, $\gamma = 2$ we see that k and n take only the values 0, 1, 2 and 3, so we can represent both k and n using two-digit binary numbers; in general γ-digit binary numbers will be required.

We write $k = k_1k_0$ and $n = n_1n_0$, where k_0, k_1, n_0 and n_1 may take the values 0 or 1 only. For example, $k = 3$ becomes $k = 11$ and $n = 2$ becomes $n = 10$. The decimal form can always be recovered easily as $k = 2k_1 + k_0$ and $n = 2n_1 + n_0$.

Using binary notation, we can write (5.99) as

$$G_{k_1k_0} = \sum_{n_0=0}^{1} \sum_{n_1=0}^{1} g_{n_1n_0} W^{(2n_1+n_0)(2k_1+k_0)} \tag{5.100}$$

The single summation of (5.99) is now replaced, when $\gamma = 2$, by two summations. Again we see that for the more general case with $N = 2^\gamma$ a total of γ summations replaces the single sum of (5.99).

The matrix factorization operation with which we are concerned is now achieved by considering the term

$$W^{(2n_1+n_0)(2k_1+k_0)}$$

in (5.100). Expanding gives

$$\begin{aligned} W^{(2n_1+n_0)(2k_1+k_0)} &= W^{(2k_1+k_0)2n_1} W^{(2k_1+k_0)n_0} \\ &= W^{4n_1k_1} W^{2n_1k_0} W^{(2k_1+k_0)n_0} \end{aligned} \tag{5.101}$$

Since $W = e^{-j2\pi/N}$, and $N = 4$ in this case, the leading term in (5.101) becomes

$$\begin{aligned} W^{4n_1k_1} &= (e^{-j2\pi/4})^{4n_1k_1} = (e^{-j2\pi})^{n_1k_1} \\ &= 1^{n_1k_1} = 1 \end{aligned}$$

Again we observe that in the more general case such a factor will always emerge.

Thus (5.101) can be written as

$$W^{(2n_1+n_0)(2k_1+k_0)} = W^{2n_1k_0} W^{(2k_1+k_0)n_0}$$

so that (5.100) becomes

$$G_{k_1k_0} = \sum_{n_0=0}^{1} \left[\sum_{n_1=0}^{1} g_{n_1n_0} W^{2n_1k_0} \right] W^{(2k_1+k_0)n_0} \tag{5.102}$$

which is the required matrix factorization. This can be seen by writing

$$g'_{k_0n_0} = \sum_{n_1=0}^{1} g_{n_1n_0} W^{2n_1k_0} \tag{5.103}$$

so that the sum in the square brackets in (5.102) defines the four relations

$$\left.\begin{aligned} g'_{00} &= g_{00}W^{2.0.0} + g_{10}W^{2.1.0} = g_{00} + g_{10}W^0 \\ g'_{01} &= g_{01}W^{2.0.0} + g_{11}W^{2.1.0} = g_{01} + g_{11}W^0 \\ g'_{10} &= g_{00}W^{2.0.1} + g_{10}W^{2.1.1} = g_{00} + g_{10}W^2 \\ g'_{11} &= g_{01}W^{2.0.1} + g_{11}W^{2.1.1} = g_{01} + g_{11}W^2 \end{aligned}\right\} \tag{5.104}$$

which, in matrix form, becomes

$$\begin{bmatrix} g'_{00} \\ g'_{01} \\ g'_{10} \\ g'_{11} \end{bmatrix} = \begin{bmatrix} 1 & 0 & W^0 & 0 \\ 0 & 1 & 0 & W^0 \\ 1 & 0 & W^2 & 0 \\ 0 & 1 & 0 & W^2 \end{bmatrix} \begin{bmatrix} g_{00} \\ g_{01} \\ g_{10} \\ g_{11} \end{bmatrix} \tag{5.105}$$

and we see that we have re-established the system of equations (5.96), this time with binary indexing. Note that in (5.104) and (5.105) we distinguished between terms in W^0 depending on how the zero is generated. When the zero is generated through the value of the summation index (that is, when $n_1 = 0$ and thus a zero will always be generated whatever the value of γ) we replace W^0 by 1. When the index is zero because of the value of k_0, we maintain W^0 as an aid to generalization.

The final stage of the factorization appears when we write the outer summation of (5.102) as

$$G'_{k_0k_1} = \sum_{n_0=0}^{1} g'_{k_0n_0} W^{(2k_1+k_0)n_0} \tag{5.106}$$

which, on writing out in full, gives

$$G'_{00} = g'_{00}W^{0.0} + g'_{01}W^{0.1} = g'_{00} + g'_{01}W^0$$

$$G'_{01} = g'_{00}W^{2.0} + g'_{01}W^{2.1} = g'_{00} + g'_{01}W^2$$

$$G'_{10} = g'_{10}W^{1.0} + g'_{11}W^{1.1} = g'_{10} + g'_{11}W^1$$

$$G'_{11} = g'_{10}W^{3.0} + g'_{11}W^{3.1} = g'_{10} + g'_{11}W^3$$

or, in matrix form,

$$\begin{bmatrix} G'_{00} \\ G'_{01} \\ G'_{10} \\ G'_{11} \end{bmatrix} = \begin{bmatrix} 1 & W^0 & 0 & 0 \\ 1 & W^2 & 0 & 0 \\ 0 & 0 & 1 & W^1 \\ 0 & 0 & 1 & W^3 \end{bmatrix} \begin{bmatrix} g'_{00} \\ g'_{01} \\ g'_{10} \\ g'_{11} \end{bmatrix} \tag{5.107}$$

The matrix in (5.107) is exactly that of (5.97), and we have completed the factorization process as we intended. Finally, to obtain the transform in a natural order, we must carry out the bit-reversal operation. From (5.102) and (5.105), we achieve this by simply writing

$$G_{k_1k_0} = G'_{k_0k_1} \tag{5.108}$$

We can therefore summarize the Cooley–Tukey algorithm for the fast Fourier transform for the case $N = 4$ by the three relations (5.103), (5.106) and (5.108), that is

$$g'_{k_0n_0} = \sum_{n_1=0}^{1} g_{n_1n_0} W^{2n_1k_0}$$

$$G'_{k_0k_1} = \sum_{n_0=0}^{1} g'_{k_0n_0} W^{(2k_1+k_0)n_0}$$

$$G_{k_1k_0} = G'_{k_0k_1}$$

The evaluation of these three relationships is equivalent to the matrix factorization process together with the bit-reversal procedure discussed above.

The fast Fourier transform is essentially a computer-orientated algorithm and highly efficient codes are available in MATLAB and other software libraries, usually requiring a simple subroutine call for their implementation. The interested reader who would prefer to produce 'home-made' code may find listings in the textbook by Brigham quoted at the beginning of this section, as well as elsewhere.

5.6.6 Exercises

28 Calculate directly the discrete Fourier transform of the sequence

$$\{1, 0, 1, 0\}$$

using the methods of Section 5.6.3 (see Example 5.19).

29 Use the fast Fourier transform method to calculate the transform of the sequence of Exercise 28 (follow Example 5.21).

30 Use the FFT algorithm in MATLAB (or an alternative) to improve the experiment with the estimation of the spectrum of the signal of Example 5.20.

31 Derive an FFT algorithm for $N = 2^3 = 8$ points. Work from (5.99), writing

$$k = 4k_2 + 2k_1 + k_0, \quad k_i = 0 \text{ or } 1 \quad \text{for all } i$$

$$n = 4n_2 + 2n_1 + n_0, \quad n_i = 0 \text{ or } 1 \quad \text{for all } i$$

to show that

$$g'_{k_0n_1n_0} = \sum_{n_2=0}^{1} g_{n_2n_1n_0} W^{4k_0n_2}$$

$$g''_{k_0k_1n_0} = \sum_{n_1=0}^{1} g'_{k_0n_1n_0} W^{(2k_1+k_0)2n_1}$$

$$G'_{k_0k_1k_2} = \sum_{n_0=0}^{1} g''_{k_0k_1n_0} W^{(4k_2+2k_1+k_0)n_0}$$

$$G_{k_2k_1k_0} = G'_{k_0k_1k_2}$$

5.7 Engineering application: the design of analogue filters

In this section we explore the ideas of mathematical design or synthesis. We shall express in mathematical form the desired performance of a system, and, utilizing the ideas we have developed, produce a system design.

This chapter has been concerned with the frequency-domain representation of signals and systems, and the system we shall design will operate on input signals to produce output signals with specific frequency-domain properties. In Figure 5.31 we illustrate the amplitude response of an ideal low-pass filter. This filter passes perfectly signals, or components of signals, at frequencies less than the cut-off frequency ω_c. Above ω_c, attenuation is perfect, meaning that signals above this frequency are not passed by this filter.

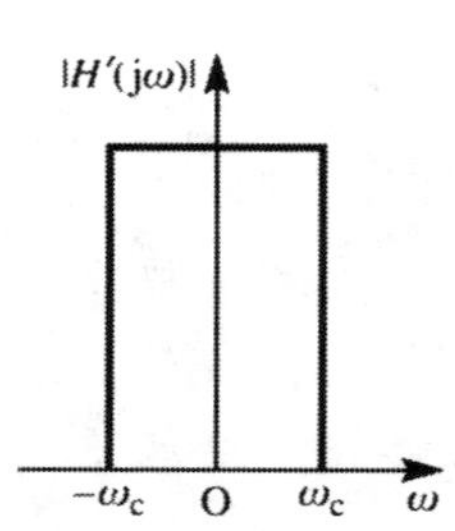

Figure 5.31 Amplitude response of an ideal low-pass filter.

The amplitude response of this ideal device is given by

$$|H'(j\omega)| = \begin{cases} 1 & (|\omega| \leqslant \omega_c) \\ 0 & (|\omega| > \omega_c) \end{cases}$$

Such an ideal response cannot be attained by a real analogue device, and our design problem is to approximate this response to an acceptable degree using a system that can be constructed. A class of functions whose graphs resemble that of Figure 5.31 is the set

$$|H_B(j\omega)| = \frac{1}{\sqrt{[1 + (\omega/\omega_c)^{2n}]}}$$

and we see from Figure 5.32, which corresponds to $\omega_c = 1$, that, as n increases, the graph approaches the ideal response. This particular approximation is known as the **Butterworth approximation**, and is only one of a number of possibilities.

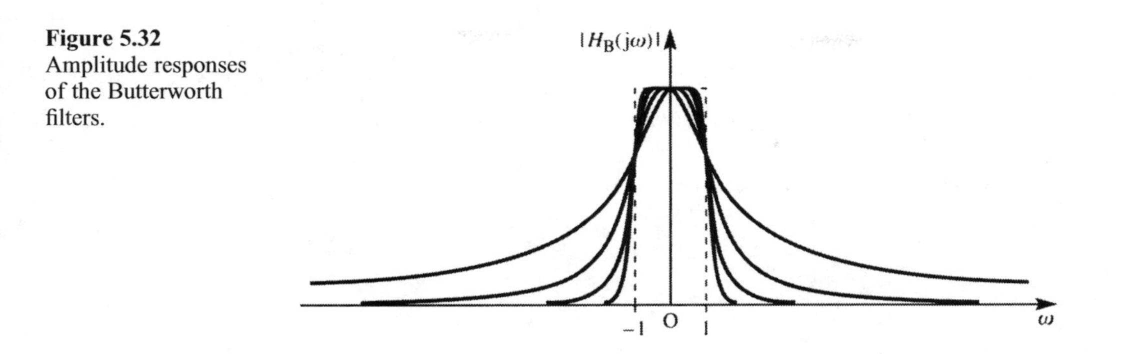

Figure 5.32 Amplitude responses of the Butterworth filters.

To explore this approach further, we must ask the question whether such a response could be obtained as the frequency response of a realizable, stable linear system. We assume that it can, although if our investigation leads to the opposite conclusion then we shall have to abandon this approach and seek another. If $H_B(j\omega)$ is the frequency response of such a system then it will have been obtained by replacing s with $j\omega$ in the system Laplace transfer function. This is at least possible since, by assumption, we are dealing with a stable system. Now

$$|H_B(j\omega)|^2 = \frac{1}{1 + (j\omega/j\omega_c)^{2n}}$$

where $|H_B(j\omega)|^2 = H_B(j\omega)H_B^*(j\omega)$. If $H_B(s)$ is to have real coefficients, and thus be realizable, then we must have $H_B^*(j\omega) = H(-j\omega)$. Thus

$$H_B(j\omega)H_B(-j\omega) = \frac{1}{1 + (\omega/\omega_c)^{2n}} = \frac{1}{1 + (j\omega/j\omega_c)^{2n}}$$

and we see that the response could be obtained by setting $s = j\omega$ in

$$H_B(s)H_B(-s) = \frac{1}{1 + (s/j\omega_c)^{2n}}$$

Our task is now to attempt to separate $H_B(s)$ from $H_B(-s)$ in such a way that $H_B(s)$ represents the transfer function of a stable system. To do this, we solve the equation

$$1 + (s/j\omega_c)^{2n} = 0$$

to give the poles of $H_B(s)H_B(-s)$ as

$$s = \omega_c \, e^{j[(2k+1)\pi/2n+\pi/2]} \quad (k = 0, 1, 2, 3, \dots) \tag{5.109}$$

Figure 5.33 shows the pole locations for the cases $n = 1$, 2, 3 and 5. The important observations that we can make from this figure are that in each case there are $2n$ poles equally spaced around the circle of radius ω_c in the Argand diagram, and that there are no poles on the imaginary axis. If $s = s_1$ is a pole of $H_B(s)H_B(-s)$ then so is $s = -s_1$, and we can thus select as poles for the transfer function $H_B(s)$ those lying in the left half-plane. The remaining poles are then those of $H_B(-s)$. By this procedure, we have generated a stable transfer function $H_B(s)$ for our filter design.

The transfer function that we have generated from the frequency-domain specification of system behaviour must now be related to a real system, and this is the next step

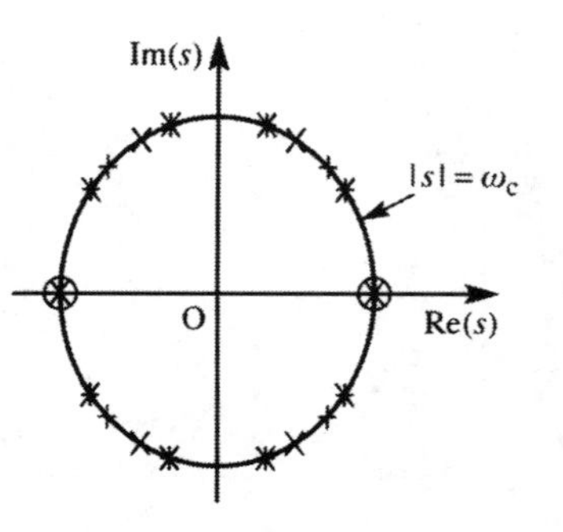

Figure 5.33
Pole locations for the Butterworth filters: (O) $n = 1$; (+) $n = 2$; (X) $n = 3$; (∗) $n = 5$.

in the design process. The form of the transfer function for the filter of order n can be shown to be

$$H_B(s) = \frac{\omega_c^n}{(s - s_1)(s - s_2) \dots (s - s_n)}$$

where $s_1, s_2, \dots, s_n$ are the stable poles generated by (5.109). The reader is invited to show that the second-order Butterworth filter has transfer function

$$H_B(s) = \frac{\omega_c^2}{s^2 + \sqrt{2}\omega_c s + \omega_c^2}$$

Writing $Y(s) = H_B(s)U(s)$, with $H_B(s)$ as above, we obtain

$$Y(s) = \frac{\omega_c^2}{s^2 + \sqrt{2}\omega_c s + \omega_c^2} U(s)$$

or

$$(s^2 + \sqrt{2}\omega_c s + \omega_c^2)Y(s) = \omega_c^2 U(s) \tag{5.110}$$

If we assume that all initial conditions are zero then (5.110) represents the Laplace transform of the differential equation

$$\frac{d^2 y(t)}{dt^2} + \sqrt{2}\omega_c \frac{dy(t)}{dt} + \omega_c^2 y(t) = \omega_c^2 u(t) \tag{5.111}$$

This step completes the mathematical aspect of the design exercise. It is possible to show that a system whose behaviour is modelled by this differential equation can be constructed using elementary circuit components, and the specification of such a circuit would complete the design. For a fuller treatment of the subject the interested reader could consult M. J. Chapman, D. P. Goodall and N. C. Steele, *Signal Processing in Electronic Communications*, Horwood Publishing, Chichester, 1997.

To appreciate the operation of this filter, the use of the Signal Processing Toolbox in MATLAB is recommended. After setting the cut-off frequency ω_c, at 4 for example, the output of the system $y(t)$ corresponding to an input signal $u(t) = \sin t + \sin 10t$ will demonstrate the almost-perfect transmission of the low-frequency ($\omega = 1$) term, with nearly total attenuation of the high-frequency ($\omega = 10$) signal. As an extension to this exercise, the differential equation to represent the third- and fourth-order filters should be obtained, and the responses compared. Using a simulation package and an FFT coding, it is possible to investigate the operation of such devices from the viewpoint of the frequency domain by examining the spectrum of samples drawn from both input and output signals.

5.8 Engineering application: modulation, demodulation and frequency-domain filtering

5.8.1 Introduction

In this section we demonstrate the practical implementation of modulation, demodulation and frequency-domain filtering. These are the processes by which an information-carrying signal can be combined with others for transmission along a channel, with the signal subsequently being recovered so that the transmitted information can be extracted. When a number of signals have to be transmitted along a single channel at the same time, one solution is to use the method of **amplitude modulation** as described in Section 5.3.4. We assume that the channel is 'noisy', so that the received signal contains noise, and this signal is then cleaned and demodulated using **frequency-domain filtering** techniques. This idea is easy to describe and to implement, but cannot usually be performed on-line in view of the heavy computational requirements. Our filtering operations are carried out on the frequency-domain version of the signal, and this is generated using the fast Fourier transform algorithm. The MATLAB code in Figure 5.34 is designed to illustrate how results can be obtained working from basic ideas. The nature and usefulness of the Toolboxes now associated with MATLAB have made it possible to work at a higher level. Nevertheless it is thought valuable to retain this figure for instructional purposes, since it is easily modified. (*Note*: In Figure 5.34 i is used instead of j to denote $\sqrt{-1}$, to conform with MATLAB convention.)

Figure 5.34 'MATLAB' M-file demonstrating frequency-domain filtering using the fast Fourier transform.

```
% Demonstration of frequency domain filtering using the FFT.
%
%
% Some MATLAB housekeeping to prevent memory problems!
clear
clg
%
% Select a value of N for the number of samples to be taken.
% Make a selection by adding or removing % symbols.
% N must be a power of 2.
%N = 512;
N = 1024;
%N = 2048;
%N = 4096;
%N = 8192;
%
% T is the sampling interval and the choice of N determines the
% interval over which the signal is processed. Also, if
% N frequency domain values are to be produced the resolution
% is determined.
T = 0.001;
t = 0:T:(N - 1)*T;
delw = 2*pi/(T*N);
%
% Generate the 'information'
f = t .*exp(-t/2);
%
```

Figure 5.34 *continued*

```
% Set the frequency of the carriers, wc is the carrier which
% will be modulated.
wc = 2*pi*50;
wca = 2*pi*120;
%
% Perform the modulation ...
x = f. *cos(wc*t) + cos(wca*t);
%
%... and add channel noise here
nfac = 0.2;
rand('normal');
x = x + nfac*rand(t);
%
% Plot the 'received' time signal
plot(t,x)
title('The time signal, modulated carrier and noise if added')
xlabel('time, t')
ylabel('x(t)')
pause
%
% Calculate the DFT using the FFT algorithm ...
y = fft(x);
z = T*abs(y);
w = 0:delw:(N - 1)*delw;
%
% ... and plot the amplitude spectrum.
plot(w,z)
title('The amplitude spectrum. Spikes at frequencies of carriers')
xlabel('frequency, w')
ylabel('amplitude')
pause
%
% Construct a filter to isolate the information-bearing carrier.
%
% 2*hwind + 1 is the length of the filter 'window'.
% Set ffac to a value less than 1.0 ffac = 0.5 gives a filter
% of half length wc/2 where wc is frequency of carrier. Don't
% exceed a value of 0.95!
ffac = 0.5;
hwind = round(ffac*wc/delw);
l = 2*hwind + 1;
%
% Set the centre of the window at peak corresponding to wc.
% Check this is ok by setting l = 1!
l1 = round(wc/delw) - hwind;
%
% Remember that we must have both ends of the filter!
mask = [zeros(1,l1),ones(1,l),zeros(1,N - (2*l + 2*l1 - 1)),ones(1,l),zeros(1,l1 - 1)];
%
% Do the frequency domain filtering ...
zz = mask.*y;
%
% ... and calculate the inverse DFT
yya = ifft(zz);
%
% Remove rounding errors ... it is real!
yy = 0.5*(yya + conj(yya));
%
```

Figure 5.34 *continued*

```
% Plot the 'cleaned' spectrum with only lower carrier present.
plot(w,T*abs(zz))
title('Upper carrier eliminated and noise reduced')
xlabel('frequency, w')
ylabel('amplitude')
pause
%
% Now the signal is cleaned but needs demodulating so
% form the product with 2*carrier signal ...
dem = yy.*cos(wc*t);
dem = 2*dem;
%
% ... and take the DFT.
demft = fft(dem);
%
% Use a low-pass filter on the result, the length is llp.
% The same factor is used as before!
llp = round(ffac*wc/delw);
masklp = [ones(1,llp),zeros(1,N - (2*llp - 1)),ones(1,llp - 1)];
%
% Carry out the filtering...
op = masklp.*demft;
%
% ... and plot the DFT of filtered signal.
plot(w,T*abs(op))
title('Result of demodulation and low-pass filtering')
xlabel('frequency, w')
ylabel('amplitude')
pause
%
% Return to the time domain...
opta = ifft(op);
opt = 0.5*(opta + conj(opta));
act = f;
vp = N;
% ... and finally plot the extracted signal vs the original.
plot(t(1:vp),opt(1:vp),'-',t(1:vp),act(1:vp),':');
title('The extracted signal, with original')
xlabel('time, t')
ylabel('f(t)')
pause
%
% Clean-up ...
clg
clear
%
% ... but responsibly!
i = sqrt(-1);
home
```

5.8.2 Modulation and transmission

We suppose that our 'information' consists of samples from the signal $f(t) = t\,e^{-t/2}$, taken at intervals $T = 0.001$ s. This signal, or more correctly, data sequence, will be used to modulate the carrier signal $\cos(50*2*\pi*t)$. A second carrier signal is given by

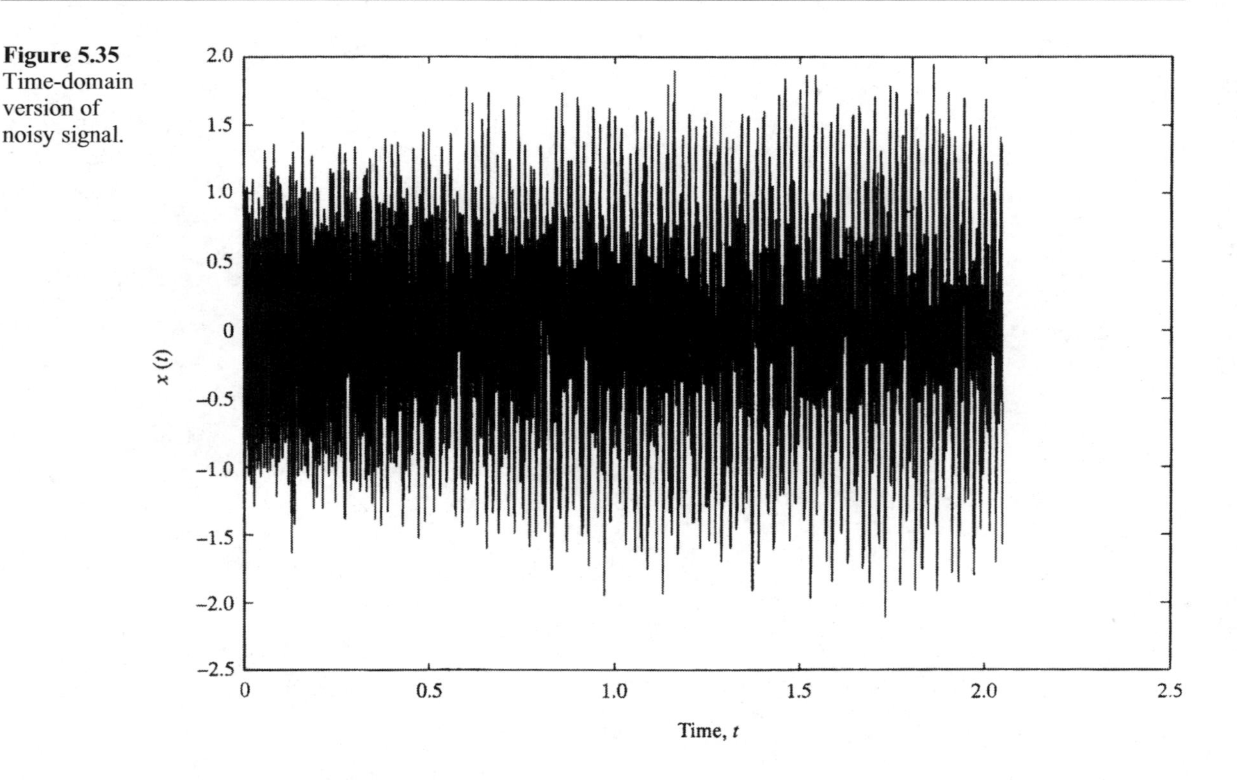

Figure 5.35 Time-domain version of noisy signal.

cos (120∗2∗π∗*t*), and this can be thought of as carrying the signal $f(t) = 1$. We combine these two signals and add 'white noise' to represent the action of the channel. This part of the exercise corresponds to the signal generation and transmission part of the overall process, and Figure 5.35 shows the time-domain version of the resulting signal

5.8.3 Identification and isolation of the information-carrying signal

Here we begin the signal-processing operations. The key to this is Fourier analysis, and we make use of the fast Fourier transform algorithm to perform the necessary transforms and their inverses. First we examine the spectrum of the received signal, shown in Figure 5.36. We immediately see two spikes corresponding to the carrier signals, and we know that the lower one is carrying the signal we wish to extract. We must design a suitable filter to operate in the frequency domain for the isolation of the selected carrier wave before using the demodulation operation to extract the information. To do this, we simply mask the transformed signal, multiplying by 1 those components we wish to pass, and by 0 those we wish to reject. Obviously we want to pass the carrier-wave frequency component itself, but we must remember that the spectrum of the information signal is centred on this frequency, and so we must pass a band of frequencies around this centre frequency. Again a frequency-domain filter is constructed. We thus have to construct a bandpass filter of suitable bandwidth to achieve this, and moreover, we must remember to include the right-hand half of the filter! There are no problems here with the Nyquist frequency – at first glance we simply need to avoid picking up

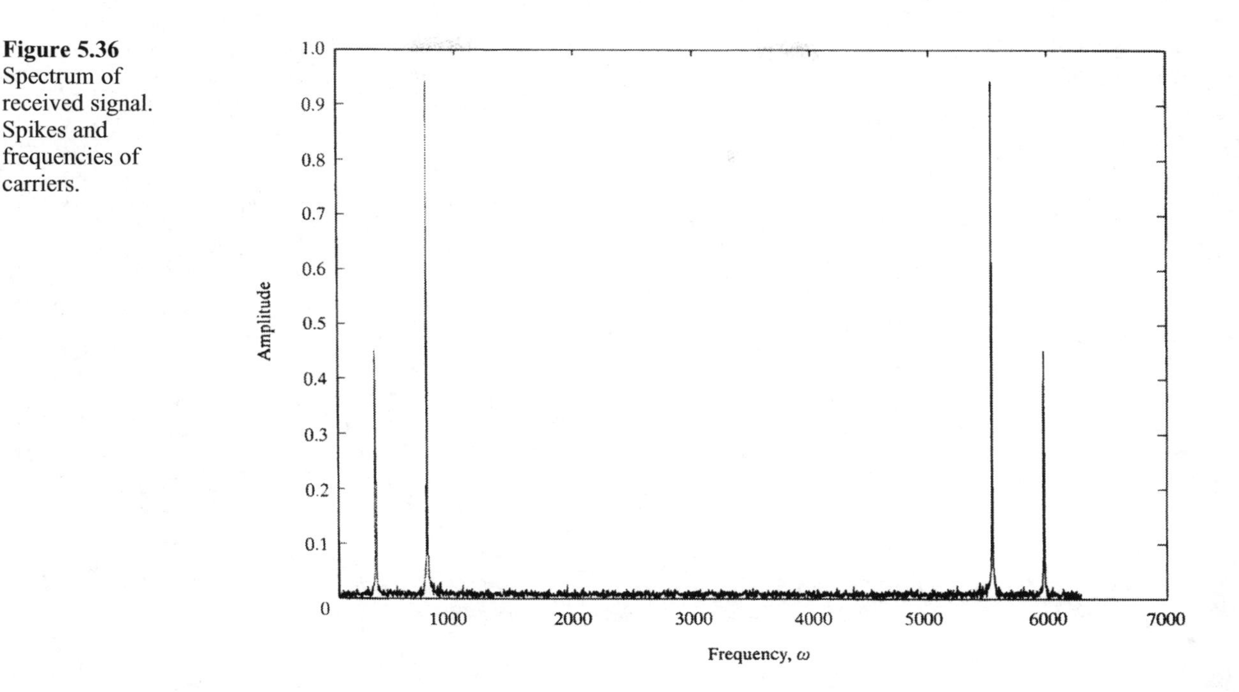

Figure 5.36 Spectrum of received signal. Spikes and frequencies of carriers.

the second carrier wave. However, the larger the bandwidth we select, the more noise we shall pass, and so a compromise has to be found between the necessary width for good signal recovery and noise elimination. Obviously, since we *know* the bandwidth of our information signal in this case, we could make our choice based on this knowledge. This, however, would be cheating, because usually the exact nature of the transmitted information is not known in advance: if it were, there would be little point in sending it! In the M file we have set the half-length of the filter to be a fraction of the carrier frequency. The carrier frequency ω_c represents the maximum possible channel bandwidth, and in practice a channel would have a specified maximum bandwidth associated with it. Figure 5.37 shows the resulting spectrum after application of the bandpass filter, with a bandwidth less than ω_c.

5.8.4 Demodulation stage

The purpose of this operation is to extract the information from the carrier wave, and it can be shown that multiplying the time signal by $\cos \omega_c T$, where ω_c is the frequency of the carrier wave, has the effect of shifting the spectrum of the modulating signal so that it is again centred on the origin. To perform the multiplication operation, we have to return to the time domain, and this is achieved by using the inverse FFT algorithm. In the frequency-domain representation of the demodulated signal there are also copies of the spectrum of the modulating signal present, centred at higher frequencies ($2\omega_c$, $4\omega_c$), and so we must perform a final low-pass filtering operation on the demodulated signal. To do this, we return to the frequency domain using the FFT algorithm again. The result of the demodulation and low-pass filtering operations is shown in Figure 5.38.

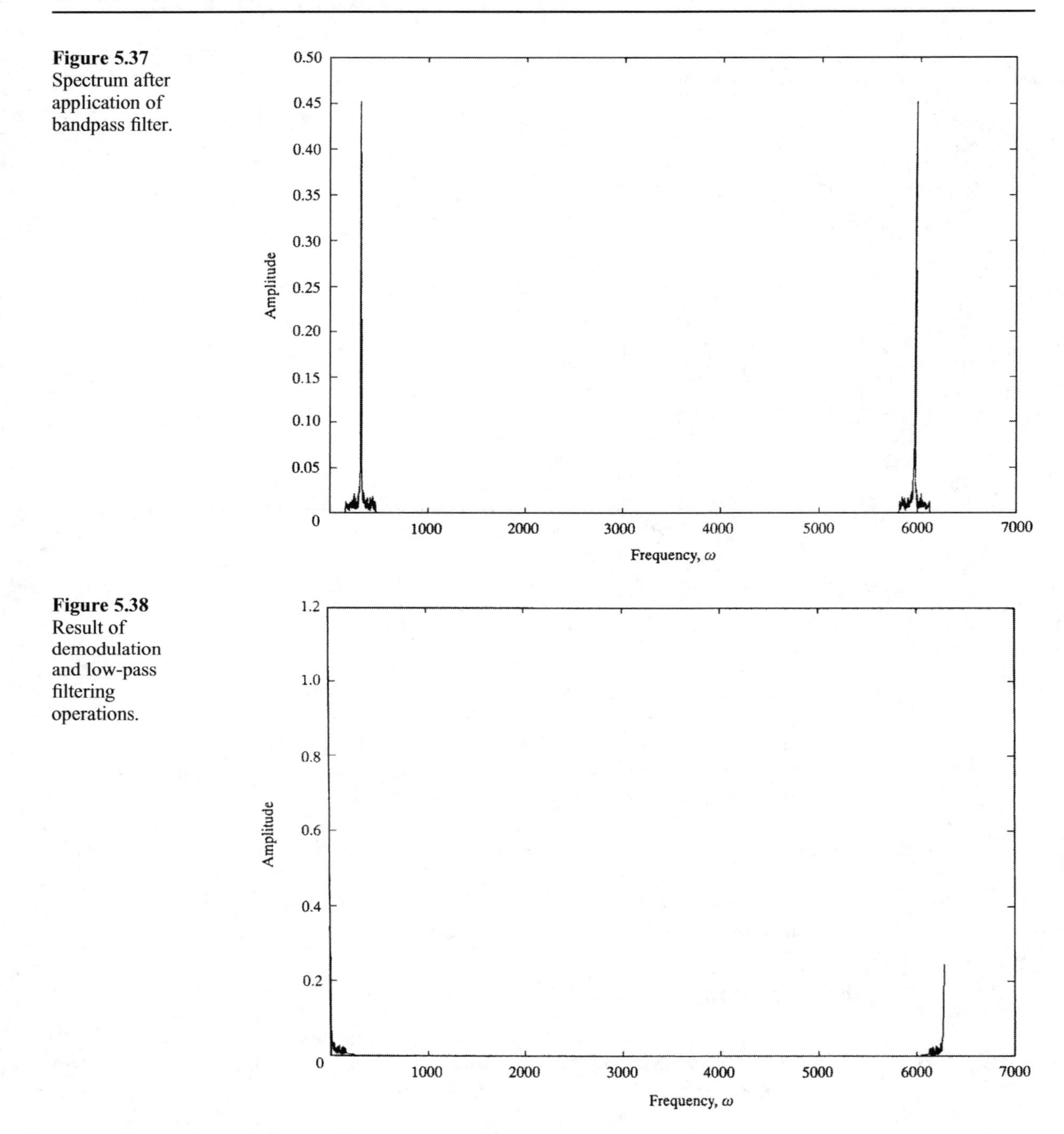

Figure 5.37 Spectrum after application of bandpass filter.

Figure 5.38 Result of demodulation and low-pass filtering operations.

5.8.5 Final signal recovery

The last operation to be performed is to return to the time domain to examine what we have achieved. After calling the inverse FFT routine, the extracted signal is plotted together with the original for comparison. The results with a fairly low value for the added noise are shown in Figure 5.39. If the process is carried out in the absence of noise altogether, excellent signal recovery is achieved, except for the characteristic 'ringing' due to the sharp edges of the filters.

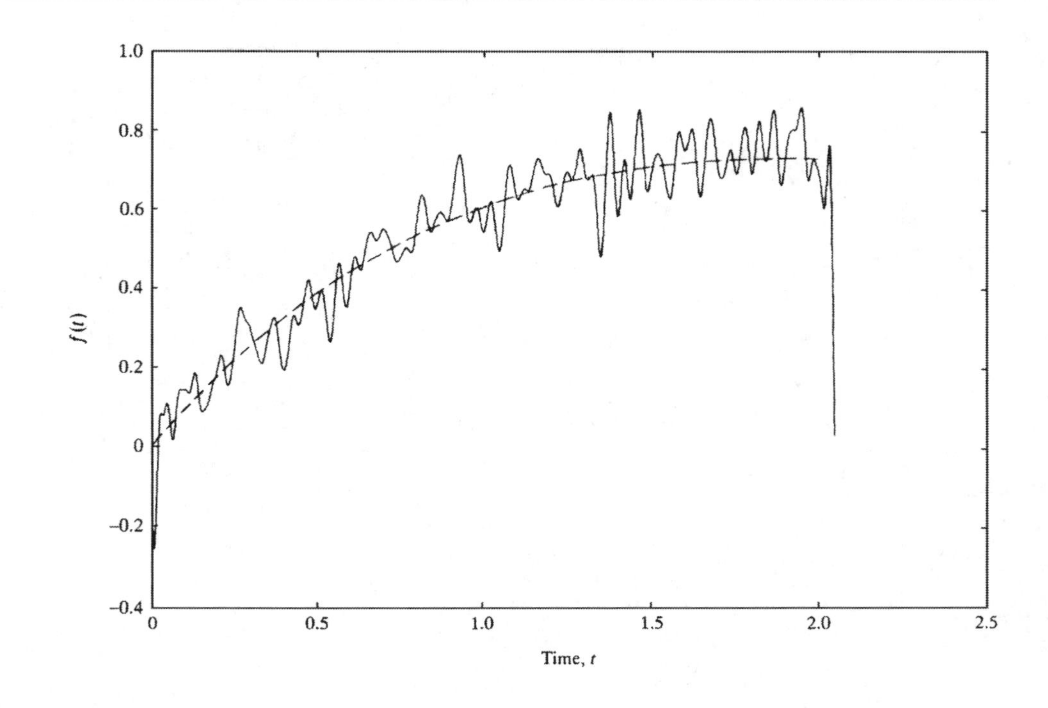

Figure 5.39 Extracted signal, shown together with the original signal.

5.8.6 Further developments

Readers are invited to develop this case study to increase their understanding. Try adding a second information signal modulating the second carrier wave, and extract both signals after 'transmission'. Also add more carrier waves and modulating signals, and investigate signal recovery. If information signal bandwidths are limited to a fixed value, how many signals can be transmitted and recovered satisfactorily? What happens if T is altered? Can the 'ringing' effect be reduced by smoothing the transition from the string of ones to the string of zeros in the filter masks? Seek references to various **window functions** in signal-processing texts to assist in resolving this question.

5.9 Review exercises (1–25)

1 Calculate the Fourier sine transform of the causal function $f(t)$ defined by

$$f(t) = \begin{cases} t & (0 \leqslant t \leqslant 1) \\ 1 & (1 < t \leqslant 2) \\ 0 & (t > 2) \end{cases}$$

2 Show that if $\mathcal{F}\{f(t)\} = F(\mathrm{j}\omega)$ then $\mathcal{F}\{f(-t)\} = F(-\mathrm{j}\omega)$. Show also that

$$\mathcal{F}\{f(-t-a)\} = \mathrm{e}^{\mathrm{j}a\omega}F(-\mathrm{j}\omega)$$

where a is real and positive.

Find $\mathcal{F}\{f(t)\}$ when

$$f(t) = \begin{cases} -\frac{1}{2}\pi & (t < -2) \\ \frac{1}{4}\pi t & (-2 \leqslant t \leqslant 2) \\ \frac{1}{2}\pi & (t > 2) \end{cases}$$

3 Use the result

$$\mathcal{F}[H(t + \tfrac{1}{2}T) - H(t - \tfrac{1}{2}T)] = T \operatorname{sinc} \tfrac{1}{2}\omega T$$

and the frequency convolution result to verify that the Fourier transform of the windowed cosine function

$$f(t) = \cos \omega_0 t\,[H(t + \tfrac{1}{2}T) - H(t - \tfrac{1}{2}T)]$$

is

$$\tfrac{1}{2}T[\operatorname{sinc} \tfrac{1}{2}(\omega - \omega_0)T + \operatorname{sinc} \tfrac{1}{2}(\omega + \omega_0)T]$$

4 Show that

$$\delta(t - t_1) * \delta(t - t_2) = \delta(t - (t_1 + t_2))$$

and hence show that

$$\mathcal{F}\{\cos \omega_0 t\, H(t)\} = \tfrac{1}{2}\pi[\delta(\omega + \omega_0) + \delta(\omega - \omega_0)] + \frac{j\omega}{\omega_0^2 - \omega^2}$$

5 Establish the demodulation property,

$$\mathcal{F}\{f(t)\cos \omega_0 t \cos \omega_0 t\} = \tfrac{1}{2}F(j\omega) + \tfrac{1}{4}[F(j\omega + 2j\omega_0) + F(j\omega + 2j\omega_0)]$$

6 Use the result $\mathcal{F}\{H(t + T) - H(t - T)\} = 2T \operatorname{sinc} \omega T$ and the symmetry property to show that

$$\mathcal{F}\{\operatorname{sinc} t\} = \pi[H(\omega + 1) - \mathrm{H}(\omega - 1)]$$

Check your result by use of the inversion integral.

7 For a wide class of frequently occurring Laplace transforms it is possible to deduce an inversion integral based on the Fourier inversion integral. If $X(s) = \mathcal{L}\{x(t)\}$ is such a transform, we have

$$x(t) = \frac{1}{j2\pi}\int_{\gamma - j\infty}^{\gamma + j\infty} X(s)\,e^{st}\,ds$$

where Re $(s) = \gamma$, with γ real, defines a line in the s plane to the right of all the poles of $X(s)$. Usually the integral can be evaluated using the residue theorem, and we then have

$$x(t) = \sum \text{residues of } X(s)\,e^{st} \text{ at all poles of } X(s)$$

(a) Write down the poles for the transform

$$X(s) = \frac{1}{(s - a)(s - b)}$$

where a and b are real. Calculate the residues of $X(s)\,e^{st}$ at these poles and invert the transform.

(b) Calculate

(i) $\mathcal{L}^{-1}\left\{\dfrac{1}{(s - 2)^2}\right\}$ (ii) $\mathcal{L}^{-1}\left\{\dfrac{1}{s^2(s + 1)}\right\}$

(c) Show that

$$\mathcal{L}^{-1}\left\{\frac{2s}{(s^2 + 1)^2}\right\} = t \sin t$$

8 A linear system has impulse response $h(t)$, so that the output corresponding to an input $u(t)$ is

$$y(t) = \int_{-\infty}^{\infty} h(t - \tau)\,u(\tau)\,d\tau$$

When $u(t) = \cos \omega_0 t$, $y(t) = -\sin \omega_0 t$ $(\omega_0 \geqslant 0)$. Find the output when $u(t)$ is given by

(a) $\cos \omega_0(t + \tfrac{1}{4}\pi)$ (b) $\sin \omega_0 t$

(c) $e^{j\omega_0 t}$ (d) $e^{-j\omega_0 t}$

This system is known as a **Hilbert transformer**.

9 In Section 5.5.1 we established that

$$\mathcal{F}^{-1}\left\{\frac{1}{j\omega}\right\} = \tfrac{1}{2}\operatorname{sgn}(t)$$

where $\operatorname{sgn}(t)$ is the signum function. Deduce that

$$\mathcal{F}\{\operatorname{sgn}(t)\} = \frac{2}{j\omega}$$

and use the symmetry result to demonstrate that

$$\mathcal{F}\left\{-\frac{1}{\pi t}\right\} = j \operatorname{sgn}(\omega)$$

10 The **Hilbert transform** of a signal $f(t)$ is defined by

$$F_{\mathrm{Hi}}(x) = \mathcal{H}\{f(t)\} = \frac{1}{\pi}\int_{-\infty}^{\infty} \frac{f(\tau)}{\tau - x}\,d\tau$$

Show that the operation of taking the Hilbert transform is equivalent to the convolution

$$-\frac{1}{\pi t} * f(t)$$

and hence deduce that the Hilbert-transformed signal has an amplitude spectrum $F_{\mathrm{Hi}}(j\omega)$ identical with $f(t)$. Show also that the phase of the transformed signal is changed by $\pm\tfrac{1}{2}\pi$, depending on the sign of ω.

11 Show that

$$\frac{t}{(t^2 + a^2)(t - x)} = \frac{1}{x^2 + a^2}\left(\frac{a^2}{t^2 + a^2} + \frac{x}{t - x} - \frac{xt}{t^2 + a^2}\right)$$

Hence show that the Hilbert transform of

$$f(t) = \frac{t}{t^2 + a^2} \quad (a > 0)$$

is

$$\frac{a}{x^2 + a^2}$$

12 If $F_{Hi}(x) = \mathcal{H}\{f(t)\}$ is the Hilbert transform of $f(t)$, establish the following properties:

(a) $\mathcal{H}\{f(a + t)\} = F_{Hi}(x + a)$

(b) $\mathcal{H}\{f(at)\} = F_{Hi}(ax) \quad (a > 0)$

(c) $\mathcal{H}\{f(-at)\} = -F_{Hi}(-ax) \quad (a > 0)$

(d) $\mathcal{H}\left\{\frac{df}{dt}\right\} = \frac{d}{dx} F_{Hi}(x)$

(e) $\mathcal{H}\{tf(t)\} = xF_{Hi}(x) + \frac{1}{\pi}\int_{-\infty}^{\infty} f(t)\,dt$

13 Show that

$$f(t) = -\frac{1}{\pi}\int_{-\infty}^{\infty} \frac{F_{Hi}(x)}{x - t}\,dx$$

14 Define the **analytic signal** associated with the real signal $f(t)$ as

$$f_a(t) = f(t) - jF_{Hi}(t)$$

where $F_{Hi}(t)$ is the Hilbert transform of $f(t)$. Use the method of Review exercise 13 to show that

$$\mathcal{F}\{f_a(t)\} = F_a(j\omega) = \begin{cases} 2F(j\omega) & (\omega > 0) \\ 0 & (\omega < 0) \end{cases}$$

15 Use the result $\mathcal{F}\{H(t)\} = 1/j\omega + \pi\delta(\omega)$ and the symmetry property to show that

$$\mathcal{F}^{-1}\{H(\omega)\} = \tfrac{1}{2}\delta(t) + \frac{j}{2\pi t}$$

(*Hint*: $H(-\omega) = 1 - H(\omega)$.)

Hence show that if $\hat{f}(t)$ is defined by $\mathcal{F}\{\hat{f}(t)\} = 2H(\omega)F(j\omega)$ then $\hat{f}(t) = f(t) - jF_{Hi}(t)$, the analytic signal associated with $f(t)$, where $F(j\omega) = \mathcal{F}\{f(t)\}$ and $F_{Hi}(t) = \mathcal{H}\{f(t)\}$.

If $f(t) = \cos\omega_0 t$ $(\omega_0 > 0)$, find $\mathcal{F}\{f(t)\}$ and hence $\hat{f}(t)$. Deduce that

$$\mathcal{H}\{\cos\omega_0 t\} = -\sin\omega_0 t$$

By considering the signal $g(t) = \sin\omega_0 t$ $(\omega_0 > 0)$, show that

$$\mathcal{H}\{\sin\omega_0 t\} = \cos\omega_0 t$$

16 A causal system has impulse response $\bar{h}(t)$, where $\bar{h}(t) = 0$ $(t < 0)$. Define the even part $\bar{h}_e(t)$ of $\bar{h}(t)$ as

$$\bar{h}_e(t) = \tfrac{1}{2}[\bar{h}(t) + \bar{h}(-t)]$$

and the odd part $\bar{h}_o(t)$ as

$$\bar{h}_o(t) = \tfrac{1}{2}[\bar{h}(t) - \bar{h}(-t)]$$

Since $\bar{h}(t) = 0$ $(t < 0)$ deduce that

$$\bar{h}_o(t) = \text{sgn}(t)\bar{h}_e(t)$$

and that

$$\bar{h}(t) = \bar{h}_e(t) + \text{sgn}(t)\bar{h}_e(t) \quad \text{for all } t$$

Verify this result for $\bar{h}(t) = \sin t\, H(t)$. Take the Fourier transform of this result to establish that

$$\bar{H}(j\omega) = \bar{H}_e(j\omega) + j\mathcal{H}\{\bar{H}_e(j\omega)\}$$

Let $\bar{h}(t) = e^{-at}H(t)$ be such a causal impulse response. By taking the Fourier transform, deduce the Hilbert transform pair

$$\mathcal{H}\left\{\frac{a}{a^2 + t^2}\right\} = -\frac{x}{a^2 + x^2}$$

Use the result

$$\mathcal{H}\{tf(t)\} = x\mathcal{H}\{f(t)\} + \frac{1}{\pi}\int_{-\infty}^{\infty} f(t)\,dt$$

to show that

$$\mathcal{H}\left\{\frac{t}{a^2 + t^2}\right\} = \frac{a}{x^2 + a^2}$$

17 The **Hartley transform** is defined as

$$F_H(s) = \mathrm{H}\{f(t)\} = \int_{-\infty}^{\infty} f(t)\,\text{cas}\,2\pi st\,dt$$

where $\text{cas}\,t = \cos t + \sin t$. Find the Hartley transform of the functions

(a) $f(t) = e^{-at}H(t) \quad (a > 0)$

(b) $f(t) = \begin{cases} 0 & (|t| > T) \\ 1 & (|t| \leqslant T) \end{cases}$

18 An alternative form of the Fourier transform pair is given by

$$F(jp) = \int_{-\infty}^{\infty} f(t)\,e^{-j2\pi pt}\,dt$$

$$g(t) = \int_{-\infty}^{\infty} G(\mathrm{j}p)\,\mathrm{e}^{\mathrm{j}2\pi pt}\,\mathrm{d}t$$

where the frequency p is now measured in hertz. Define the even part of the Hartley transform as

$$E(s) = \tfrac{1}{2}[F_{\mathrm{H}}(s) + F_{\mathrm{H}}(-s)]$$

and the odd part as

$$O(s) = \tfrac{1}{2}[F_{\mathrm{H}}(s) - F_{\mathrm{H}}(-s)]$$

Show that the Fourier transform of $f(t)$ is given by

$$F(\mathrm{j}p) = E(p) - \mathrm{j}O(p)$$

and confirm your result for $f(t) = \mathrm{e}^{-2t}H(t)$.

19 Prove the **time-shift result** for the Hartley transform in the form

$$\mathsf{H}\{f(t-T)\} = \sin(2\pi Ts)\,F_{\mathrm{H}}(-s) + \cos(2\pi Ts)\,F_{\mathrm{H}}(s)$$

20 Using the alternative form of the Fourier transform given in Review exercise 18, it can be shown that the Fourier transform of the Heaviside step function is

$$\mathscr{F}\{H(t)\} = \frac{1}{\mathrm{j}p\pi} + \tfrac{1}{2}\delta(p)$$

Show that the Hartley transform of $H(t)$ is then

$$\tfrac{1}{2}\delta(s) + \frac{1}{s\pi}$$

and deduce that the Hartley transform of $H(t - \tfrac{1}{2})$ is

$$\tfrac{1}{2}\delta(s) + \frac{\cos \pi s - \sin \pi s}{s\pi}$$

21 Show that $\mathsf{H}\{\delta(t)\} = 1$ and deduce that $\mathsf{H}\{1\} = \delta(s)$. Show also that $\mathsf{H}\{\delta(t - t_0)\} = \operatorname{cas} 2\pi s t_0$ and that

$$\mathsf{H}\{\operatorname{cas} 2\pi s_0 t\} = \mathsf{H}\{\cos 2\pi s_0 t\} + \mathsf{H}\{\sin 2\pi s_0 t\} = \delta(s - s_0)$$

22 Prove the Hartley transform **modulation theorem** in the form

$$\mathsf{H}\{f(t)\cos 2\pi s_0 t\} = \tfrac{1}{2}F_{\mathrm{H}}(s - s_0) + \tfrac{1}{2}F_{\mathrm{H}}(s + s_0)$$

Hence show that

$$\mathsf{H}\{\cos 2\pi s_0 t\} = \tfrac{1}{2}[\delta(s - s_0) + \delta(s + s_0)]$$

$$\mathsf{H}\{\sin 2\pi s_0 t\} = \tfrac{1}{2}[\delta(s - s_0) - \delta(s + s_0)]$$

23 Show that

$$\mathscr{F}\{\tan^{-1} t\} = \frac{\pi\,\mathrm{e}^{-|\omega|}}{\mathrm{j}\omega}$$

$$\left(\textit{Hint:}\ \text{Consider} \int_{-\infty}^{t} (1 + t^2)^{-1}\,\mathrm{d}t.\right)$$

24 Show that

$$x(t) = \tfrac{1}{2}(1 + \cos \omega_0 t)[H(t + \tfrac{1}{2}T) - H(t - \tfrac{1}{2}T)]$$

has Fourier transform

$$T[\operatorname{sinc} \omega + \tfrac{1}{2}\operatorname{sinc}(\omega - \omega_0) + \tfrac{1}{2}\operatorname{sinc}(\omega + \omega_0)]$$

25 The **discrete Hartley transform** of the sequence $\{f(r)\}_{r=0}^{N-1}$ is defined by

$$\mathsf{H}(v) = \frac{1}{N}\sum_{r=0}^{N-1} f(r)\operatorname{cas}\left(\frac{2\pi vr}{N}\right) \quad (v = 0, 1, \ldots, N-1)$$

The inverse transform is

$$f(r) = \sum_{v=0}^{N-1} \mathsf{H}(v)\operatorname{cas}\left(\frac{2\pi vr}{N}\right) \quad (r = 0, \ldots, N-1)$$

Show that in the case $N = 4$,

$$\mathbf{H} = \boldsymbol{T}\boldsymbol{f}$$

$$\mathbf{H} = [\mathsf{H}(0)\ \ \mathsf{H}(1)\ \ \mathsf{H}(2)\ \ \mathsf{H}(3)]^{\mathrm{T}}$$

$$\boldsymbol{f} = [f(0)\ \ f(1)\ \ f(2)\ \ f(3)]^{\mathrm{T}}$$

$$\boldsymbol{T} = \frac{1}{4}\begin{bmatrix} 1 & 1 & 1 & 1 \\ 1 & 1 & -1 & -1 \\ 1 & -1 & 1 & -1 \\ 1 & -1 & -1 & 1 \end{bmatrix}$$

Hence compute the discrete Hartley transform of the sequence $\{1, 2, 3, 4\}$. Show that $\boldsymbol{T}^2 = \frac{1}{4}\boldsymbol{I}$ and hence that $\boldsymbol{T}^{-1} = 4\boldsymbol{T}$, and verify that applying the $\boldsymbol{T}^{-1}$ operator regains the original sequence.

6 Applied Probability and Statistics

Chapter 6 Contents

6.1 Introduction

Applications of probability and statistics in engineering are very far-reaching. Data from experiments have to be analysed and conclusions drawn, decisions have to be made, production and distribution have to be organized and monitored, and quality has to be controlled. In all of these activities probability and statistics have at least a supporting role to play, and sometimes a central one.

The distinction between applied probability and statistics is blurred, but essentially it is this: **applied probability** is about mathematical modelling of a situation that involves random uncertainty, whereas **statistics** is the business of handling data and drawing conclusions, and can be regarded as a branch of applied probability. Most of this chapter is about statistics, but Section 6.10 on queueing theory is applied probability.

When applying statistical methods to a practical problem, the most visible activity is the processing of data, using either a hand calculator or, increasingly often, a computer statistical package. Either way, a formula or standard procedure from a textbook is being applied to the data. The relative ease and obviousness of this activity sometimes leads to a false sense that there is nothing more to it. On the contrary, the handling of the data (by whatever means) is quite superficial compared with the essential task of trying to understand both the problem at hand and the assumptions upon which the various statistical procedures are based. If the wrong procedure is chosen, a wrong conclusion may be drawn.

It is, unfortunately, all too easy to use a formula while overlooking its theoretical basis, which largely determines its applicability. It is true that there are some statistical methods that continue to work reliably even where the assumptions upon which they are based do not hold (such methods are called **robust**), but it is unwise to rely too heavily upon this and even worse to be unaware of the assumptions at all.

The conclusions of a statistical analysis are often expressed in a qualified way such as 'We can be 95% sure that . . .'. At first this seems vague and inadequate. Perhaps a decision has to be made, but the statistical conclusion is not expressed simply as 'yes' or 'no'. A statistical analysis is rather like a legal case in which the witness is required to tell 'the whole truth and nothing but the truth'. In the present context 'the whole truth' means that the statistician must glean as much information from the data as is possible until nothing but pure randomness remains. 'Nothing but the truth' means that the statistician must not state the conclusion with any greater degree of certainty or confidence than is justified by the analysis. In fact there is a practical compromise between truth and precision that will be explained in Section 6.3.3. The result of all this is that the decision-maker is aided by the analysis but not pre-empted by it.

In this chapter we shall first review the basic theory of probability and then cover some applications that are beneficial in engineering and many other fields: the statistics of means, proportions and correlation, linear regression and goodness-of-fit testing, queueing theory and quality control.

6.2 Review of basic probability theory

This section contains an overview of the basic theory used in the remainder of this chapter. No attempt is made to explain or justify the ideas or results. For the same reason there are no examples or exercises. In the process of reviewing the basic theory, this section also establishes the pattern of notation used throughout the chapter, which follows standard conventions as far as possible. No reader should embark on this chapter without having a fairly thorough understanding of the material in this section.

6.2.1 The rules of probability

We associate a probability $P(A)$ with an **event** A, which in general is a subset of a **sample space** S. The usual set-theoretic operations apply to the events (subsets) in S, and there are corresponding rules that must be satisfied by the probabilities.

Complement rule

$$P(S - A) = 1 - P(A)$$

The **complement** of an event A is often written as $\bar{A}$.

Addition rule

$$P(A \cup B) = P(A) + P(B) - P(A \cap B)$$

For **disjoint** events, $A \cap B = \varnothing$, and the addition rule takes the simple form

$$P(A \cup B) = P(A) + P(B)$$

Product rule

$$P(A \cap B) = P(A)P(B \mid A)$$

This is actually the definition of the **conditional probability** $P(B \mid A)$ of B given A. If A and B are **independent** then the product rule takes the simple form

$$P(A \cap B) = P(A)P(B)$$

6.2.2 Random variables

A **random variable** has a sample space of possible numerical values together with a **distribution** of probabilities. Random variables can be either **discrete** or **continuous**. For a discrete random variable (X, say) the possible values can be written as a list $\{v_1, v_2, v_3, \ldots\}$ with corresponding probabilities $P(X = v_1)$, $P(X = v_2)$, $P(X = v_3)$, $\ldots$. The **mean** of X is then defined as

$$\mu_X = \sum_k v_k P(X = v_k)$$

(sum over all possible values), and is a measure of the central location of the distribution. The **variance** of X is defined as

$$\mathrm{Var}(X) = \sigma_X^2 = \sum_k (v_k - \mu_X)^2 P(X = v_k)$$

and is a measure of dispersion of the distribution about the mean. The symbols μ and σ^2 are conventional for these quantities. In general, the **expected value** of a function $h(X)$ of X is defined as

$$E\{h(X)\} = \sum_k h(v_k) P(X = v_k)$$

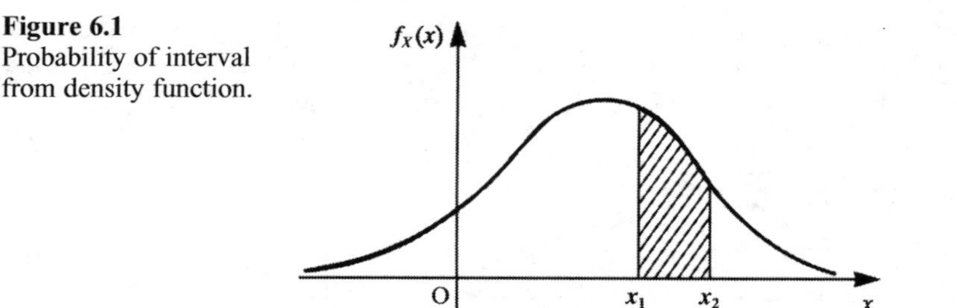

Figure 6.1
Probability of interval from density function.

of which the mean and variance are special cases. The **standard deviation** σ_X is the square root of the variance.

For a **continuous** random variable (X, say), there is a **probability density function** $f_X(x)$ and a **cumulative distribution function** $F_X(x)$. The cumulative distribution function is defined as

$$F_X(x) = P(X \leqslant x)$$

and is the indefinite integral of the density function:

$$F_X(x) = \int_{-\infty}^{x} f_X(t)\,\mathrm{d}t$$

These functions determine the probabilities of events for the random variable. The probability that the variable X takes a value within the real interval (x_1, x_2) is the area under the density function over that interval, or equivalently the difference in values of the distribution function at its ends:

$$P(x_1 < X < x_2) = \int_{x_1}^{x_2} f_X(t)\,\mathrm{d}t = F_X(x_2) - F_X(x_1)$$

(see Figure 6.1). Note that the events $x_1 < X < x_2$, $x_1 \leqslant X < x_2$, $x_1 < X \leqslant x_2$ and $x_1 \leqslant X \leqslant x_2$ are all equivalent in probability terms for a continuous random variable X because the probability of X being exactly equal to either x_1 or x_2 is zero. The mean and variance of X, and the expected value of a function $h(X)$, are defined in terms of the density function by

$$\mu_X = \int_{-\infty}^{\infty} x f_X(x)\,\mathrm{d}x$$

$$\mathrm{Var}(X) = \sigma_X^2 = \int_{-\infty}^{\infty} (x - \mu_X)^2 f_X(x)\,\mathrm{d}x$$

$$E\{h(X)\} = \int_{-\infty}^{\infty} h(x) f_X(x)\,\mathrm{d}x$$

These definitions assume that the random variable is defined for values of x from $-\infty$ to ∞. If the random variable is defined in general for values in some real interval, say (a, b), then the domain of integration can be restricted to that interval, or alternatively the density function can be defined to be zero outside that interval.

Just as events can be independent (and then obey a simple product rule of probabilities), so can random variables be independent. We shall consider this in more detail in Section 6.4. Means and variances of random variables (whether discrete or continuous) have the following important properties (X and Y are random variables, and c is an arbitrary constant):

$$E(cX) = cE(X) = c\mu_X$$

$$\text{Var}(cX) = c^2\text{Var}(X) = c^2\sigma_X^2$$

$$E(X + c) = E(X) + c = \mu_X + c$$

$$\text{Var}(X + c) = \text{Var}(X) = \sigma_X^2$$

$$E(X + Y) = E(X) + E(Y) = \mu_X + \mu_Y$$

(this applies whether or not X and Y are independent),

$$\text{Var}(X + Y) = \text{Var}(X) + \text{Var}(Y) = \sigma_X^2 + \sigma_Y^2$$

(this applies only when X and Y are independent).
It is also useful to note that $\text{Var}(X) = E(X^2) - [E(X)]^2$.

6.2.3 The Bernoulli, binomial and Poisson distributions

The simplest example of a discrete distribution is the **Bernoulli distribution**. This has just two values: $X = 1$ with probability p and $X = 0$ with probability $1 - p$, from which the mean and variance are p and $p(1 - p)$ respectively.

The binomial and Poisson distributions are families of discrete distributions whose probabilities are generated by formulae, and which arise in many real situations. The **binomial distribution** governs the number (X, say) of 'successes' in n independent 'trials', with a probability p of 'success' at each trial:

$$P(X = k) = \binom{n}{k} p^k (1 - p)^{n-k}$$

where the range of possible values (k) is $\{0, 1, 2, \ldots, n\}$. The binomial distribution can be thought of as the sum of n independent Bernoulli random variables. This distribution (more properly, *family* of distributions) has two **parameters**, n and p. In terms of these parameters, the mean and variance are

$$\mu_X = np$$

$$\sigma_X^2 = np(1 - p)$$

The **Poisson distribution** is defined as

$$P(X = k) = \frac{\lambda^k e^{-\lambda}}{k!}$$

where the range of possible values (k) is the set of non-negative integers $\{0, 1, 2, \ldots\}$. This has mean and variance both equal to the single parameter λ (see Section 6.7.1), and, by setting $\lambda = np$, provides a useful approximation to the binomial distribution that works when n is large and p is small (see Section 6.7.2). As a guide, the approximation can be used when $n \geqslant 25$ and $p \leqslant 0.1$. The Poisson distribution has many other uses, as will be seen in Section 6.10.

6.2.4 The normal distribution

This is a family of continuous distributions with probability density function given by

$$f_X(x) = \frac{1}{\sigma_X\sqrt{(2\pi)}}\exp\left[-\tfrac{1}{2}\left(\frac{x-\mu_X}{\sigma_X}\right)^2\right]$$

for $-\infty < x < +\infty$, where the parameters μ_X and σ_X are the mean and standard deviation of the distribution. It is conventional to denote the fact that a random variable X has a normal distribution by

$$X \sim N(\mu_X, \sigma_X^2)$$

The **standard normal distribution** is a special case with zero mean and unit variance, often denoted by Z:

$$Z \sim N(0, 1)$$

Tables of the standard normal cumulative distribution function

$$\Phi(z) = P(Z \leqslant z) = \frac{1}{\sqrt{(2\pi)}}\int_{-\infty}^{z} \mathrm{e}^{-t^2/2}\,\mathrm{d}t$$

are widely available (see for example Figure 6.2). These tables can be used for probability calculations involving arbitrary normal random variables. For example, if $X \sim N(\mu_X, \sigma_X^2)$ then

$$P(X \leqslant a) = P\left(\frac{X-\mu_X}{\sigma_X} \leqslant \frac{a-\mu_X}{\sigma_X}\right) = \Phi\left(\frac{a-\mu_X}{\sigma_X}\right)$$

The key result for applications of the normal distribution is the **central limit theorem**: if $\{X_1, X_2, X_3, \ldots, X_n\}$ are independent and identically distributed random variables (the distribution being arbitrary), each with mean μ_X and variance σ_X^2, and if

$$W_n = \frac{X_1 + \ldots + X_n}{n}, \qquad Z_n = \frac{X_1 + \ldots + X_n - n\mu_X}{\sigma_X\sqrt{n}}$$

then, as $n \to \infty$, the distributions of W_n and Z_n tend to $W_n \sim N(\mu_X, \sigma_X^2/n)$ and $Z_n \sim N(0, 1)$ respectively. Loosely speaking, the sum of independent identically distributed random variables tends to a normal distribution.

This theorem is proved in Section 6.7.3, and in the key to many statistical processes, some of which are described in Section 6.3. One corollary is that the normal distribution can be used to approximate the binomial distribution when n is sufficiently large: if X is binomial with parameters n and p then the approximating distribution (by equating the means and variances) is $Y \sim N(np, np(1-p))$.

$$P(X \leqslant k) \simeq \Phi\left(\frac{k+0.5-np}{\sqrt{[np(1-p)]}}\right)$$

$$P(X = k) \simeq \Phi\left(\frac{k+0.5-np}{\sqrt{[np(1-p)]}}\right) - \Phi\left(\frac{k-0.5-np}{\sqrt{[np(1-p)]}}\right)$$

As a guide, the approximation can be used when $n \geqslant 25$ and $0.1 \leqslant p \leqslant 0.9$.

Figure 6.2 Table of the standard normal cumulative distribution function $\Phi(z)$.

z	.00	.01	.02	.03	.04	.05	.06	.07	.08	.09
.0	.5000	.5040	.5080	.5120	.5160	.5199	.5239	.5279	.5319	.5359
.1	.5398	.5438	.5478	.5517	.5557	.5596	.5636	.5675	.5714	.5753
.2	.5793	.5832	.5871	.5910	.5948	.5987	.6026	.6064	.6103	.6141
.3	.6179	.6217	.6255	.6293	.6331	.6368	.6406	.6443	.6480	.6517
.4	.6554	.6591	.6628	.6664	.6700	.6736	.6772	.6808	.6844	.6879
.5	.6915	.6950	.6985	.7019	.7054	.7088	.7123	.7157	.7190	.7224
.6	.7257	.7291	.7324	.7357	.7389	.7422	.7454	.7486	.7517	.7549
.7	.7580	.7611	.7642	.7673	.7704	.7734	.7764	.7794	.7823	.7852
.8	.7881	.7910	.7939	.7967	.7995	.8023	.8051	.8078	.8106	.8133
.9	.8159	.8186	.8212	.8238	.8264	.8289	.8315	.8340	.8365	.8389
1.0	.8413	.8438	.8461	.8485	.8508	.8531	.8554	.8577	.8599	.8621
1.1	.8643	.8665	.8686	.8708	.8729	.8749	.8770	.8790	.8810	.8830
1.2	.8849	.8869	.8888	.8907	.8925	.8944	.8962	.8980	.8997	.9015
1.3	.9032	.9049	.9066	.9082	.9099	.9115	.9131	.9147	.9162	.9177
1.4	.9192	.9207	.9222	.9236	.9251	.9265	.9279	.9292	.9306	.9319
1.5	.9332	.9345	.9357	.9370	.9382	.9394	.9406	.9418	.9429	.9441
1.6	.9452	.9463	.9474	.9484	.9495	.9505	.9515	.9525	.9535	.9545
1.7	.9554	.9564	.9573	.9582	.9591	.9599	.9608	.9616	.9625	.9633
1.8	.9641	.9649	.9656	.9664	.9671	.9678	.9686	.9693	.9699	.9706
1.9	.9713	.9719	.9726	.9732	.9738	.9744	.9750	.9756	.9761	.9767
2.0	.9772	.9778	.9783	.9788	.9793	.9798	.9803	.9808	.9812	.9817
2.1	.9821	.9826	.9830	.9834	.9838	.9842	.9846	.9850	.9854	.9857
2.2	.9861	.9864	.9868	.9871	.9875	.9878	.9881	.9884	.9887	.9890
2.3	.9893	.9896	.9898	.9901	.9904	.9906	.9909	.9911	.9913	.9916
2.4	.9918	.9920	.9922	.9925	.9927	.9929	.9931	.9932	.9934	.9936
2.5	.9938	.9940	.9941	.9943	.9945	.9946	.9948	.9949	.9951	.9952
2.6	.9953	.9955	.9956	.9957	.9959	.9960	.9961	.9962	.9963	.9964
2.7	.9965	.9966	.9967	.9968	.9969	.9970	.9971	.9972	.9973	.9974
2.8	.9974	.9975	.9976	.9977	.9977	.9978	.9979	.9979	.9980	.9981
2.9	.9981	.9982	.9982	.9983	.9984	.9984	.9985	.9985	.9986	.9986
3.0	.9987	.9987	.9987	.9988	.9988	.9989	.9989	.9989	.9990	.9990
3.1	.9990	.9991	.9991	.9991	.9992	.9992	.9992	.9992	.9993	.9993
3.2	.9993	.9993	.9994	.9994	.9994	.9994	.9994	.9995	.9995	.9995
3.3	.9995	.9995	.9995	.9996	.9996	.9996	.9996	.9996	.9996	.9997
3.4	.9997	.9997	.9997	.9997	.9997	.9997	.9997	.9997	.9997	.9998

z	1.282	1.645	1.960	2.326	2.576	3.090	3.291	3.891	4.417
$\Phi(z)$	.90	.95	.975	.99	.995	.999	.9995	.999 95	.999 995
$2[1-\Phi(z)]$	.20	.10	.05	.02	.01	.002	.001	.000 1	.000 01

6.2.5 Sample measures

It is conventional to denote a random variable by an upper-case letter (X, say), and an actual observed value of it by the corresponding lower-case letter (x, say). An observed value x will be one of the set of possible values (sample space) for the random variable, which for a discrete random variable may be written as a list of the form $\{v_1, v_2, v_3, \ldots\}$.

It is possible to observe a random variable many times (say n times) and obtain a series of values. In this case we assume that the random variable X refers to a **population** (whose characteristics may be unknown), and the series of random variables $\{X_1, X_2, \ldots, X_n\}$ as a **sample**. Each X_i is assumed to have the characteristics of the population, so they all have the same distribution. The actual series of values $\{x_1, x_2, \ldots, x_n\}$ consists of data upon which we can work, but it is useful to define certain sample measures in terms of the random variables $\{X_1, X_2, \ldots, X_n\}$ in order to interpret the data. Principal among these measures are the **sample average** and **sample variance**, defined as

$$\bar{X} = \frac{1}{n}\sum_{i=1}^{n} X_i, \qquad S_X^2 = \frac{1}{n}\sum_{i=1}^{n}(X_i - \bar{X})^2$$

respectively, and it is useful to note that the sample variance is the average of the squares minus the square of the average:

$$S_X^2 = \overline{X^2} - (\bar{X})^2$$

We shall also need the following alternative definition of sample variance in Section 6.3.5:

$$S_{X,n-1}^2 = \frac{1}{n-1}\sum_{i=1}^{n}(X_i - \bar{X})^2$$

We can use the properties of means and variances (summarized in Section 6.2.2) to find the mean and variance of the sample average as follows:

$$\begin{aligned} E(\bar{X}) &= \frac{1}{n}E(X_1 + \ldots + X_n) = \frac{1}{n}[E(X_1) + \ldots + E(X_n)] \\ &= \frac{n\mu_X}{n} = \mu_X \end{aligned}$$

$$\begin{aligned} \mathrm{Var}(\bar{X}) &= \frac{1}{n^2}\mathrm{Var}(X_1 + \ldots + X_n) = \frac{1}{n^2}[\mathrm{Var}(X_1) + \ldots + \mathrm{Var}(X_n)] \\ &= \frac{n\sigma_X^2}{n^2} = \frac{\sigma_X^2}{n} \end{aligned}$$

Here we are assuming that the population mean and variance are μ_X and σ_X^2 respectively (which may be unknown values in practice), and that the observations of the random variables X_i are *independent*, a very important requirement in statistics.

6.3 Estimating parameters

6.3.1 Interval estimates and hypothesis tests

The first step in statistics is to take some data from an experiment and make inferences about the values of certain parameters. Such parameters could be the mean and variance of a population, or the correlation between two variables for a population. The data are never sufficient to determine the values exactly, but two kinds of inferences can be made:

(a) a range of values can be quoted, within which it is believed with high probability that the population parameter value lies, or

(b) a decision can be made as to whether or not the data are compatible with a particular value of the parameter.

The first of these is called **interval estimation**, and provides an assessment of the value that is rather more honest than merely quoting a single number derived from the sample data, which may be more or less uncertain depending upon the sample size. The second approach is called **hypothesis testing** and allows a value of particular interest to be assessed. These two approaches are usually covered in separate chapters in introductory textbooks on statistics, but they are closely related and are often used in conjunction with each other. Tests of simple hypotheses about parameter values will therefore be covered here within the context of interval estimation.

6.3.2 Distribution of the sample average

Suppose that a clearly identified population has a numerical characteristic with an unknown mean value, such as the mean lifetime for a kind of electronic component or the mean salary for a job category. A natural way to estimate this unknown mean is to take a sample from the population, measure the appropriate characteristic, and find the average value. If the sample size is n and the measured values are $\{x_1, x_2, \dots, x_n\}$ then the average value

$$\bar{x} = \frac{1}{n}\sum_{i=1}^{n} x_i$$

is a reasonable estimate of the population mean μ_X provided that the sample is *representative* and *independent*, and the size n is sufficiently large.

We can be more precise about how useful this estimate is if we treat the sample average as a random variable. Now we have a sample $\{X_1, X_2, \dots, X_n\}$ with average

$$\bar{X} = \frac{1}{n}\sum_{i=1}^{n} X_i$$

and the mean and variance of $\bar{X}$ are given by

$$E(\bar{X}) = \mu_X, \qquad \mathrm{Var}(\bar{X}) = \frac{\sigma_X^2}{n}$$

(see Section 6.2.5). This shows that the expected value of the average is indeed equal to the population mean, and that the variance is smaller for larger samples. However, we can go further. The central limit theorem (Section 6.2.4) tells us that sums of identical random variables tend to have a normal distribution regardless of the distribution of the variables themselves. The only requirement is that a sufficient number of variables contribute to the sum (the actual number required depends very much on the shape of the underlying distribution).

The sample average is a sum of random variables, and therefore has (approximately) a normal distribution for a sufficiently large sample:

$$\bar{X} \sim N(\mu_X, \sigma_X^2/n)$$

This allows us to use a general method of inference concerning means instead of a separate method for each underlying distribution – even if this were known, which is usually not the case. In practice, a sample size of 25 or more is usually sufficient for the normal approximation.

Example 6.1 For all children taking an examination, the mean mark was 60%, with a standard deviation of 8%. A particular class of 30 children achieved an average of 63%. Is this unusual?

Solution The average of 63% is higher than the mean, but not by very much. We do not know the true distribution of marks, but the sample average has (approximately) a normal distribution. We can test the idea that this particular class result is a fluke by reducing the sample average to a standard normal in the manner described in Section 6.2.4 and checking its value against the table of the cumulative distribution function $\Phi(z)$ (Figure 6.2):

$$P(\bar{X} \geqslant 63) = P\left(\frac{\bar{X} - 60}{8/\sqrt{30}} \geqslant \frac{63 - 60}{8/\sqrt{30}}\right) = 1 - \Phi(2.054) = 0.020$$

It is unlikely (one chance in 50) that an average as high as this could occur by chance, assuming that the ability of the class is typical. Figure 6.3 illustrates that the result is towards the tail of the distribution. It therefore seems that this class is unusually successful.

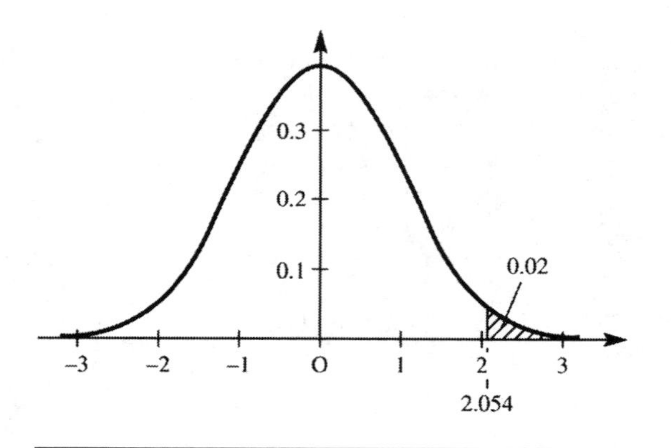

Figure 6.3 Normal density function for Example 6.1.

6.3.3 Confidence interval for the mean

A useful notation will be introduced here. For the standard normal distribution, define z_α to be the point on the z axis for which the area under the density function to its right is equal to α:

$$P(Z > z_\alpha) = \alpha$$

or equivalently

$$\Phi(z_\alpha) = 1 - \alpha$$

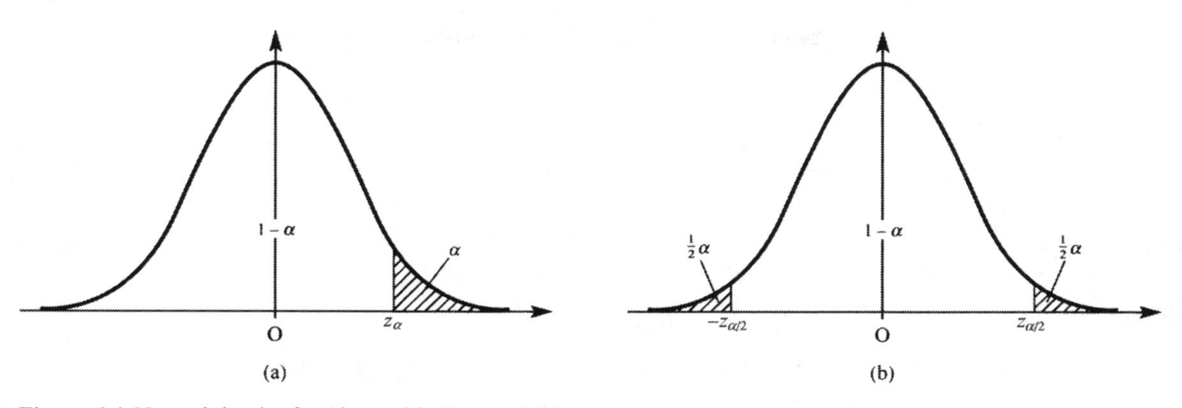

Figure 6.4 Normal density functions with (a) z_α and (b) $z_{\alpha/2}$.

(see Figure 6.4a). From the standard normal table we have $z_{0.05} = 1.645$ and $z_{0.025} = 1.96$. By symmetry

$$P(-z_{\alpha/2} < Z < z_{\alpha/2}) = 1 - \alpha$$

(see Figure 6.4b). Assuming normality of the sample average, we have

$$P\left(-z_{\alpha/2} < \frac{\bar{X} - \mu_X}{\sigma_X/\sqrt{n}} < z_{\alpha/2}\right) = (1 - \alpha)$$

which, after multiplying through the inequality by $\sigma_X/\sqrt{n}$ and changing the sign, gives

$$P\left(-z_{\alpha/2}\frac{\sigma_X}{\sqrt{n}} < \mu_X - \bar{X} < z_{\alpha/2}\frac{\sigma_X}{\sqrt{n}}\right) = 1 - \alpha$$

so that

$$P\left(\bar{X} - z_{\alpha/2}\frac{\sigma_X}{\sqrt{n}} < \mu_X < \bar{X} + z_{\alpha/2}\frac{\sigma_X}{\sqrt{n}}\right) = 1 - \alpha$$

Assume for now that the standard deviation of X is known (it is actually very rare for σ_X to be known when μ_X is unknown, but we shall discuss this case first for simplicity and later consider the more general situation where both μ_X and σ_X are unknown).

The interval defined by $(\bar{X} \pm z_{\alpha/2}\sigma_X/\sqrt{n})$ is called a **100(1 − α)% confidence interval for the mean**, with variance known. If a value for α is specified, the upper and lower limits of this interval can be calculated from the sample average. The probability is $1 - \alpha$ that the true mean lies between them.

Example 6.2

The temperature (in degrees Celsius) at ten points chosen at random in a large building is measured, giving the following list of readings:

$$\{18°, 16.5°, 17.5°, 18°, 19.5°, 16.5°, 18°, 17°, 19°, 17.5°\}$$

The standard deviation of temperature through the building is known from past experience to be 1 °C. Find a 90% confidence interval for the mean temperature in the building.

Solution The average of the ten readings is 17.75 °C, and, using $z_{0.05} = 1.645$, the 90% confidence interval is

$$(17.75 \pm 1.645(1/\sqrt{10})) = (17.1, 18.3)$$

The confidence interval is used to indicate the degree of uncertainty in the sample average. The simplicity of the calculation is deceptive because the idea is very important and easily misunderstood. It is not the mean that is random but rather the interval that would enclose it $100(1 - \alpha)\%$ of the times the experiment is performed. It is tempting to think of the interval as fixed by the experiment and the mean as a random variable that has a probability $1 - \alpha$ of lying within it, but this is not correct.

Typical values of α are 0.1, 0.05 and 0.01, giving 90%, 95% and 99% confidence intervals respectively. The value chosen is a compromise between truth and precision, as illustrated in Figure 6.5. A statement saying that the mean lies within the interval $(-\infty, \infty)$ is 100% true (certain to be the case), but totally uninformative because of its total imprecision. None of the possible values is ruled out. On the other hand, saying that the mean equals the exact value given by the sample average is maximally precise, but again of limited value because the statement is false – or rather the probability of its truth is zero. A statement quoting a finite interval for the mean has a probability of being true, chosen to be quite high, and at the same time it rules out most of the possible values and therefore is highly informative. The higher the probability of truth, the lower the informativeness, and vice versa.

The width of the interval also depends on the sample size. A larger experiment yields a more precise result. If figures for the confidence $1 - \alpha$ and precision (width of the interval) are specified in advance then the sample size can be chosen sufficiently large to satisfy these requirements. In some experimental situations (for example, destructive testing) there are incentives to keep sample sizes as small as possible. The experimenter must weigh up these conflicting objectives and design the experiment accordingly.

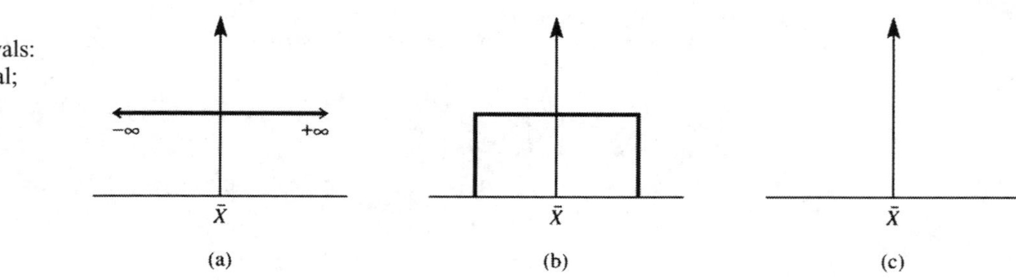

Figure 6.5
Confidence intervals:
(a) infinite interval;
(b) finite interval;
(c) point value.

Example 6.3 A machine fills cartons of liquid; the mean fill is adjustable but the dial on the gauge is not very accurate. The standard deviation of the quantity of fill is 6 ml. A sample of 30 cartons gave a measured average content of 570 ml. Find 90% and 95% confidence intervals for the mean.

Solution Using $\alpha = 0.05$ and $z_{0.025} = 1.96$, the 95% confidence interval is

$$(570 \pm 1.960(6/\sqrt{30})) = (567.8, 572.1)$$

Likewise, using $\alpha = 0.1$ and $z_{0.05} = 1.645$, the 90% confidence interval is

$$(570 \pm 1.645(6/\sqrt{30})) = (568.2, 571.8)$$

As expected, the 95% interval is slightly wider.

6.3.4 Testing simple hypotheses

As explained in Section 6.3.1, the testing of hypotheses about parameter values is complementary to the estimation process involving an interval. A 'simple' hypothesis is one that specifies a particular value for the parameter, as opposed to an interval, and it is this type that we shall consider. The following remarks apply generally to parameter hypothesis testing, but will be directed in particular to hypotheses concerning means.

There are two kinds of errors that can occur when testing hypotheses:

(a) a true hypothesis can be rejected (this is usually referred to as a **type I error**), or

(b) a false hypothesis can be accepted (this is usually called a **type II error**).

In reality, all hypotheses that prescribe particular values for parameters are false, but they may be approximately true and rejection may be the result of an experimental fluke. This is the sense in which a type I error can occur. Any hypothesis will be rejected if the sample size is large enough. Acceptance really means that there is insufficient evidence to reject the hypothesis, but this is not an entirely negative view because if the hypothesis has survived the test then it has some degree of dependability.

Normally a simple hypothesis is tested by evaluating a **test statistic**, a quantity that depends upon the sample and leads to rejection of the hypothesized parameter value if its magnitude exceeds a certain threshold. If the hypothesized mean is μ_0 then the test statistic for the mean is

$$Z = \frac{\bar{X} - \mu_0}{\sigma_X/\sqrt{n}}$$

with the hypothesis 'rejected at significance level α' if $|Z| > z_{\alpha/2}$.

The **significance level** can be regarded as the probability of false rejection, an error of type I. If the hypothesis is true then Z has a standard normal distribution and the probability that it will exceed $z_{\alpha/2}$ in magnitude is α. If Z does exceed this value then either the hypothesis is wrong or else a rare event has occurred. It is easy to show that the test statistic lies on this threshold (for significance level α) exactly when the hypothesized value lies at one or other extreme of the $100(1 - \alpha)$% confidence interval (see Figure 6.6). An alternative way to test the hypothesis is therefore to see whether or not the value lies within the confidence interval.

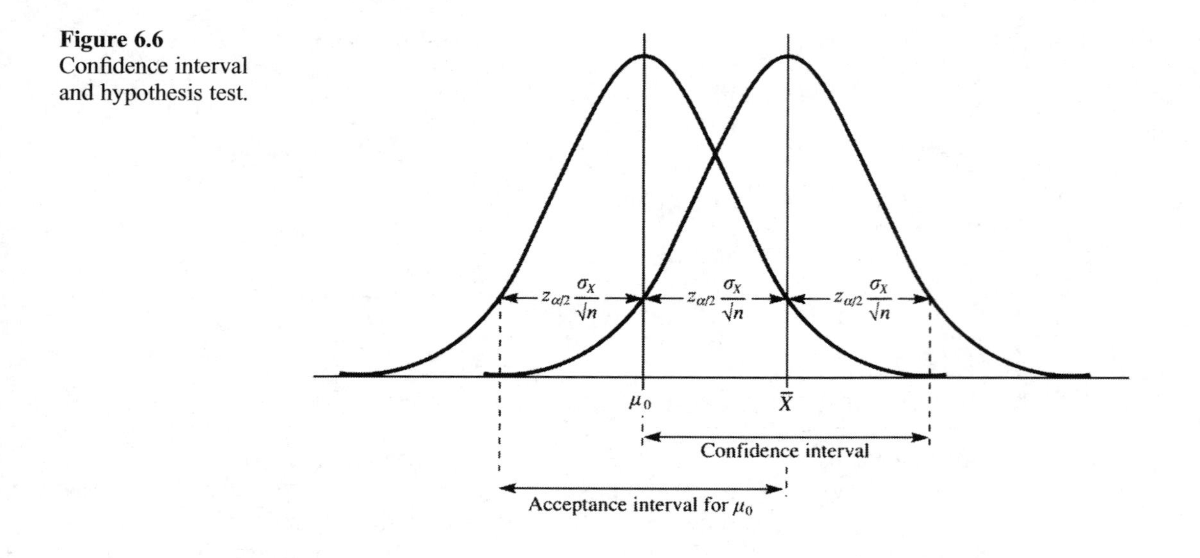

Figure 6.6 Confidence interval and hypothesis test.

Example 6.4 For the situation described in Example 6.3 test the hypothesis that the mean fill of liquid is 568 ml (one imperial pint).

Solution The value of the test statistic is

$$Z = \frac{570 - 568}{6/\sqrt{30}} = 1.83$$

This exceeds $z_{0.05} = 1.645$ (10% significance), but is less than $z_{0.025} = 1.96$ (5% significance). Alternatively, the quoted figure lies within the 95% confidence interval but outside the 90% confidence interval. Either way, the hypothesis is rejected at the 10% significance level but accepted at the 5% level. If the actual mean is 568 ml then there is less than one chance in 10 (but more than one in 20) that a result as extreme as 570 ml will be obtained. It looks as though the true mean is larger than the intended value, but the evidence is not particularly strong. The probability of false rejection (type I error) is somewhere between 5% and 10%, which is small but not negligible.

Examples 6.3 and 6.4 set the pattern for the interpretation and use of confidence intervals. We shall now see how to apply these ideas more generally.

6.3.5 Other confidence intervals and tests concerning means

Mean when variance is unknown

With the basic ideas of interval estimation and hypothesis testing established, it is relatively easy to cover other cases. The first and most obvious is to remove the assumption that the variance is known. If the sample size is large then there is essentially no problem, because the sample standard deviation $S_{X,n-1}$ can be used in place of σ_X in the confidence interval, where

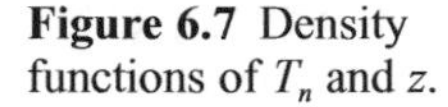

Figure 6.7 Density functions of T_n and z.

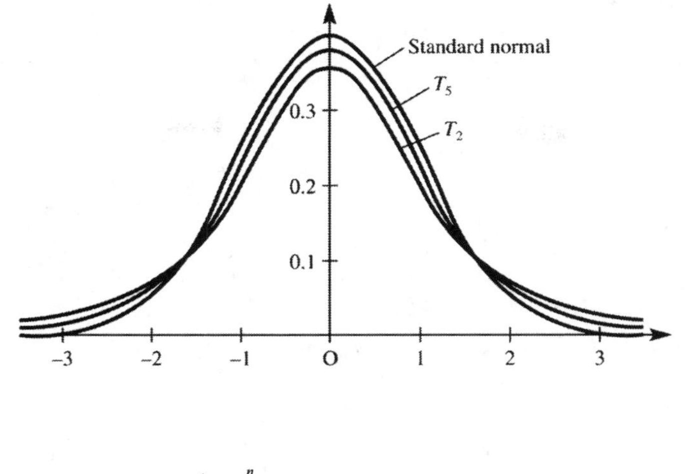

$$S_{X,n-1}^2 = \frac{1}{n-1}\sum_{i=1}^{n}(X_i - \bar{X})^2$$

This definition was introduced in Section 6.2.5. Note that the sum is divided by $n - 1$ rather than n. For a large sample this makes little difference, but for a small sample this form must be used because the 't distribution' requires it.

Suppose that the sample size is small, say less than 25. Using $S_{X,n-1}$ in place of σ_X adds an extra uncertainty because this estimate is itself subject to error. Furthermore, the central limit theorem cannot be relied upon to ensure that the sample average has a normal distribution. We have to assume that the data themselves are normal. In this situation the random variable

$$T_n = \frac{\bar{X} - \mu_X}{S_{X,n-1}/\sqrt{n}}$$

has a ***t* distribution** with parameter $n - 1$. This distribution resembles the normal distribution, as can be seen in Figure 6.7, which shows the density functions of T_2 and T_5 together with that of the standard normal distribution. In fact T_n tends to the standard normal distribution as $n \to \infty$. The parameter of the t distribution (whose value here is one less than the size of the sample) is usually called the **number of degrees of freedom**.

Defining $t_{\alpha,n-1}$ by

$$P(T_n > t_{\alpha,n-1}) = \alpha$$

(by analogy with z_α), we can derive a $100(1 - \alpha)\%$ confidence interval for the mean by the method used in Section 6.3.3:

$$\left(\bar{X} \pm t_{\alpha/2,n-1}\frac{S_{X,n-1}}{\sqrt{n}}\right)$$

This takes explicit account of the uncertainty caused by the use of $S_{X,n-1}$ in place of σ_X. Values of $t_{\alpha,n-1}$ for typical values of α can be read directly from the table of the t distribution, an example of which is shown in Figure 6.8. To obtain a test statistic for an assumed mean μ_0, simply replace μ_X by μ_0 in the definition of T_n.

Figure 6.8 Table of the t distribution $t_{\alpha,n}$. (Based on Table 12 of *Biometrika Tables for Statisticians*, Volume 1. Cambridge University Press, 1954. By permission of the *Biometrika* trustees.)

n	$\alpha = 0.10$	$\alpha = 0.05$	$\alpha = 0.025$	$\alpha = 0.01$	$\alpha = 0.005$	n
1	3.078	6.314	12.706	31.821	63.657	1
2	1.886	2.920	4.303	6.965	9.925	2
3	1.638	2.353	3.182	4.541	5.841	3
4	1.533	2.132	2.776	3.747	4.604	4
5	1.476	2.015	2.571	3.365	4.032	5
6	1.440	1.943	2.447	3.143	3.707	6
7	1.415	1.895	2.365	2.998	3.499	7
8	1.397	1.860	2.306	2.896	3.355	8
9	1.383	1.833	2.262	2.821	3.250	9
10	1.372	1.812	2.228	2.764	3.169	10
11	1.363	1.796	2.201	2.718	3.106	11
12	1.356	1.782	2.179	2.681	3.055	12
13	1.350	1.771	2.160	2.650	3.012	13
14	1.345	1.761	2.145	2.624	2.977	14
15	1.341	1.753	2.131	2.602	2.947	15
16	1.337	1.746	2.120	2.583	2.921	16
17	1.333	1.740	2.110	2.567	2.898	17
18	1.330	1.734	2.101	2.552	2.878	18
19	1.328	1.729	2.093	2.539	2.861	19
20	1.325	1.725	2.086	2.528	2.845	20
21	1.323	1.721	2.080	2.518	2.831	21
22	1.321	1.717	2.074	2.508	2.819	22
23	1.319	1.714	2.069	2.500	2.807	23
24	1.318	1.711	2.064	2.492	2.797	24
25	1.316	1.708	2.060	2.485	2.787	25
26	1.315	1.706	2.056	2.479	2.779	26
27	1.314	1.703	2.052	2.473	2.771	27
28	1.313	1.701	2.048	2.467	2.763	28
29	1.311	1.699	2.045	2.462	2.756	29
∞	1.282	1.645	1.960	2.326	2.576	∞

Example 6.5

The measured lifetimes of a sample of 20 electronic components gave an average of 1250 h, with a sample standard deviation of 96 h. Assuming that the lifetime has a normal distribution, find a 95% confidence interval for the mean lifetime of the population, and test the hypothesis that the mean is 1300 h.

Solution

The appropriate figure from the t table is $t_{0.025,19} = 2.093$, so the 95% confidence interval is

$$(1250 \pm 2.093(96)/\sqrt{20}) = (1205,\ 1295)$$

The claim that the mean lifetime is 1300 h is therefore rejected at the 5% significance level. The same conclusion is reached by evaluating

$$T_n = \frac{1250 - 1300}{96/\sqrt{20}} = -2.33$$

which exceeds $t_{0.025,19}$ in magnitude.

Difference between means

Now suppose that we have not just a single sample but two samples from different populations, and that we wish to compare the separate means. Assume also that the variances of the two populations are equal but unknown (the most common situation). Then it can be shown that the $100(1-\alpha)\%$ confidence interval for the difference $\mu_1 - \mu_2$ between the means is

$$\left(\bar{X}_1 - \bar{X}_2 \pm t_{\alpha/2,n} S_p \sqrt{\left(\frac{1}{n_1} + \frac{1}{n_2}\right)}\right)$$

where $\bar{X}_1$ and $\bar{X}_2$ are the respective sample averages, n_1 and n_2 are the respective sample sizes, S_1^2 and S_2^2 are the respective sample variances (using the '$n-1$' form as above),

$$S_p^2 = \frac{(n_1 - 1)S_1^2 + (n_2 - 1)S_2^2}{n_1 + n_2 - 2}$$

is a pooled estimate of the unknown variance, and

$$n = n_1 + n_2 - 2$$

is the parameter for the t table. The corresponding test statistic for an assumed difference $d_0 = \mu_1 - \mu_2$ is

$$T_n = \frac{\bar{X}_1 - \bar{X}_2 - d_0}{S_p \sqrt{(1/n_1 + 1/n_2)}}$$

For small samples the populations have to be normal, but for larger samples this is not required and the t-table figure can be replaced by $z_{\alpha/2}$.

Example 6.6

Two kinds of a new plastic material are to be compared for strength. From tensile strength measurements of 10 similar pieces of each type, the sample averages and standard deviations were as follows:

$$\bar{X}_1 = 78.3, \quad S_1 = 5.6, \quad \bar{X}_2 = 84.2, \quad S_2 = 6.3$$

Compare the mean strengths, assuming normal data.

Solution

The pooled estimate of the standard deviation is 5.960, the t table gives $t_{0.025,18} = 2.101$, and the 95% confidence interval for the difference between means is

$$(78.3 - 84.2 \pm 2.101(5.96)/\sqrt{5}) = (-11.5, -0.3)$$

The difference is significant at the 5% level because zero does not lie within the interval. Also, assuming zero difference gives

$$T_n = \frac{78.3 - 84.2}{5.96/\sqrt{5}} = -2.21$$

which confirms the 5% significance.

It is also possible to set up confidence intervals and tests for the variance σ_X^2, or for comparing two variances for different populations. The process of testing means and variances within and between several populations is called **analysis of variance**. This has many applications, and is well covered in statistics textbooks.

6.3.6 Interval and test for proportion

The ideas of interval estimation do not just apply to means. If probability is interpreted as a long-term proportion (which is one of the common interpretations) then measuring a sample proportion is a way of estimating a probability. The binomial distribution (Section 6.2.3) points the way. We count the number of 'successes', say X, in n 'trials', and estimate the probability p of success at each trial, or the long-term proportion, by the sample proportion

$$\hat{p} = \frac{X}{n}$$

(it is common in statistics to place the 'hat' symbol ^ over a parameter to denote an estimate of that parameter). This only provides a point estimate. To obtain a confidence interval, we can exploit the normal approximation to the binomial (Section 6.2.4)

$$X \sim N(np, np(1-p))$$

approximately, for large n. Dividing by n preserves normality, so

$$\hat{p} \sim N\left(p, \frac{p(1-p)}{n}\right)$$

Following the argument in Section 6.3.3, we have

$$P\left(p - z_{\alpha/2}\sqrt{\left[\frac{p(1-p)}{n}\right]} < \hat{p} < p + z_{\alpha/2}\sqrt{\left[\frac{p(1-p)}{n}\right]}\right) = 1 - \alpha$$

and, after rearranging the inequality,

$$P\left(\hat{p} - z_{\alpha/2}\sqrt{\left[\frac{p(1-p)}{n}\right]} < p < \hat{p} + z_{\alpha/2}\sqrt{\left[\frac{p(1-p)}{n}\right]}\right) = 1 - \alpha$$

Because p is unknown, we have to make a further approximation by replacing p by $\hat{p}$ inside the square root, to give an approximate $100(1-\alpha)\%$ confidence interval for p:

$$\left(\hat{p} \pm z_{\alpha/2}\sqrt{\left[\frac{\hat{p}(1-\hat{p})}{n}\right]}\right)$$

The corresponding test statistic for an assumed proportion p_0 is

$$Z = \frac{X - np_0}{\sqrt{[np_0(1-p_0)]}}$$

with $\pm z_{\alpha/2}$ as the rejection points for significance level α.

Example 6.7

In an opinion poll conducted with a sample of 1000 people chosen at random, 30% said that they support a certain political party. Find a 95% confidence interval for the actual proportion of the population who support this party.

Solution

The required confidence interval is obtained directly as

$$\left(0.3 \pm 1.96\sqrt{\left[\frac{(0.3)(0.7)}{1000}\right]}\right) = (0.27, 0.33)$$

A variation of about 3% either way is therefore to be expected when conducting opinion polls with sample sizes of this order, which is fairly typical, and this figure is often quoted in the news media as an indication of maximum likely error.

A similar argument that also exploits the fact that the difference between two independent normal random variables is also normal leads to the following $100(1-\alpha)\%$ confidence interval for the difference between two proportions, when $\hat{p}_1$ and $\hat{p}_2$ are the respective sample proportions:

$$\left(\hat{p}_1 - \hat{p}_2 \pm z_{\alpha/2}\sqrt{\left[\frac{\hat{p}_1(1-\hat{p}_1)}{n_1} + \frac{\hat{p}_2(1-\hat{p}_2)}{n_2}\right]}\right)$$

Again it is assumed that n_1 and n_2 are reasonably large. The test statistic for equality of proportions is

$$Z = \frac{\hat{p}_1 - \hat{p}_2}{\sqrt{[p(1-\hat{p})(1/n_1 + 1/n_2)]}}$$

where $\hat{p} = (X_1 + X_2)/(n_1 + n_2)$ is a pooled estimate of the proportion.

Example 6.8

One hundred samples of an alloy are tested for resistance to fatigue. Half have been prepared using a new process and the other half by a standard process. Of those prepared by the new process, 35 exhibit good fatigue resistance, whereas only 25 of those prepared in the standard way show the same performance. Is the new process better than the standard one?

Solution

The proportions of good samples are 0.7 for the new process and 0.5 for the standard one, so a 95% confidence interval for the difference between the true proportions is

$$\left(0.7 - 0.5 \pm 1.96\sqrt{\left[\frac{(0.7)(0.3)}{50} + \frac{(0.5)(0.5)}{50}\right]}\right) = (0.01, 0.39)$$

The pooled estimate of proportion is

$$\hat{p} = (35 + 25)/(50 + 50) = 0.6$$

so that

$$Z = \frac{0.7 - 0.5}{\sqrt{[(0.6)(0.4)/25]}} = 2.04$$

Both approaches show that the difference is significant at the 5% level. However, it is only just so: if one more sample for the new process had been less fatigue-resistant, the difference would not have been significant at this level. This suggests that the new process is effective – but, despite the apparently large difference in success rates, the evidence is not very strong.

This method only applies to independent sample proportions. It would not be legitimate to apply it, for instance, to a more elaborate version of the opinion poll (Example 6.7) in which respondents can choose between two (or more) political parties or else support neither. Support for one party usually precludes support for another, so the proportions of those interviewed who support the two parties are not independent. More elaborate confidence intervals, based on the multinomial distribution, can handle such situations. This shows how important it is to understand the assumptions upon which statistical methods are based. It would be very easy to look up 'difference between proportions' in an index and apply an inappropriate formula.

6.3.7 Exercises

1. An electrical firm manufactures light bulbs whose lifetime is approximately normally distributed with a standard deviation of 50 h.

   (a) If a sample of 30 bulbs has an average life of 780 h, find a 95% confidence interval for the mean lifetime of the population.
   (b) How large a sample is needed if we wish to be 95% confident that our sample average will be within 10 h of the population mean?

2. Monthly rainfall measurements (in mm) were taken at a certain location for three years, with results as follows:

   38 48 50 94 105 53 81 91 110 103 90 84

   115 113 35 130 77 67 72 113 98 37 61 91

   9 112 29 16 56 61 82 132 48 68 114 55

   Find the average monthly rainfall for this period. Also find a 95% confidence interval for the mean monthly rainfall, using the measured standard deviation as an estimate of the true value.

3. Quantities of a trace impurity in 12 specimens of a new material are measured (in parts per million) as follows:

   8.8, 7.1, 7.9, 10.2, 8.9, 7.7, 10.6, 9.4, 9.2, 7.5, 9.0, 8.4

   Find a 95% confidence interval for the population mean, assuming that the distribution is normal.

4. A sample of 30 pieces of a semiconductor material gave an average resistivity of 73.2 mΩ m, with a sample standard deviation of 5.4 mΩ m. Obtain a 95% confidence interval for the resistivity of the material, and test the hypothesis that this is 75 mΩ m.

5. The mean weight loss of 16 grinding balls after a certain length of time in mill slurry is 3.42 g, with a standard deviation of 0.68 g. Construct a 99% confidence interval for the true mean weight loss of such grinding balls under the stated conditions.

6. While performing a certain task under simulated weightlessness, the pulse rate of 32 astronaut trainees increased on the average by 26.4 beats per minute, with a standard deviation of 4.28 beats per minute. Construct a 95% confidence interval for the true average increase in the pulse rate of astronaut trainees performing the given task.

7 The quality of a liquid being used in an etching process is monitored automatically by measuring the attenuation of a certain wavelength of light passing through it. The criterion is that when the attenuation reaches 58%, the liquid is declared as 'spent'. Ten samples of the liquid are used until they are judged as 'spent' by the experts. The light attenuation is then measured, and gives an average result of 56%, with a standard deviation of 3%. Is the criterion satisfactory?

8 A fleet car company has to decide between two brands A and B of tyre for its cars. An experiment is conducted using 12 of each brand, run until they wear out. The sample averages and standard deviations of running distance (in km) are respectively 36 300 and 5000 for A, and 39 100 and 6100 for B. Obtain a 95% confidence interval for the difference in means, assuming the distributions to be normal, and test the hypothesis that brand B tyres outrun brand A tyres.

9 A manufacturer claims that the lifetime of a particular electronic component is unaffected by temperature variations within the range 0–60 °C. Two samples of these components were tested, and their measured lifetimes (in hours) recorded as follows:

0 °C: 7250, 6970, 7370, 7910, 6790, 6850, 7280, 7830

60 °C: 7030, 7270, 6510, 6700, 7350, 6770, 6220, 7230

Assuming that the lifetimes have a normal distribution, find 90% and 95% confidence intervals for the difference between the mean lifetimes at the two temperatures, and hence test the manufacturer's claim at the 5% and 10% significance levels.

10 Suppose that out of 540 drivers tested at random, 38 were found to have consumed more than the legal limit of alcohol. Find 90% and 95% confidence intervals for the true proportion of drivers who were over the limit during the time of the tests. Are the results compatible with the hypothesis that this proportion is less than 5%?

11 It is known that approximately one-quarter of all houses in a certain area have inadequate loft insulation. How many houses should be inspected if the difference between the estimated and true proportions having inadequate loft insulation is not to exceed 0.05, with probability 90%? If in fact 200 houses are inspected, and 55 of them have inadequate loft insulation, find a 90% confidence interval for the true proportion.

12 A drug-manufacturer claims that the proportion of patients exhibiting side-effects to their new anti-arthritis drug is at least 8% lower than for the standard brand X. In a controlled experiment 31 out of 100 patients receiving the new drug exhibited side-effects, as did 74 out of 150 patients receiving brand X. Test the manufacturer's claim using 90% and 95% confidence intervals.

13 Suppose that 10 years ago 500 people were working in a factory, and 180 of them were exposed to a material which is now suspected as being carcinogenic. Of those 180, 30 have since developed cancer, whereas 32 of the other workers (who were not exposed) have also since developed cancer. Obtain a 95% confidence interval for the difference between the proportions with cancer among those exposed and not exposed, and assess whether the material should be considered carcinogenic, on this evidence.

6.4 Joint distributions and correlation

Just as it is possible for events to be dependent upon one another in that information to the effect that one has occurred changes the probability of the other, so it is possible for random variables to be associated in value. In this section we show how the degree of dependence between two random variables can be defined and measured.

6.4.1 Joint and marginal distributions

The idea that two variables, each of which is random, can be associated in some way might seem mysterious at first, but can be clarified with some familiar examples. For instance, if one chooses a person at random and measures his or her height and weight, each measurement is a random variable – but we know that taller people also tend to be heavier than shorter people, so the outcomes will be related. On the other hand, a person's birthday and telephone number are not likely to be related in any way. In general, we need a measure of the simultaneous distribution of two random variables.

For two discrete random variables X and Y with possible values $\{u_1, \dots, u_m\}$ and $\{v_1, \dots, v_n\}$ respectively, the **joint distribution** of X and Y is the set of all joint probabilities of the form

$$P(X = u_k \cap Y = v_j\} \quad (k = 1, \dots, m; j = 1, \dots, n)$$

The joint distribution contains all relevant information about the random variables separately, as well as their joint behaviour. To obtain the distribution of one variable, we sum over the possible values of the other:

$$P(X = u_k) = \sum_{j=1}^{n} P(X = u_k \cap Y = v_j) \quad (k = 1, \dots, m)$$

$$P(Y = v_j) = \sum_{k=1}^{m} P(X = u_k \cap Y = v_j) \quad (j = 1, \dots, n)$$

The distributions obtained in this way are called **marginal distributions** of X and Y.

Example 6.9 Two textbooks are selected at random from a shelf containing three statistics texts, two mathematics texts and three engineering texts. Denoting the number of books selected in each subject by S, M and E respectively, find (a) the joint distribution of S and M, and (b) the marginal distributions of S, M and E.

Solution (a)

Figure 6.9 Joint distribution for Example 6.9.

	M			
S	0	1	2	Total
0	$\frac{3}{28}$	$\frac{3}{14}$	$\frac{1}{28}$	$\frac{5}{14}$
1	$\frac{9}{28}$	$\frac{3}{14}$		$\frac{15}{28}$
2	$\frac{3}{28}$			$\frac{3}{28}$
Total	$\frac{15}{28}$	$\frac{3}{7}$	$\frac{1}{28}$	1

The joint distribution (shown in Figure 6.9) is built up element by element using the addition and product rules of probability as follows:

$$P(S = M = 0) = P(E = 2) = (\tfrac{3}{8})(\tfrac{2}{7}) = \tfrac{3}{28}$$

that is, the probability that the first book is an engineering text (three chances out of eight) times the probability that the second book is also (two remaining chances out of seven). Continuing,

$$P(S = 0 \cap M = 1) = P(M = 1 \cap E = 1)$$
$$= (\tfrac{2}{8})(\tfrac{3}{7}) + (\tfrac{3}{8})(\tfrac{2}{7}) = \tfrac{3}{14}$$

that is, the probability that the first book is a mathematics text and the second an engineering text, plus the (equal) probability of the books being the other way round. The other probabilities are derived similarly.

(b) The marginal distributions of S and M are just the row and column totals as shown in Figure 6.9. The marginal distribution of E can also be derived from the table:

$$P(E = 2) = P(S = M = 0) = \tfrac{3}{28}$$
$$P(E = 1) = P(S = 1 \cap M = 0) + P(S = 0 \cap M = 1) = \tfrac{15}{28}$$
$$P(E = 0) = P(S = 2) + P(S = 1 \cap M = 1) + P(M = 2) = \tfrac{5}{14}$$

This is the same as the marginal distribution of S, which is not surprising, because there are the same numbers of engineering and statistics books on the shelf.

In order to apply these ideas of joint and marginal distributions to continuous random variables, we need to build on the interpretation of the probability density function. The **joint density function** of two continuous random variables X and Y, denoted by $f_{X,Y}(x, y)$, is such that

$$P(x_1 < X < x_2 \quad \text{and} \quad y_1 < Y < y_2) = \int_{x_1}^{x_2} \int_{y_1}^{y_2} f_{X,Y}(x, y)\, dy\, dx$$

for all intervals (x_1, x_2) and (y_1, y_2). This involves a double integral over the two variables x and y. This is necessary because the joint density function must indicate the relative likelihood of every combination of values of X and Y, just as the joint distribution does for discrete random variables. The joint density function is transformed into a probability by integrating over an interval for both variables. The double integral here can be regarded as a pair of single-variable integrations, with the outer variable (x) held constant during the integration with respect to the inner variable (y). In fact the same answer is obtained if the integration is performed the other way around.

The **marginal density functions** for X and Y are obtained from the joint density function in a manner analogous to the discrete case: by integrating over all values of the unwanted variable:

$$f_X(x) = \int_{-\infty}^{\infty} f_{X,Y}(x, y)\, dy \quad (-\infty < x < \infty)$$

$$f_Y(y) = \int_{-\infty}^{\infty} f_{X,Y}(x, y)\, dx \quad (-\infty < y < \infty)$$

Example 6.10 The joint density function of random variables X and Y is

$$f_{X,Y}(x, y) = \begin{cases} 1 & (0 \leqslant x \leqslant 1,\ cx \leqslant y \leqslant cx + 1) \\ 0 & \text{otherwise} \end{cases}$$

where c is a constant such that $0 \leqslant c \leqslant 1$ (which means that $f_{X,Y}(x, y)$ is unity over the trapezoidal area shown in Figure 6.10 and zero elsewhere). Find the marginal distributions of X and Y. Also find the probability that neither X nor Y exceeds one-half, assuming $c = 1$.

Solution To find the marginal distribution of X, we integrate with respect to y:

$$f_X(x) = \begin{cases} \displaystyle\int_{cx}^{cx+1} dy = 1 & (0 \leqslant x \leqslant 1) \\ 0 & \text{otherwise} \end{cases}$$

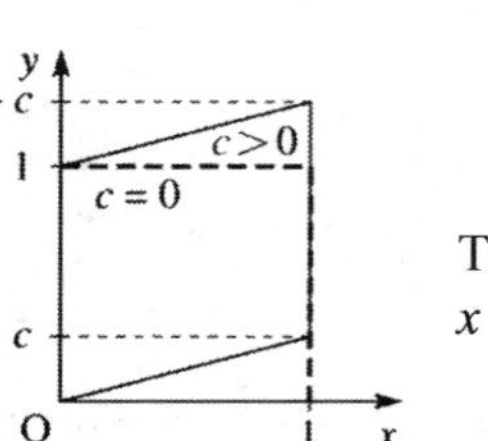

Figure 6.10
Density function for Example 6.10.

The marginal distribution for Y is rather more complicated. Integrating with respect to x and assuming that $0 < c \leqslant 1$,

$$f_Y(y) = \begin{cases} 1 - \dfrac{1}{c}(y-1) & (1 \leqslant y \leqslant 1 + c) \\ 1 & (c \leqslant y \leqslant 1) \\ \dfrac{y}{c} & (0 \leqslant y \leqslant c) \end{cases}$$

(Exercise 16). When $c = 0$, the marginal distribution for Y is the same as that for X. Finally, when $c = 1$,

$$P(X \leqslant \tfrac{1}{2} \quad \text{and} \quad Y \leqslant \tfrac{1}{2}) = \int_0^{1/2}\int_x^{1/2} 1\,dy\,dx = \int_0^{1/2} (\tfrac{1}{2} - x)\,dx = \tfrac{1}{8}$$

Here the inner integral (with respect to y) is performed with x treated as constant, and the resulting function of x is integrated to give the answer.

The definitions of joint and marginal distributions can be extended to any number of random variables.

6.4.2 Independence

The idea of independence of events can be extended to random variables to give us the important case in which no information is shared between them. This is important in experiments where essentially the same quantity is measured repeatedly, either within a single experiment involving repetition or between different experiments. As mentioned before, independence within a sample is one of the properties that qualifies the sample for analysis and conclusion.

Two random variables X and Y are called **independent** if their joint distribution factorizes into the product of their marginal distributions:

$$P(X = u_k \cap Y = v_j) = P(X = u_k)P(Y = v_j) \quad \text{in the discrete case}$$

$$f_{X,Y}(x, y) = f_X(x)f_Y(y) \quad \text{in the continuous case}$$

For example, the random variables X and Y in Example 6.10 are independent if and only if $c = 0$.

Example 6.11

The assembly of a complex piece of equipment can be divided into two stages. The times (in hours) required for the two stages are random variables (X and Y, say) with density functions e^{-x} and $2\,e^{-2y}$ respectively. Assuming that the stage assembly times are independent, find the probability that the assembly will be completed within four hours.

Solution

The assumption of independence implies that

$$f_{X,Y}(x, y) = f_X(x)f_Y(y) = 2\,e^{-(x+2y)}$$

If the time for the first stage is x, the total time will not exceed four hours if

$$Y < 4 - x$$

so the required value is

$$P(X + Y < 4) = \int_0^4 \int_0^{4-x} f_{X,Y}(x, y)\,dy\,dx = \int_0^4 \int_0^{4-x} 2\,e^{-(x+2y)}\,dy\,dx$$

$$= \int_0^4 (e^{-x} - e^{-(8-x)})\,dx = 0.964$$

Where random variables are dependent upon one another, it is possible to express this dependence by defining a **conditional distribution** analogous to conditional probability, in terms of the joint distribution (or density function) and the marginal distributions. Instead of pursuing this idea here, we shall consider a numerical measure of dependence that can be estimated from sample data.

6.4.3 Covariance and correlation

The use of mean and variance for a random variable is motivated partly by the difficulty in determining the full probability distribution in many practical cases. The joint distribution of two variables presents even greater difficulties. Since we already have numerical measures of location and dispersion for the variables individually, it seems reasonable to define a measure of association of the two variables that is independent of their separate means and variances so that the new measure provides essentially new information about the variables.

There are four objectives that it seems reasonable for such a measure to satisfy. Its value should

(a) be zero for independent variables,

(b) be non-zero for dependent variables,

(c) indicate the degree of dependence in some well-defined sense, detached from the individual means and variances,

(d) be easy to estimate from sample data.

It is actually rather difficult to satisfy all of these, but the most popular measure of association gets most of the way.

The **covariance** of random variables X and Y, denoted by $\mathrm{Cov}(X, Y)$, is defined as

$$\mathrm{Cov}(X, Y) = E\{(X - \mu_X)(Y - \mu_Y)\}$$

$$= \begin{cases} \sum_{k=1}^{m} \sum_{j=1}^{n} (u_k - \mu_X)(v_j - \mu_Y) P(X = u_k \cap Y = v_j) \\ \int_{-\infty}^{\infty} \int_{-\infty}^{\infty} (x - \mu_X)(y - \mu_Y) f_{X,Y}(x, y)\, dx\, dy \end{cases}$$

for discrete and continuous variables respectively. The **correlation** $\rho_{X,Y}$ is the covariance divided by the product of the standard deviations:

$$\rho_{X,Y} = \frac{\mathrm{Cov}(X, Y)}{\sigma_X \sigma_Y}$$

If whenever the random variable X is larger than its mean the random variable Y also tends to be larger than its mean then the product $(X - \mu_X)(Y - \mu_Y)$ will tend to be positive. The same will be true if both variables tend to be smaller than their means simultaneously. The covariance is then positive. A negative covariance implies that the variables tend to move in opposite directions with respect to their means. Both covariance and correlation therefore measure association relative to the mean values of the variables. It turns out that correlation measures association relative to the standard deviations as well.

It should be noted that the variance of a random variable X is the same as the covariance with itself:

$$\mathrm{Var}(X) = \mathrm{Cov}(X, X)$$

Also, by expanding the product within the integral or sum in the definition of covariance, it is easy to show that an alternative expression is

$$\mathrm{Cov}(X, Y) = E(XY) - E(X)E(Y)$$

Although the sign of the covariance indicates the direction of the dependence, its magnitude depends not only on the degree of dependence but also upon the variances of the random variables, so it fails to satisfy the objective (c). In contrast, the correlation is limited in range

$$-1 \leqslant \rho_{X,Y} \leqslant +1$$

and it adopts the limiting values of this range only when the random variables are linearly related:

$$\rho_{X,Y} = \pm 1 \quad \text{if and only if there exist } a, b \text{ such that } Y = aX + b$$

(this is proved in most textbooks on probability theory). The magnitude of the correlation indicates the degree of linear relationship, so that objective (c) is satisfied.

Example 6.12 Find the correlation of the random variables S and M in Example 6.9.

Solution The joint and marginal distributions of S and M are shown in Figure 6.9. First we find the expected values of S and S^2 from the marginal distribution, and hence the variance and standard deviation:

$$E(S) = \tfrac{15}{28} + (2)(\tfrac{3}{28}) = \tfrac{21}{28}, \qquad E(S^2) = \tfrac{15}{28} + (4)(\tfrac{3}{28}) = \tfrac{27}{28}$$

$$\text{Var}(S) = \tfrac{27}{28} - (\tfrac{21}{28})^2$$

from which

$$\sigma_S = \tfrac{3}{28}\sqrt{35}$$

Next we do the same for M:

$$E(M) = \tfrac{3}{7} + (2)(\tfrac{1}{28}) = \tfrac{1}{2}, \qquad E(M^2) = \tfrac{3}{7} + (4)(\tfrac{1}{28}) = \tfrac{4}{7}$$

$$\text{Var}(M) = \tfrac{4}{7} - \tfrac{1}{4} = \tfrac{9}{28}$$

from which

$$\sigma_M = \tfrac{3}{2}\sqrt{\tfrac{1}{7}}$$

All products of S and M are zero except when both are equal to one, so the expected value of the product is

$$E(SM) = \tfrac{3}{14}$$

The correlation now follows easily:

$$\rho_{S,M} = \frac{E(SM) - E(S)E(M)}{\sigma_S \sigma_M} = \frac{\tfrac{3}{14} - (\tfrac{21}{28})(\tfrac{1}{2})}{(\tfrac{3}{28}\sqrt{35})(\tfrac{3}{2}\sqrt{\tfrac{1}{7}})} = -\frac{1}{\sqrt{5}}$$

The correlation is negative because if there are more statistics books in the selection then there will tend to be fewer mathematics books, and vice versa.

Example 6.13 Find the correlation of the random variables X and Y in Example 6.10.

Solution Proceeding as in Example 6.12, we have for X

$$E(X) = \int_0^1 x\,\mathrm{d}x = \tfrac{1}{2}$$

$$E(X^2) = \int_0^1 x^2\,\mathrm{d}x = \tfrac{1}{3}$$

so that $\text{Var}(X) = E(X^2) - [E(X)]^2 = \frac{1}{12}$. Also, for Y

$$E(Y) = \int_0^c \frac{y^2}{c}\,dy + \int_c^1 y\,dy + \int_1^{1+c} y\left[1 - \frac{1}{c}(y-1)\right] dy$$

$$= \tfrac{1}{2}(1+c) \quad \text{after simplification}$$

$$E(Y^2) = \int_0^c \frac{y^3}{c}\,dy + \int_c^1 y^2\,dy + \int_1^{1+c} y^2\left[1 - \frac{1}{c}(y-1)\right] dy$$

$$= \tfrac{1}{3}(1+c^2) + \tfrac{1}{2}c \quad \text{after simplification}$$

so that $\text{Var}(Y) = E(Y^2) - [E(Y)]^2 = \frac{1}{12}(1 + c^2)$. For the expected value of the product we have

$$E(XY) = \int_0^1 \int_{cx}^{cx+1} xy\,dy\,dx = \tfrac{1}{2}\int_0^1 x(1+2cx)\,dx = \tfrac{1}{4} + \tfrac{1}{3}c$$

Finally, the correlation between X and Y is

$$\rho_{X,Y} = \frac{E(XY) - E(X)E(Y)}{\sqrt{[\text{Var}(X)\,\text{Var}(Y)]}}$$

$$= \frac{\frac{1}{4} + \frac{1}{3}c - \frac{1}{4}(1+c)}{\frac{1}{12}\sqrt{(1+c^2)}} = \frac{c}{\sqrt{(1+c^2)}}$$

Note that in fact the result of Example 6.13 holds for any value of c, and not just for the range $0 \leqslant c \leqslant 1$ assumed in Example 6.10. As the value of c increases (positive or negative), the correlation increases also, but its magnitude never exceeds one. It is also clear that if X and Y are independent then $c = 0$ and the correlation is zero. Refer to Figure 6.10 for a geometrical interpretation. When $c = 0$, the sample space is a square within which all points are equally likely, so there is no association between the variables. As c increases (positive or negative), the sample space becomes more elongated as the variables become more tightly coupled to one another.

The general relationship between independence and correlation is expressed as follows: if the random variables X and Y are independent then their correlation is zero. This is easily shown as follows for continuous random variables (or by a similar argument for discrete random variables). First we have

$$f_{X,Y}(x, y) = f_X(x)\,f_Y(y)$$

and then

$$\int_{-\infty}^{\infty}\int_{-\infty}^{\infty} (x - \mu_X)(y - \mu_Y)\,f_X(x)\,f_Y(y)\,dx\,dy$$

$$= \int_{-\infty}^{\infty} (x - \mu_X)\,f_X(x)\,dx \int_{-\infty}^{\infty} (y - \mu_Y)\,f_Y(y)\,dy = (\mu_X - \mu_X)(\mu_Y - \mu_Y) = 0$$

Unfortunately, the converse does not hold: zero correlation does not imply independence. In general, correlation is a measure of linear dependence, and may be zero or very small for variables that are dependent in a *nonlinear* way (see Exercise 15). Objective (a) is satisfied, therefore, but not objective (b) in general.

Another problem with correlation is that a non-zero value does not imply the presence of a causal relationship between the variables or the phenomena that they measure. Correlation can be 'spurious', deriving from some third variable that may be unrecognized at the time. For example, among the economic statistics that are gathered together from many countries and published, there are figures for the number of telephones per head of population, birth rate, and the gross domestic product per capita (GDP). It turns out that there is a large negative correlation between number of telephones per head and the birth rate, but no-one would suggest that telephones have any direct application in birth control. The GDP is a measure of wealth, and there is a large positive correlation between this and the number of telephones per head, and a large negative correlation between GDP and birth rate, both for quite genuine reasons. The correlation between telephones and birth rate is therefore spurious, and a more sophisticated measure called the **partial correlation** can be used to eliminate the third variable (provided that it is recognized and measured).

We have considered all the objectives except (d); that this is satisfied is shown in Section 6.4.4.

6.4.4 Sample correlation

There are two kinds of situations where we take samples of values of two random variables X and Y. First we might be interested in the same property for two different populations. Perhaps there is evidence that the mean values are different, so we take samples of each and compare them. This situation was discussed in Section 6.3.5. The second kind involves two different properties for the same population. It is to this situation that correlation applies. We take a single sample from the population and measure the pair of random variables (X_i, Y_i) for each $i = 1, \dots, n$.

For a sample $\{(X_1, Y_1), \dots, (X_n, Y_n)\}$ the **sample correlation coefficient** is defined as

$$r_{X,Y} = \frac{\frac{1}{n}\sum_{i=1}^{n}[(X_i - \bar{X})(Y_i - \bar{Y})]}{S_X S_Y}$$

Like the true correlation, the sample correlation is limited in value to the range $[-1, 1]$ and $r_{X,Y} = \pm 1$ when (and only when) all of the points lie along a line. Figure 6.11 contains four typical **scatter diagrams** of samples plotted on the (x, y) plane, with an indication of the correlation for each one. The range of behaviour is shown from independence (a) through imperfect correlation (b) and (c) to a perfect linear relationship (d).

By expanding the product within the outer bracket in the numerator, it is easy to show that an alternative expression is

$$r_{X,Y} = \frac{\overline{XY} - (\bar{X})(\bar{Y})}{S_X S_Y}$$

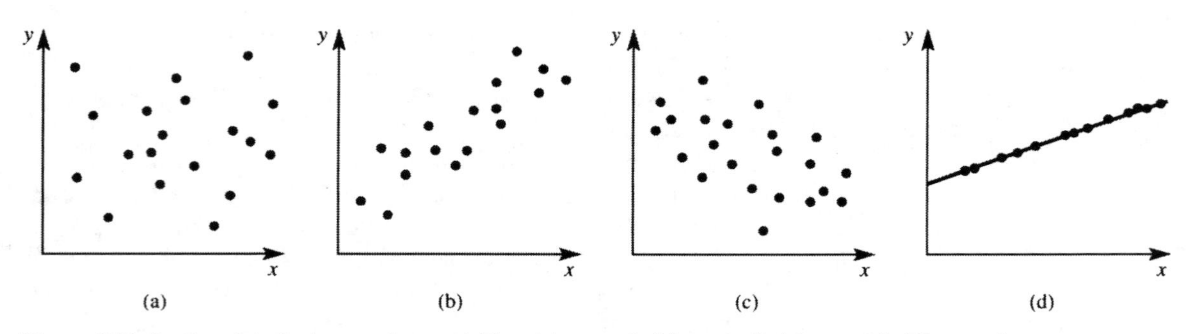

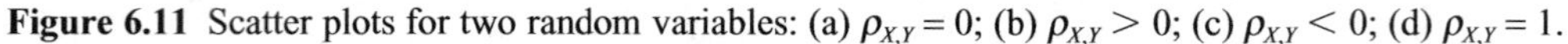

Figure 6.11 Scatter plots for two random variables: (a) $\rho_{X,Y} = 0$; (b) $\rho_{X,Y} > 0$; (c) $\rho_{X,Y} < 0$; (d) $\rho_{X,Y} = 1$.

Figure 6.12 Pseudocode listing for sample correlation.

```
{ Program to compute sample correlation.
x(k) and y(k) are the arrays of data,
n is the sample size,
xbar and ybar are the sample averages,
sx and sy are the sample standard deviations,
rxy is the sample correlation,
Mx, My, Qx, Qy, Qxy hold running totals. }

Mx ← 0; My ← 0
Qx ← 0; Qy ← 0
Qxy ← 0
for k is 1 to n do
  diffx ← x(k) – Mx
  diffy ← y(k) – My
  Mx ← ((k – 1)*Mx + x(k))/k
  My ← ((k – 1)*My + y(k))/k
  Qx ← Qx + (1 – 1/k)*diffx*diffx
  Qy ← Qy + (1 – 1/k)*diffy*diffy
  Qxy ← Qxy + (1 – 1/k)*diffx*diffy
endfor
xbar ← Mx; ybar ← My
sx ← sqr(Qx/n); sy ← sqr(Qy/n)
rxy ← Qxy/(n*sx*sy)
```

which is useful for hand calculation. For computer calculation the best method involves the successive sums of products:

$$Q_{XY,k} = \sum_{i=1}^{k} (X_i - M_{X,k})(Y_i - M_{Y,k})$$

where

$$M_{X,k} = \frac{1}{k}\sum_{i=1}^{k} X_i, \qquad M_{Y,k} = \frac{1}{k}\sum_{i=1}^{k} Y_i$$

and then $r_{X,Y} = Q_{XY,n}/nS_XS_Y$. The pseudocode listing in Figure 6.12 exploits the recurrence relation

$$Q_{XY,k} = Q_{XY,k-1} + \left(1 - \frac{1}{k}\right)(X_k - M_{X,k-1})(Y_k - M_{Y,k-1})$$

which allows for a single pass through the data with no loss of accuracy.

Example 6.14

A material used in the construction industry contains an impurity suspected of having an adverse effect upon the material's performance in resisting long-term operational stresses. Percentages of impurity and performance indexes for 22 specimens of this material are as follows:

% Impurity X_i	4.4	5.5	4.2	3.0	4.5	4.9	4.6	5.0	4.7	5.1	4.4
Performance Y_i	12	14	18	35	23	29	16	12	18	21	27
% Impurity X_i	4.1	4.9	4.7	5.0	4.6	3.6	4.9	5.1	4.8	5.2	5.2
Performance Y_i	13	19	22	20	16	27	21	13	18	17	11

Find the sample correlation coefficient.

Solution The following quantities are easily obtained from the data:

$$\bar{X} = 4.6545, \quad S_X = 0.550\,81, \quad \bar{Y} = 19.1818, \quad S_Y = 6.0350, \quad \overline{XY} = 87.3591$$

(Note that it is advisable to record these results to several significant digits in order to avoid losing precision when calculating the difference within the numerator of $r_{X,Y}$.) The sample correlation is then $r_{X,Y} = -0.58$, the negative value suggesting that the impurity has an adverse effect upon performance. It remains to be seen whether this is statistically significant.

6.4.5 Interval and test for correlation

Correlation is more difficult to deal with than mean and proportion, but for normal random variables X and Y with a true correlation $\rho_{X,Y}$ the sample statistic

$$Z = \frac{\sqrt{(n-3)}}{2} \ln\left[\frac{(1 + r_{X,Y})(1 - \rho_{X,Y})}{(1 - r_{X,Y})(1 + \rho_{X,Y})}\right]$$

is approximately standard normal for large n. This can be used directly as a test statistic for an assumed value of $\rho_{X,Y}$. Alternatively, an approximate $100(1 - \alpha)\%$ confidence interval for $\rho_{X,Y}$ can be derived:

$$\left(\frac{1 + r - c(1 - r)}{1 + r + c(1 - r)}, \frac{1 + r - (1 - r)/c}{1 + r + (1 - r)/c}\right)$$

where

$$c = \exp\left[\frac{2z_{\alpha/2}}{\sqrt{(n-3)}}\right]$$

(the subscripts X and Y have been dropped from $r_{X,Y}$ in this formula).

Example 6.15

For the data in Example 6.14 find 95% and 99% confidence intervals for the true correlation between percentage of impurity and performance index, and test the hypothesis that these are independent.

Solution The sample correlation (from the 22 specimens) was found in Example 6.14 to be −0.58. For the 95% confidence interval the constant $c = 2.458$ and the interval itself is (−0.80, −0.21). Similarly, the 99% confidence interval is (−0.85, −0.07). Assuming $\rho_{XY} = 0$, the value of the test statistic is $Z = -2.89$, which exceeds $z_{0.005} = 2.576$ in magnitude. Either way, we can be more than 99% confident that the impurity has an adverse effect upon performance.

6.4.6 Rank correlation

As has been previously emphasized the correlation only works as a measure of dependence if

(1) n is reasonably large,

(2) X and Y are *numerical* characteristics,

(3) the dependence is *linear*, and

(4) X and Y each have a *normal* distribution.

There is an alternative form of sample correlation, which has greater applicability, requiring only that

(1) n is reasonably large,

(2) X and Y are *rankable* characteristics, and

(3) the dependence is *monotonic* (that is, always in the same direction, which may be forward or inverse, but not necessarily linear).

The variables X and Y can have any distribution. For a set of data $X_1, \ldots, X_n$, a **rank** of 1 is assigned to the smallest value, 2 to the next-smallest and so on up to a rank of n assigned to the largest. This applies wherever the values are distinct. Tied values are given the mean of the ranks they would receive if slightly different. The following is an example:

X_i	8	3	5	8	1	9	6	5	3	5	7	2
Rank	10.5	3.5	6	10.5	1	12	8	6	3.5	6	9	2

The **Spearman rank correlation coefficient** r_S for data $(X_1, Y_1), \ldots, (X_n, Y_n)$ is the correlation of the ranks of X_i and Y_i, where the data $X_1, \ldots, X_n$ and $Y_1, \ldots, Y_n$ are ranked separately. If the number of tied values is small compared with n then

$$r_S \simeq 1 - \frac{6}{n(n^2-1)} \sum_{i=1}^{n} d_i^2$$

where d_i is the difference between the rank of X_i and that of Y_i. The value of r_S always lies in the interval [−1, 1], and adopts its extreme values only when the rankings precisely match (forwards or in reverse).

To test for dependence, special tables must be used for small samples ($n < 20$), but for larger samples the test statistic

$$Z = r_S\sqrt{(n-1)}$$

is approximately standard normal.

Example 6.16 Find and test the rank correlation for the data in Example 6.14.

Solution The data with their ranks are as follows:

X_i	4.4	5.5	4.2	3.0	4.5	4.9	4.6	5.0	4.7	5.1	4.4
Rank	5.5	22	4	1	7	14	8.5	16.5	10.5	18.5	5.5
Y_i	12	14	18	35	23	29	16	12	18	21	27
Rank	2.5	6	11	22	18	21	7.5	2.5	11	15.5	19.5

X_i	4.1	4.9	4.7	5.0	4.6	3.6	4.9	5.1	4.8	5.2	5.2
Rank	3	14	10.5	16.5	8.5	2	14	18.5	12	20.5	20.5
Y_i	13	19	22	20	16	27	21	13	18	17	11
Rank	4.5	13	17	14	7.5	19.5	15.5	4.5	11	9	1

From this, the rank correlation is $r_S = -0.361$, and $Z = -1.66$, which exceeds $z_{0.05} = 1.645$ and is therefore just significant at the 10% level. If the approximate formula is used, the sum of squares of differences is 2398, so

$$r_S \simeq 1 - \frac{(6)(2398)}{(22)(483)} = -0.354$$

and $Z = -1.62$, which is just short of significance.

These results show that the rank correlation is a more conservative test than the sample correlation $r_{X,Y}$, in that a larger sample tends to be needed before the hypothesis of independence is rejected. A price has to be paid for the wider applicability of the method.

6.4.7 Exercises

14 Suppose that the random variables X and Y have the following joint distribution:

	X		
Y	1	2	3
1	0	0.17	0.08
2	0.20	0.11	0
3	0.14	0.25	0.05

Find (a) the marginal distributions of X and Y, (b) $P(Y = 3 \mid X = 2)$, and (c) the mean, variance and correlation coefficient of X and Y.

15 Consider the random variable X with density function

$$f_X(x) = \begin{cases} 1 & (-\frac{1}{2} < x < \frac{1}{2}) \\ 0 & \text{otherwise} \end{cases}$$

Show that the covariance of X and X^2 is zero. (This shows that zero covariance does not imply independence, because obviously X^2 is dependent on X.)

16 The joint density function of random variables X and Y is

$$f_{X,Y}(x, y) = \begin{cases} 1 & (0 \leqslant x \leqslant 1;\ cx \leqslant y \leqslant cx + 1) \\ 0 & \text{otherwise} \end{cases}$$

where c is a constant such that $0 \leqslant c \leqslant 1$. Find the marginal density function for Y (see Example 6.10).

17 Let the random variables X and Y represent the lifetimes (in hundreds of hours) of two types of components used in an electronic system. The joint density function is given by

$$f_{X,Y}(x, y) = \begin{cases} \frac{1}{8} x \, e^{-(x+y)/2} & (x > 0, y > 0) \\ 0 & \text{otherwise} \end{cases}$$

Find (a) the probability that two components (one of each type) will each last longer than 100 h, and (b) the probability that a component of the second type (Y) will have a lifetime in excess of 200 h.

18 The following are the measured heights and weights of eight people:

Height (cm)	182.8	162.5	175.2	185.4	170.1	167.6	177.8	172.7
Weight (kg)	86.1	58.3	83.0	92.4	60.2	69.3	83.6	72.7

Find the sample correlation coefficient.

19 The number of minutes it took 10 mechanics to assemble a piece of machinery in the morning (X) and in the late afternoon (Y) were measured, with the following results:

X	11.1	10.3	12.0	15.1	13.7	18.5	17.3	14.2	14.8	15.3
Y	10.9	14.2	13.8	21.5	13.2	21.1	16.4	19.3	17.4	19.0

Find the sample correlation coefficient.

20 If the sample correlation between resistance and failure time for 30 overloaded resistors is 0.7, find a 95% confidence interval for the true correlation.

21 Find a 95% confidence interval for correlation between height and weight using the data in Exercise 18.

22 Marks obtained by 20 students taking examinations in mathematics and computer studies were as follows:

Math.	45	77	43	64	58	64	58	54	71	45
	57	52	67	57	54	54	61	58	55	42
Comp.	64	67	47	75	42	65	58	42	70	44
	44	67	49	70	51	58	37	60	42	36

Find the sample correlation coefficient and the 90% and 95% confidence intervals. Hence test the hypothesis that the two marks are independent at the 5% and 10% significance levels. Also find and test the rank correlation.

23 Let the random variables X and Y have joint density function given by

$$f_{X,Y}(x, y) = \begin{cases} c(1-y) & (0 \leqslant x \leqslant y \leqslant 1) \\ 0 & \text{otherwise} \end{cases}$$

Find (a) the value of the constant c, (b) $P(x < \frac{3}{4}, y > \frac{1}{2})$, and (c) the marginal density functions for X and Y.

24 The ball and socket of a joint are separately moulded and then assembled together. The diameter of the ball is a random variable X between 29.8 and 30.3 mm, all values being equally likely. The internal diameter of the socket is a random variable Y between 30.1 and 30.6 mm, again with all values equally likely. The condition for an acceptable fit is that $0 \leqslant Y - X \leqslant 0.6$ mm. Find the probability of this condition being satisfied, assuming that the random variables are independent.

6.5 Regression

A procedure that is very familiar to engineers is that of drawing a good straight line through a set of points on a graph. When calibrating a measuring instrument, for example, known inputs are applied, the readings are noted and plotted, a straight line is drawn as close to the points as possible (there are bound to be small errors, so they will not all lie on the line), and the graph is then used to interpret the readings for unknown inputs. It is possible to draw the line by eye, but there is a better way, which involves calculating the slope and intercept of the line from the data. The given line then minimizes the total

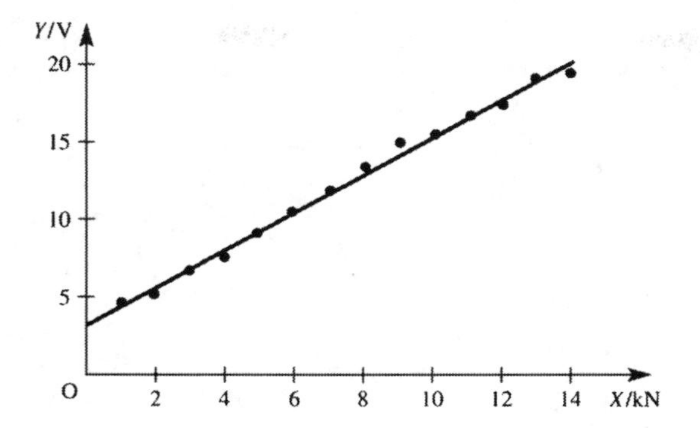

Figure 6.13 Scatter plot with regression line (Example 6.17).

squared error for the data points. This procedure (which for historical reasons is called **regression**) can be applied in general to pairs of random variables.

Computer packages are very often used to carry out the regression calculations and display the results. This is of special value when the data tend to follow a curve and various nonlinear models are tried and compared (see Section 6.5.4).

6.5.1 The method of least squares

The correlation was introduced in Section 6.4.3 as a way of measuring the dependence between random variables. Subsequently, we have seen how the correlation can be estimated and the dependence tested using sample data. We can take the idea of correlation between variables (say X and Y) a stage further by assuming that the sample pairs $\{(X_1, Y_1), \dots, (X_n, Y_n)\}$ satisfy a linear relationship of the form

$$Y_i = a + bX_i + E_i \quad (i = 1, \dots, n)$$

where a and b are unknown coefficients and the random variables E_i have zero mean and represent residual errors. This assumption is prompted by the scatter diagrams in Figure 6.11, which illustrate how the points may be concentrated around a line. Figure 6.13 shows a typical scatter diagram again, this time with the line drawn in. If we can estimate the coefficients a and b so as to give the best fit, we shall be able to predict the value of Y when the value of X is known.

The least-squares approach is to choose estimates $\hat{a}$ and $\hat{b}$ to minimize the sum of squares of the values E_i:

$$Q = \sum_{i=1}^{n} E_i^2 = \sum_{i=1}^{n} [Y_i - (\hat{a} + \hat{b}X_i)]^2$$

Equating to zero the partial derivatives of this sum with respect to the two coefficients gives a pair of equations that determine the minimum:

$$\frac{\partial Q}{\partial \hat{a}} = 0 = -2\sum_{i=1}^{n} [Y_i - (\hat{a} + \hat{b}X_i)]$$

$$\frac{\partial Q}{\partial \hat{b}} = 0 = -2\sum_{i=1}^{n} X_i[Y_i - (\hat{a} + \hat{b}X_i)]$$

These can be rewritten as

$$n\hat{a} + (\Sigma_i X_i)\hat{b} = (\Sigma_i Y_i)$$

$$(\Sigma_i X_i)\hat{a} + (\Sigma_i X_i^2)\hat{b} = (\Sigma_i X_i Y_i)$$

(where $\Sigma_i = \Sigma_{i=1}^{n}$) from which the solution is

$$\hat{b} = \frac{S_{XY}}{S_X^2}, \quad \hat{a} = \bar{Y} - \hat{b}\bar{X}$$

where

$$\bar{X} = \frac{1}{n}\Sigma_i X_i, \quad \bar{Y} = \frac{1}{n}\Sigma_i Y_i$$

and

$$S_{XY} = \frac{1}{n}\Sigma_i (X_i - \bar{X})(Y_i - \bar{Y}) = \overline{XY} - (\bar{X})(\bar{Y})$$

$$S_X^2 = \frac{1}{n}\Sigma_i (X_i - \bar{X})^2 = \overline{X^2} - (\bar{X})^2$$

$$S_Y^2 = \frac{1}{n}\Sigma_i (Y_i - \bar{Y})^2 = \overline{Y^2} - (\bar{Y})^2$$

are the sample variances and covariance.

This process of fitting a straight line through a set of data of the form $\{(X_1, Y_1), \ldots, (X_n, Y_n)\}$ is called **linear regression**, and the coefficients are called **regression coefficients**.

Example 6.17

A strain gauge has been bonded to a steel beam, and is being calibrated. The resistance of the strain gauge is converted into a voltage appearing on a meter. Known forces (X, in kN) are applied and voltmeter measurements (Y, in V) are as follows:

X	1	2	3	4	5	6	7	8	9	10	11	12	13	14
Y	4.4	4.9	6.4	7.3	8.8	10.3	11.7	13.2	14.8	15.3	16.5	17.2	18.9	19.3

Fit a regression line through the data and estimate the tension in the beam when the meter reading is 13.8 V.

Solution

The following quantities are calculated from the data:

$$\bar{X} = 7.5, \quad S_X = 4.031\,13, \quad \bar{Y} = 12.0714, \quad S_Y = 4.950\,68, \quad \overline{XY} = 110.421$$

(When using a hand calculator to solve linear regression problems, it is advisable to work to at least five or six significant digits during intermediate calculations, because the subtraction in the numerator of $\hat{b}$ often results in the loss of some leading digits.) From these results, $\hat{b} = 1.22$ and $\hat{a} = 2.89$ (Figure 6.13). The estimated value of tension for a reading of $Y = 13.8$ V is given by

$$13.8 = 2.89 + 1.22X$$

from which $X = 8.9$ kN.

Figure 6.14 shows a pseudocode listing for linear regression. The program is very similar to that in Figure 6.12 for the sample correlation, and the link between these will be explained in Section 6.5.3. In addition to the regression coefficients $\hat{a}$ and $\hat{b}$, an estimate of the residual standard deviation is returned, which is explained below.

Figure 6.14
Pseudocode listing for linear regression.

```
{ Program to compute linear regression coefficients.
x(k) and y(k) are the arrays of data,
n is the sample size,
xbar and ybar are the sample averages,
sx and sy are the sample standard deviations,
bhat is the regression slope result,
ahat is the regression intercept result,
se is the residual standard deviation,
Mx, My, Qx, Qy, Qxy hold running totals.  }

Mx ← 0; My ← 0
Qx ← 0; Qy ← 0
Qxy ← 0
for k is 1 to n do
  diffx ← x(k) – Mx
  diffy ← y(k) – My
  Mx ← ((k – 1)*Mx+x(k))/k
  My ← ((k – 1)*My+y(k))/k
  Qx ← Qx+(1–1/k)*diffx*diffx
  Qy ← Qy+(1–1/k)*diffy*diffy
  Qxy ← Qxy+(1–1/k)*diffx*diffy
endfor
xbar ← Mx; ybar ← My
sx ← sqr(Qx/n); sy ← sqr(Qy/n)
bhat ← Qxy/(n*sx*sx)
ahat ← ybar – bhat*xbar
se ← sqr(sy*sy – bhat*bhat*sx*sx)
```

6.5.2 Normal residuals

The process of fitting a straight line through the data by minimizing the sum of squares of the errors does not involve any statistics as such. However, we often need to test whether the slope of the regression line is significantly different from zero, because this will reveal whether there is any dependence between the random variables. For this purpose we must make the assumption that the errors E_i, called the **residuals**, have a normal distribution:

$$E_i \sim N(0, \sigma_E^2)$$

The unknown variance σ_E^2 can be estimated by defining

$$S_E^2 = \frac{1}{n}\sum_{i=1}^{n} E_i^2 = \frac{1}{n}\sum_{i=1}^{n} [Y_i - (\hat{a} + \hat{b}X_i)]^2$$

Using the earlier result that $\hat{a} = \bar{Y} - \hat{b}\bar{X}$ gives a more convenient form:

$$\begin{aligned} S_E^2 &= \frac{1}{n}\sum_i [(Y_i - \bar{Y}) - \hat{b}(X_i - \bar{X})]^2 \\ &= \frac{1}{n}\sum_i [(Y_i - \bar{Y})^2 - 2\hat{b}(X_i - \bar{X})(Y_i - \bar{Y}) + \hat{b}^2(X_i - \bar{X})^2] \\ &= S_Y^2 - 2\hat{b}S_{XY} + \hat{b}^2 S_X^2 \\ &= S_Y^2 - \hat{b}^2 S_X^2 \end{aligned}$$

This result is used in the pseudocode listing (Figure 6.14).

Various confidence intervals are derived in more advanced texts covering linear regression. Here the most useful results will simply be quoted. The $100(1-\alpha)\%$ confidence interval for the regression slope b is given by

$$\left(\hat{b} \pm t_{\alpha/2,n-2}\frac{S_E}{S_X\sqrt{(n-2)}}\right)$$

It is often useful to have an estimate of the mean value of Y for a given value of X, say $X=x$. The point estimate is $\hat{a}+\hat{b}x$, and the $100(1-\alpha)\%$ confidence interval for this is

$$\left(\hat{a}+\hat{b}x \pm t_{\alpha/2,n-2}S_E\sqrt{\left[\frac{1+(x-\bar{X})^2/S_X^2}{n-2}\right]}\right)$$

Example 6.18 Estimate the residual standard deviation and find a 95% confidence interval for the regression slope for the data in Example 6.17. Also test the hypothesis that the tension in the beam is 10 kN when a voltmeter reading of 15 V is obtained.

Solution Using the results obtained in Example 6.17, the residual standard deviation is

$$S_E = 0.418$$

and, using $t_{0.025,12} = 2.179$, the 95% confidence interval for b is

$$\left(1.22 \pm 2.179\frac{0.418}{(4.031)\sqrt{12}}\right) = (1.16,\ 1.29)$$

Obviously the regression slope is significant – but this is not in doubt. To test the hypothesis that the tension is 10 kN, we can use the 95% confidence interval for the corresponding voltage, which is

$$\left(2.89 + 1.22(10) \pm 2.179(0.418)\sqrt{\left[\frac{1+(10-7.5)^2/(4.031)^2}{12}\right]}\right)$$

$$= (14.8,\ 15.4)$$

The measured value of 15 V lies within this interval, so the hypothesis is accepted at the 5% level. A better way to approach this would be to reverse the regression (use force as the Y variable and voltage as the X variable), so that a confidence interval for the tension in the beam for a given voltage could be obtained and the assumed value tested. For the present data this gives (9.6, 10.1) at 95%, so again the hypothesis is accepted (Exercise 27).

6.5.3 Regression and correlation

Both regression and correlation are statistical methods for measuring the linear dependence of one random variable upon another, so it is not surprising that there is a connection between them. From the definition of the sample correlation $r_{X,Y}$ (Section 6.4.4) and the result for the regression slope $\hat{b}$, it follows immediately that

$$r_{X,Y} = \frac{S_{XY}}{S_X S_Y} = \frac{\hat{b} S_X}{S_Y}$$

Another expression for the residual variance is then

$$S_E^2 = S_Y^2 - \left(\frac{S_Y r_{X,Y}}{S_X}\right)^2 S_X^2 = S_Y^2(1 - r_{X,Y}^2)$$

This result has an important interpretation. S_Y^2 is the total variation in the Y values, and S_E^2 is the residual variation after the regression line has been identified, so $r_{X,Y}^2$ is the proportion of the total variation in the Y values that is accounted for by the regression on X: informally, it represents how closely the points are clustered about the line. This is a measure of goodness of fit that is especially useful when the dependence between X and Y is nonlinear and different models are to be compared.

6.5.4 Nonlinear regression

Sometimes the dependence between two random variables is nonlinear, and this shows clearly in the scatter plot; see for instance Figure 6.15. Fitting a straight line through the data would hardly be appropriate. Instead, various models of the dependence can be assumed and tested. In each case the value of $r_{X,Y}^2$ indicates the success of the model in capturing the dependence. One form of nonlinear regression model involves a quadratic or higher-degree polynomial:

$$Y_i = a_0 + a_1 X_i + a_2 X_i^2 + E_i \quad (i = 1, \ldots, n)$$

The three coefficients a_0, a_1 and a_2 can be identified by a multivariate regression method that is beyond the scope of this text. A simpler approach is to try models of the form

$$Y_i = a X_i^b F_i \quad (i = 1, \ldots, n)$$

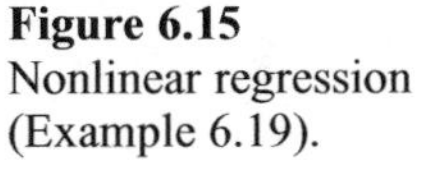

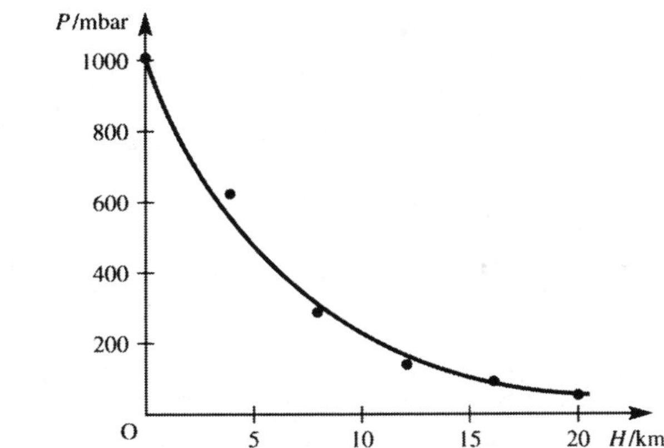

Figure 6.15
Nonlinear regression (Example 6.19).

or

$$Y_i = F_i \exp(a + bX_i) \quad (i = 1, \ldots, n)$$

where each F_i is a residual multiplicative error. On taking logarithms, these models reduce to the standard linear form:

$$\ln Y_i = \ln a + b \ln X_i + E_i \quad (i = 1, \ldots, n)$$

or

$$\ln Y_i = a + bX_i + E_i \quad (i = 1, \ldots, n)$$

which can be solved by the usual method.

Example 6.19 The following data for atmospheric pressure (P, in mbar) at various heights (H, in km) have been obtained:

Height H	0	4	8	12	16	20
Pressure P	1012	621	286	141	104	54

The relationship between height and pressure is believed to be of the form

$$P = e^{a+bH}$$

where a and b are constants. Fit and assess a model of this form and predict the atmospheric pressure at a height of 14 km.

Solution Taking logarithms and setting $Y = \ln P$ gives

$$Y_i = a + bH_i + E_i$$

for which the following results are easily obtained:

$$\bar{H} = 10, \quad S_H = 6.831\,30, \quad \bar{Y} = 5.431\,52, \quad S_Y = 1.016\,38, \quad \overline{HY} = 47.4081$$

Hence

$$\hat{b} = \frac{\overline{HY} - (\bar{H})(\bar{Y})}{S_H^2} = -0.148$$

$$\hat{a} = \bar{Y} - \hat{b}\bar{H} = 6.91$$

Also, $r_{H,Y}^2 = 0.99$, which implies that the fit is very good (Figure 6.15). In this case there is not much point in trying other models. Finally, the predicted pressure at a height of 14 km is

$$P = e^{6.91-0.148(14)} = 126\,\text{mbar}$$

6.5.5 Exercises

25 Ten files of audio data are annotated by a human labeller. The time (s) this takes per file is a function of the length of the file (s) as follows:

File length (X)	5.4	7.9	10.0	14.2	16.1	16.8	19.6	22.0	25.0	26.7
Annotation time (Y)	13.1	17.3	23.9	30.1	33.5	40.0	43.6	46.5	52.4	60.7

Find the linear regression coefficients.

26 Measured deflections (in mm) of a structure under a load (in kg) were recorded as follows:

Load X	1	2	3	4	5	6	7	8	9	10	11	12
Deflection Y	16	35	45	74	86	96	106	124	134	156	164	182

Draw a scatter plot of the data. Find the linear regression coefficients and predict the deflection for a load of 15 kg.

27 Using the data in Example 6.17, carry out a regression of force against voltage, and obtain a 95% confidence interval for the tension in the beam when the voltmeter reads 15 V, as described in Example 6.18.

28 Weekly advertising expenditures X_i and sales Y_i for a company are as follows (in units of £100):

X_i	40	20	25	20	30	50	40	20	50	40	25	50
Y_i	385	400	395	365	475	440	490	420	560	525	480	510

(a) Fit a regression line and predict the sales for an advertising expenditure of £6000.
(b) Estimate the residual standard deviation and find a 95% confidence interval for the regression slope. Hence test the hypothesis that the sales do not depend upon advertising expenditure.
(c) Find a 95% confidence interval for the mean sales when advertising expenditure is £6000.

29 A machine that can be run at different speeds produces articles, of which a certain number are defective. The number of defective items produced per hour depends upon machine speed (in rev s^{-1}) as indicated in the following experimental run:

Speed	8	9	10	11	12	13	14	15
Defectives per hour	7	12	13	13	13	16	14	18

Find the regression line for number of defectives against speed, and a 90% confidence interval for the mean number of defectives per hour when the speed is 14 rev s^{-1}.

30 Sometimes it is required that the regression line passes through the origin, in which case the only regression coefficient is the slope of the line. Use the least-squares procedure to show that the estimate of the slope is then

$$\hat{b} = (\Sigma_i X_i Y_i)/\Sigma_i X_i^2$$

31 A series of measurements of voltage across and current through a resistor produced the following results:

Voltage (V)	1	2	3	4	5	6	7	8	9	10	11	12
Current (mA)	6	18	27	30	42	48	58	69	74	81	94	99

Estimate the resistance, using the result of the previous exercise.

32 The pressure P of a gas corresponding to various volumes V was recorded as follows:

V (cm^3)	50	60	70	90	100
P (kg cm^{-2})	64.7	51.3	40.5	25.9	7.8

The ideal gas law is given by the equation

$$PV^{\lambda} = C$$

where λ and C are constants. By taking logarithms and using the least-squares method, estimate λ and C from the data and predict P when $V = 80$ cm^3.

33 The following data show the unit costs of producing certain electronic components and the number of units produced:

Lot size X_i	50	100	250	500	1000	2000	5000
Unit cost Y_i	108	65	21	13	4	2.2	1

Fit a model of the form $Y = aX^b$ and predict the unit cost for a lot size of 300.

6.6 Goodness-of-fit tests

The common classes of distributions, especially the binomial, Poisson and normal distributions, which often govern the data in experimental contexts, are used as the basis for statistical methods of estimation and testing. A question that naturally arises is whether or not a given set of data actually follows an assumed distribution. If it does then the statistical methods can be used with confidence. If not then some alternative should be considered. The general procedure used for testing this can also be used to test for dependence between two variables.

6.6.1 Chi-square distribution and test

No set of data will follow an assumed distribution exactly, but there is a general method for testing a distribution as a statistical hypothesis. If the hypothesis is accepted then it is reasonable to use the distribution as an approximation to reality.

First the data must be partitioned into classes. If the data consist of observations from a discrete distribution then they will be in classes already, but it may be appropriate to combine some classes if the numbers of observations are small. For each class the number of observations that would be expected to occur under the assumed distribution can be worked out. The following quantity acts as a test statistic for comparing the observed and expected class numbers:

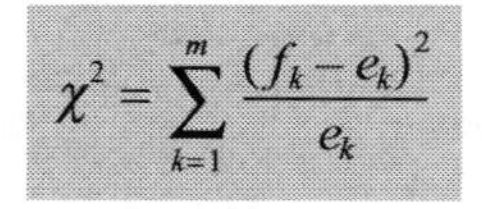

$$\chi^2 = \sum_{k=1}^{m} \frac{(f_k - e_k)^2}{e_k}$$

where f_k is the number of observations in the kth class, e_k is the expected number in the kth class and m is the number of classes. Clearly, χ^2 is a non-negative quantity whose magnitude indicates the extent of the discrepancy between the histogram of data and the assumed distribution. For small samples the histogram is erratic and the comparison invalid, but for large samples the histogram should approximate the true distribution. It can be shown that for a large sample the random variable χ^2 has a **'chi-square' distribution**. This class of distributions is widely used in statistics, and a typical chi-square probability density function is shown in Figure 6.16. We are interested in particular in the value of $\chi^2_{\alpha,n}$ to the right of which the area under the density function curve is α, where n is the (single) parameter of the distribution. These values are extensively tabulated; a typical table is shown in Figure 6.17.

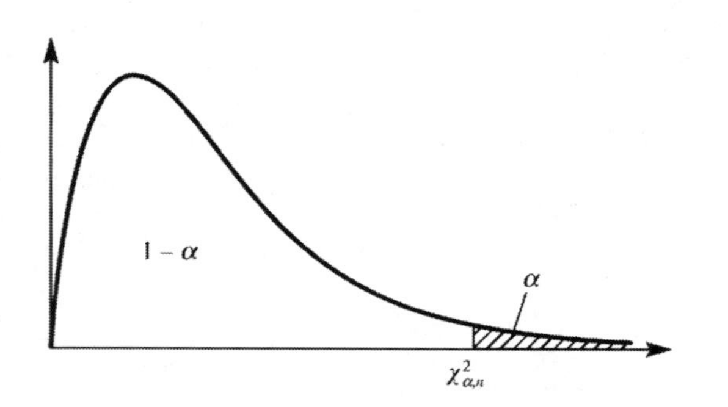

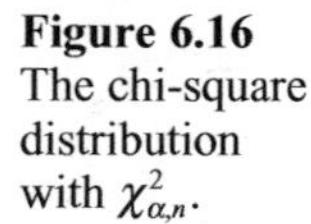

Figure 6.16 The chi-square distribution with $\chi^2_{\alpha,n}$.

Figure 6.17
Table of the chi-square distribution $\chi^2_{\alpha,n}$.

n	$\alpha = 0.05$	$\alpha = 0.025$	$\alpha = 0.01$	$\alpha = 0.005$	n
1	3.841	5.024	6.635	7.879	1
2	5.991	7.378	9.210	10.597	2
3	7.815	9.348	11.345	12.838	3
4	9.488	11.143	13.277	14.860	4
5	11.070	12.832	15.086	16.750	5
6	12.592	14.449	16.812	18.548	6
7	14.067	16.013	18.475	20.278	7
8	15.507	17.535	20.090	21.955	8
9	16.919	19.023	21.666	23.589	9
10	18.307	20.483	23.209	25.188	10
11	19.675	21.920	24.725	26.757	11
12	21.026	23.337	26.217	28.300	12
13	22.362	24.736	27.688	29.819	13
14	23.685	26.119	29.141	31.319	14
15	24.996	27.488	30.578	32.801	15
16	26.296	28.845	32.000	34.267	16
17	27.587	30.191	33.409	35.718	17
18	28.869	31.526	34.805	37.156	18
19	30.144	32.852	36.191	38.582	19
20	31.410	34.170	37.566	39.997	20
21	32.671	35.479	38.932	41.401	21
22	33.924	36.781	40.289	42.796	22
23	35.172	38.076	41.638	44.181	23
24	36.415	39.364	42.980	45.558	24
25	37.652	40.646	44.314	46.928	25
26	38.885	41.923	45.642	48.290	26
27	40.113	43.194	46.963	49.645	27
28	41.337	44.461	48.278	50.993	28
29	42.557	45.722	49.588	52.336	29
30	43.773	46.979	50.892	53.672	30

The hypothesis of the assumed distribution is rejected if

$$\chi^2 > \chi^2_{\alpha,m-t-1}$$

where α is the significance level and t is the number of independent parameters estimated from the data and used for computing the e_k values. The significance level is the probability of false rejection, as discussed in Section 6.3.4. The only difference is that there is now no estimation procedure underlying the hypothesis test, which must stand alone. Sometimes the hypothesis is deliberately vague, for example a parameter value may be left unspecified. If the data themselves are used to fix parameter values in the assumed distribution before testing then the test must be strengthened to allow for this in the form of a correction t in the chi-square parameter.

A useful rule of thumb when using this test is that there should be at most a small number (one or two) of classes with an expected number of observations less than five. If necessary, classes in the tails of the distribution can be merged.

Example 6.20 A die is tossed 600 times, and the numbers of occurrences of the numbers one to six are recorded respectively as 89, 113, 98, 104, 117 and 79. Is the die fair or biased?

Solution The expected values are $e_k = 100$ for all k, and the test value is $\chi^2 = 10.4$. This is less than $\chi^2_{0.05,5} = 11.07$, so we should expect results as erratic as this at least once in 20 similar experiments. The die may well be biased, but the data are insufficient to justify this conclusion.

Example 6.21 The numbers of trucks arriving per hour at a warehouse are counted for each of 500 h. Counts of zero up to eight arrivals are recorded on respectively 52, 151, 130, 102, 45, 12, 5, 1 and 2 occasions. Test the hypothesis that the numbers of arrivals have a Poisson distribution, and estimate how often there will be nine or more arrivals in one hour.

Solution The hypothesis stipulates a Poisson distribution, but without specifying the parameter λ. Since the mean of the Poisson distribution is λ and the average number of arrivals per hour is 2.02 from the data, it is reasonable to assume that $\lambda = 2$. The columns in the table in Figure 6.18 show the observed counts f_k, the Poisson probabilities p_k, the expected counts $e_k = 500p_k$ and the individual χ^2 values for each class. The last two classes have been combined because the numbers are so small. One parameter has been estimated from the data, so the total χ^2 value is compared with $\chi^2_{0.05,6} = 12.59$. The Poisson hypothesis is accepted, and on that basis the probability of nine or more trucks arriving in one hour is

$$P(9 \text{ or more}) = 1 - \sum_{k=0}^{8} \frac{2^k e^{-2}}{k!} = 0.000\,237$$

This will occur roughly once in every 4200 h of operation.

Figure 6.18
Chi-square calculation for Example 6.21.

Trucks	f_k	p_k	e_k	χ^2
0	52	0.1353	67.7	3.63
1	151	0.2707	135.3	1.81
2	130	0.2707	135.3	0.21
3	102	0.1804	90.2	1.54
4	45	0.0902	45.1	0.00
5	12	0.0361	18.0	2.02
6	5	0.0120	6.0	0.17
7	3	0.0046	2.3	0.24
Totals	500	1.0	500	9.62

Because so many statistical methods assume normal data, it is important to have a test for normality, and the chi-square method can be used (Exercise 38 and Section 6.8.4).

6.6.2 Contingency tables

In Section 6.4.3 the correlation was introduced as a measure of dependence between two random variables. The sample correlation (Section 6.4.4) provides an estimate from data. This measure only applies to numerical random variables, and then only works for linear dependence (Exercise 15). The rank correlation (Section 6.4.6) has more general applicability, but still requires that the data be classified in order of rank. The chi-square testing procedure can be adapted to provide at least an indicator of dependence that has the widest applicability of all.

Suppose that each item in a sample of size n can be separately classified as one of $A_1, \ldots, A_r$ by one criterion, and as one of $B_1, \ldots, B_c$ by another (these may be numerical values, but not necessarily). The number f_{ij} of items in the sample that are classified as 'A_i and B_j' can be counted for each $i = 1, \ldots, r$ and $j = 1, \ldots, c$. The table of these numbers (with r rows and c columns) is called a **contingency table** (Figure 6.19). The question is whether the two criteria are independent. If not then some combinations of A_i and B_j will occur significantly more often (and others less often) than would be expected under the assumption of independence. We first have to work out how many would be expected under an assumption of independence.

Figure 6.19
Contingency table.

Class	B_1	...	B_c	Total
A_1	f_{11}	...	f_{1c}	f_{1+}
⋮	⋮		⋮	⋮
A_r	f_{r1}	...	f_{rc}	f_{r+}
Total	f_{+1}	...	f_{+c}	n

Let the row and column totals be denoted by

$$f_{i+} = \sum_{j=1}^{c} f_{ij} \quad (i = 1, \ldots, r)$$

$$f_{+j} = \sum_{i=1}^{r} f_{ij} \quad (j = 1, \ldots, c)$$

If the criteria are independent then the joint probability for each combination can be expressed as the product of the separate marginal probabilities:

$$P(A_i \cap B_j) = P(A_i)P(B_j)$$

The chi-square procedure will be used to see how well the data fit this assumption. To test it, we can estimate the marginal probabilities from the row and column totals,

$$P(A_i) \simeq \frac{f_{i+}}{n}, \qquad P(B_j) \simeq \frac{f_{+j}}{n}$$

and multiply the product of these by n to obtain the expected number e_{ij} for each combination:

$$e_{ij} = n\frac{f_{i+}}{n}\frac{f_{+j}}{n} = \frac{f_{i+}f_{+j}}{n}$$

The chi-square goodness-of-fit statistic follows from the actual and expected numbers (f_{ij} and e_{ij}) as a sum over all the rows and columns:

$$\chi^2 = \sum_{i=1}^{r}\sum_{j=1}^{c}\frac{(f_{ij}-e_{ij})^2}{e_{ij}}$$

If the value of this is large then the hypothesis of independence is rejected, because the actual and expected counts differ by more than can be attributed to chance. As explained in Section 6.6.1, the largeness is judged with respect to $\chi^2_{\alpha,m-t-1}$ from the chi-square table. The number of classes, m, is the number of rows times the number of columns, rc. The number of independent parameters estimated from the data, t, is the number of independent marginal probabilities $P(A_i)$ and $P(B_j)$:

$$t = (r-1) + (c-1)$$

The number is not $r + c$, because the row and column totals must equal one, so when all but one are specified, the last is determined. Finally,

$$m - t - 1 = rc - (r + c - 2) - 1 = (r-1)(c-1)$$

The hypothesis of independence is therefore rejected (at significance level α) if

$$\chi^2 > \chi^2_{\alpha,(r-1)(c-1)}$$

Example 6.22

An accident inspector makes spot checks on working practices during visits to industrial sites chosen at random. At one large construction site the numbers of accidents occurring per week were counted for a period of three years, and each week was also classified as to whether or not the inspector had visited the site during the previous week. The results are shown in bold print in Figure 6.20. Do visits by the inspector tend to reduce the number of accidents, at least in the short term?

Figure 6.20
Contingency table for Example 6.22.

	Number of accidents				
	0	1	2	3	Total
Visit Residual	**20** (13.38) 2.96	**3** (7.08) –1.99	**1** (2.46) –1.07	**0** (1.08) –1.16	24
No visit Residual	**67** (73.62) –2.96	**43** (38.92) 1.99	**15** (13.54) 1.07	**7** (5.92) 1.16	132
Total	87	46	16	7	156

Solution The respective row and column totals are shown in Figure 6.20, together with the expected numbers e_{ij} in parentheses in each cell. For example, the top left cell has observed number 20, row total 24, column total 87, $n = 156$, and hence the expected number

$$e_{11} = (24)(87)/156 = 13.38$$

The chi-square sum is

$$\chi^2 = \frac{(20 - 13.38)^2}{13.38} + \ldots + \frac{(7 - 5.92)^2}{5.92}$$

$$= 8.94$$

With two rows, four columns and a significance level of 5%, the appropriate number from the chi-square table is $\chi^2_{0.05,3} = 7.815$. The calculated value exceeds this, and by comparing the observed and expected numbers in the table, it seems clear that the visits by the inspector do tend to reduce the number of accidents. This is not, however, significant at the 2.5% level.

A significant chi-square value does not by itself reveal what part or parts of the table are responsible for the lack of independence. A procedure that is often helpful in this respect is to work out the **adjusted residual** for each cell, defined as

$$d_{ij} = \frac{f_{ij} - e_{ij}}{\sqrt{[e_{ij}(1 - f_{i+}/n)(1 - f_{+j}/n)]}}$$

Under the assumption of independence, these are approximately standard normal, so a significant value for a cell suggests that that cell is partly responsible for the dependence overall. The adjusted residuals for the contingency table in Example 6.22 are shown in Figure 6.20, and support the conclusion that visits by the inspector tend to reduce the number of accidents.

For a useful survey of procedures for analysing contingency tables see B. S. Everitt, *The Analysis of Contingency Tables*, 2nd edn (Chapman & Hall, London, 1992).

6.6.3 Exercises

34 In a genetic experiment, outcome A is expected to occur twice as often as outcome B, which in turn is expected to occur twice as often as outcome C, and exactly one of these three outcomes must occur. In a sample of size 100, outcomes A, B, C occurred 63, 22, 15 times respectively. Test the hypothesis at 5% significance.

35 The number of books borrowed from a library that is open five days a week is as follows: Monday 153, Tuesday 108, Wednesday 120, Thursday 114, Friday 145. Test (at 5% significance) whether the number of books borrowed depends on the day of the week.

36 A new process for manufacturing light fibres is being tested. Out of 50 samples, 32 contained no flaws, 12 contained one flaw and 6 contained two flaws. Test the hypothesis that the number of flaws per sample has a Poisson distribution.

37 In an early experiment on the emission of α-particles from a radioactive source, Rutherford obtained the following data on counts of particles during constant time intervals:

Number of particles	0	1	2	3	4	5	6	7	8	9	10	>10
Number of intervals	57	203	383	525	532	408	273	139	45	27	10	6

Test the hypothesis that the number of particles emitted during an interval has a Poisson distribution.

38 Two samples of 100 data have been grouped into classes as shown in Figure 6.21. The sample average and standard deviation in each case were 10.0 and 2.0 respectively.

(a) Draw the histogram for each sample.
(b) Test each sample for normality using the measured parameters.

Class	Sample 1	Sample 2
<6.5	4	3
6.5–7.5	6	6
7.5–8.5	16	16
8.5–9.5	16	13
9.5–10.5	17	26
10.5–11.5	20	7
11.5–12.5	12	19
12.5–13.5	6	5
>13.5	3	5

Figure 6.21 Data classification for Exercise 38.

39 Shipments of electronic devices have been received by a firm from three sources: A, B and C. Each device is classified as either perfect, intermediate (imperfect but acceptable), or unacceptable. From source A 89 were perfect, 23 intermediate and 12 unacceptable. Corresponding figures for source B were 62, 12 and 8 respectively, and for source C 119, 30 and 21 respectively. Is there any significant difference in quality between the devices received from the three sources?

40 Cars produced at a factory are chosen at random for a thorough inspection. The number inspected and the number of those that were found to be unsuitable for shipment were counted monthly for one year as follows:

Month	Jan.	Feb.	Mar.	Apr.	May	Jun.
Inspected	450	550	550	400	600	450
Defective	8	14	6	3	7	8
Month	**Jul.**	**Aug.**	**Sep.**	**Oct.**	**Nov.**	**Dec.**
Inspected	450	200	450	600	600	550
Defective	16	5	12	6	15	9

Is there a significant variation in quality through the year?

41 Customers ordering regularly from an on-line clothing catalogue are classed as low, medium and high spenders. Considering four products from the catalogue (a jacket, a shirt, a pair of trousers, and a pair of shoes), the numbers of customers in each class buying these products over a fixed period of time are given in the following table:

Spending level	Jacket	Shirt	Trousers	Shoes
Low	21	94	57	113
Medium	66	157	94	209
High	58	120	41	125

Does this table provide evidence that customers with different spending levels tend to choose different products?

42 A quality control engineer takes daily samples of four television sets coming off an assembly line. In a total of 200 working days he found that on 110 days no sets required adjustments, on 73 days one set requires adjustments, on 16 days two sets and on 1 day three sets. Use these results to test the hypothesis that 10% of sets coming off the assembly line required adjustments, at 5% and 1% significance levels. Also test this using the confidence interval for proportion (Section 6.3.6), using the total number of sets requiring adjustments.

6.7 Moment generating functions

This section is more difficult than the rest of this chapter, and can be treated as optional during a first reading. It contains the proofs of theoretical results, such as the central limit theorem, that are of great importance, as seen earlier in this chapter. The technique introduced here is the moment generating function, which is a useful tool for finding means and variances of random variables as well as for proving these essential results. The moment generating function also bears a striking resemblance to the Laplace transform considered in Chapter 2.

6.7.1 Definition and simple applications

The **moment generating function** of a random variable X is defined as

$$M_X(t) = E(e^{tX}) = \begin{cases} \displaystyle\sum_{k=1}^{m} e^{tv_k} P(X = v_k) & \text{in the discrete case} \\ \displaystyle\int_{-\infty}^{\infty} e^{tx} f_X(x)\,dx & \text{in the continuous case} \end{cases}$$

where t is a real variable. This is an example of the expected value of a function $h(X)$ of the random variable X (Section 6.2.2). The moment generating function does not always exist, or it may exist only for certain values of t. In cases where it fails to exist there is an alternative (called the **characteristic function**) which always exists and has similar properties. When the moment generating function does exist, it is unique in the sense that no two distinct distributions can have the same moment generating function.

To see how the moment generating function earns its name, the first step is to differentiate it with respect to t and then let t tend to zero:

$$\frac{d}{dt} M_X(t)\big|_{t=0} = E(X e^{tX})\big|_{t=0} = E(X) = \mu_X$$

Thus the first derivative gives the mean. Differentiating again gives

$$\frac{d^2}{dt^2} M_X(t)\big|_{t=0} = E(X^2 e^{tX})\big|_{t=0} = E(X^2)$$

From this result we obtain the variance (from Section 6.2.2)

$$\text{Var}(X) = E(X^2) - [E(X)]^2$$

We can summarize these results as follows. If a random variable X has mean μ_X, variance σ_X^2 and moment generating function $M_X(t)$ defined for t in some neighbourhood of zero then

$$\mu_X = M_X^{(1)}(0), \qquad \sigma_X^2 = (M_X^{(2)}(0) - [M_X^{(1)}(0)]^2)$$

where the superscript in parentheses denotes the order of the derivative. Furthermore,

$$E(X^k) = M_X^{(k)}(0) \quad k = (1, 2, \dots)$$

Example 6.23 Show that the mean and variance of the Poisson distribution with parameter λ are both equal to λ (Section 6.2.3).

Solution If X has a Poisson distribution then

$$P(X = k) = \frac{\lambda^k e^{-\lambda}}{k!} \quad (k = 0, 1, 2, \ldots)$$

and the moment generating function is

$$M_X(t) = \sum_{k=0}^{\infty} e^{kt} \frac{\lambda^k e^{-\lambda}}{k!} = e^{-\lambda} \sum_{k=0}^{\infty} \frac{(\lambda e^t)^k}{k!} = \exp[\lambda(e^t - 1)]$$

Differentiating this with respect to t gives

$$M_X^{(1)}(t) = \lambda e^t \exp[\lambda(e^t - 1)]$$

$$M_X^{(2)}(t) = (\lambda^2 e^{2t} + \lambda e^t) \exp[\lambda(e^t - 1)]$$

from which

$$\mu_X = M_X^{(1)}(0) = \lambda$$

$$\sigma_X^2 = M_X^{(2)}(0) - \mu_X^2 = \lambda$$

as expected.

Example 6.24 Show that the mean and standard deviation of the exponential distribution

$$f_X(x) = \begin{cases} \lambda e^{-\lambda x} & (x \geqslant 0) \\ 0 & (x < 0) \end{cases}$$

are both equal to $1/\lambda$ (Section 6.10.2).

Solution The moment generating function is

$$M_X(t) = \int_0^{\infty} \lambda e^{-(\lambda - t)x} \, dx = \frac{\lambda}{\lambda - t}$$

Note that the integral only exists for $t < \lambda$, but we can differentiate it and set $t = 0$ for any positive value of λ:

$$M_X^{(1)}(0) = \lambda^{-1} = \mu_X$$

$$M_X^{(2)}(0) = 2\lambda^{-2}$$

from which $\sigma_X^2 = \lambda^{-2}$.

6.7.2 The Poisson approximation to the binomial

In addition to its utility for finding means and variances, the moment generating function is a very useful theoretical tool. In this section and the next we shall use it to prove two of the most important results in probability theory, but first we need the following general property of moment generating functions.

Suppose that X and Y are independent random variables with moment generating functions $M_X(t)$ and $M_Y(t)$. Then the moment generating function of their sum is given by

$$M_{X+Y}(t) = M_X(t)M_Y(t)$$

To prove this, we shall assume that X and Y are continuous random variables with a joint density function $f_{X,Y}(x, y)$; however, the proof is essentially the same if either or both are discrete. By definition,

$$M_{X+Y}(t) = E[\mathrm{e}^{t(X+Y)}] = \int_{-\infty}^{\infty}\int_{-\infty}^{\infty} \mathrm{e}^{t(x+y)} f_{X,Y}(x, y)\,\mathrm{d}x\,\mathrm{d}y$$

Both factors of the integrand themselves factorize (noting the independence of X and Y) to give

$$M_{X+Y}(t) = \int_{-\infty}^{\infty}\int_{-\infty}^{\infty} [\mathrm{e}^{tx} f_X(x)][\mathrm{e}^{ty} f_Y(y)]\,\mathrm{d}x\,\mathrm{d}y$$

The two integrals can now be separated, and the result follows:

$$M_{X+Y}(t) = \int_{-\infty}^{\infty} \mathrm{e}^{tx} f_X(x)\,\mathrm{d}x \int_{-\infty}^{\infty} \mathrm{e}^{ty} f_Y(y)\,\mathrm{d}y$$

$$= M_X(x)M_Y(y)$$

It follows that if $\{X_1, \ldots, X_n\}$ are independent and identically distributed random variables, each with moment generating function $M_X(t)$, and if $Z = X_1 + \ldots + X_n$, then

$$M_Z(t) = [M_X(t)]^n$$

We now proceed to the main result. If the random variable Y has a binomial distribution with parameters n and p and the random variable X has a Poisson distribution with parameter $\lambda = np$ then as $n \to \infty$ and $p \to 0$, the distribution of X tends to that of Y.

First let the random variable B have a Bernoulli distribution with parameter p (Section 6.2.3). The moment generating function of B is then

$$M_B(t) = \mathrm{e}^t p + (1 - p) = 1 + p(\mathrm{e}^t - 1)$$

Since the binomial random variable Y is the sum of n copies of B, it follows that the moment generating function of the binomial distribution is

$$M_Y(t) = [1 + p(\mathrm{e}^t - 1)]^n$$

It can be proved that for any real z

$$\lim_{n\to\infty}\left(1+\frac{z}{n}\right)^n = e^z$$

Now let $z = np(e^t - 1)$ and assume that $\lambda = np$:

$$M_Y(t) = \left(1+\frac{z}{n}\right)^n \simeq e^z = \exp[\lambda(e^t - 1)] = M_X(t)$$

(the moment generating function for the Poisson distribution was derived in Example 6.23). The uniqueness of the moment generating function implies that the distributions of X and Y must be similar, provided that n is sufficiently large. It is also required that $p \to 0$ as $n \to \infty$, so that z does not grow without bound.

This approximation has many applications; see for example Section 6.9.2.

6.7.3 Proof of the central limit theorem

This theorem is of vital importance in statistics because it tells us that the sample average for a sample of at least moderate size tends to have a normal distribution even when the data themselves do not. The result (Section 6.2.4) is here restated and proved using the moment generating function.

Theorem 6.1 The central limit theorem

If $\{X_1, \ldots, X_n\}$ are independent and identically distributed random variables, each with mean μ_X and variance σ_X^2, and if

$$Z_n = \frac{X_1 + \ldots + X_n - n\mu_X}{\sigma_X\sqrt{n}}$$

then the distribution of Z_n tends to the standard normal distribution as $n \to \infty$.

Proof First let the random variables Y_i be defined by

$$Y_i = \frac{X_i - \mu_X}{\sigma_X\sqrt{n}} \quad (i = 1, \ldots, n)$$

so that

$$E(Y_i) = 0$$

$$E(Y_i^2) = \frac{1}{n}$$

$$E(Y_i^3) = \frac{c}{n\sqrt{n}}, \quad \text{where } c \text{ is a constant}$$

Expanding the moment generating function $M_Y(t)$ for each Y_i as a Maclaurin series (to four terms) gives

$$M_Y(t) \simeq M_Y(0) + M_Y^{(1)}(0)t + M_Y^{(2)}(0)\frac{t^2}{2!} + M_Y^{(3)}(0)\frac{t^3}{3!}$$

By the results in Section 6.7.1, the coefficients of this series can be replaced by the successive moments $E(Y_i^k)$:

$$M_Y(t) \simeq E(1) + E(Y_i)t + E(Y_i^2)\frac{t^2}{2!} + E(Y_i^3)\frac{t^3}{3!} \simeq 1 + \frac{t^2}{2n} + \frac{ct^3}{6n\sqrt{n}}$$

Now Z_n is the sum of the variables Y_i,

$$Z_n = \sum_{i=1}^{n} Y_i$$

so the moment generating function of Z_n is the nth power of that of Y_i:

$$M_{Z_n}(t) = [M_Y(t)]^n$$

Retaining only the first two terms of a binomial expansion of this gives

$$M_{Z_n}(t) = \left(1 + \frac{t}{2n}\right)^n + n\left(1 + \frac{t^2}{2n}\right)^{n-1}\left(\frac{ct^3}{6n\sqrt{n}}\right) + \ldots$$

$$\to \mathrm{e}^{t^2/2} \quad \text{as } n \to \infty$$

because all terms except the first will tend to zero.

It only remains to show that this is the moment generating function for the standard normal distribution; see Exercise 47.

end of theorem

6.7.4 Exercises

43 A continuous random variable X has density function

$$f_X(x) = \begin{cases} cx\,\mathrm{e}^{-2x} & (x > 0) \\ 0 & (x \leqslant 0) \end{cases}$$

Find the value of the constant c. Derive the moment generating function, and hence find the mean and variance of X.

44 Prove that if $X_1, \ldots, X_n$ are independent Poisson random variables with parameters $\lambda_1, \ldots, \lambda_n$ then their sum

$$Y = X_1 + \ldots + X_n$$

is also Poisson, with parameter $\lambda = \lambda_1 + \ldots + \lambda_n$.

45 A factory contains 30 machines each with breakdown probability 0.01 in any one hour and 40 machines each with breakdown probability 0.005 in any one hour. Use the result of Exercise 44, together with the Poisson approximation to the binomial, to find the probability that a total of three or more machine breakdowns will occur in any one hour.

46 A manufacturer has agreed to dispatch small servomechanisms in cartons of 100 to a distributor. The distributor requires that 90% of cartons contain at most one defective servomechanism. Assuming the Poisson approximation to the binomial, obtain an equation for the Poisson parameter λ such that the distributor's requirements are just satisfied. Solve for λ by one of the standard methods for nonlinear equations (approximate solution 0.5), and hence find the required proportion of manufactured servomechanisms that must be satisfactory.

47 Show that the moment generating function of the standard normal distribution is $\mathrm{e}^{t^2/2}$. (*Hint*: Complete the square in the exponential.)

6.8 Engineering application: analysis of engine performance data

6.8.1 Introduction

Statistical methods are often used in conjunction with each other. So far in this chapter the examples and exercises have almost always been designed to illustrate the various topics one at a time. This section contains an example of a more extended problem to which several topics are relevant, and correspondingly there are several stages to the analysis.

The background to the problem is this. Suppose that the fuel consumption of a car engine is tested by measuring the time that the engine runs at constant speed on a litre of standard fuel. Two prototype engines, A and B, are being compared for fuel consumption. For each engine a series of tests is performed in various ambient temperatures, which are also recorded. Figure 6.22 contains the data. There are 30 observations each for the four random variables concerned:

A, running time in minutes for engine A;

T, ambient temperature in degrees Celsius for engine A;

B, running time in minutes for engine B;

U, ambient temperature in degrees Celsius for engine B.

The histograms for the running times are compared in Figure 6.23(a) and those for the temperatures in Figure 6.23(b). The overall profile of temperatures is very similar for the two series of tests, differing only in the number of unusually high or low figures encountered. The profiles of running times appear to differ rather more markedly. It is clear that displaying the data in this way is useful, but some analysis will have to be done in order to determine whether the differences are significant.

Figure 6.22 Data for engine case study.

Engine A				Engine B			
A	T	A	T	B	U	B	U
27.7	24	24.1	7	24.9	13	24.3	17
24.3	25	23.1	14	21.4	19	24.5	16
23.7	18	23.4	16	24.1	18	26.1	18
22.1	15	23.1	9	27.5	19	27.7	14
21.8	19	24.1	14	27.5	21	24.3	19
24.7	16	28.6	23	25.7	17	26.1	5
23.4	17	20.2	14	24.9	17	24.0	17
21.6	14	25.7	18	23.3	19	24.9	18
24.5	18	24.6	18	22.5	21	26.7	23
26.1	20	24.0	12	28.5	12	27.3	28
24.8	15	24.9	18	25.9	17	23.9	18
23.7	15	21.9	20	26.9	13	23.1	10
25.0	22	25.1	16	27.7	17	25.5	25
26.9	18	25.7	16	25.4	23	24.9	22
23.7	19	23.5	11	25.3	30	25.9	16

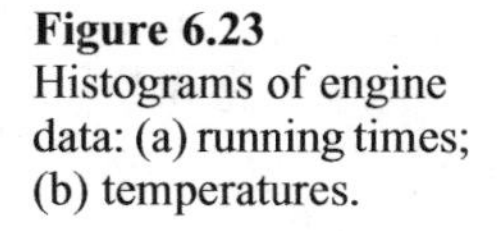

Figure 6.23
Histograms of engine data: (a) running times; (b) temperatures.

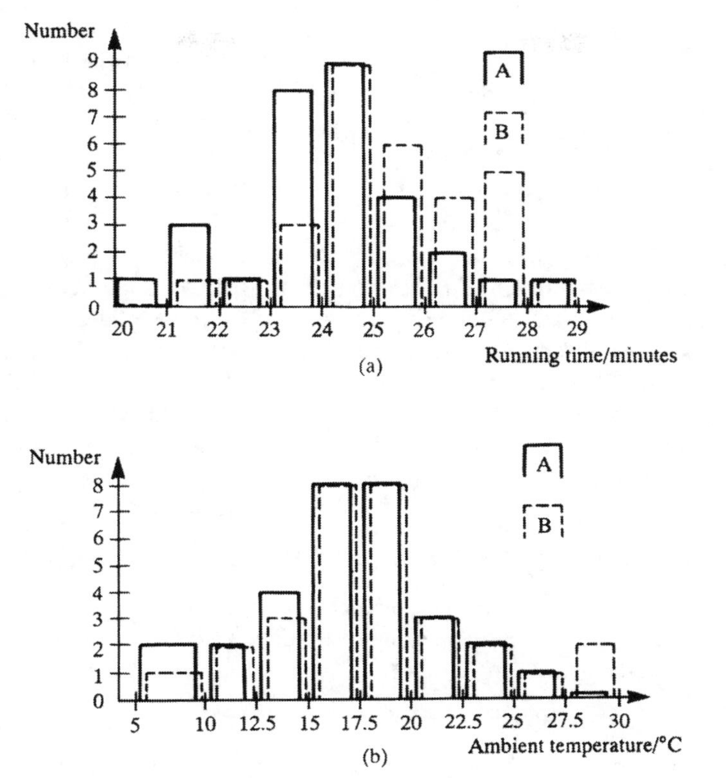

When planning the analysis, it is as well to consider the questions to which most interest attaches. Do the mean running times for the two engines differ? Does the running time depend on temperature? If so, and if there is a difference in the temperatures for the test series on engines A and B, can this account for any apparent difference in fuel consumption? More particularly, are the data normal? This has a bearing on the methods used, and hence on the conclusions drawn.

6.8.2 Difference in mean running times and temperatures

The sample averages and both versions of standard deviation for the data in Figure 6.22 are as follows:

$$\bar{A} = 24.20, \quad \bar{T} = 16.70, \quad \bar{B} = 25.36, \quad \bar{U} = 18.07$$

$$S_A = 1.761, \quad S_T = 4.001, \quad S_B = 1.657, \quad S_U = 4.932$$

$$S_{A,n-1} = 1.791, \quad S_{T,n-1} = 4.070, \quad S_{B,n-1} = 1.685, \quad S_{U,n-1} = 5.017$$

The average running time for engine B is slightly higher than for engine A. The sample standard deviations are very similar, so we can assume that the true standard deviations are equal and use the method for comparing means discussed in Section 6.3.5. The pooled estimate of the variance is

$$S_p^2 = \frac{(n-1)(S_{A,n-1}^2 + S_{B,n-1}^2)}{2(n-1)} = \frac{3.208 + 2.839}{2} = 3.023$$

and the relevant value from the t-table is $t_{0.025,58} = 1.960$. In fact the sample is large enough for the value for the normal distribution to be taken. The 95% confidence interval for the difference $\mu_B - \mu_A$ is

$$(\bar{B} - \bar{A} \pm 1.96S_p/\sqrt{15}) = (0.28, 2.04)$$

Even the 99% confidence interval (0.12, 2.20) does not contain the zero point, so we can be almost certain that the difference in mean running times is significant.

Following the same procedure for the temperatures gives the 95% confidence interval for the difference $\mu_U - \mu_T$ to be (−0.94, 3.68). Superficially, this is not significant – and even if the running times do depend on temperature, the similarity of the two test series in this respect enables this factor to be discounted. If so, the fuel performance for engine B is superior to that for engine A. However, if the temperature sensitivity were very high then even a difference in the average too small to give a significant result by this method could create a misleading difference in the fuel consumption figures. This possibility needs to be examined.

6.8.3 Dependence of running time on temperature

The simplest way to test for dependence is to correlate times and temperatures for each engine. To compute the sample correlations, we need the following additional results from the data:

$$\overline{AT} = 407.28, \qquad \overline{BU} = 457.87$$

The sample correlations (Section 6.4.4) of A and T and of B and U are then

$$r_{A,T} = \frac{\overline{AT} - (\bar{A})(\bar{T})}{S_A S_T} = 0.445, \qquad r_{B,U} = \frac{\overline{BU} - (\bar{B})(\bar{U})}{S_B S_U} = -0.030$$

and the respective 95% confidence intervals (Section 10.4.5) are

$$(0.10, 0.69), \quad (-0.39, 0.34)$$

This is a quite definitive result: the running time for engine A depends positively upon the ambient temperature, but that for engine B does not. The confidence intervals are based on the assumption that all the variables A, T, B and U are normal. The histograms have this character, and a test for normality will be covered later.

Linear regression also reveals the dependence of running time on temperature. Here we assume that the variables are related by a linear model as follows:

$$\left.\begin{aligned} A_i &= c_A + d_A T_i + E_i \\ B_i &= c_B + d_B U_i + F_i \end{aligned}\right\} \quad (i = 1, \ldots, n)$$

where c_A, d_A, c_B and d_B are constants, and the random variables E_i and F_i represent residual errors. Using the results of the least-squares analysis in Section 6.5.1, for engine A we have

$$\hat{d}_A = \frac{\overline{AT} - (\bar{A})(\bar{T})}{S_T^2} = 0.196, \qquad \hat{c}_A = \bar{A} - \hat{d}_A\bar{T} = 20.9$$

Likewise, for engine B

$$\hat{d}_B = -0.010, \qquad \hat{c}_B = 25.5$$

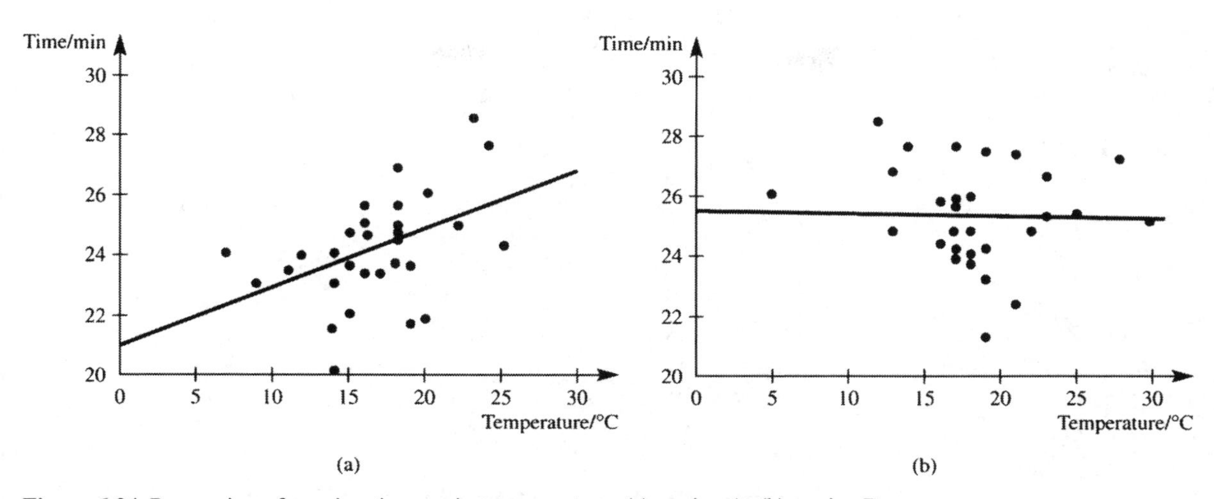

Figure 6.24 Regression of running time against temperature: (a) engine A; (b) engine B.

Figure 6.24 contains scatter plots of the data with these regression lines drawn. The points are well scattered about the lines. The residual variances, using the results in Sections 6.5.2 and 6.5.3, are

$$S_E^2 = S_A^2 - \hat{d}_A S_T^2 = S_A^2(1 - r_{A,T}^2) = 2.49$$

$$S_F^2 = 2.74$$

As explained in Section 6.5.3, the respective values of r^2 indicate the extent to which the variation in running times is due to the dependence on temperature. For engine B there is virtually no such dependence. For engine A we have $r_{A,T}^2 = 0.198$, so nearly 20% of the variation in running times is accounted for in this way.

If we assume that the residuals E_i and F_i are normal, we can obtain confidence intervals for the regression slopes. The appropriate value from the t table is $t_{\alpha/2,n-2} = t_{0.025,28} = 2.048$, so the 95% confidence interval for d_A is

$$\left(\hat{d}_A \pm 2.048 \frac{S_E}{S_T\sqrt{28}}\right) = (0.04, 0.35)$$

The significance shown here confirms that found for the correlation. The 95% confidence interval for d_B is $(-0.14, 0.12)$.

We now return to the main question. We know that the average running time for engine A was significantly lower than that for engine B. However, we also know that the running time for engine A depends on temperature, and that the average temperature during the test series for engine A was somewhat lower than for engine B. Could this account for the difference?

A simple way to test this is to look at the average values. The difference in average temperatures is $(18.07 - 16.70) = 1.37$ and the regression slope d_A is estimated to be 0.196, so that a deficit in the average running time of $(1.37)(0.196) \simeq 0.27$ min is predicted on this basis. This cannot account for the actual difference of 1.16 min, and does not even bring the zero point within the 95% confidence interval for the difference in means $\mu_B - \mu_A$.

To examine this more carefully, we can try using the regression slopes to correct all running times to the same temperature. Choosing the average temperature for the series B for this purpose, we can let

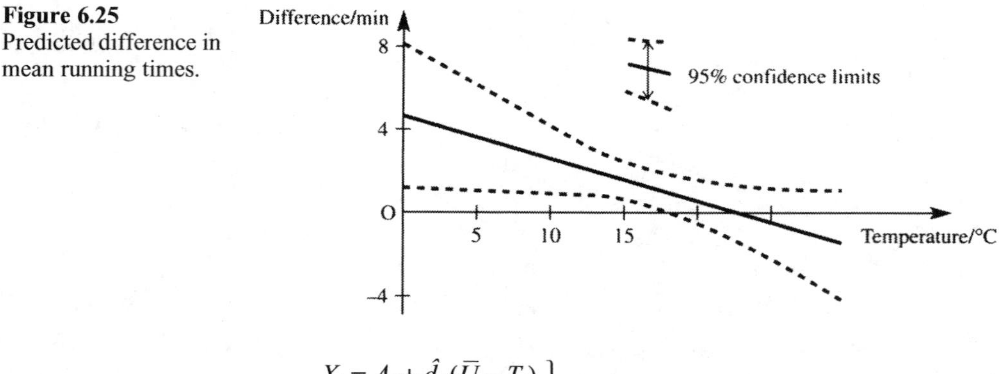

Figure 6.25
Predicted difference in mean running times.

$$\left.\begin{aligned} X_i &= A_i + \hat{d}_A(\bar{U} - T_i) \\ Y_i &= B_i + \hat{d}_B(\bar{U} - U_i) \end{aligned}\right\} \quad (i = 1, \ldots, n)$$

The 95% confidence interval for the difference between mean running times, $\mu_Y - \mu_X$, at this temperature is then (0.06, 1.72), using the method in Section 6.3.5. The problem with this is that the estimates of d_A and d_B themselves have rather wide confidence intervals, and it is not satisfactory to adopt a point value to apply the temperature correction.

We need a more direct way to obtain the confidence interval for the difference between mean running times at any particular temperature. This is possible using a more general theory of linear regression, formulated using matrix algebra, which allows for any number of regression coefficients instead of just two; see for example G. A. F. Seber, *Linear Regression Analysis* (Wiley, New York, 1977). Applied to the present problem, estimates of the regression slopes d_A and d_B and intercepts c_A and c_B are obtained simultaneously, with the same values as before, and it now becomes possible to obtain a confidence interval for any linear combination of these four unknowns. In particular, the confidence interval for the difference between mean running times at any temperature t is based on the linear combination

$$(c_B + d_B t) - (c_A + d_A t)$$

Space precludes coverage of the analysis here, but the results can be seen in Figure 6.25. At any temperature below 22.4 °C engine B is predicted to have the advantage over engine A (this temperature being the point at which the regression lines cross). At any temperature below 18.1 °C the 95% confidence interval for the difference is entirely positive, and we should say that engine B has a significant advantage. This is the best comparison of the engines that is possible using the data presented.

6.8.4 Test for normality

The confidence interval statistics are all based on the assumption of normality of the data. Although the sample sizes are reasonably large, so that the central limit theorem can be relied upon to weaken this requirement, it is worth applying a test for normality to see whether there is any clear evidence to the contrary. Here the regression residuals E_i and F_i will be tested using the method described in Section 6.6.1.

Figure 6.26 shows the histogram of all 60 'standardized' residuals. The residuals have zero mean in any case, and are standardized by dividing by the standard deviation so that they can be compared with a standard normal distribution. It is convenient to use intervals of width 0.4, and the comparison is developed in Figure 6.27.

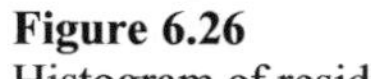

Figure 6.26
Histogram of residuals.

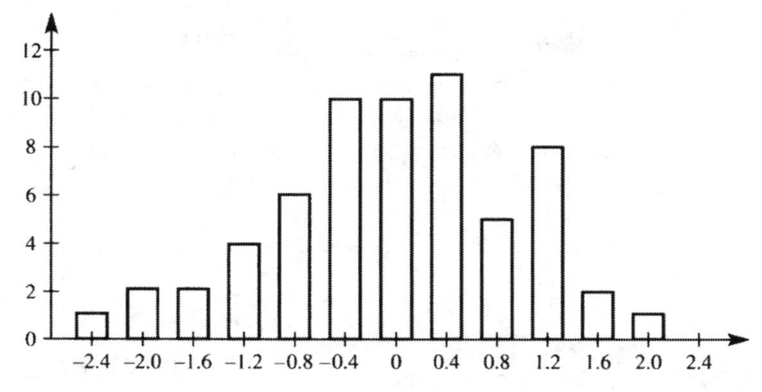

Figure 6.27 Table of the test for normality.

Interval	Observed (f_k)	Probability	Expected (e_k)	Chi-square
$(-\infty, -1.4)$	5	0.0808	4.848	0.005
$(-1.4, -1.0)$	4	0.0779	4.674	0.097
$(-1.0, -0.6)$	6	0.1156	6.936	0.126
$(-0.6, -0.2)$	10	0.1464	8.784	0.168
$(-0.2, +0.2)$	8	0.1586	9.516	0.242
$(+0.2, +0.6)$	11	0.1464	8.784	0.559
$(+0.6, +1.0)$	5	0.1156	6.936	0.540
$(+1.0, +1.4)$	8	0.0779	4.674	2.367
$(+1.4, +\infty)$	3	0.0808	4.848	0.704
Totals	60	1.0	60	4.809

The normal probabilities for each interval are obtained from the standard normal table of the cumulative distribution function $\Phi(z)$, Figure 6.2, taking successive differences:

$$P(z_1 < Z < z_2) = \Phi(z_2) - \Phi(z_1)$$

These probabilities are multiplied by 60 to obtain the expected number in each interval, and the difference between the observed and expected number for each interval is squared and then divided by the expected number to give the contribution to the total chi-square:

$$\chi^2 = \sum_{k=1}^{m} \frac{(f_k - e_k)^2}{e_k} = 4.81$$

This is small compared with $\chi^2_{0.05,8} = 15.507$, so the hypothesis of normality is accepted.

It is unwise when applying this test in general to have many classes with expected numbers less than five, so the intervals in the tails of the histogram have been merged.

6.8.5 Conclusions

All the questions posed in Section 6.8.1 have now been answered. Engine B has an average running time that is significantly higher than that for engine A, showing that it has the advantage in fuel consumption. However, this statement requires qualification.

The running time for engine A depends upon ambient temperature. The temperature difference between the two test series was not significant, and does not account for the difference in average running times. However, engine B will only maintain its fuel advantage up to a certain point. This point has been estimated, but cannot be identified very precisely because of considerable residual scatter in the data. There are many potential sources of this scatter, such as errors in measuring out the fuel, or variations in the quantity and consistency of the engine oil. The scatter has a normal distribution, which justifies the statistics behind the conclusions reached.

6.9 Engineering application: statistical quality control

6.9.1 Introduction

Every manufacturer recognizes the importance of quality, and every manufacturing process involves some variation in the quality of its output, however that is to be measured. Experience shows that tolerating a lack of quality tends to be more costly in the end than promoting a quality approach. It follows that quality control is a major and increasing concern, and methods of statistical quality control are more important than ever. The domain of these methods now extends to the construction and service industries as well as to manufacturing – wherever there is a process that can be monitored in quantitative terms.

Traditionally, quality control involved the accumulation of batches of manufactured items, the testing of samples extracted from these batches, and the acceptance or rejection (with appropriate rectifying action) of these batches depending upon the outcome. The essential problem with this is that it is too late within the process: it is impossible to inspect or test quality into a product. More recently the main concern has been to design the quality into the product or service and to monitor the process to ensure that the standard is maintained, in order to prevent any deficiency. Assurance can then be formally given to the customer that proper procedures are in place.

Control charts play an important role in the implementation of quality. In order for this section to be as self-contained as possible, some of that material is repeated here. This section then covers more powerful control charts and extends the scope of what they monitor.

First note that there are two main alternative measures of quality: **attribute** and **variable**. In attribute measure, regular samples from the process are inspected and for each sample the number that fail according to some criterion is plotted on a chart. In variable measure, regular samples are again taken, but this time the sample average for some numerical measure (such as dimension or lifetime) is plotted.

6.9.2 Shewhart attribute control charts

Figure 6.28 is an example of a Shewhart control chart: a plot of the count of 'defectives' (the number in the sample failing according to some chosen criterion) against sample number. It is assumed that a small (specified) proportion of 'defective' items in the process is permitted. Also shown on the chart are two limits on the count of defectives,

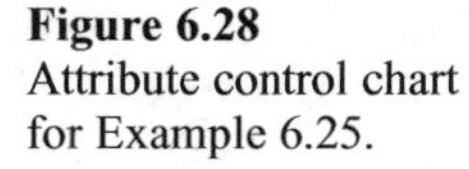
Figure 6.28
Attribute control chart for Example 6.25.

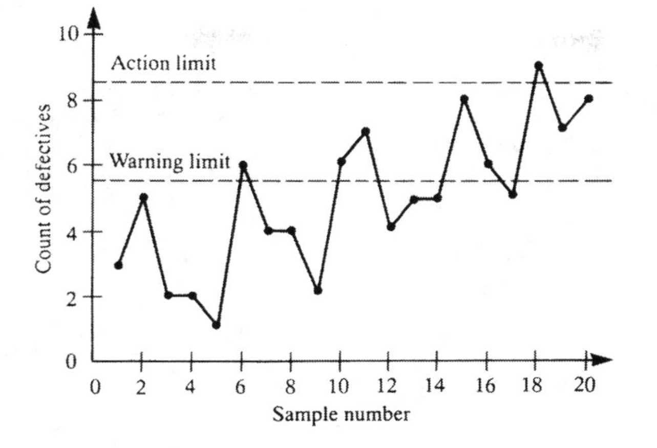

corresponding to probabilities of one in 40 and one in 1000 of a sample count falling outside if the process is 'in control'; that is, conforming to the specification. These are called **warning** and **action limits** respectively, and are denoted by c_W and c_A.

Any sample point falling outside the action limit would normally result in the process being suspended and the problem corrected. Roughly one in 40 sample points will fall outside the warning limit purely by chance, but if this occurs repeatedly or if there is a clear trend upwards in the counts of defectives then action may well be taken before the action limit itself is crossed.

To obtain the warning and action limits, we use the Poisson approximation to the binomial. If the acceptable proportion of defective items is p, usually small, and the sample size is n then for a process in control the defective count C, say, will be a binomial random variable with parameters n and p. Provided that n is not too small, the Poisson approximation can be used (Section 6.7.2):

$$P(C \geqslant c) \simeq \sum_{k=c}^{\infty} \frac{(np)^k \mathrm{e}^{-np}}{k!}$$

Equating this to $\frac{1}{40}$ and then to $\frac{1}{1000}$ gives equations that can be solved for the warning limit c_W and the action limit c_A respectively, in terms of the product np. This is the basis for the table shown in Figure 6.29, which enables c_W and c_A to be read directly from the value of np.

Example 6.25

Regular samples of 50 are taken from a process making electronic components, for which an acceptable proportion of defectives is 5%. Successive counts of defectives in each sample are as follows:

Sample	1	2	3	4	5	6	7	8	9	10	11	12	13	14	15	16	17	18	19	20
Count	3	5	2	2	1	6	4	4	2	6	7	4	5	5	8	6	5	9	7	8

At what point would the decision be taken to stop and correct the process?

Solution The control chart is shown in Figure 6.28. From $np = 2.5$ and Figure 6.29 we have the warning limit $c_W = 5.5$ and the action limit $c_A = 8.5$. The half-integer values are to avoid ambiguity when the count lies on a limit. There are warnings at samples 6, 10, 11, 15 and 16 before the action limit is crossed at sample 18. Strictly, the decision should be taken at that point, but the probability of two consecutive warnings is less than one in 1600 by the product rule of probabilities, which would justify taking action after sample 11.

Figure 6.29
Shewhart attribute control limits: n is sample size, p is probability of defect, c_W is warning limit and c_A is action limit.

c_W or c_A	np for c_W	np for c_A
1.5	<0.44	<0.13
2.5	0.44–0.87	0.13–0.32
3.5	0.87–1.38	0.32–0.60
4.5	1.38–1.94	0.60–0.94
5.5	1.94–2.53	0.94–1.33
6.5	2.53–3.16	1.33–1.77
7.5	3.16–3.81	1.77–2.23
8.5	3.81–4.48	2.23–2.73
9.5	4.48–5.17	2.73–3.25
10.5	5.17–5.87	3.25–3.79
11.5	5.87–6.59	3.79–4.35
12.5	6.59–7.31	4.35–4.93
13.5	7.31–8.05	4.93–5.52
14.5	8.05–8.80	5.52–6.12
15.5	8.80–9.55	6.12–6.74
16.5	9.55–10.31	6.74–7.37
17.5	10.31–11.08	7.37–8.01
18.5	11.08–11.85	8.01–8.66
19.5	11.85–12.63	8.66–9.31
20.5	12.63–13.42	9.31–9.98
21.5	13.42–14.21	9.98–10.65
22.5	14.21–15.00	10.65–11.33
23.5	15.00–15.80	11.33–12.02
24.5	15.80–16.61	12.02–12.71
25.5	16.61–17.41	12.71–13.41
26.5	17.41–18.23	13.41–14.11
27.5	18.23–19.04	14.11–14.82
28.5	19.04–19.86	14.82–15.53
29.5	19.86–20.68	15.53–16.25
30.5		16.25–16.98
31.5		16.98–17.70
32.5		17.70–18.44
33.5		18.44–19.17
34.5		19.17–19.91
35.5		19.91–20.66

An alternative practice (especially popular in the USA) is to dispense with the warning limit and to set the action limit (called the **upper control limit**, **UCL**) at three standard deviations above the mean. Because the count of defectives is binomial with mean np and variance $np(1-p)$, this means that

$$\text{UCL} = np + 3\sqrt{[np(1-p)]}$$

Example 6.26 Find the UCL and apply it to the data in Example 6.25.

Solution From $n = 50$ and $p = 0.05$ we infer that UCL = 7.1, which is between the warning limit c_W and the action limit c_A in Example 6.25. The decision to correct the process would be taken after the 15th sample, the first to exceed the UCL.

6.9.3 Shewhart variable control charts

Suppose now that the appropriate assessment of quality involves measurement on a continuous scale rather than success or failure under some criterion. This arises whenever some dimension of the output is critical for applications. Again we take samples, but this time we measure this critical dimension and average the results. The Shewhart chart for this variable measure is a plot of successive sample averages against sample number.

The warning and action limits c_W and c_A on a Shewhart chart are those points for which the probabilities of a false alarm (where the result exceeds the limit even though the process is in control) are one in 40 and one in 1000 respectively. For variable measure the critical quantity can be either too high or too low, so the sample average must be tested in each direction with the stated probability of exceedance for each limit. It follows that the limits are determined by

$$P(\bar{X} > \mu_X + c_W) = P(\bar{X} < \mu_X - c_W) = \tfrac{1}{40}$$

$$P(\bar{X} > \mu_X + c_A) = P(\bar{X} < \mu_X - c_A) = \tfrac{1}{1000}$$

where $\bar{X}$ is the sample average and μ_X the design mean.

Provided that the sample size n is not too small, the central limit theorem allows the sample average to be assumed normal (Section 6.3.2),

$$\bar{X} \sim N(\mu_X, \sigma_X^2/n)$$

and the normal distribution table (Figure 6.2) then gives

$$c_W = \frac{1.96\sigma_X}{\sqrt{n}}, \qquad c_A = \frac{3.09\sigma_X}{\sqrt{n}}$$

Example 6.27 Measurements of sulphur dioxide concentration (in $\mu g\ m^{-3}$) in the air are taken daily at five locations, and successive average readings are as follows:

64.2, 56.9, 57.7, 67.9, 61.7, 59.7, 55.6, 63.7
58.3, 66.4, 67.2, 65.2, 63.1, 67.6, 64.1, 66.7

It is suspected that the mean increased during that time. Assuming normal data with a long-term mean of 60.0 and standard deviation of 8.0, investigate whether an increase occurred.

Solution From $n = 5$ and $\sigma_X = 8$ we have $c_W = 7.0$ and $c_A = 11.1$ (Figure 6.30). The warning limit is 67.0, which is exceeded by sample numbers 4, 11 and 14. The action limit is 71.1, which is not exceeded. The readings are suspiciously high – but not sufficiently so for the conclusion to be justified.

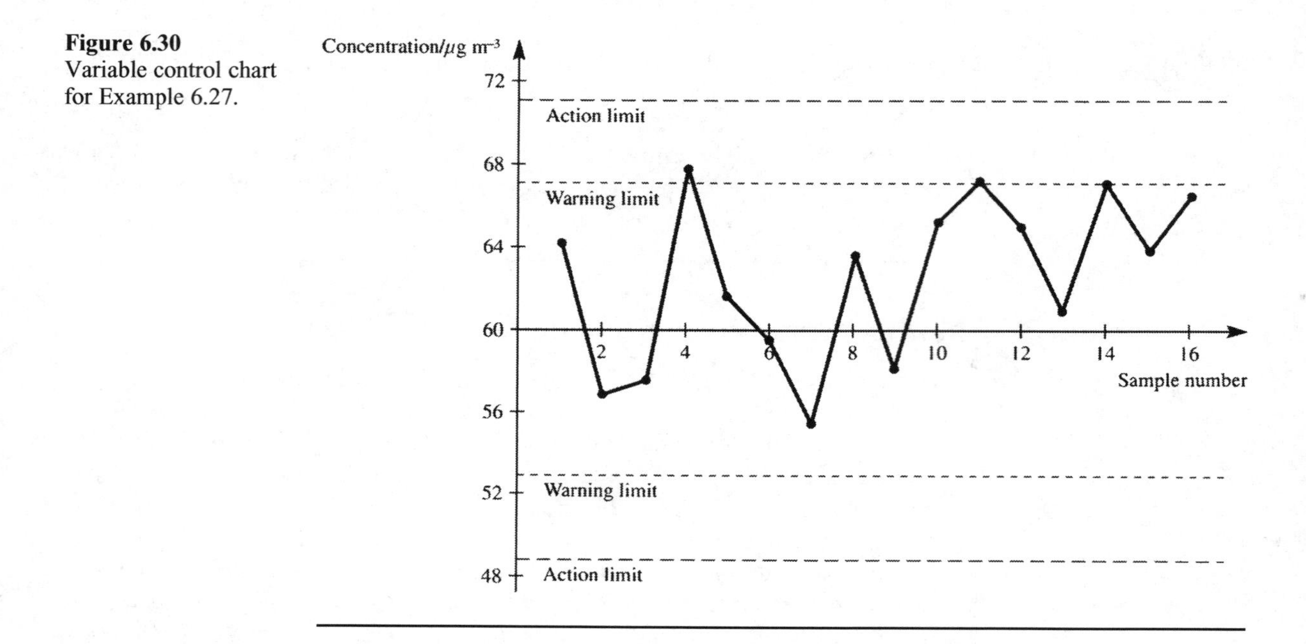

Figure 6.30 Variable control chart for Example 6.27.

As discussed in Section 6.9.2, the practice in the USA is somewhat different: there are no warning limits, only action limits at three standard deviations on either side of the mean. For a variable chart this allows a deviation from the mean of at most $3\sigma_X/\sqrt{n}$, which is very close to the action limit usually used in the UK.

6.9.4 Cusum control charts

The main concern in designing a control chart is to achieve the best compromise between speedy detection of a fault on the one hand and avoidance of a proliferation of false alarms on the other. If the chart is too sensitive, it will lead to a large number of unnecessary shutdowns. The Shewhart charts, on the other hand, are rather conservative in that they are slow to indicate a slight but genuine shift in performance away from the design level. This derives from the fact that each sample point is judged independently and may well lie inside the action limits, whereas the cumulative evidence over several samples might justify an earlier decision. Rather informal methods involving repeated warnings and trends are used, but it is preferable to employ a more powerful control chart. The **cumulative sum (cusum)** chart achieves this, and is easily implemented on a small computer.

Suppose that we have a sequence $\{Y_1, Y_2, \ldots\}$ of observations, which may be either counts of defectives or sample averages. From this a new sequence $\{S_0, S_1, \ldots\}$ is obtained by setting

$$S_0 = 0,$$

$$S_m = \max\{0, S_{m-1} + Y_m - r\} \quad (m = 1, 2, \ldots)$$

where r is a constant 'reference value'. This gives a cumulative sum of values of $Y_m - r$, which is reset to zero whenever it goes negative. The out-of-control decision is made when

$$S_m > h$$

Figure 6.31 Cusum attribute chart control data.

np	r	h	np	r	h
0.22	1	1.5	2.35	4	4.5
0.39	1	2.5	2.60	4	5.5
0.51	2	1.5	2.95	5	4.5
0.62	1	4.5	3.24	5	5.5
0.69	1	5.5	3.89	6	5.5
0.79	2	2.5	4.16	6	6.5
0.86	3	1.5	5.32	7	8.5
1.05	2	3.5	6.07	8	8.5
1.21	3	2.5	7.04	9	9.5
1.52	3	3.5	8.01	10	10.5
1.96	3	5.5	9.00	11	11.5
2.16	5	2.5	10.00	12	12.5

where h is a constant 'decision interval'. This will detect an increasing mean; a separate but similar procedure can be used to detect a decreasing mean. Values of r and h for both attribute and variable types of control can be obtained from tables such as those in J. Murdoch, *Control Charts* (Macmillan, London, 1979), from which the attribute table in Figure 6.31 has been extracted. For variable measure (with process design mean μ_X and standard deviation σ_X) the following are often used:

$$r = \mu_X + \frac{\sigma_X}{2\sqrt{n}}, \qquad h = 5\frac{\sigma_X}{\sqrt{n}}$$

Example 6.28

Regular samples of 50 are taken from a process making electronic components, for which an acceptable proportion of defectives is 5%. Successive counts of defectives in each sample are as follows:

Sample	1	2	3	4	5	6	7	8	9	10	11	12	13	14	15	16	17	18	19	20
Count	3	5	2	2	1	6	4	4	2	6	7	4	5	5	8	6	5	9	7	8

At what point would the decision be taken to stop and correct the process?

Solution

The acceptable proportion of defectives is $p = 0.05$ and the regular sample size is $n = 50$. From the table in Figure 6.31, with $np = 2.5$ the nearest figures for reference value and decision interval are $r = 4$ and $h = 5.5$. The following shows the cusum S_m below each count of defectives Y_m, and the cusum is also plotted in Figure 6.32:

Count	3	5	2	2	1	6	4	4	2	6	7	4	5	5	8	6	5	9	7	8
Cusum	0	1	0	0	0	2	2	2	0	2	5	5	6	7	11	13	14	19	22	26

For example,

$$S_{13} = S_{12} + Y_{13} - r = 5 + 5 - 4 = 6$$

and because this exceeds $h = 5.5$, the decision to take action would be made after the 13th sample. This result can be compared with that of a Shewhart chart applied to the same data (Example 6.25), which suggests that action should be taken after 18 samples.

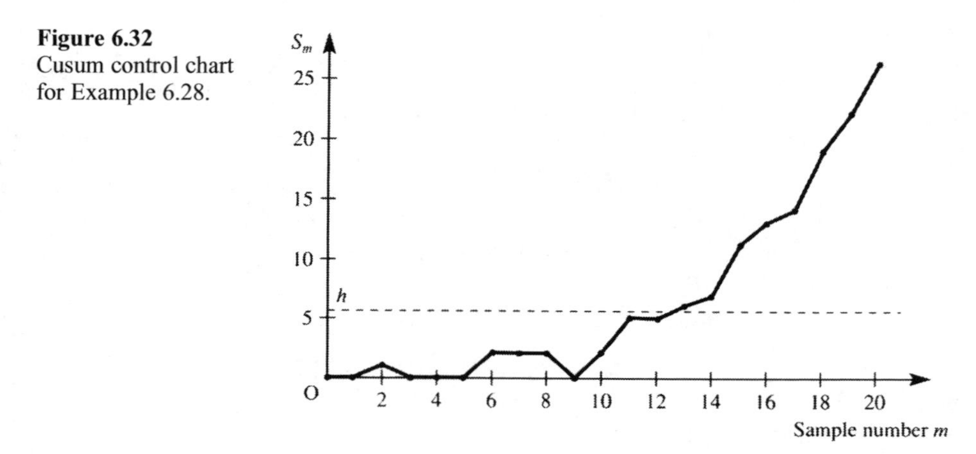

Figure 6.32
Cusum control chart for Example 6.28.

Example 6.29

Construct a cusum chart for the sulphur dioxide data in Example 6.27.

Solution

From $\mu_X = 60$, $\sigma_X = 8$ and $n = 5$ we have

$$r = 60 + \frac{8}{2\sqrt{5}} = 61.8, \qquad h = 5\frac{8}{\sqrt{5}} = 17.9$$

The following table shows the sample average $\bar{X}_m$ and cusum S_m for $1 \leqslant m \leqslant 16$, and the cusum is also plotted in Figure 6.33:

Average	64.2	56.9	57.7	67.9	61.7	59.7	55.6	63.7
Cusum	2.4	0	0	6.1	6.0	3.9	0	1.9
Average	58.3	66.4	67.2	65.2	63.1	67.6	64.1	66.7
Cusum	0	4.6	10.0	13.4	14.7	20.5	22.8	27.7

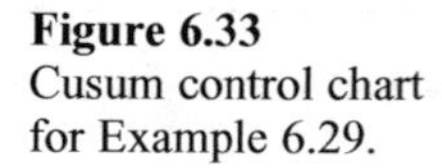

Figure 6.33
Cusum control chart for Example 6.29.

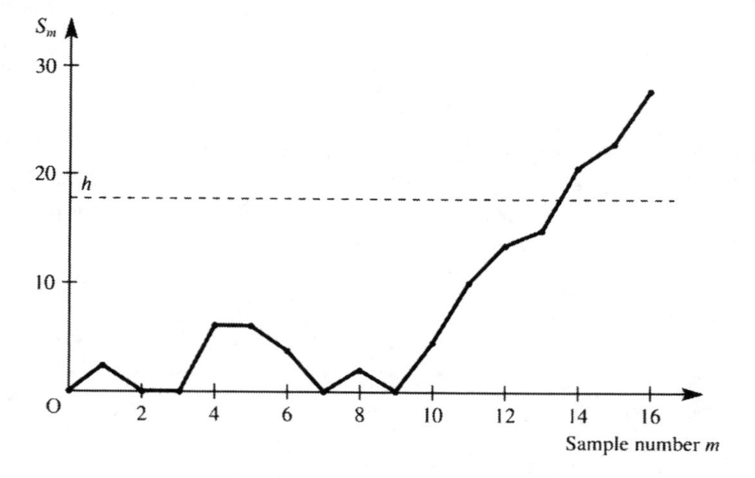

Because $S_{14} = 20.5$ exceeds $h = 17.9$, this chart suggests that the SO_2 concentration did increase during the experiment, a stronger result than that obtained from the Shewhart chart in Example 6.27.

It can be shown that the cusum method will usually detect an out-of-control condition (involving a slight process shift) much sooner than the strict Shewhart method, but with essentially the same risk of a false alarm. For instance, the cusum method leads to a decision after 13 samples in Example 6.28 compared with 18 samples in Example 6.25 for the same data. The measure used to compare the two methods is the **average run length (ARL)**, which is the mean number of samples required to detect an increase in proportion of defectives (or process average) to some specified level. It has been shown that the ARL for the Shewhart chart can be up to four times that for the cusum chart (J. Murdoch, *Control Charts*, Macmillan, London, 1979).

6.9.5 Moving-average control charts

The cusum chart shows that the way to avoid the relative insensitivity of the Shewhart chart is to allow the evidence of a shift in performance to accumulate over several samples. There are also **moving-average control charts**, which are based upon a weighted sum of a number of observations. The best of these, which is very similar to the cusum chart in operation, is the **geometric moving-average (GMA) chart**. This will be described here for variable measure, but it also works for attribute measure (Exercise 56).

Suppose that the successive sample averages are $\bar{X}_1, \bar{X}_2, \dots$, each from a sample of size n. Also suppose that the design mean and variance are μ_X and σ_X^2. Then the GMA is the new sequence given by

$$S_0 = \mu_X$$

$$S_m = r\bar{X}_m + (1 - r)S_{m-1} \quad (m = 1, 2, \dots)$$

where $0 < r \leqslant 1$ is a constant. The statistical properties of this sequence are simpler than for the cusum sequence. First, by successively substituting for S_{m-1}, S_{m-2} and so on, we can express S_m directly in terms of the sample averages:

$$S_m = r\sum_{i=0}^{m-1}[(1-r)^i\bar{X}_{m-i}] + (1-r)^m\mu_X$$

Then, using the summation formula

$$\sum_{i=0}^{m-1} x^i = \frac{1-x^m}{1-x} \quad (|x| < 1)$$

it is easy to show (Exercise 57) that the mean and variance of S_m are

$$\mu_{S_m} = E(S_m) = \mu_X$$

$$\sigma_{S_m}^2 = \text{Var}(S_m) = \frac{r}{2-r}[1-(1-r)^{2m}]\frac{\sigma_X^2}{n}$$

After the first few samples the variance of S_m tends to a constant value:

$$\sigma_{S_m}^2 \to \left(\frac{r}{2-r}\right)\frac{\sigma_X^2}{n} \quad \text{as } m \to \infty$$

If US practice is followed then the upper and lower control limits can be set at $(\mu_X \pm 3\sigma_{S_m})$. If UK practice is followed then, from the approximate normality of the sample averages and the fact that sums of normal random variables are also normal, it follows that S_m is approximately normal, so the warning and action limits can be set at

$(\mu_X \pm 1.96\sigma_{S_m})$ and $(\mu_X \pm 3.09\sigma_{S_m})$ respectively (although the warning limits now have less significance).

It remains to choose a value for r. If we set $r = 1$, the whole approach reduces to the standard Shewhart charts. Small values of r (say around 0.2) lead to early recognition of small shifts of process mean, but if r is too small, a large shift may remain undetected for some time.

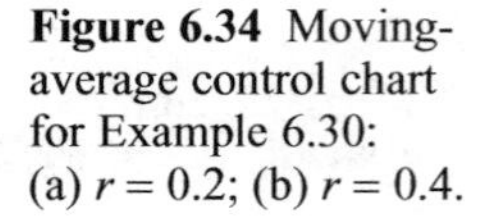

Construct GMA charts for the sulphur dioxide data in Example 6.27, using $r = 0.2$ and $r = 0.4$.

Solution The control charts can be seen in Figure 6.34. Clearly the warning and action limits converge fairly quickly to constant values, so little is lost by using those values in practice. The warning limit is exceeded from sample 11 for both values of r. The action limit is exceeded from sample 14 for $r = 0.2$ (as for the cusum chart in Example 6.29) and at sample 16 for $r = 0.4$.

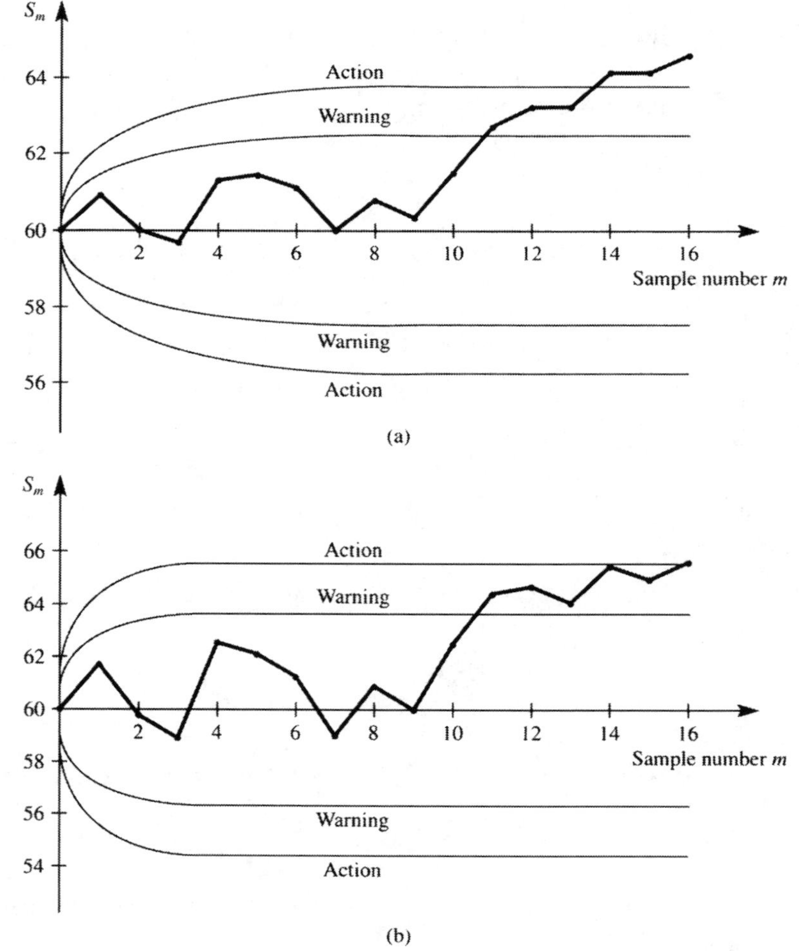

Figure 6.34 Moving-average control chart for Example 6.30: (a) $r = 0.2$; (b) $r = 0.4$.

6.9.6 Range charts

The **sample range** is defined as the difference between the largest and smallest values in the sample. The range has two functions in quality control where the quality is of the variable rather than the attribute type. First, if the data are normal then the range (R, say) provides an estimate $\hat{\sigma}$ of the standard deviation σ by

$$\hat{\sigma} = R/d$$

where d is a constant that depends upon the sample size n as follows:

n	2	3	4	5	6	7	8	9	10	11	12
d	1.128	1.693	2.059	2.326	2.534	2.704	2.847	2.970	3.078	3.173	3.258

It is clearly quicker to evaluate this than the sample standard deviation S, and for the small samples typically used in quality control the estimate is almost as good.

The other reason why the range is important is because the quality of production can vary in dispersion as well as (or instead of) in mean. Control charts for the range R are more commonly used than charts for the sample standard deviation S when monitoring variability within the manufacturing process, and all three types of chart discussed above (Shewhart, cusum and moving-average) can be applied to the range. **Range charts** (or **R charts**) are designed using tables that can be found in specialized books on quality control, for example D. C. Montgomery, *Introduction to Statistical Quality Control*, 2nd edn (Wiley, New York, 1991).

6.9.7 Exercises

48 It is intended that 90% of electronic devices emerging from a machine should pass a simple on-the-spot quality test. The numbers of defectives among samples of 50 taken by successive shifts are as follows:

5, 8, 11, 5, 6, 4, 9, 7, 12, 9, 10, 14

Find the action and warning limits, and the sample number at which an out-of-control decision is taken. Also find the UCL (US practice) and the sample number for action.

49 Thirty-two successive samples of 100 castings each, taken from a production line, contained the following numbers of defectives

3, 3, 5, 3, 5, 0, 3, 1, 3, 5, 4, 2, 4, 3, 5, 4
3, 4, 5, 6, 5, 6, 4, 4, 7, 5, 4, 8, 5, 6, 6, 7

If the proportion that are defective is to be maintained at 0.02, use the Shewhart method (both UK and US standards) to indicate whether this proportion is being maintained, and if not then give the number of samples after which action should be taken.

50 A bottling plant is supposed to fill bottles with 568 ml (one imperial pint) of liquid. The standard deviation of the quantity of fill is 3 ml. Regular samples of 10 bottles are taken and their contents measured. After subtracting 568 from the sample averages, the results are as follows:

−0.2, 1.3, 2.1, 0.3, −0.8, 1.7, 1.3, 0.6, 2.5, 1.4, 1.6, 3.0

Using a Shewhart control chart, determine whether the mean fill requires readjustment.

51 Average reverse-current readings (in nA) for samples of 10 transistors taken at half-hour intervals are as follows:

12.8, 11.2, 13.4, 12.1, 13.6, 13.9, 12.3, 12.9, 13.8, 13.1, 12.9, 14.0, 13.7, 13.4, 14.2, 13.1, 14.0, 14.0, 15.1, 14.3

The standard deviation is 3 nA. At what point, if any, does the Shewhart control method indicate that the reverse current has increased from its design value of 12 nA?

52 Using the data in Exercise 50, apply (a) a cusum control chart and (b) a moving-average control chart with $r = 0.3$.

53 Using the data in Exercise 51, apply (a) a cusum control chart and (b) a moving-average control chart with $r = 0.3$.

54 Apply a cusum control chart to the data in Exercise 48.

55 Apply a cusum control chart to the data in Exercise 49.

56 The diameters of the castings in Exercise 49 are also important. Twelve of each sample of 100 were taken, and their diameters measured and averaged. The differences (in mm) between the successive averages and the design mean diameter of 125 mm were as follows:

0.1, 0.3, –0.2, 0.4, 0.1, 0.0, 0.2, –0.1, 0.2, 0.4, 0.5, 0.1, 0.4, 0.6, 0.3, 0.4, 0.3, 0.6, 0.5, 0.4, 0.2, 0.3, 0.5, 0.7, 0.3, 0.1, 0.6, 0.5, 0.6, 0.7, 0.4, 0.5

Use (a) Shewhart, (b) cusum and (c) moving-average (with $r = 0.2$) control methods to test for an increase in actual mean diameter, assuming a standard deviation of 1 mm.

57 Prove that the mean and variance of the geometric moving-average S_m defined in Section 6.9.5 for variable measure are given by

$$E(S_m) = \mu_X$$

$$\sigma_{S_m}^2 = \mathrm{Var}(S_m) = \frac{r}{2-r}[1-(1-r)^{2m}]\frac{\sigma_X^2}{n}$$

58 Suppose that the moving-average control chart is to be applied to the counts of defectives in attribute quality control. Find the mean and variance of S_m in terms of the sample size n, the design proportion of defectives p and the coefficient r. Following US practice, set the upper control limit at three standard deviations above the mean, and apply the method to the data in Example 6.28, using $r = 0.2$.

59 The design diameter of a moulded plastic component is 6.00 cm, with a standard deviation of 0.2 cm. The following data consist of successive averages of samples of 10 components:

6.04, 6.12, 5.99, 6.02, 6.04, 6.11, 5.97, 6.06, 6.05, 6.06, 6.17, 6.03, 6.13, 6.05, 6.17, 5.97, 6.07, 6.14, 6.03, 5.99, 6.10, 6.01, 5.96, 6.12, 6.02, 6.20, 6.11, 5.98, 6.02, 6.12

After how many samples do the Shewhart, cusum and moving-average (with $r = 0.2$) control methods indicate that action is needed?

6.10 Poisson processes and the theory of queues

Probability theory is often applied to the analysis and simulation of systems, and this can be a valuable aid to design and control. This section, which is therefore applied probability rather than statistics, will illustrate how this progresses from an initial mathematical model through the analysis stage to a simulation.

6.10.1 Typical queueing problems

Queues are everywhere: in banks and ticket offices, at airports and seaports, traffic intersections and hospitals, and in computer and communication networks. Somebody has to decide on the level of service facilities. The problem, in essence, is that it is costly to keep customers waiting for a long time, but it is also costly to provide enough service facilities so that no customer ever has to wait at all. Queues of trucks, aeroplanes or ships may be costly because of the space they occupy or the lost earnings during the idle time. Queues of people may be costly because of lost productivity or because people will often go elsewhere in preference to joining a long queue. Queues

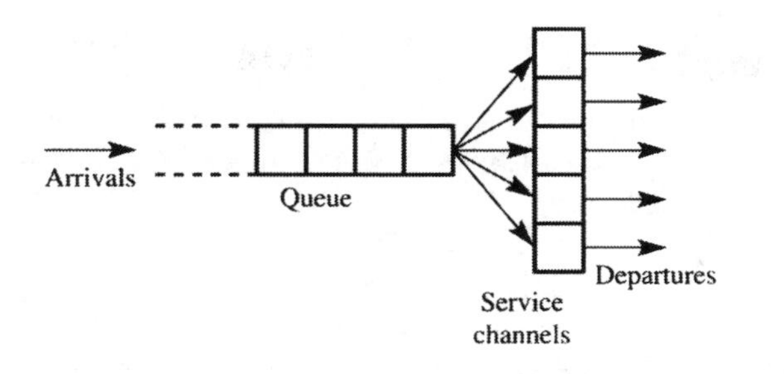

Figure 6.35 A typical queueing system.

of jobs or packets in computer networks are costly in loss of time-efficiency. Service facilities are costly in capital, staffing and maintenance. Probabilistic modelling, often combined with simulation, allows performance evaluation for queues and networks, which can be of great value in preparing the ground for design decisions.

The mathematical model of a simple queueing system is based on the situation shown in Figure 6.35. **Customers** join the queue at random times that are independent of each other – the **inter-arrival time** (between successive arrivals) is a random variable. When a **service channel** is free, the next customer to be served is selected from the queue in a manner determined by the **service discipline**. After being served the customer departs from the queueing system. The **service time** for each customer is another random variable. The distributions of inter-arrival time and service time are usually assumed to take one of a number of standard patterns. The commonest assumption about service discipline is that the next customer to be served is the one who has been queueing the longest time (first in, first out).

The queueing system may be regarded from either a static or a dynamic viewpoint. Dynamically, the system might start from an initial state of emptiness and build up with varying rates of arrivals and varying numbers of service channels depending upon queue length. This is hard to deal with mathematically, but can be treated by computer simulation. Useful information about queues can, however, be obtained from the static viewpoint, in which the rate at which arrivals occur is constant, as is the number of service channels, and the system is assumed to have been in operation sufficiently long to have reached a steady state. At any time the queue length will be a random variable, but the distribution of queue length is then independent of time.

We need to find the distributions of queue length and of waiting time for the customer, and how these vary with the number of service channels. Costs can be worked out from these results.

6.10.2 Poisson processes

Consider the arrivals process for a queueing system. We shall assume that the customers join the queue at random times that are independent of each other. Other assumptions about the pattern of arrivals would give different results, but this is the most common one. We can therefore think of the arrivals as a stream of events occurring at random along a time axis, as depicted in Figure 6.36. The inter-arrival time T, say, will be a continuous random variable with probability density function $f_T(t)$ and cumulative distribution function $F_T(t)$.

Time

Figure 6.36 Random events (×) on a time axis.

One way to formulate the assumption of independent random arrivals is to assert that at any moment the distribution of the time until the next arrival is independent of the time elapsed since the previous arrival (because arrivals are 'blind' to each other). This is known as the **memoryless property**, and can be expressed as

$$P(T \leqslant t+h \mid T > t) = P(T \leqslant h) \quad (t, h \geqslant 0)$$

where t denotes the actual time since the previous arrival and h denotes a possible time until the next arrival. Using the definition of conditional probability (Section 6.2.1), we can write this in terms of the distribution function $F_T(t)$ as

$$\frac{P(t < T \leqslant t+h)}{1 - P(T \leqslant t)} = \frac{F_T(t+h) - F_T(t)}{1 - F_T(t)} = F_T(h)$$

Rearranging at the second equality and then dividing through by h gives

$$\frac{1}{h}[F_T(t+h) - F_T(t)] = \frac{F_T(h)}{h}[1 - F_T(t)]$$

Letting $h \to 0$, we obtain a first-order linear differential equation for $F_T(t)$:

$$\frac{\mathrm{d}}{\mathrm{d}t} F_T(t) = \lambda[1 - F_T(t)]$$

where

$$\lambda = \lim_{h \to 0} \frac{F_T(h)}{h}$$

With the initial condition $F_T(0) = 0$ (because inter-event times must be positive), the solution is

$$F_T(t) = 1 - \mathrm{e}^{-\lambda t} \quad (t \geqslant 0)$$

and hence the probability density function is

$$f_T(t) = \frac{\mathrm{d}}{\mathrm{d}t} F_T(t) = \lambda \mathrm{e}^{-\lambda t} \quad (t \geqslant 0)$$

This is the density function of an **exponential distribution with parameter λ**, and it follows that the mean time between arrivals is $1/\lambda$ (see Section 6.7.1). The parameter λ is the **rate of arrivals** (number per unit time).

Example 6.31

A factory contains 30 machines of a particular type, each of which breaks down every 100 operating hours on average. It is suspected that the breakdowns are not independent. The operating time intervals between 10 consecutive breakdowns (of any machine) are measured and the shortest such interval is only six minutes. Does this lend support to the suspicion of non-independent breakdowns?

Solution

Collectively, the machines break down at the rate of 30/100 or 0.3 per hour. If the breakdowns are independent then the interval between successive breakdowns will have an exponential distribution with parameter 0.3. The probability that such an interval will exceed six minutes is

$$P(\text{interval} > 0.1) = \int_{0.1}^{\infty} 0.3\,\mathrm{e}^{-0.3t}\,\mathrm{d}t = \mathrm{e}^{-0.3(0.1)} = 0.9704$$

and the probability that all nine intervals (between 10 breakdowns) will exceed this time is $(0.9704)^9 = 0.763$. Hence the probability that the shortest interval will be six minutes or less is one minus this, or 0.237. This is quite likely to have happened by chance, so it does not support the suspicion of non-independent intervals.

The assumption of independent random arrivals therefore leads to a particular distribution of inter-arrival time, parametrized by the rate of arrivals. Two further conclusions also emerge. First, the number of arrivals that occur during a fixed interval of length H has a Poisson distribution with parameter λH:

$$P(k \text{ arrivals during interval of length } H) = \frac{(\lambda H)^k \mathrm{e}^{-\lambda H}}{k!} \qquad (k = 0, 1, 2, \dots)$$

This will not be proved here, but is easily seen to be consistent with an exponential distribution of inter-arrival time T because

$$\begin{aligned} F_T(t) &= P(T \leqslant t) = 1 - P(T > t) \\ &= 1 - P\,(\text{no event during interval of length } t) \\ &= 1 - \mathrm{e}^{-\lambda t} \end{aligned}$$

using the Poisson distribution. Because of this distribution, events conforming to these assumptions are known as a **Poisson process**.

The other conclusion is that the probability that an arrival occurs during a short interval of length h is equal to $\lambda h + O(h^2)$, regardless of the history of the process. Suppose that a time t has elapsed since the previous arrival, and consider a short interval of length h starting from that point:

$$\begin{aligned} P(\text{arrival during } (t, t+h)) &= P(T \leqslant t + h \mid T > t) = F_T(h) \\ &= 1 - \mathrm{e}^{-\lambda h} = \lambda h + O(h^2) \end{aligned}$$

using the memoryless property and the expansion of $\mathrm{e}^{\lambda h}$ to first order. Furthermore, the probability of more than one arrival during a short interval of length h is $O(h^2)$.

Example 6.32

A computer receives on average 60 batch jobs per day. They arrive at a constant rate throughout the day and independently of each other. Find the probability that more than four jobs will arrive in any one hour.

Solution

The assumptions for a Poisson process hold, so the number of jobs arriving in one hour is a Poisson random variable with parameter $\lambda H = 60/24$. Hence

$$\begin{aligned} P(\text{more than four jobs}) &= 1 - P(0 \text{ or } 1 \text{ or } 2 \text{ or } 3 \text{ or } 4 \text{ jobs}) \\ &= 1 - \mathrm{e}^{-\lambda H}\left[1 + \lambda H + \frac{(\lambda H)^2}{2!} + \frac{(\lambda H)^3}{3!} + \frac{(\lambda H)^4}{4!}\right] = 0.109 \end{aligned}$$

6.10.3 Single service channel queue

Consider a queueing system with a Poisson arrival process with mean rate λ per unit time, and a single service channel. The behaviour of the queueing system depends not only on the arrival process but also upon the distribution of service times. A common assumption here is that the service time distribution (like that of inter-arrival time) is exponential. Thus the probability density function of service time S is

$$f_S(s) = \mu e^{-\mu s} \quad (s \geqslant 0)$$

Unlike the inter-arrival time distribution in Section 6.10.2, this is not based on an assumption of independence or the memoryless property, but simply on the fact that in many queueing situations most customers are served quickly but a few take a lot longer, and the form of the distribution conforms with this fact. This assumption is therefore on much weaker ground than that for the arrival time distribution. The parameter μ is the mean number of customers served in unit time (with no idle periods), and the mean service time is $1/\mu$. With this service distribution, the probability that a customer in the service channel will have departed after a short time h is equal to $\mu h + O(h^2)$, independent of the time already spent in the service channel.

Distribution of the number of customers in the system

We can now derive the distribution of the number of customers in the queueing system. Considering the system as a whole (queue plus service channel), the number of customers in the system at time t is a random variable. Let $p_n(t)$ be the distribution of this random variable:

$$p_n(t) = P(n \text{ customers in the system at time } t) \quad (n = 0, 1, 2, \ldots)$$

Consider the time $t + h$, where h is small. The probability of more than one arrival or more than one departure during this time is $O(h^2)$, and will be ignored. There are four ways in which there can be n (assumed greater than zero) customers in the system at that time:

(1) there are n in the system at t, and no arrival or departure by $t + h$; the probability of this is given by

$$p_n(t)(1 - \lambda h)(1 - \mu h) + O(h^2) = p_n(t)(1 - \lambda h - \mu h) + O(h^2)$$

(2) there are n in the system at t, and one arrival and one departure by $t + h$; the probability is given by

$$p_n(t)(\lambda h)(\mu h) + O(h^2) = O(h^2)$$

(3) there are $n - 1$ in the system at t, and one arrival but no departure by $t + h$; the probability is given by

$$p_{n-1}(t)(\lambda h)(1 - \mu h) + O(h^2) = p_{n-1}(t)(\lambda h) + O(h^2)$$

(4) there are $n + 1$ in the system at t, and no arrivals but one departure by $t + h$; the probability is given by

$$p_{n+1}(t)(1 - \lambda h)(\mu h) + O(h^2) = p_{n+1}(t)(\mu h) + O(h^2)$$

Summing the probabilities of these mutually exclusive events gives the probability of n customers in the system at time $t + h$ as

$$p_n(t+h) = p_n(t)(1 - \lambda h - \mu h) + p_{n-1}(t)(\lambda h) + p_{n+1}(t)(\mu h) + O(h^2) \quad (n = 1, 2, \dots) \tag{6.1}$$

Similarly, there are two ways in which the system can be empty ($n = 0$) at time $t + h$: empty at t and no arrival before $t + h$, or one customer at t who departs before $t + h$. This gives

$$p_0(t+h) = p_0(t)(1 - \lambda h) + p_1(t)(\mu h) + O(h^2) \tag{6.2}$$

Rearranging equations (6.1) and (6.2) and taking the limit as $h \to 0$, we obtain

$$\begin{aligned}\frac{\mathrm{d}}{\mathrm{d}t}p_n(t) &= \lim_{h\to 0}\frac{1}{h}[p_n(t+h) - p_n(t)]\\ &= -(\lambda + \mu)p_n(t) + \lambda p_{n-1}(t) + \mu p_{n+1}(t) \quad (n = 1, 2, \dots)\end{aligned}$$

$$\frac{\mathrm{d}}{\mathrm{d}t}p_0(t) = -\lambda p_0(t) + \mu p_1(t)$$

This is a rather complex set of recursive differential equations for the probabilities $p_n(t)$. If we assume that the arrival and service parameters λ and μ are constant and that the system has been in operation for a long time then the distribution will not depend upon t; the derivatives therefore vanish, and we are left with the following algebraic equations for the *steady-state* distribution p_n:

$$0 = -(\lambda + \mu)p_n + \lambda p_{n-1} + \mu p_{n+1} \quad (n = 1, 2, \dots)$$

$$0 = -\lambda p_0 + \mu p_1$$

Defining the ratio of arrival and service parameters λ and μ as $\rho = \lambda/\mu$ and dividing through by μ, we have

$$p_{n+1} = (1 + \rho)p_n - \rho p_{n-1} \quad (n = 1, 2, \dots)$$

$$p_1 = \rho p_0$$

To solve these, we first assume that $p_n = \rho^n p_0$. Clearly this works for $n = 0$ and $n = 1$. Substituting,

$$p_{n+1} = (1 + \rho)\rho^n p_0 - \rho\rho^{n-1}p_0 = \rho^{n+1}p_0$$

so the assumed form holds for $n + 1$, and therefore for all n by induction. It remains only to identify p_0 from the fact that the distribution must sum to unity over $n = 0, 1, 2, \dots$:

$$1 = p_0\sum_{n=0}^{\infty}\rho^n = \frac{p_0}{1 - \rho}$$

Hence $p_0 = 1 - \rho$ and

$$p_n = (1 - \rho)\rho^n \quad (n = 0, 1, 2, \dots)$$

This is known as the **geometric distribution**, and is a discrete version of the exponential distribution (Figure 6.37). Note that this result requires that $\rho < 1$, or equivalently $\lambda < \mu$. If this condition fails to hold, the arrival rate swamps the capacity of the service channel, the queue gets longer and longer, and no steady-state condition exists.

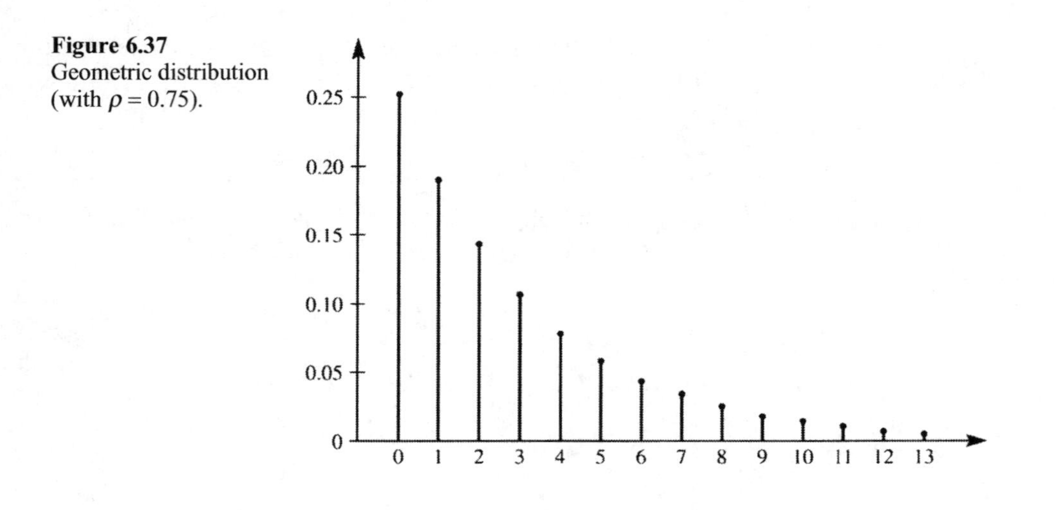

Figure 6.37
Geometric distribution (with $\rho = 0.75$).

Queue length and waiting time

The queue length distribution now follows easily:

$$P(\text{queue empty}) = p_0 + p_1$$
$$= 1 - \rho^2$$
$$P(n \text{ in queue}) = P(n + 1 \text{ in system})$$
$$= (1 - \rho)\rho^{n+1} \quad (n = 1, 2, \ldots)$$

Denoting the mean numbers of customers in the system and in the queue by N_S and N_Q respectively,

$$N_S = \sum_{n=0}^{\infty} np_n = \frac{\rho}{1-\rho}, \qquad N_Q = \sum_{n=1}^{\infty} (n-1)p_n = \frac{\rho^2}{1-\rho}$$

(Exercise 62). Since in the steady state the mean time between departures must equal the mean time between arrivals ($1/\lambda$), it is plausible that the mean total time in the system for each customer, W_S say, is given by

$$W_S = \text{mean number in system} \times \text{mean time between departures}$$
$$= \frac{\rho/\lambda}{1-\rho} = \frac{1}{\mu - \lambda}$$

The mean waiting time in the queue, W_Q say, is then

$$W_Q = \text{mean time in system} - \text{mean service time}$$
$$= W_S - \frac{1}{\mu} = \frac{\rho}{\mu - \lambda}$$

These results for W_S and W_Q can be derived more formally from the respective waiting time distributions. For example, the distribution of total time in the system can be shown to be exponential with parameter $\mu - \lambda$, and the waiting time in the queue can be expressed as

$$P(\text{waiting time in queue} \geqslant t) = \rho\, e^{-(\mu-\lambda)t} \quad (t > 0)$$

Example 6.33

If customers in a shop arrive at a single check-out point at the rate of 30 per hour and if the service times have an exponential distribution, what mean service time will ensure that 80% of customers do not have to wait more than five minutes in the queue and what will be the mean queue length?

Solution

With $\lambda = 0.5$ and $t = 5$, the queue waiting time gives

$$0.2 = \rho \, e^{-(\mu-\lambda)t}$$

that is,

$$0.2\mu = 0.5 \, e^{2.5-5\mu}$$

This is a nonlinear equation for μ, which may be solved by standard methods to give $\mu = 0.743$. The mean service time is therefore $1/\mu$ or 1.35 min, and the mean queue length is

$$N_Q = \frac{\rho^2}{1-\rho} = 1.39, \qquad \text{using } \rho = \frac{\lambda}{\mu} = 0.673$$

Example 6.34

Handling equipment is to be installed at an unloading bay in a factory. An average of 20 trucks arrive during each 10 h working day, and these must be unloaded. The following three schemes are being considered:

Scheme	Fixed cost/ £ per day	Operating cost/ £ per hour	Mean handling rate/ trucks per hour
A	90	45	3
B	190	50	4
C	450	60	6

Truck waiting time is costed at £30 per hour. Assuming an exponential distribution of truck unloading time, find the best scheme.

Solution

Viewing this as a queueing problem, we have

λ = arrival rate per hour = 2.0

μ = unloading rate per hour

mean waiting time for each truck = $1/(\mu - \lambda)$

Hence the mean delay cost per truck is

$$\frac{30}{\mu - 2}$$

and the mean delay cost per day is

$$\frac{20 \times 30}{\mu - 2}$$

The proportion of time that the equipment is running is equal to the probability that the system is not empty (the **utilization**), which is

$$1 - p_0 = \frac{\lambda}{\mu} = \rho$$

Hence the mean operating cost per day is 10ρ times operating cost per hour. The total cost per day (in £) is the sum of the fixed, operating and delay costs, as follows:

Scheme	μ	ρ	Fixed	Operating	Delay	Total
A	3	0.6667	90	300	600	990
B	4	0.5	190	250	300	740
C	6	0.3333	450	200	150	800

Hence scheme B minimizes the total cost.

6.10.4 Queues with multiple service channels

For the case where there are c service channels, all with an exponential service time distribution with parameter μ, a line of argument similar to that in Section 6.10.3 can be found in many textbooks on queueing theory. In particular, it can be shown that the distribution p_n of the number of customers in the system is

$$p_n = \begin{cases} \dfrac{\rho^n}{n!} p_0 & (0 \leqslant n \leqslant c) \\ \dfrac{\rho^n}{c^{n-c} c!} p_0 & (n > c) \end{cases}$$

where $\rho = \lambda/\mu$ and

$$p_0 = \left[\sum_{n=0}^{c-1} \frac{\rho^n}{n!} + \frac{\rho^c}{(c-1)!(c-\rho)} \right]^{-1}$$

The mean numbers in the queue and in the system are

$$N_Q = \frac{\rho^{c+1}}{(c-1)!(c-\rho)^2} p_0, \qquad N_S = N_Q + \rho$$

and the mean waiting times in the queue and in the system are

$$W_Q = \frac{N_Q}{\lambda}, \qquad W_S = W_Q + \frac{1}{\mu}$$

Example 6.35

For the unloading bay problem in Example 6.34 a fourth option would be to install two sets of equipment under scheme A (there is space available to do this). The fixed costs would then double but the operating costs per bay would be the same. Evaluate this possibility.

Solution With two bays under scheme A, we have $\lambda = 2$, $\mu = 3$ and $c = 2$, so that $\rho = \frac{2}{3}$, and the probability that the system is empty at any time is

$$p_0 = \left(1 + \rho + \frac{\rho^2}{2 - \rho}\right)^{-1} = \tfrac{1}{2}$$

The probabilities of one truck (one bay occupied) and of two or more trucks (both bays occupied) are then

$$P_1 = \rho p_0 = \tfrac{1}{3}$$

$$P(\text{two or more trucks}) = 1 - \tfrac{1}{2} - \tfrac{1}{3} = \tfrac{1}{6}$$

The total operating cost per day is the operating cost for when one or other bay is working (£45 per hour) plus that for when both bays are working (£90 per hour), which is

$$10[\tfrac{1}{3}(45) + \tfrac{1}{6}(90)] = 300$$

The mean number in the queue is

$$\frac{\rho^3}{(2-\rho)^2} p_0 = 0.083\,33$$

so that the mean total time in the system for each truck is

$$\tfrac{1}{2}(0.083\,33) + \tfrac{1}{3} = 0.375$$

Multiplying by the cost per hour and the number of trucks gives the delay cost per day:

$$20(30)(0.375) = 225$$

The total cost per day of this scheme is therefore

$$2(90) + 300 + 225 = £705$$

This is less than the £740 under scheme B, the best of the single-bay options.

6.10.5 Queueing system simulation

The assumption that the service time distribution is exponential, which underlies the results in Sections 6.10.3 and 6.10.4, is often unrealistic. It is known that it leads to predicted waiting times that tend to be pessimistic, as a result of which costs based on these predictions are often overestimated. Theoretical results for other service distributions exist (see for example E. Page, *Queueing Theory in OR*. Butterworth, London, 1972), but it is often instructive to simulate a queueing system and find the various answers numerically. It is then easy to vary the arrival and service distributions, and the transient (non-steady-state) behaviour of the system also reveals itself.

Figure 6.38 shows a pseudocode listing of a single-channel queueing system simulation, which is easily modified to cope with multiple channels. Each event consists of either an arrival or a departure. The variables next_arrival and next_departure are used to represent the time to the next arrival and the time to the next departure respectively, and the type of the next event is determined by whichever is the smaller. New arrival and departure times are returned by the functions arrival_time and departure_time, which generate values from appropriate exponential distributions. The distribution of the number of customers in the system is built up as an array, normalized at the end of the simulation, from which the mean and other results can be obtained.

Figure 6.38 Pseudocode listing for queueing system simulation.

```
{  Procedure to simulate a single-channel queueing system.
time is the running time elapsed,
limit is the simulation length,
number is the number of items in the system,
maximum is the maximum number allowed in the system,
system[i] is the distribution (array) of times with i in the
   system, assumed initialized to zero,
mean is the mean number in the system,
infinity contains a very large number,
arrival_rate is the arrival distribution parameter,
service_rate is the service distribution parameter,
next_arrival is the time to the next arrival,
next_departure is the time to the next departure,
rnd() is a function assumed to return a uniform random (0,1)
   number.
The simulation starts with the system empty,
limit, maximum, arrival_rate and service_rate must be set.   }

time ← 0
next_arrival ← arrival_time(arrival_rate)
next_departure ← infinity
number ← 0
repeat
   if next_arrival < next_departure then
      time ← time + next_arrival
      system[number] ← system[number] + next_arrival
      arrival()
   else
      time ← time + next_departure
      system[number] ← system[number] + next_departure
      departure()
   endif
until time > limit
mean ← 0
for i is 0 to maximum do
   system[i] ← system[i]/time
   mean ← mean + i* system[i]
endfor
********************
procedure arrival()
{  procedure to handle an arrival,
changes the values of next_arrival, next_departure, and number   }
   if number = 0 then
      next_departure ← departure_time(service_rate)
   else
      next_departure ← next_departure – next_arrival
   endif
   number ← number + 1
   if number = maximum then
      next_arrival ← infinity
   else
      next_arrival ← arrival_time(arrival_rate)
   endif
endprocedure
********************
procedure departure()
{  procedure to handle a departure,
changes the values of next_arrival, next_departure, and number   }
```

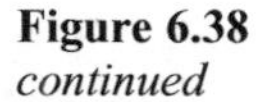

Figure 6.38 *continued*

```
    if number = maximum then
      next_arrival ← arrival_time(arrival_rate)
    else
      next_arrival ← next_arrival – next_departure
    endif
    number ← number – 1
    if number = 0 then
      next_departure ← infinity
    else
      next_departure ← departure_time(service_rate)
    endif
endprocedure
********************
function arrival_time(arrival_rate)
{  function to generate a new arrival time  }
    U ← rnd()
    return( – (log(U))/arrival_rate)
endfunction
function departure_time(service_rate)
{  function to generate a new departure time  }
    U ← rnd()
    return ( – (log/U))/service_rate)
endfunction
```

What is typically found from such a simulation (with Poisson arrivals and an exponential service distribution) is that there is good agreement with the predicted results as long as $\rho = \lambda/\mu$ is small, but the results become more erratic as $\rho \to 1$. It takes a very long time for the distribution to reach its steady-state form when the value of ρ is close to unity. In that situation the theoretical steady-state results may be of limited value.

6.10.6 Exercises

60 A sea area has on average 15 gales annually, evenly distributed throughout the year. Assuming that the gales occur independently, find the probability that more than two gales will occur in any one month.

61 Suppose that the average number of telephone calls arriving at a switchboard is 30 per hour, and that they arrive independently. What is the probability that no calls will arrive in a three-minute period? What is the probability that more than five calls will arrive in a five-minute period?

62 Show that for a single-channel queue with Poisson arrivals and exponential service time distribution the mean numbers of customers in the system and in the queue are

$$N_S = \frac{\rho}{1-\rho}, \qquad N_Q = \frac{\rho^2}{1-\rho}$$

where ρ is the ratio of arrival and service rates. (*Hint*: Differentiate the equation

$$\sum_{n=0}^{\infty} \rho^n = \frac{1}{1-\rho}$$

with respect to ρ.)

63 Patients arrive at the casualty department of a hospital at random, with a mean arrival rate of three per hour. The department is served by one doctor, who spends on average 15 minutes with each patient, actual consulting times being exponentially distributed. Find

(a) the proportion of time that the doctor is idle;
(b) the mean number of patients waiting to see the doctor;
(c) the probability of there being more than three patients waiting;
(d) the mean waiting time for patients;

(e) the probability of a patient having to wait longer than one hour.

64 A small company operates a cleaning and re-catering service for passenger aircraft at an international airport. Aircraft arrive requiring this service at a mean rate of λ per hour, and arrive independently of each other. They are serviced one at a time, with an exponential distribution of service time. The cost for each aircraft on the ground is put at c_1 per hour, and the cost of servicing the planes at a rate μ is $c_2\mu$ per hour. Prove that the service rate that minimizes the total cost per hour is

$$\mu = \lambda + \sqrt{\left(\frac{c_1\lambda}{c_2}\right)}$$

65 The machines in a factory break down in a Poisson pattern at an average rate of three per hour during the eight-hour working day. The company has two service options, each involving an exponential service time distribution. Option A would cost £20 per hour, and the mean repair time would be 15 min. Option B would cost £40 per hour, with a mean repair time of 12 min. If machine idle time is costed at £60 per hour, which option should be adopted?

66 Ships arrive independently at a port at a mean rate of one every three hours. The time a ship occupies a berth for unloading and loading has an exponential distribution with a mean of 12 hours. If the mean delay to ships waiting for berths is to be kept below six hours, how many berths should there be at the port?

67 In a self-service store the arrival process is Poisson, with on average one customer arriving every 30 s. A single cashier can serve customers every 48 s on average, with an exponential distribution of service time. The store managers wish to minimize the mean waiting time for customers. To do this, they can either double the service rate by providing an additional server to pack the customer's goods (at a single cash desk) or else provide a second cash desk. Which option is preferable?

6.11 Bayes' theorem and its applications

To end this chapter, we return to the foundations of probability and inference. The definition of conditional probability is fundamental to the subject, and from it there follows the theorem of Bayes, which has far-reaching implications.

6.11.1 Derivation and simple examples

The definition in Section 6.2.1 of the conditional probability of an event B given that another event A occurs can be rewritten as

$$P(A \cap B) = P(B \mid A)P(A)$$

If A and B are interchanged then this becomes

$$P(A \cap B) = P(A \mid B)P(B)$$

The left-hand sides are equal, so we can equate the right-hand sides and rearrange, giving

$$P(A \mid B) = \frac{P(B \mid A)P(A)}{P(B)}$$

Now suppose that B is known to have occurred, and that this can only happen if one of the mutually exclusive events

$$\{A_1, \ldots, A_n\}, \quad A_i \cap A_j = \varnothing \quad (i \neq j)$$

has also occurred, but which one is not known. The relevance of the various events A_i to the occurrence of B is expressed by the conditional probabilities $P(B|A_i)$. Suppose that the probabilities $P(A_i)$ are also known. The examples below will show that this is a common situation, and we should like to work out the conditional probabilities

$$P(A_i|B) = \frac{P(B|A_i)P(A_i)}{P(B)}$$

To find the denominator, we sum from 1 to n:

$$\sum_{i=1}^{n} P(A_i|B) = 1 = \frac{1}{P(B)} \sum_{i=1}^{n} P(B|A_i)P(A_i)$$

The sum is equal to 1 by virtue of the assumption that B could not have occurred without one of the A_i occurring. We therefore obtain a formula for $P(B)$:

$$P(B) = \sum_{i=1}^{n} P(B|A_i)P(A_i)$$

which is sometimes called the **rule of total probability**. Hence we have the following theorem.

Theorem 6.2 **Bayes' theorem**

If $\{A_1, \ldots, A_n\}$ are mutually exclusive events, one of which must occur given that another event B occurs, then

$$P(A_i|B) = \frac{P(B|A_i)P(A_i)}{\sum_{j=1}^{n} P(B|A_j)P(A_j)} \quad (i = 1, \ldots, n)$$

end of theorem

Example 6.36

Three machines produce similar car parts. Machine A produces 40% of the total output, and machines B and C produce 25% and 35% respectively. The proportions of the output from each machine that do not conform to the specification are 10% for A, 5% for B and 1% for C. What proportion of those parts that do not conform to the specification are produced by machine A?

Solution

Let D represent the event that a particular part is defective. Then, by the rule of total probability, the overall proportion of defective parts is

$$\begin{aligned} P(D) &= P(D|A)P(A) + P(D|B)P(B) + P(D|C)P(C) \\ &= (0.1)(0.4) + (0.05)(0.25) + (0.01)(0.35) = 0.056 \end{aligned}$$

Using Bayes' theorem,

$$P(A|D) = \frac{P(D|A)P(A)}{P(D)} = \frac{(0.1)(0.4)}{0.056} = 0.714$$

so that machine A produces 71.4% of the defective parts.

Example 6.37 Suppose that 0.1% of the people in a certain area have a disease D and that a mass screening test is used to detect cases. The test gives either a positive or a negative result for each person. Ideally, the test would always give a positive result for a person who has D, and would never do so for a person who has not. In practice the test gives a positive result with probability 99.9% for a person who has D, and with probability 0.2% for a person who has not. What is the probability that a person for whom the test is positive actually has the disease?

Solution Let T represent the event that the test gives a positive result. Then the proportion of positives is

$$P(T) = P(T\,|\,D)P(D) + P(T\,|\,\bar{D})P(\bar{D})$$

$$= (0.999)(0.001) + (0.002)(0.999) \simeq 0.003$$

and the desired result is

$$P(D\,|\,T) = \frac{P(T\,|\,D)P(D)}{P(T)} = \frac{(0.999)(0.001)}{0.003} = \tfrac{1}{3}$$

Despite the high basic reliability of the test, only one-third of those people receiving a positive result actually have the disease. This is because of the low incidence of the disease in the population, which means that a positive result is twice as likely to be a false alarm as it is to be correct.

In connection with Example 6.37, it might be wondered why the reliability of the test was quoted in the problem in terms of

$$P(\text{positive result}\,|\,\text{disease}) \quad \text{and} \quad P(\text{positive result}\,|\,\text{no disease})$$

instead of the seemingly more useful

$$P(\text{disease}\,|\,\text{positive result}) \quad \text{and} \quad P(\text{disease}\,|\,\text{negative result})$$

The reason is that the latter figures are contaminated, in a sense, by the incidence of the disease in the population. The figures quoted for reliability are intrinsic to the test, and may be used anywhere the disease occurs, regardless of the level of incidence.

6.11.2 Applications in probabilistic inference

The scope for applications of Bayes' theorem can be widened considerably if we assume that the calculus of probability can be applied not just to events as subsets of a sample space but also to more general statements about the world. Events are essentially statements about facts that may be true on some occasions and false on others. Scientific theories and hypotheses are much deeper statements, which have great explanatory and predictive power, and which are not so much true or false as gaining or lacking in evidence. One way to assess the extent to which some evidence E supports a hypothesis H is in terms of the conditional probability $P(H\,|\,E)$. The relative frequency interpretation of probability does not normally apply in this situation, so a subjective interpretation is adopted. The quantity $P(H|E)$ is regarded as a **degree of belief** in hypothesis H on the basis of evidence E. In an attempt to render the theory as objective as possible, the rules of probability are strictly applied, and an inference mechanism based on Bayes' theorem is employed.

Suppose that there are in fact two competing hypotheses H_1 and H_2. Let X represent all background information and evidence relevant to the two hypotheses. The probabilities $P(H_1|X)$ and $P(H_1|X \cap E)$ are called the **prior** and **posterior probabilities** of H_1, where E is a new piece of evidence. Similarly, there are prior and posterior probabilities of H_2. Applying Bayes' theorem to both H_1 and H_2 and cancelling the common denominator $P(E)$ gives

$$\frac{P(H_1|X \cap E)}{P(H_2|X \cap E)} = \frac{P(E|H_1 \cap X)}{P(E|H_2 \cap X)} \frac{P(H_1|X)}{P(H_2|X)}$$

The left-hand side and the second factor on the right-hand side are called the **posterior odds** and **prior odds** respectively, favouring H_1 over H_2. The first factor on the right-hand side is called the **likelihood ratio**, and it measures how much more likely it is that the evidence event E would occur if the hypothesis H_1 were true than if H_2 were true. The new evidence E therefore 'updates' the odds, and the process can be repeated as often as desired, provided that the likelihood ratios can be calculated.

Example 6.38

From experience it is known that when a particular type of single-board microcomputer fails, this is twice as likely to be caused by a short on the serial interface (H_1) as by a faulty memory circuit (H_2). The standard diagnostic test is to measure the voltage at a certain point on the board, and from experience it is also known that a drop in voltage there occurs nine times out of ten when the memory circuit is faulty but only once in six occasions of an interface short. How does the observed drop in voltage (E) affect the assessment of the cause of failure?

Solution

The prior odds are two to one in favour of H_1, and the likelihood ratio is (1/6)/(9/10), so the posterior odds are given by

$$\frac{P(H_1|E)}{P(H_2|E)} = (\tfrac{10}{54})(2) = 0.370$$

The evidence turns the odds around to about 2.7 to one in favour of H_2.

Example 6.39

An oil company is prospecting for oil in a certain area, and is conducting a series of seismic experiments. It is known from past experience that if oil is present in the rock strata below then there is on average one chance in three that a characteristic pattern will appear on the trace recorded by the seismic detector after a test. If oil is absent then the pattern can still appear, but is less likely, appearing only once in four tests on average. After 150 tests in the area the pattern has been seen on 48 occasions. Assuming prior odds of 3:1 against the presence of oil, find the updated odds. Also find the 90% confidence interval for the true probability of the pattern appearing after a test, and hence consider whether oil is present or not.

Solution Let H_1 and H_2 represent the hypotheses that oil is present and that it is absent respectively. There were effectively 150 pieces of evidence gathered, and the odds need to be multiplied by the likelihood ratio for each. Each time the pattern is present the likelihood ratio is

$$\frac{P(\text{pattern} \mid H_1)}{P(\text{pattern} \mid H_2)} = \tfrac{1}{3}\Big/\tfrac{1}{4} = \tfrac{4}{3}$$

and each time it is absent the likelihood ratio is

$$\frac{P(\text{no pattern} \mid H_1)}{P(\text{no pattern} \mid H_2)} = \tfrac{2}{3}\Big/\tfrac{3}{4} = \tfrac{8}{9}$$

The updated odds, letting E represent the total evidence, become

$$\frac{P(H_1 \mid E)}{P(H_2 \mid E)} = \left(\tfrac{4}{3}\right)^{48}\left(\tfrac{8}{9}\right)^{102}\left(\tfrac{1}{3}\right) = 2.01$$

The odds that there is oil present are therefore raised to 2:1 in favour.

Confidence intervals for proportions were covered in Section 6.3.6. The proportion of tests for which the pattern was observed is 48/150 or 0.32, so the 90% confidence interval for the probability of appearance is

$$\left(0.32 \pm 1.645\sqrt{\left[\frac{(0.32)(0.68)}{150}\right]}\right) = (0.26, 0.38)$$

The hypothesis that oil is absent is not compatible with this, because the pattern should then appear with probability 0.25, whereas the hypothesis that oil is present is fully compatible.

For the problem in Example 6.38 it is conceivable that there could be enough repetitions for the relative frequency interpretation to be placed on the probabilities of the two hypotheses. In contrast, in Example 6.39 the probability of the presence or absence of oil is not well suited to a frequency interpretation, but the subjective interpretation is available.

Example 6.39 also provides a contrast between the ‘Bayesian’ and ‘classical’ inference approaches. The classical confidence interval appears to lead to a definite result: H_1 is true and H_2 is false. This definiteness is misleading, because it is possible (although not likely) that the opposite is the case, but the evidence supports one hypothesis more than the other. The Bayesian approach has the merit of indicating this relative support quantitatively.

One area where Bayesian inference is very important is in decision support and expert systems. In classical decision theory Bayesian inference is used to update the probabilities of various possible outcomes of a decision, as further information becomes available. This allows an entire programme of decisions and their consequences to be planned (see D. V. Lindley, *Making Decisions*, 2nd edn. Wiley, London, 1985). Expert systems often involve a process of reasoning from evidence to hypothesis with a Bayesian treatment of uncertainty (see for example R. Forsyth, ed., *Expert Systems, Principles and Case Studies*. Chapman & Hall, London, 1984).

6.11.3 Exercises

68 A telephone-based automated customer care system has three main menu options: 45% of customers choose option 1, 32% choose option 2, and 23% choose option 3. Of those who choose option 1, 28% eventually get routed to a service agent, as do 41% of those who choose option 2 and 16% of those who choose option 3. What is the overall proportion of customers who eventually get routed to a service agent?

69 An explosion at a construction site could have occurred as a result of (a) static electricity, (b) malfunctioning of equipment, (c) carelessness or (d) sabotage. It is estimated that such an explosion would occur with probability 0.25 as a result of (a), 0.20 as a result of (b), 0.40 as a result of (c) and 0.75 as a result of (d). It is also judged that the prior probabilities of the four causes of the explosion are (a) 0.20, (b) 0.40, (c) 0.25, (d) 0.15. Find the posterior probabilities and hence the most likely cause of the explosion.

70 Three marksmen (A, B and C) fire at a target. Their success rates at hitting the target are 60% for A, 50% for B and 40% for C. If each marksman fires one shot at the target and two bullets hit it, then which is more probable: that C hit the target, or did not?

71 An accident has occurred on a busy highway between city A, of 100 000 people, and city B, of 200 000 people. It is known only that the victim is from one of the two cities and that his name is Smith. A check of the records reveals that 10% of city A's population is named Smith and 5% of city B's population has that name. The police want to know where to start looking for relatives of the victim. What is the probability that the victim is from city A?

72 In a certain community, 8% of all adults over 50 have diabetes. If a health service in this community correctly diagnoses 95% of all persons with diabetes as having the disease, and incorrectly diagnoses 2% of all persons without diabetes as having the disease, find the probabilities that

(a) the community health service will diagnose an adult over 50 as having diabetes,
(b) a person over 50 diagnosed by the health service as having diabetes actually has the disease.

73 A stockbroker correctly identifies a stock as being a good one 60% of the time and correctly identifies a stock as being a bad one 80% of the time. A stock has a 50% chance of being good. Find the probability that a stock is good if

(a) the stockbroker identifies it as good,
(b) k out of n stockbrokers of equal ability independently identify it as good.

74 On a communications channel, one of three sequences of letters can be transmitted: AAAA, BBBB and CCCC, where the prior probabilities of the sequences are 0.3, 0.4 and 0.3 respectively. It is known from the noise in the channel that the probability of correct reception of a transmitted letter is 0.6, and the probability of incorrect reception of the other two letters is 0.2 for each. It is assumed that the letters are distorted independently of each other. Find the most probable transmitted sequence if ABCA is received.

75 The number of accidents per day occurring at a road junction was recorded over a period of 100 days. There were no accidents on 84 days, one accident on 12 days, and two accidents on four days. One hypothesis is that the number of accidents per day has a Poisson distribution with parameter λ (unspecified), and another is that the distribution is binomial with parameters $n = 3$ and p (unspecified). Use the average number of accidents per day to identify the unspecified parameters and compare the hypotheses assuming that the binomial is initially thought to be twice as likely as the Poisson.

76 The following **multinomial distribution** is a generalization of the binomial distribution. Suppose that there are k distinct possible outcomes of an experiment, with probabilities $p_1, \ldots, p_k$, and that the experiment is repeated n times. The probability of obtaining a number n_1 of occurrences of the first possible outcome, n_2 of the second, and so on up to n_k of the kth is

$$P(n_1, \ldots, n_k) = \frac{n!}{n_1! \ldots n_k!}(p_1)^{n_1} \ldots (p_k)^{n_k}$$

Suppose now that there are two competing hypotheses H_1 and H_2. H_1 asserts that the probabilities are $p_1, \ldots, p_k$ as above, and H_2 asserts that they are $q_1, \ldots, q_k$. Prove that the logarithm of the likelihood ratio is

$$\ln\left[\frac{P(n_1, \ldots, n_k|H_1)}{P(n_1, \ldots, n_k|H_2)}\right] = \sum_{i=1}^{k} n_i \ln\left(\frac{p_i}{q_i}\right)$$

77 According to the design specification, of the components produced by a machine, 92% should have no defect, 5% should have defect A alone, 2% should have defect B alone and 1% should have both defects. Call this hypothesis H_1. The user suspects that the machine is producing more components (say a proportion p_B) with defect B alone, and also more components (say a proportion p_{AB}) with both defects, but is satisfied that 5% have defect A alone. Call this hypothesis H_2. Of a sample of 1000 components, 912 had no defects, 45 had A alone, 27 had B alone and 16 had both. Using the multinomial distribution (as in Exercise 76), maximize $\ln P(912, 45, 27, 16|H_2)$ with respect to p_B and p_{AB}, and find the posterior odds assuming prior odds of 5:1 in favour of H_1.

78 It is suggested that higher-priced cars are assembled with greater care than lower-priced cars. To investigate this, a large luxury model A and a compact hatchback B were compared for defects when they arrived at the dealer's showroom. All cars were manufactured by the same company. The numbers of defects for several of each model were recorded:

A: {5, 4, 3, 5, 3, 4}

B: {8, 6, 8, 9, 5}

The number of defects in each car can be assumed to be governed by a Poisson distribution with parameter λ. Compare the hypothesis H_1 that $\lambda_A \neq \lambda_B$ with H_2 that $\lambda_A = \lambda_B = \lambda$, using the average numbers of defects to identify the λ values and assuming no initial preference between the hypotheses.

6.12 Review exercises (1–10)

1 Eight cases each of 12 bottles of wine from a vineyard were tested for evidence of oxidation in the wine. Five of the cases were bottled using standard corks and, of these, six bottles were found to have oxidized. The remaining cases were bottled using plastic bungs and, of these, three bottles were found to have oxidized. Test the hypothesis that there is no difference in the proportion of bottles oxidized for the different types of cork.

2 The amplitude d of vibration of a damped pendulum is expected to diminish by

$$d = d_0 e^{-\lambda t}$$

Successive amplitudes are measured from a trace as follows:

t	1.01	2.04	3.12	4.09	5.22	6.30	7.35	8.39	9.44	10.50
d	2.46	1.75	1.26	0.94	0.90	0.79	0.52	0.49	0.31	0.21

Find a 95% confidence interval for the damping coefficient λ.

3 Successive masses of 1 kg were hung from a wire, and the position of a mark at its lower end was measured as follows:

Load/kg	0	1	2	3	4	5	6	7
Position/cm	6.12	6.20	6.26	6.32	6.37	6.44	6.50	6.57

It is expected that the extension Y is related to the force X by

$$Y = LX/EA$$

where $L = 101.4$ cm is the length, $A = 1.62 \times 10^{-5}$ cm^2 is the area and E is the Young's modulus of the material. Find a 95% confidence interval for the Young's modulus.

4 The table in Figure 6.39 gives the intervals, in hours, between arrivals of cargo ships at a port during a period of six weeks. It is helpful to the port authorities to know whether the times of arrival are random or whether they show any regularity. Fit an exponential distribution to the data and test for goodness-of-fit.

6.8	2.1	1.0	28.1	5.8	19.7	2.9	16.3	10.7	25.3	12.5	1.6	3.0	9.9	15.9
21.3	9.1	6.9	5.6	2.0	2.2	10.2	6.5	6.8	42.5	2.9	7.3	3.1	2.6	1.0
3.8	14.7	3.8	13.9	2.9	4.1	22.7	5.8	7.6	6.4	11.3	51.6	15.6	2.6	7.6
1.2	0.7	1.9	1.8	0.7	0.4	72.0	10.7	8.3	15.1	3.6	6.0	0.1	3.1	12.9
2.2	17.6	3.6	2.4	3.2	0.4	4.4	17.1	7.1	10.1	18.8	3.4	0.2	4.9	12.9
1.8	22.4	11.6	4.2	18.0	3.0	16.2	6.8	3.7	13.6	15.7	0.7	2.7	18.8	29.8
4.9	6.8	10.7	0.9	2.4	3.8	9.0	8.8	4.8	0.3	4.6	4.9	6.1	33.0	6.5

Figure 6.39 Time interval data for Review exercise 4.

5 When large amounts of data are processed, there is a danger of transcription errors occurring (for example, a decimal point in the wrong place), which could bias the results. One way to avoid this is to test for **outliers** in the data. Suppose that $X_1, \ldots, X_n$ are independent exponential random variables, each with a common parameter λ. Let the random variable Y be the largest of these divided by the sum:

$$Y = X_{\max} \Big/ \sum_i X_i$$

It can be shown (V. Barnett and T. Lewis, *Outliers in Statistical Data.* Wiley, Chichester, 1978) that the distribution function of Y is given by

$$F_Y(y) = \sum_{k=0}^{[1/y]} (-1)^k \binom{n}{k} (1 - ky)^{n-1} \qquad \left(\frac{1}{n} \leqslant y \leqslant 1\right)$$

where $[1/y]$ denotes the integer part of $1/y$. For the data in the Review exercise 4 (Figure 6.39) test the largest value to see whether it is reasonable to expect such a value if the data truly have an exponential distribution. Find 95% confidence intervals for the mean inter-arrival time with this value respectively included and excluded from the data.

6 Language courses in French, German and Spanish are offered by an adult learning institute. At the end of each course, the students are asked to grade their response to the course as either very satisfied, fairly satisfied, neutral, fairly dissatisfied, or very dissatisfied. After gathering data for several terms the results are as follows:

Grade	French	German	Spanish
Very satisfied	16	6	22
Fairly satisfied	63	13	76
Neutral	40	27	60
Fairly dissatisfied	10	13	32
Very dissatisfied	3	5	12

Is there evidence of different levels of satisfaction with the different courses?

7 A surgeon has to decide whether or not to perform an operation on a patient suspected of suffering from a rare disease. If the patient has the disease, he has a 50:50 chance of recovering after the operation but only a one in 20 chance of survival if the operation is not performed. On the other hand, there is a one in five chance that a patient who has not got the disease would die as a result of the operation. How will the decision depend upon the surgeon's assessment of the probability p that the patient has the disease? (*Hint*: Use $P(B \mid A) = P(B \mid A \cap C)P(C) + P(B \mid A \cap \bar{C})P(\bar{C})$, where A and C are independent.)

8 A factory contains 200 machines, each of which becomes misaligned on average every 200 h of operation, the misalignments occurring at random and independently of each other and of other machines. To detect the misalignments, a quality control chart will be followed for each machine, based on one sample of output per machine per hour. Two options have been worked out: option A would cost £1 per hour per machine, whereas option B would cost £1.50 per hour per machine. The control charts differ in their average run lengths (ARLs) to a signal of action required. Option A (Shewhart) has an ARL of 20 for a misaligned machine, but will also generate false alarms with an ARL of 1000 for a well-adjusted machine. Option B (cusum) has an ARL of four for a misaligned machine and an ARL of 750 for a well-adjusted machine.

When a control chart signals action required, the machine will be shut down and will join a queue of machines awaiting servicing. A single server will operate, with a mean service time of 30 min and standard deviation of 15 min, regardless of whether the machine was actually misaligned. This is all that is known of the service time distribution, but use can be made of the **Pollaczek–Khintchine formula**, which applies to single-channel queues with arbitrary service distributions:

$$N_S = \rho + \frac{(\lambda\sigma_S)^2 + \rho^2}{2(1-\rho)}$$

(the notation is as in Section 6.10.3, with σ_S the standard deviation of service time).

During the time that a machine is in the queue and being serviced, its lost production is costed at £200 per hour. In addition, if the machine is found to have been misaligned then its output for the previous several hours (given on average by the ARL) must be examined and if necessary rectified, at a cost of £10 per production hour.

Find the total cost per hour for each option, and hence decide which control scheme should be implemented.

9 A transmission channel for binary data connects a source to a receiver. The source emits a 0 with probability α and a 1 with probability $1 - \alpha$, each symbol independent of every other. The noise in the channel causes some bits to be interpreted incorrectly. The probability that a bit will be inverted is p (whether a 0 or a 1, the channel is 'symmetric').

(a) Using Bayes' theorem, express the four probabilities that the source symbol is a 0 or a 1 given that the received symbol is a 0 or a 1.

(b) If p is small and the receiver chooses to deliver whichever source symbol is the more likely given the received symbol, find the conditions on α such that the source symbol is assumed to be the same as the received symbol.

10 If discrete random variables X and Y can take possible values $\{u_1, \dots, u_m\}$ and $\{v_1, \dots, v_n\}$ respectively, with joint distribution $P(u_k, v_j)$ (see Section 6.4.1), the **mutual information** between X and Y is defined as

$$I(X; Y) = \sum_{k=1}^{m} \sum_{j=1}^{n} P(u_k, v_j) \log_2 \frac{P(u_k, v_j)}{P(X = u_k)P(Y = v_j)}$$

Show that for the binary symmetric transmission channel referred to in Review exercise 9, if X is the source symbol, Y the received symbol and $\alpha = \frac{1}{2}$ then

$$I(X; Y) = 1 + p \log_2 p + (1 - p) \log_2(1 - p)$$

The interpretation of this quantity is that it measures (in 'bits') the average amount of information received for each bit of data transmitted. Show that $I(X; Y) = 0$ when $p = \frac{1}{2}$ and that $I(X; Y) \to 1$ as $p \to 0$ and as $p \to 1$. Interpret this result.

Answers to Exercises

CHAPTER 1

Exercises

1 (a) $y = \frac{5}{2}x + \frac{5}{4}$ (b) $y = \frac{1}{4}x - \frac{3}{4}$

2 $z = 2, \frac{1}{2}\pi$

3 $u = 6v$

6 Semi-infinite strip $v > 0, |u| < 1$

7 (a) $u = v\sqrt{3} - 4$
(b) $v = -u\sqrt{3}$
(c) $(u + 1)^2 + (v - \sqrt{3})^2 = 4$
(d) $u^2 + v^2 = 8$

8 (a) $\alpha = \frac{1}{5}(-2 + \text{j}), \beta = \frac{3}{5}(1 + 2\text{j})$
(b) $u + 2v < 3$
(c) $(5u - 3)^2 + (5v - 6)^2 < 20$
(d) $\frac{3}{10}(1 + 3\text{j})$

9 Interior of circle, centre $(0, -1/2c)$, radius $1/2c$; half-plane $v < 0$; region outside the circle, centre $(0, -1/2c)$, radius $1/2c$

10 Circle, centre $(\frac{1}{2}, -\frac{2}{3})$, radius $\frac{7}{6}$

11 $\text{Re}(w) = 1/2a$, half-plane $\text{Re}(w) > 1/2a$

12 $w = \dfrac{z + 1}{\text{j}z - \text{j}}$,
$\text{Re}(z) = \text{const}(k)$ to circles

$$u^2 + \left(v - \frac{k}{1 - k}\right)^2 = \frac{1}{(1 - k)^2} \text{ plus } v = -1 \ (k = 1)$$

$\text{Im}(z) = \text{const}(l)$ to circles $\left(u + \dfrac{1}{l}\right)^2 + (v + 1)^2 = \dfrac{1}{l^2}$

plus $u = 0$ $(l = 0)$

13 (a) $1 + \text{j}, \text{j}, \infty$
(b) $|w| > \sqrt{2}$
(c) $v = 0, (u - 1)^2 + v^2 = 1$
(d) $\pm 2^{1/4}\text{e}^{\text{j}\pi/8}$

14 Segment of the imaginary axis $|v| \geq 1$

15 (a) Upper segment of the circle, centre $(\frac{2}{3}, -\frac{2}{3})$, radius $\frac{1}{3}\sqrt{5}$, cut off by the line $u - 3v = 1$

16 Circle, centre $(\frac{5}{3}, 0)$, radius $\frac{4}{3}$

17 $z_0 = \text{j}, \theta_0 = \pi$

18 $|w - 1| < 1; \left|w - \frac{4}{3}\right| > \frac{2}{3}$

19 $w = \text{e}^{\text{j}\theta_0} \dfrac{z - z_0}{z_0^* z - 1}$, where θ_0 is any real number

20 Region enclosed between the inverted parabola $v = 2 - (u^2/8)$ and the real axis

21 $u = 0, 2mu = (1 - m^2)v$

23 $u = x + \dfrac{x}{x^2 + y^2}, v = y - \dfrac{y}{x^2 + y^2}$; $v = 0$; ellipses, $u^2 + v^2 = r^2$ and $x^2 + y^2 = r^2$, r large

24 (a) $\text{e}^z(z + 1)$ (b) $4 \cos 4z$ (d) $-2 \sin 2z$

25 $a = -1, b = 1$
$w = z^2 + \text{j}z^2, \text{d}w/\text{d}z = 2(1 + \text{j})z$

26 $v = 2y + x^2 - y^2$

27 $\text{e}^x(x \sin y + y \cos y), z\,\text{e}^z$

28 $\cos x \sinh y, \sin z$

29 (a) $x^4 - 6x^2y^2 + y^4 = \beta$
(b) $2\,\text{e}^{-x} \sin y + x^2 - y^2 = \beta$

30 (a) $(x^2 - y^2) \cos 2x - 2xy \sin 2y + \text{j}[2xy \cos 2x + (x^2 - y^2) \sin 2y]$
(b) $\sin 2x \cosh 2y + \text{j} \cos 2x \sinh 2y$

31 $u = \cos^{-1}\{2y^2\{x^2 + y^2 - 1 + \sqrt{[(x^2 + y^2 - 1)^2 + 4y^2]}\}\}$
$v = \sinh^{-1}\sqrt{\{\frac{1}{2}(x^2 + y^2 - 1) + \frac{1}{2}\sqrt{[(x^2 + y^2 - 1)^2 + 4y^2]}\}}$

33 (a) 0
(b) 3, 4
(c) $\frac{1}{2}, \frac{1}{4}(-1 + \text{j}\sqrt{3}), \frac{1}{4}(-1 - \text{j}\sqrt{3})$

34 $z = \pm j$

35 (a) region outside unit circle
(b) $1 \leqslant u^2 + v^2 < e^2,\ 0 \leqslant v \leqslant u \tan 1$
(c) outside unit circle, u and v of opposite sign

36

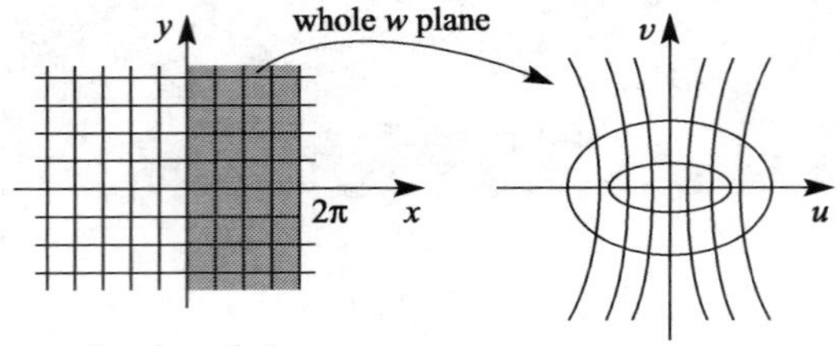

whole w plane; y, x, 2π; v, u

$x = k \to$ hyperbola
$y = k \to$ ellipse

37 $4a$, ellipse centred at origin, semi axes are $\dfrac{a^2+b^2}{b}$ and $\dfrac{|b^2-a^2|}{b}$

38 (a) $j + z - jz^2 - z^3 + jz^4 + \ldots$
(b) $\dfrac{1}{z} + \dfrac{j}{z^2} - \dfrac{1}{z^3} - \dfrac{j}{z^4} + \dfrac{1}{z^5} + \ldots$
(c) $1 - (z - 1 - j) + (z - 1 - j)^2 - (z - 1 - j)^3 + \ldots$

39 (a) $1 - 2z^2 + 3z^4 - 4z^6 + \ldots$
(b) $1 - 3z^2 + 6z^4 - 10z^6 + \ldots$

40 (a) $\frac{1}{2} - \frac{1}{4}(z-1) + \frac{1}{8}(z-1)^2 - \frac{1}{16}(z-1)^3$; 2
(b) $\frac{1}{4} - \frac{1}{16}(z-2j)^2 + \frac{1}{64}(z-2j)^4 - \frac{1}{256}(z-2j)^6$; 2
(c) $-\frac{1}{2}j + \frac{1}{2}(1+j)(z-1-j) + \frac{3}{4}(z-1-j)^2$
$+ \frac{1}{2}(j-1)(z-1-j)^3$; $\sqrt{2}$

41 $1 - z + z^3 + \ldots$

42 $1, 1, \sqrt{5}$; f is singular at $z = j$

43 $z + \frac{1}{3}z^2 + \frac{2}{15}z^5 + \ldots$; $\frac{1}{2}\pi$

44 (a) $\dfrac{1}{z} + 2 + 3z + 4z^2 + \ldots\ (0 < |z| < 1)$
(b) $\dfrac{1}{(z-1)^2} - \dfrac{1}{z-1} + 1 - (z-1) + (z-1)^2 - \ldots$
$(0 < |z-1| < 1)$

45 (a) $\ldots + \dfrac{1}{5!z^3} - \dfrac{1}{3!z} + z$
(b) $z - \dfrac{1}{3!z} + \dfrac{1}{5!z^3} - \ldots$
(c) $a^2 \sin \dfrac{1}{a} + zf'(a) + z^2 f''(a) + \ldots$

46 (a) $\frac{1}{2}z + \frac{3}{4}z^2 + \frac{7}{8}z^3 + \frac{15}{16}z^4 + \ldots$
(b) $\ldots - \dfrac{1}{z^2} - \dfrac{1}{z} - 1 - \dfrac{1}{2}z - \dfrac{1}{4}z^2 - \dfrac{1}{8}z^3 - \ldots$
(c) $\dfrac{1}{z} + \dfrac{3}{z^2} + \dfrac{7}{z^3} + \dfrac{15}{z^4} + \ldots$
(d) $\dfrac{1}{z-1} + \dfrac{2}{(z-1)^2} + \dfrac{2}{(z-1)^3} + \ldots$
(e) $-1 + \dfrac{2}{z-2} + (z-2) - (z-2)^2 + (z-2)^3$
$+ (z-2)^4 - \ldots$

47 (a) $z = 0$, double pole
(b) $z = j$, simple pole; $z = -j$, double pole
(c) $z = \pm 1, \pm j$, simple poles
(d) $z = jn\pi$ (n an integer), simple poles
(e) $z = \pm j\pi$, simple poles
(f) $z = 1$, essential singularity
(g) Simple zero at $z = 1$ and simple poles at $z = \pm j$
(h) Simple zero at $z = -j$, simple pole at $z = 3$ and a pole of order 3 at $z = -2$
(i) Simple poles at $z = 2 + j,\ 2 - j$ and a pole of order 2 at $z = 0$

48 (a) $\dfrac{z}{2!} - \dfrac{z^3}{4!} + \dfrac{z^5}{5!} - \ldots$ (removable singularity)
(b) $\dfrac{1}{z^3} + \dfrac{1}{z} + \dfrac{z}{2!} + \dfrac{z^3}{3!} + \dfrac{z^5}{4!} + \dfrac{z^7}{5!} + \ldots$ (pole of order 3)
(c) $\dfrac{1}{z} + \dfrac{1}{2!z^3} + \dfrac{1}{4!z^5} - \ldots$ (essential singularity)
(d) $\tan^{-1}2 + \dfrac{2}{5}z - \dfrac{6}{25}z^2 + \ldots$ (analytic point)

50 (a) Simple poles at $z = -1, 2$; residues $\frac{1}{3}, \frac{5}{3}$
(b) Simple pole at $z = 1$, double pole at $z = 0$; residues $-1, 1$
(c) Simple poles at $z = 1, 3j, -3j$; residues $\frac{1}{2}$, $\frac{5}{12}(3 - j)$, $\frac{5}{12}(3 + j)$
(d) Simple poles at $z = 0, 2j, -2j$; residues $-\frac{1}{4}$, $-\frac{3}{8} + \frac{3}{4}j$, $-\frac{3}{8} - \frac{3}{4}j$
(e) Pole of order 5 at $z = 1$, residue 19
(f) Pole of order 2 at $z = 1$, residue 4
(g) Simple pole at $z = -3$, double pole at $z = 1$; residues $-\frac{1}{8}, \frac{1}{8}$
(h) Simple poles at $z = 0, -2, -1$; residues $\frac{3}{2}, -\frac{5}{2}, 1$

51 (a) 1 (simple pole)
(b) $-\frac{1}{12}(3 + j\sqrt{3}) \sin[\frac{1}{2}(1 + j\sqrt{3})]$ (simple pole)
(c) $\frac{1}{4}(1 + j)\sqrt{2}$ (simple pole)
(d) $-\pi$ (simple pole) (e) $-j\frac{1}{4}$ (double pole)

52 (a) $-\frac{1}{2}$ (triple pole) (b) $-\frac{14}{25}$ (double pole)
(c) $e^{n\pi}$ (double pole)

53 $-\frac{44}{3} - j\frac{8}{3}$, all cases

54 0, all cases

56 $0, 2\pi j$

57 $\frac{4}{5}\pi j$, $\frac{12}{5}\pi j$

58 $\frac{4}{17}\pi(9+j2)$, 0

59 (a) $-\frac{3}{8}\pi j$ (b) 0

60 (a) 0 (b) $2\pi j$

61 (a) $-\frac{4}{9}\pi j$ (b) $2\pi j$

62 $z = j,\ -\frac{3}{10}j$; $z = -j,\ \frac{3}{10}j$; $z = j\sqrt{6},\ \frac{2}{15}j\sqrt{6}$; $z = -j\sqrt{6},\ -\frac{2}{15}j\sqrt{6}$
(a) 0, (b) $\frac{3}{5}\pi$, (c) 0

63 (a) 0 (b) 0

64 (a) $2\pi j$, $\frac{5}{2}\pi j$
(b) $\frac{2}{25}\pi(25 - j39)$
(c) 0, $\frac{19}{108}\pi j$, $-\frac{19}{108}\pi j$
(d) $0 - \frac{487}{162}\pi j$, $-3\pi j$

65 (a) $2\pi/\sqrt{3}$ (b) $\frac{1}{2}\pi$ (c) $\frac{5}{288}\pi$ (d) $\frac{1}{12}\pi$
(e) $\frac{8}{3}\pi$ (f) $\frac{7}{10}\pi$ (g) π (h) $\pi/2\sqrt{2}$
(i) $\frac{1}{2}\pi$ (j) $\pi(1 - 3/\sqrt{5})$

66 $2axV_0/(x^2 + y^2)$

67 (a) (0, 0), (0, 1), (0, 7), (7, 0)
(b) $v = 0$ (c) $u = 0$

68 $H(x, y) = 2y - y^2 + x^2$;
$W = 2z - jz^2$

70 (a) (0, 0), (1, 0), (−1, 0)
(b) $u = 0$ (c) $v = 0$

1.9 Review exercises

1 (a) 3j (b) 7 + j4 (c) 1 (d) j2

2 $y = 2x$ gives $3u + v = 3$, $u + 2v = 3$ and $3v - u = 1$ respectively
$x + y = 1$ gives $v = 1$, $v - u = 3$ and $u = 1$ respectively

3 (a) $\alpha = -\frac{1}{5}(3 + j4)$, $\beta = 3 + j$
(b) $13 \leqslant 3u + 4v$
(c) $|w - 3 - j| \leqslant 1$ (d) $\frac{1}{4}(7 - j)$

4 (a) $u^2 + v^2 + u - v = 0$ (b) $u = 3v$
(c) $u^2 + v^2 + u - 2v = 0$ (d) $4(u^2 + v^2) = u$

5 Left hand Right hand

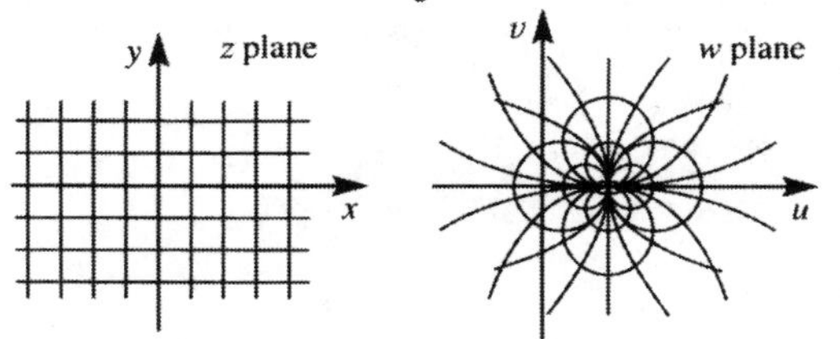

$$x = k \rightarrow \left(u - \frac{k}{k-1}\right)^2 + v^2 = \frac{1}{(k-1)^2}$$

$$y = l \rightarrow (u-1)^2 + \left(v + \frac{1}{l}\right)^2 = \frac{1}{l^2}$$

Fixed points: $1 \pm \sqrt{2}$

6 Fixed points $z = \pm\sqrt{2}/2$
$r = 1 \Rightarrow u = 0$

7 $u = x^3 - 3xy^2$, $v = 3x^2y - y^3$

8 $(z \sin z)$ $v = y \sin x \cosh y + x \cos x \sinh y$

9 $w = 1/z$

10 Ellipse is given by $\dfrac{x^2}{(R + a^2/4k)^2} + \dfrac{y^2}{(R - a^2/4k)^2} = 1$

11 $1 - z^3 + z^6 - z^9 + z^{12} - \ldots$;
$1 - 2z^3 + 3z^6 - 4z^9 + \ldots$

12 (a) $1 - 2z + 2z^2 - 2z^3$; 1
(b) $\frac{1}{2} - \frac{1}{2}(z-1) + \frac{1}{4}(z-1)^2 - \frac{1}{6}(z-1)^4$; $\sqrt{2}$
(c) $\frac{1}{2}(1+j) + \frac{1}{2}j(z-j) - \frac{1}{4}(1+j)(z-j)^2 - \frac{1}{8}(z-j)^3$; $\sqrt{2}$

13 1, 1, 1, $\frac{1}{2}\sqrt{5}$, $2\sqrt{2}$ respectively

14 (a) $\dfrac{1}{z} - z + z^3 - z^5 + \ldots\ (0 < |z| < 1)$
(b) $\frac{1}{2} - (z-1) + \frac{5}{4}(z-1)^2 + \ldots\ (|z-1| < 1)$

15 (a) Taylor series
(b) and (c) are essential singularities, the principal parts are infinite

16 (a) $\frac{1}{2}(e^{2x}\cos 2y - 1) + j\frac{1}{2}e^{2x}\sin 2y$
(b) $\cos 2x \cosh 2y - j \sin 2x \sinh 2y$
(c)
$$\frac{x\sin x\cosh y + y\cos x\sinh y + j(x\cos x\sinh y - y\sin x\cosh y)}{x^2 + y^2}$$
(d) $\dfrac{\tan x(1 - \tanh^2 y) + j\tanh y(1 + \tan^2 x)}{1 + \tan^2 x \tanh^2 y}$

17 (a) Conformal (b) j, −1 − j (c) ±0.465, ±j0.465

18

$x = k \rightarrow$ hyperbolas, $\dfrac{u^2}{\cos^2 k} - \dfrac{v^2}{\sin^2 k} = 1$

$y = l \rightarrow$ ellipses, $\dfrac{u^2}{\cosh^2 l} + \dfrac{v^2}{\sinh^2 l} = 1$

19 (a) Simple pole at $z = 0$
(b) Double poles at $z = 2, 2e^{2\pi j/3}, 2e^{4\pi j/3}$
(c) Simple poles at $z = +1, \pm j$, removable singularity at $z = -1$
(d) Simple poles at $z = \frac{1}{2}(2n + 1)\pi j$ $(n = 0, \pm 1, \pm 2, \dots)$
(e) No singularities in finite plane (entire)
(f) Essential singularity at $z = 0$
(g) Essential (non-isolated) singularity at $z = 0$

20 (a) $2e^{-2}$ (b) 0 (c) 0 (d) 0

21 Zeros: $\pm 1, -\frac{3}{2} \pm \frac{1}{2}j\sqrt{11}$
Poles: $0, e^{\pi j/4}, e^{3\pi j/4}, e^{5\pi j/4}, e^{7\pi j/4}$
Residues (respectively) $-5, \frac{6+3\sqrt{2}}{4} - j,$
$\frac{6-3\sqrt{2}}{4} + \frac{j}{4}, \frac{6-3\sqrt{2}}{4} - \frac{j}{-j}, \frac{6+3\sqrt{2}}{4} + \frac{j}{4}$

22 $-204 - 324j$

23 (a) $-\frac{2}{5}\pi j$ (b) 0 (c) (i) 0, (ii) $3\pi j$ (d) 0, 0
(e) $-\pi$ (f) $j\frac{\pi}{6}, -\frac{4\pi}{3}j$

24 (a) $\frac{7}{50}\pi$ (b) $\frac{1}{8}\pi\sqrt{2}$ (c) $-\frac{11\pi}{24}$ (d) $\frac{19\pi}{12}$

CHAPTER 2

Exercises

1 (a) $\frac{s}{s^2-4}$, $\text{Re}(s) > 2$ (b) $\frac{2}{s^3}$, $\text{Re}(s) > 0$
(c) $\frac{3s+1}{s^2}$, $\text{Re}(s) > 0$ (d) $\frac{1}{(s+1)^2}$, $\text{Re}(s) > -1$

2 (a) 5 (b) -3 (c) 0 (d) 3 (e) 2
(f) 0 (g) 0 (h) 0 (i) 2 (j) 3

3 (a) $\frac{5s-3}{s^2}$, $\text{Re}(s) > 0$
(b) $\frac{42}{s^4} - \frac{6}{s^2+9}$, $\text{Re}(s) > 0$
(c) $\frac{3s-2}{s^2} + \frac{4s}{s^2+4}$, $\text{Re}(s) > 0$
(d) $\frac{s}{s^2-9}$, $\text{Re}(s) > 3$
(e) $\frac{2}{s^2-4}$, $\text{Re}(s) > 2$
(f) $\frac{5}{s+2} + \frac{3}{s} - \frac{2s}{s^2+4}$, $\text{Re}(s) > 0$
(g) $\frac{4}{(s+2)^2}$, $\text{Re}(s) > -2$
(h) $\frac{4}{s^2+6s+13}$, $\text{Re}(s) > -3$
(i) $\frac{2}{(s+4)^3}$, $\text{Re}(s) > -4$
(j) $\frac{36-6s+4s^2-2s^3}{s^4}$, $\text{Re}(s) > 0$
(k) $\frac{2s+15}{s^2+9}$, $\text{Re}(s) > 0$
(l) $\frac{s^2-4}{(s^2+4)^2}$, $\text{Re}(s) > 0$
(m) $\frac{18s^2-54}{(s^2+9)^3}$, $\text{Re}(s) > 0$
(n) $\frac{2}{s^3} - \frac{3s}{s^2+16}$, $\text{Re}(s) > 0$
(o) $\frac{2}{(s+2)^3} + \frac{s+1}{s^2+2s+5} + \frac{3}{s}$, $\text{Re}(s) > 0$

4 (a) $\frac{1}{4}(e^{-3t} - e^{-7t})$ (b) $-e^{-t} + 2e^{3t}$
(c) $\frac{4}{9} - \frac{1}{3}t - \frac{4}{9}e^{-3t}$ (d) $2\cos 2t + 3\sin 2t$
(e) $\frac{1}{64}(4t - \sin 4t)$ (f) $e^{-2t}(\cos t + 6\sin t)$
(g) $\frac{1}{8}(1 - e^{-2t}\cos 2t + 3e^{-2t}\sin 2t)$
(h) $e^t - e^{-t} + 2te^{-t}$
(i) $e^{-t}(\cos 2t + 3\sin 2t)$ (j) $\frac{1}{2}e^t - 3e^{2t} + \frac{11}{2}e^{3t}$
(k) $-2e^{-3t} + 2\cos(\sqrt{2}t) - \sqrt{\tfrac{1}{2}}\sin(\sqrt{2}t)$
(l) $\frac{1}{5}e^t - \frac{1}{5}e^{-t}(\cos t - 3\sin t)$
(m) $e^{-t}(\cos 2t - \sin 2t)$ (n) $\frac{1}{2}e^{2t} - 2e^{3t} + \frac{3}{2}e^{-4t}$
(o) $-e^t + \frac{3}{2}e^{2t} - \frac{1}{2}e^{-2t}$
(p) $4 - \frac{9}{2}\cos t + \frac{1}{2}\cos 3t$
(q) $9e^{-2t} - e^{-3t/2}[7\cos(\frac{1}{2}\sqrt{3}t) - \sqrt{3}\sin(\frac{1}{2}\sqrt{3}t)]$
(r) $\frac{1}{9}e^{-t} - \frac{1}{10}e^{-2t} - \frac{1}{90}e^{-t}(\cos 3t + 3\sin 3t)$

5 (a) $x(t) = e^{-2t} + e^{-3t}$
(b) $x(t) = \frac{35}{78}e^{4t/3} - \frac{3}{26}(\cos 2t + \frac{2}{3}\sin 2t)$
(c) $x(t) = \frac{1}{5}(1 - e^{-t}\cos 2t - \frac{1}{2}e^{-t}\sin 2t)$
(d) $y(t) = \frac{1}{25}(12e^{-t} + 30te^{-t} - 12\cos 2t + 16\sin 2t)$
(e) $x(t) = -\frac{7}{5}e^t + \frac{4}{3}e^{2t} + \frac{1}{15}e^{-4t}$
(f) $x(t) = e^{-2t}(\cos t + \sin t + 3)$
(g) $x(t) = \frac{13}{12}e^t - \frac{1}{3}e^{-2t} + \frac{1}{4}e^{-t}(\cos 2t - 3\sin 2t)$
(h) $y(t) = -\frac{2}{3} + t + \frac{2}{3}e^{-t}[\cos(\sqrt{2}t) + \sqrt{\tfrac{1}{2}}\sin(\sqrt{2}t)]$
(i) $x(t) = (\frac{1}{8} + \frac{3}{4}t)e^{-2t} + \frac{1}{2}t^2e^{-2t} + \frac{3}{8} - \frac{1}{2}t + \frac{1}{4}t^2$
(j) $x(t) = \frac{1}{5} - \frac{1}{5}e^{-2t/3}(\cos\frac{1}{3}t + 2\sin\frac{1}{3}t)$
(k) $x(t) = te^{-4t} - \frac{1}{2}\cos 4t$
(l) $y(t) = e^{-t} + 2te^{-2t/3}$
(m) $x(t) = \frac{5}{4} + \frac{1}{2}t - e^t + \frac{5}{12}e^{2t} - \frac{2}{3}e^{-t}$
(n) $x(t) = \frac{9}{20}e^{-t} - \frac{7}{16}\cos t + \frac{25}{16}\sin t - \frac{1}{80}\cos 3t - \frac{3}{80}\sin 3t$

6 (a) $x(t)=\frac{1}{4}(\frac{15}{4}e^{3t}-\frac{11}{4}e^{t}-e^{-2t}),\ y(t)=\frac{1}{8}(3e^{3t}-e^{t})$
(b) $x(t)=5\sin t+5\cos t-e^{t}-e^{2t}-3$
$y(t)=2e^{t}-5\sin t+e^{2t}-3$
(c) $x(t)=3\sin t-2\cos t+e^{-2t}$
$y(t)=-\frac{7}{2}\sin t+\frac{9}{2}\cos t-\frac{1}{2}e^{-3t}$
(d) $x(t)=\frac{3}{2}e^{t/3}-\frac{1}{2}e^{t},\ y(t)=-1+\frac{1}{2}e^{t}+\frac{3}{2}e^{t/3}$
(e) $x(t)=2e^{t}+\sin t-2\cos t$
$y(t)=\cos t-2\sin t-2e^{t}$
(f) $x(t)=-3+e^{t}+3e^{-t/3}$
$y(t)=t-1-\frac{1}{2}e^{t}+\frac{3}{2}e^{-t/3}$
(g) $x(t)=2t-e^{t}+e^{-2t},\ y(t)=t-\frac{7}{2}+3e^{t}+\frac{1}{2}e^{-2t}$
(h) $x(t)=3\cos t+\cos(\sqrt{3}t)$
$y(t)=3\cos t-\cos(\sqrt{3}t)$
(i) $x(t)=\cos(\sqrt{\frac{3}{10}}t)+\frac{3}{4}\cos(\sqrt{6}t)$
$y(t)=\frac{5}{4}\cos(\sqrt{\frac{3}{10}}t)-\frac{1}{4}\cos(\sqrt{6}t)$
(j) $x(t)=\frac{1}{3}e^{t}+\frac{2}{3}\cos 2t+\frac{1}{3}\sin 2t$
$y(t)=\frac{2}{3}e^{t}-\frac{2}{3}\cos 2t-\frac{1}{3}\sin 2t$

7 $I_1(s)=\dfrac{E_1(50+s)s}{(s^2+10^4)(s+100)^2}$
$I_2(s)=\dfrac{Es^2}{(s^2+10^4)(s+100)^2}$
$i_2(t)=E(-\frac{1}{200}e^{-100t}+\frac{1}{2}te^{-100t}+\frac{1}{200}\cos 100t)$

9 $i_1(t)=20\sqrt{\frac{1}{7}}e^{-t/2}\sin(\frac{1}{2}\sqrt{7}t)$

10 $x_1(t)=-\frac{3}{10}\cos(\sqrt{3}t)-\frac{7}{10}\cos(\sqrt{13}t)$
$x_2(t)=-\frac{1}{10}\cos(\sqrt{3}t)+\frac{21}{10}\cos(\sqrt{13}t)$, $\sqrt{3}$, $\sqrt{13}$

13 $f(t)=tH(t)-tH(t-1)$

14 (a) $f(t)=3t^2-[3(t-4)^2+22(t-4)+43]H(t-4)$
$-[2(t-6)+4]H(t-6)$
$F(s)=\dfrac{6}{s^3}-\left(\dfrac{6}{s^3}+\dfrac{22}{s^2}+\dfrac{43}{s}\right)e^{-4s}-\left(\dfrac{2}{s^3}+\dfrac{4}{s}\right)e^{-6s}$
(b) $f(t)=t-2(t-1)H(t-1)+(t-2)H(t-2)$
$F(s)=\dfrac{1}{s^2}-\dfrac{2}{s^2}e^{-s}+\dfrac{1}{s^2}e^{-2s}$

15 (a) $\frac{1}{6}(t-5)^3e^{2(t-5)}H(t-5)$
(b) $\frac{3}{2}[e^{-(t-2)}-e^{-3(t-2)}]H(t-2)$
(c) $[t-\cos(t-1)-\sin(t-1)]H(t-1)$
(d) $\sqrt{\frac{1}{3}}e^{-(t-\pi)/2}\{\sqrt{3}\cos[\frac{1}{2}\sqrt{3}(t-\pi)]$
$+\sin[\frac{1}{2}\sqrt{3}(t-\pi)]\}H(t-\pi)$
(e) $H(t-\frac{4}{5}\pi)\cos 5t$
(f) $[t-\cos(t-1)-\sin(t-1)]H(t-1)$

16 $x(t)=e^{-t}+(t-1)[1-H(t-1)]$

17 $x(t)=2e^{-t/2}\cos(\frac{1}{2}\sqrt{3}t)+t-1-2H(t-1)$
$\{t-2+e^{-(t-1)/2}\{\cos[\frac{1}{2}\sqrt{3}(t-1)]$
$-\sqrt{\frac{1}{3}}\sin[\frac{1}{2}\sqrt{3}(t-1)]\}\}$
$+H(t-2)\{t-3+e^{-(t-2)/2}$
$\{\cos[\frac{1}{2}\sqrt{3}(t-2)]-\sqrt{\frac{1}{3}}\sin[\frac{1}{2}\sqrt{3}(t-2)]\}\}$

18 $x(t)=e^{-t}+\frac{1}{10}(\sin t-3\cos t+4e^{\pi}e^{-2t}$
$-5e^{\pi/2}e^{-t})H(t-\frac{1}{2}\pi)$

19 $f(t)=3+2(t-4)H(t-4)$
$F(s)=\dfrac{3}{s}+\dfrac{2}{s^2}e^{-4s}$
$x(t)=3-2\cos t+2[t-4-\sin(t-4)]H(t-4)$

20 $\theta_0(t)=\frac{3}{10}(1-e^{-3t}\cos t-3e^{-3t}\sin t)$
$-\frac{3}{10}[1-e^{3a}e^{-3t}\cos(t-a)$
$-3e^{3a}e^{-3t}\sin(t-a)]H(t-a)$

21 $\theta_0(t)=\frac{1}{32}(3-2t-3e^{-4t}-10te^{-4t})$
$+\frac{1}{32}[2t-3+(2t-1)e^{-4(t-1)}]H(t-1)$

23 $\dfrac{3-3e^{-2s}-6se^{-4s}}{s^2(1-e^{-4s})}$

24 $\dfrac{K}{T}\dfrac{1}{s^2}-\dfrac{K}{s}\dfrac{e^{-sT}}{1-e^{-sT}}$

25 (a) $2\delta(t)+9e^{-2t}-19e^{-3t}$
(b) $\delta(t)-\frac{5}{2}\sin 2t$
(c) $\delta(t)-e^{-t}(2\cos 2t+\frac{1}{2}\sin 2t)$

26 (a) $x(t)=(\frac{1}{6}-\frac{2}{3}e^{-3t}+\frac{1}{2}e^{-4t})$
$+(e^{-3(t-2)}-e^{-4(t-2)})H(t-2)$
(b) $x(t)=\frac{1}{2}e^{6\pi}e^{-3t}H(t-2\pi)\sin 2t$
(c) $x(t)=5e^{-3t}-4e^{-4t}+(e^{-3(t-3)}-e^{-4(t-3)})H(t-3)$

27 (a) $f'(t)=g'(t)-43\delta(t-4)-4\delta(t-6)$
$$g'(t)=\begin{cases}6t & (0\leqslant t<4)\\ 2 & (4\leqslant t<6)\\ 0 & (t\geqslant 6)\end{cases}$$
(b) $$g'(t)=\begin{cases}1 & (0\leqslant t<1)\\ -1 & (1\leqslant t<2)\\ 0 & (t\geqslant 2)\end{cases}$$
(c) $f'(t)=g'(t)+5\delta(t)-6\delta(t-2)+15\delta(t-4)$
$$g'(t)=\begin{cases}2 & (0\leqslant t<2)\\ -3 & (2\leqslant t<4)\\ 2t-1 & (t\geqslant 4)\end{cases}$$

28 $x(t)=-\frac{19}{9}e^{-5t}+\frac{19}{9}e^{-2t}-\frac{4}{3}te^{-2t}$

30 $q(t) = \dfrac{E}{Ln}\,e^{-\mu t}\sin nt,\ n^2 = \dfrac{1}{LC} - \dfrac{R^2}{4L^2},\ \mu = \dfrac{R}{2L}$

$i(t) = \dfrac{E}{Ln}\,e^{-\mu t}(n\cos nt - \mu\sin nt)$

31 $y(x) = \dfrac{1}{48EI}[2Mx^4/l + 8W(x - \tfrac{1}{2}l)^3H(x - \tfrac{1}{2}l) - 4(M + W)x^3 + (2M + 3W)l^2x]$

32 $y(x) = \dfrac{w(x_2^2 - x_1^2)x^2}{4EI} - \dfrac{w(x_2 - x_1)x^3}{6EI} + \dfrac{w}{24EI}[(x - x_1)^4H(x - x_1) - (x - x_2)^4H(x - x_2)]$

$y_{\max} = wl^4/8EI$

33 $y(x) = \dfrac{W}{EI}[\tfrac{1}{6}x^3 - \tfrac{1}{6}(x - b)^3H(x - b) - \tfrac{1}{2}bx^2]$

$$= \begin{cases} -\dfrac{Wx^2}{6EI}(3b - x) & (0 < x \leqslant b) \\ -\dfrac{Wb^2}{6EI}(3x - b) & (b < x \leqslant l) \end{cases}$$

34 (a) $\dfrac{3s + 2}{s^2 + 2s + 5}$

(b) $s^2 + 2s + 5 = 0$, order 2

(c) Poles $-1 \pm j2$; zero $-\tfrac{2}{3}$

35 $\dfrac{s^2 + 5s + 6}{s^3 + 5s^2 + 17s + 13}$, $s^3 + 5s^2 + 17s + 13 = 0$

order 3, zeros $-3, -2$, poles $-1, -2 \pm j3$

36 (a) Marginally stable (b) Unstable (c) Stable (d) Stable (e) Unstable

37 (a) Unstable
(b) Stable
(c) Marginally stable
(d) Stable
(e) Stable

40 $K > \tfrac{2}{3}$

41 (a) $3e^{-7t} - 3e^{-8t}$ (b) $\tfrac{1}{3}e^{-4t}\sin 3t$

(c) $\tfrac{2}{3}(e^{4t} - e^{-2t})$ (d) $\tfrac{1}{3}e^{2t}\sin 3t$

42 $\dfrac{s + 8}{(s + 1)(s + 2)(s + 4)}$

47 $\tfrac{2}{7}, \tfrac{4}{5}$

49 (a) $\tfrac{1}{54}[2 - e^{-3t}(9t^2 + 6t + 2)]$

(b) $\tfrac{1}{125}[e^{-3t}(5t + 2) + e^{2t}(5t - 2)]$

(c) $\tfrac{1}{16}(4t - 1 + e^{-4t})$

51 $e^{-3t} - e^{-4t}$

$x(t) = \tfrac{1}{12}A[1 - 4e^{-3t} + 3e^{-4t} - (1 - 4e^{-3(t-T)} + 3e^{-4(t-T)})H(t - T)]$

52 $e^{-2t}\sin t$, $\tfrac{1}{5}[1 - e^{-2t}(\cos t + 2\sin t)]$

2.8 Review exercises

1 (a) $x(t) = \cos t + \sin t - e^{-2t}(\cos t + 3\sin t)$

(b) $x(t) = -3 + \tfrac{13}{7}e^{t} + \tfrac{15}{7}e^{-2t/5}$

2 (a) $e^{-t} - \tfrac{1}{2}e^{-2t} - \tfrac{1}{2}e^{-t}(\cos t + \sin t)$

(b) $i(t) = 2e^{-t} - 2e^{-2t} + V[e^{-t} - \tfrac{1}{2}e^{-2t} - \tfrac{1}{2}e^{-t}(\cos t + \sin t)]$

3 $x(t) = -t + 5\sin t - 2\sin 2t$,
$y(t) = 1 - 2\cos t + \cos 2t$

4 $\tfrac{1}{5}(\cos t + 2\sin t)$

$e^{-t}[(x_0 - \tfrac{1}{5})\cos t + (x_1 + x_0 - \tfrac{3}{5})\sin t]$

$\sqrt{\tfrac{1}{5}}$, 63.4° lag

6 (a) (i) $\dfrac{s\cos\phi - \omega\sin\phi}{s^2 + \omega^2}$

(ii) $\dfrac{s\sin\phi + \omega(\cos\phi + \sin\phi)}{s^2 + 2\omega s + 2\omega^2}$

(b) $\tfrac{1}{20}(\cos 2t + 2\sin 2t) + \tfrac{1}{20}e^{-2t}(39\cos 2t + 47\sin 2t)$

7 (a) $e^{-2t}(\cos 3t - 2\sin 3t)$

(b) $y(t) = 2 + 2\sin t - 5e^{-2t}$

8 $x(t) = e^{-8t} + \sin t$, $y(t) = e^{-8t} - \cos t$

9 $q(t) = \tfrac{1}{500}(5e^{-100t} - 2e^{-200t}) - \tfrac{1}{500}(3\cos 100t - \sin 100t)$,

current leads by approximately 18.5°

10 $x(t) = \tfrac{29}{20}e^{-t} + \tfrac{445}{1212}e^{-t/5} + \tfrac{1}{3}e^{-2t} - \tfrac{1}{505}(76\cos 2t - 48\sin 2t)$

11 (a) $\theta = \tfrac{1}{100}(4e^{-4t} + 10te^{-4t} - 4\cos 2t + 3\sin 2t)$

(b) $i_1 = \tfrac{1}{7}(e^{4t} + 6e^{-3t})$, $i_2 = \tfrac{1}{7}(e^{-3t} - e^{4t})$

12 $i = \dfrac{E}{R}[1 - e^{-nt}(\cos nt + \sin nt)]$

13 $i_1 = \dfrac{E(4 - 3e^{-Rt/L} - e^{-3Rt/L})}{6R}$, $i_2 \to E/3R$

14 $x_1(t) = \tfrac{1}{3}[\sin t - 2\sin 2t + \sqrt{3}\sin(\sqrt{3}t)]$

$x_2(t) = \tfrac{1}{3}[\sin t + \sin 2t - \sqrt{3}\sin(\sqrt{3}t)]$

15 (a) (i) $e^{-t}(\cos 3t + \sin 3t)$

(ii) $e^{t} - e^{2t} + 2te^{t}$

(b) $y(t) = \tfrac{1}{2}e^{-t}(8 + 12t + t^3)$

16 (a) $\frac{5}{2}e^{7t}\sin 2t$

(b) $\dfrac{n^2 i}{Ks(s^2+2Ks+n^2)}$, $\theta(t)=\dfrac{i}{K}(1-e^{-Kt})-it\,e^{-Kt}$

17 (a) (ii) $e^{-(t-\alpha)}[\cos 2(t-\alpha)-\frac{1}{2}\sin 2(t-\alpha)]H(t-\alpha)$

(b) $y(t)=\frac{1}{10}[e^{-t}(\cos 2t-\frac{1}{2}\sin 2t)+2\sin t-\cos t]$
$+\frac{1}{10}[e^{-(t-\pi)}(\cos 2t-\frac{1}{2}\sin 2t)+\cos t$
$-2\sin t]H(t-\pi)$

18 $i(t)=\frac{1}{250}[e^{-40t}-2H(1-\frac{1}{2}T)\,e^{-40(t-T/2)}$
$+2H(t-T)\,e^{-40(t-T)}$
$-2H(t-\frac{3}{2}T)\,e^{-40(t-3T/2)}+\ldots]$
Yes, since time constant is large compared with T

19 $e^{-t}\sin t$, $\frac{1}{2}[1-e^{-t}(\cos t+\sin t)]$

20 $EI\dfrac{d^4y}{dx^4}=12+12H(x-4)-R\delta(x-4)$,
$y(0)=y'(0)=y(4)=y^{(2)}(5)=y^{(3)}(0)=0$
$$y(x)=\begin{cases}\frac{1}{2}x^4-4.25x^3+9x^2 & (0\leqslant x\leqslant 4)\\ \frac{1}{2}x^4-4.25x^3+9x^2+\frac{1}{2}(x-4)^4-7.75(x-4)^3 & (4\leqslant x\leqslant 5)\end{cases}$$
25.5 kN, 18 kN m

21 (a) $f(t)=H(t-1)-H(t-2)$
$x(t)=H(t-1)(1-e^{-(t-1)})-H(t-2)(1-e^{-(t-2)})$
(b) 0, E/R

23 (a) $t-2+(t+2)e^{-t}$
(b) $y=t+2-2e^t+2te^t$, $y(t)=\frac{1}{2}t^2+y_1$

24 $EIy=-\frac{2}{9}Wlx^2+\frac{10}{81}Wx^3-\dfrac{W(x-l)^3}{6}H(x-l)$
$EI\dfrac{d^4y}{dx^4}=-W\delta(x-l)-w[H(x)-H(x-l)]$

25 (a) $x(t)=$
$\frac{1}{6}\{1+e^{3(t-a)/2}[\sqrt{3}\sin(\frac{1}{2}\sqrt{3}t)-\cos(\frac{1}{2}\sqrt{3}t)]H(t-a)\}$

26 (a) No (b) $\dfrac{1}{s^2+2s+(K-3)}$ (d) $K>3$

27 (a) 4 (b) $\frac{1}{10}$

28 (a) $\dfrac{K}{s^2+(1+KK_1)s+K}$
(c) $K=12.5$, $K_1=0.178$ (d) 0.65 s, 2.48 s, 1.86 s

29 (a) $K_2=M_2\omega^2$

30 (b) Unstable (c) $\beta=2.5\times10^{-5}$, 92 dB
(d) −8 dB, 24°
(e) $K=10^6$, $\tau_1=10^{-6}$, $\tau_2=10^{-7}$, $\tau_3=4\times10^{-8}$
(f) $s^3+36\times10^6s^2+285\times10^{12}s$
$+25\times10^{18}(1+10^7\beta)=0$

CHAPTER 3

Exercises

1 (a) $\dfrac{4z}{4z-1}$, $|z|>\frac{1}{4}$ (b) $\dfrac{z}{z-3}$, $|z|>3$
(c) $\dfrac{z}{z+2}$, $|z|>2$ (d) $\dfrac{-z}{z-2}$, $|z|>2$
(e) $3\dfrac{z}{(z-1)^2}$, $|z|>1$

2 $e^{-2\omega kT}\leftrightarrow\dfrac{z}{z-e^{-2\omega T}}$

4 $\dfrac{1}{z^3}\dfrac{2z}{2z-1}=\dfrac{2}{z^2(2z-1)}$

5 (a) $\dfrac{5z}{5z+1}$ (b) $\dfrac{z}{z+1}$

6 $\dfrac{2z}{2z-1}$, $\dfrac{2z}{(2z-1)^2}$

8 (a) $\{e^{-4kT}\}\leftrightarrow\dfrac{z}{z-e^{-4T}}$
(b) $\{\sin kT\}\leftrightarrow\dfrac{z\sin T}{z^2-2z\cos T+1}$
(c) $\{\cos 2kT\}\leftrightarrow\dfrac{z(z-\cos 2T)}{z^2-2z\cos 2T+1}$

11 (a) 1 (b) $(-1)^k$ (c) $(\frac{1}{2})^k$ (d) $\frac{1}{3}(-\frac{1}{3})^k$
(e) j^k (f) $(-j\sqrt{2})^k$
(g) 0 $(k=0)$, 1 $(k>0)$
(h) 1 $(k=0)$, $(-1)^{k+1}$ $(k>0)$

12 (a) $\frac{1}{3}[1-(-2)^k]$ (b) $\frac{1}{7}[3^k-(-\frac{1}{2})^k]$
(c) $\frac{1}{3}+\frac{1}{6}(-\frac{1}{2})^k$ (d) $\frac{2}{3}(\frac{1}{2})^k+\frac{2}{3}(-1)^{k+1}$
(e) $\sin\frac{1}{2}k\pi$ (f) $2^k\sin\frac{1}{6}k\pi$
(g) $\frac{5}{2}k+\frac{1}{4}(1-3^k)$ (h) $k+2\sqrt{\frac{1}{3}}\cos(\frac{1}{3}k-\frac{3}{2}\pi)$

13 (a) $\{0,1,0,0,0,0,0,2\}$
(b) $\{1,0,3,0,0,0,0,0,0,-2\}$
(c) $\{5,0,0,1,3\}$ (d) $\{0,0,1,1\}+\{(-\frac{1}{3})^k\}$
(e) $1(k=0)$, $\frac{5}{2}(k=1)$ $\frac{5}{4}(k=2)$ $-\frac{1}{8}(-\frac{1}{2})^{k-3}(k\geqslant3)$
(f) $\begin{cases}0 & (k=0)\\ 3-2k+2^{k-1} & (k\geqslant1)\end{cases}$
(g) $\begin{cases}0 & (k=0)\\ 2-2^{k-1} & (k\geqslant1)\end{cases}$

14 $y_{k+2}+\frac{1}{2}y_{k+1}=x_k$, $y_{k+2}+\frac{1}{4}y_{k+1}-\frac{1}{5}y_k=x_k$

15 (a) $y_k=k$ (b) $y_k=\frac{3}{10}(9^k)+\frac{17}{10}(-1)^k$
(c) $2^{k-1}\sin\frac{1}{2}k\pi$ (d) $2(-\frac{1}{2})^k+3^k$

16 (a) $y_k = \frac{2}{5}(-\frac{1}{2})^k - \frac{9}{10}(\frac{1}{3})^k + \frac{1}{2}$
(b) $y_k = \frac{7}{2}(3^k) - 6(2^k) + \frac{5}{2}$
(c) $y_n = \frac{2}{5}(3^n) - \frac{2}{3}(2^n) + \frac{4}{15}(\frac{1}{2})^n$
(d) $y_n = -2(\sqrt{3})^{n-1} \sin \frac{1}{6}n\pi + 1$
(e) $y_n = -\frac{2}{5}(-\frac{1}{2})^n + \frac{12}{5}(2)^n - 2n - 1$
(f) $y_n = -\frac{1}{2}[2^n + (-2)^n] + 1 - n$

17 (b) 7, £4841

18 $y_k = 2^k - \frac{1}{2}(3^k) + \frac{1}{2}$

19 As $k \to \infty$, $I_k \to 2G$ as a damped oscillation

21 (a) $\dfrac{1}{z^2 - 3z + 2}$
(b) $\dfrac{z - 1}{z^2 - 3z + 1}$
(c) $\dfrac{z + 1}{z^3 - z^2 + 2z + 1}$

22

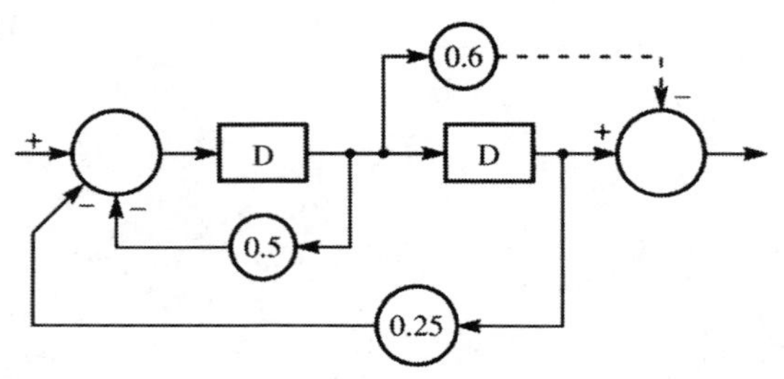

23 (a) $\frac{1}{2}\{(-\frac{1}{4})^k - (-\frac{1}{2})^k\}$ (b) $2(3^k) \sin \frac{1}{6}(k+1)\pi$
(c) $\frac{2}{3}(0.4)^k + \frac{1}{3}(-0.2)^k$ (d) $4^{k+1} + 2^k$

24 $\begin{cases} 0 & (k = 0) \\ 2^{k-1} - 1 & (k \geqslant 1) \end{cases}$

$\begin{cases} 0 & (k = 0) \\ 2^{k-1} & (k \geqslant 1) \end{cases}$

25 (a), (b) and (c) are stable; (d) is unstable; (e) is marginally stable

26 $2 - (\frac{1}{2})^k$

27 $y_n = -4(\frac{1}{2})^n + 2(\frac{1}{3})^n + 2(\frac{2}{3})^n$

29 q form:
$(Aq^2 + Bq + C)y_k = \Delta^2(q^2 + 2q + 1)u_k$
δ form:
$[A\Delta^2\delta^2 + (2\Delta A + \Delta B)\delta + (A + B + C)]y_k$
$= \Delta^2(4 + 4\Delta\delta + \Delta^2\delta^2)u_k$
$A = 2\Delta^2 + 6\Delta + 4$
$B = 4\Delta^2 - 8$
$C = 2\Delta^2 - 6\Delta + 4$

30 $\dfrac{1}{s^3 + 2s^2 + 2s + 1}$
$[(\Delta^3 + 4\Delta^2 + 8\Delta + 8)\delta^3 + (6\Delta^2 + 16\Delta + 16)\delta^2 + (12\Delta + 16)\delta + 8]y_k = (2 + T\delta)^3 u_k$

32 $\dfrac{12(z^2 - z)}{(12 + 5\Delta)z^2 + (8\Delta - 12)z - \Delta}$
$\dfrac{12\gamma(1 + \Delta\gamma)}{\Delta(12 + 5\Delta)\gamma^2 + (8\Delta - 12)\gamma + 12}$

3.10 Review exercises

4 $3 + 2k$

5 $\frac{1}{6} + \frac{1}{3}(-2)^k - \frac{1}{2}(-1)^k$

7 $\dfrac{2z}{(z - e)^{3T}} - \dfrac{z}{z - e^{-2T}}$

8 (a) $\left\{\dfrac{1}{a - b}(a^n - b^n)\right\}$
(b) (i) $3^{k-1}k$ (ii) $2\sqrt{\frac{1}{3}} \sin \frac{1}{3}k\pi$

9 $\frac{3}{2} - \frac{1}{2}(-1)^k - 2^k$

10 $(-1)^k$

13 $\frac{1}{2}A[2 - 2(\frac{1}{2})^k - k(\frac{1}{2})^{k-1}]$

CHAPTER 4

Exercises

1 (a) $f(t) = -\dfrac{1}{4}\pi - \dfrac{2}{\pi}\displaystyle\sum_{n=1}^{\infty} \dfrac{\cos(2n-1)t}{(2n-1)^2} + \sum_{n=1}^{\infty}\left[\dfrac{3\sin(2n-1)t}{2n-1} - \dfrac{\sin 2nt}{2n}\right]$
(b) $f(t) = \dfrac{1}{4}\pi + \dfrac{2}{\pi}\displaystyle\sum_{n=1}^{\infty} \dfrac{\cos(2n-1)t}{(2n-1)^2} - \sum_{n=1}^{\infty} \dfrac{\sin nt}{n}$
(c) $f(t) = \dfrac{2}{\pi}\displaystyle\sum_{n=1}^{\infty} \dfrac{\sin nt}{n}$
(d) $f(t) = \dfrac{2}{\pi} + \dfrac{4}{\pi}\displaystyle\sum_{n=1}^{\infty} \dfrac{(-1)^{n+1}\cos 2nt}{4n^2 - 1}$
(e) $f(t) = \dfrac{2}{\pi} + \dfrac{4}{\pi}\displaystyle\sum_{n=1}^{\infty} \dfrac{(-1)^{n+1}\cos nt}{4n^2 - 1}$
(f) $f(t) = \dfrac{1}{2}\pi - \dfrac{4}{\pi}\displaystyle\sum_{n=1}^{\infty} \dfrac{\cos(2n-1)t}{(2n-1)^2}$
(g) $f(t) = -\dfrac{4}{\pi}\displaystyle\sum_{n=1}^{\infty} \dfrac{\cos(2n-1)t}{(2n-1)^2} - \sum_{n=1}^{\infty} \dfrac{\sin 2nt}{n}$

(h) $f(t)=\left(\frac{1}{2}\pi+\frac{1}{\pi}\sinh\pi\right)$

$$+\frac{2}{\pi}\sum_{n=1}^{\infty}\left[\frac{(-1)^n-1}{n^2}+\frac{(-1)^n\sinh\pi}{n^2+1}\right]\cos nt$$

$$-\frac{2}{\pi}\sum_{n=1}^{\infty}\frac{n(-1)^n}{n^2+1}\sinh\pi\sin nt$$

2 $f(t)=\frac{1}{3}\pi^2+4\sum_{n=1}^{\infty}\frac{\cos nt}{n^2}$

Taking $t=\pi$ gives the required result.

3 $q(t)=Q\left[\frac{1}{2}-\frac{4}{\pi^2}\sum_{n=1}^{\infty}\frac{\cos(2n-1)t}{(2n-1)^2}\right]$

4 $f(t)=\frac{5}{\pi}+\frac{5}{2}\sin t-\frac{10}{\pi}\sum_{n=1}^{\infty}\frac{\cos 2nt}{4n^2-1}$

5 Taking $t=0$ and $t=\pi$ gives the required answers.

6 $f(t)=\frac{1}{4}\pi-\frac{2}{\pi}\sum_{n=1}^{\infty}\frac{\cos(4n-2)t}{(2n-1)^2}$

Taking $t=0$ gives the required series.

7 $f(t)=\frac{3}{2}+\frac{4}{\pi^2}\sum_{n=1}^{\infty}\frac{\cos(2n-1)t}{(2n-1)^2}$

Replacing t by $t-\frac{1}{2}\pi$ gives the following sine series of odd harmonics:

$$f\left(t-\frac{1}{2}\pi\right)-\frac{3}{2}=-\frac{4}{\pi^2}\sum_{n=1}^{\infty}\frac{(-1)^n\sin(2n-1)t}{(2n-1)^2}$$

8 $f(t)=\frac{2l}{\pi}\sum_{n=1}^{\infty}\frac{(-1)^{n+1}}{n}\sin\frac{n\pi t}{l}$

9 $f(t)=\frac{2K}{\pi}\sum_{n=1}^{\infty}\frac{1}{n}\sin\frac{n\pi t}{l}$

10 $f(t)=\frac{3}{2}+\frac{6}{\pi}\sum_{n=1}^{\infty}\frac{1}{(2n-1)}\frac{\sin(2n-1)\pi t}{5}$

11 $v(t)=\frac{A}{\pi}\left(1+\frac{1}{2}\pi\sin\omega t-2\sum_{n=1}^{\infty}\frac{\cos 2n\omega t}{4n^2-1}\right)$

12 $f(t)=\frac{1}{3}T^2+\frac{4T^2}{\pi^2}\sum_{n=1}^{\infty}\frac{(-1)^n}{n^2}\cos\frac{n\pi t}{T}$

13 $e(t)=\frac{E}{2}\left(1-\frac{2}{\pi}\sum_{n=1}^{\infty}\frac{1}{n}\sin\frac{2\pi nt}{T}\right)$

15 $f(t)=-\frac{8}{\pi^2}\sum_{n=1}^{\infty}\frac{1}{(2n-1)^2}\cos(2n-1)\pi t$

16 (a) $f(t)=\frac{2}{3}-\frac{1}{\pi^2}\sum_{n=1}^{\infty}\frac{1}{n^2}\cos 2n\pi t$

$$+\frac{1}{\pi}\sum_{n=1}^{\infty}\frac{1}{n}\sin 2n\pi t$$

(b) $f(t)=\frac{1}{\pi}\sum_{n=1}^{\infty}\frac{1}{n}\sin 2n\pi t$

$$+\frac{2}{\pi}\sum_{n=1}^{\infty}\left[\frac{1}{2n-1}+\frac{4}{\pi^2(2n-1)^3}\right]$$

$$\times\sin(2n-1)\pi t$$

(c) $f(t)=\frac{2}{3}+\frac{4}{\pi^2}\sum_{n=1}^{\infty}\frac{(-1)^{n+1}}{n^2}\cos n\pi t$

17 $f(t)=\frac{1}{6}\pi^2-\sum_{n=1}^{\infty}\frac{1}{n^2}\cos 2nt$

$$f(t)=\frac{8}{\pi}\sum_{n=1}^{\infty}\frac{1}{(2n-1)^3}\sin(2n-1)t$$

18 $f(x)=\frac{8a}{\pi^2}\sum_{n=1}^{\infty}\frac{(-1)^{n+1}}{(2n-1)^2}\sin\frac{(2n-1)\pi x}{l}$

19 $f(x)=\frac{2l}{\pi^2}\sum_{n=1}^{\infty}\frac{(-1)^{n+1}}{(2n-1)^2}\sin\frac{2(2n-1)\pi x}{l}$

20 $f(t)=\frac{1}{2}\sin t+\frac{4}{\pi}\sum_{n=1}^{\infty}\frac{n(-1)^{n+1}}{4n^2-1}\sin 2nt$

21 $f(x)=-\frac{1}{2}A-\frac{4A}{\pi^2}\sum_{n=1}^{\infty}\frac{1}{(2n-1)^2}\cos\frac{(2n-1)\pi x}{l}$

22 $T(x)=\frac{8KL^2}{\pi^3}\sum_{n=1}^{\infty}\frac{1}{(2n-1)^3}\sin\frac{(2n-1)\pi x}{L}$

23 $f(t)=\frac{1}{2}+\frac{1}{2}\cos\pi t+\frac{4}{\pi}\sum_{n=1}^{\infty}\frac{1}{4n^2-1}\sin 2n\pi t$

$$-\frac{2}{\pi}\sum_{n=1}^{\infty}\frac{1}{2n-1}\sin(2n-1)\pi t$$

26 (c) $1+4\sum_{n=1}^{\infty}\frac{(-1)^{n+1}}{n}\sin nt$

29 (a) $\frac{1}{6}\pi^2+\sum_{n=1}^{\infty}\frac{2}{n^2}(-1)^n\cos nt$

$$+\sum_{n=1}^{\infty}\frac{1}{\pi}\left[-\frac{\pi^2}{n}(-1)^n+\frac{2}{n^3}(-1)^n-\frac{2}{n^3}\right]\sin nt$$

(b) $a_n = 0$

$$b_n = \frac{4}{n\pi}\left(\cos n\pi - \cos \frac{1}{2}n\pi\right) + 2\left(\frac{3\pi}{4n^2} \sin \frac{1}{2}n\pi - \frac{\pi^2}{8n} \cos \frac{1}{2}n\pi + \frac{3}{n^3} \cos \frac{1}{2}n\pi - \frac{6}{\pi n^4} \sin \frac{1}{2}n\pi\right),$$

$$\frac{1}{\pi}\left[\left(\frac{3}{2}\pi^2 - 16\right)\sin t + \frac{1}{8}(32 + \pi^3 - 6\pi)\sin 2t - \frac{1}{3}\left(\frac{32}{9} + \frac{1}{2}\pi^2\right)\sin 3t + \dots\right]$$

(c) $-\dfrac{4}{\pi^2}\displaystyle\sum_{n=1}^{\infty}\frac{\cos(2n-1)\pi t}{(2n-1)^2} + \frac{2}{\pi}\sum_{n=1}^{\infty}\frac{\sin(2n-1)t}{(2n-1)}$

(d) $\dfrac{1}{4} + \dfrac{2}{\pi^2}\displaystyle\sum_{n=1}^{\infty}\frac{1}{(2n-1)^2}\cos 2(2n-1)\pi t$

30 $e(t) = 5 + \dfrac{20}{\pi}\displaystyle\sum_{n=1}^{\infty}\frac{1}{2n-1}\sin(2n-1)100\pi t$

$i_{ss}(t) \simeq 0.008\cos(100\pi t - 1.96) + 0.005\cos(300\pi t - 0.33)$

31 $f(t) = \dfrac{400}{\pi}\displaystyle\sum_{n=1}^{\infty}\frac{1}{2n-1}\sin(2n-1)t$

$x_{ss}(t) \simeq 0.14\sin(\pi t - 0.1) + 0.379\sin(3\pi t - 2.415) + 0.017\sin(5\pi t - 2.83)$

32 $f(t) = \dfrac{100}{\pi}\displaystyle\sum_{n=1}^{\infty}\frac{(-1)^{n+1}}{n}\sin 2\pi n t$

$x_{ss}(t) \simeq 0.044\sin(2\pi t - 3.13) - 0.0052\sin(4\pi t - 3.14)$

33 $e(t) = \dfrac{100}{\pi} + 50\sin 50\pi t - \dfrac{200}{\pi}\displaystyle\sum_{n=1}^{\infty}\frac{\cos 100\pi n t}{4n^2 - 1}$

$i_{ss}(t) \simeq 0.78\cos(50\pi t + (-0.17)) - 0.01\sin(100\pi t + (-0.48))$

35 $f(t) = \dfrac{1}{2} + \displaystyle\sum_{\substack{n=-\infty\\ n\neq 0}}^{\infty}\frac{j}{2n\pi}[(-1)^n - 1]\,e^{jn\pi t/2}$

36 (a) $\dfrac{3}{4}\pi + \displaystyle\sum_{\substack{n=-\infty\\ n\neq 0}}^{\infty}\frac{1}{2\pi}\left\{\frac{j\pi}{n} - \frac{1}{n^2}[1 + (-1)^n]\right\}e^{jnt}$

(b) $\dfrac{a}{2}\sin \omega t - \displaystyle\sum_{n=-\infty}^{\infty}\frac{a}{2\pi(n^2 - 1)}[(-1)^n + 1]\,e^{jn\omega t}$

(c) $\dfrac{3}{2} + \displaystyle\sum_{\substack{n=-\infty\\ n\neq 0}}^{\infty}\frac{j}{2\pi n}[1 - (-1)^n]\,e^{jnt}$

(d) $\dfrac{2}{\pi}\displaystyle\sum_{n=-\infty}^{\infty}\frac{1}{1 - 4n^2}e^{2jnt}$

38 (b) (i) 17.74, (ii) 17.95
(c) 18.14; (i) 2.20%, (ii) 1.05%

39 (a) $c_0 = 15,\ c_n = \dfrac{30}{jn\pi}(1 - e^{-jn\pi/2})$

$15,\ \dfrac{30}{\pi}(1 - j),\ -\dfrac{30}{\pi}j,\ -\dfrac{10}{\pi}(1 + j),\ 0,\ \dfrac{6}{\pi}(1 - j)$

(b) 15 W, 24.30 W, 12.16 W, 2.70 W, 0.97 W
(c) 60 W
(d) 91.9%

40 0.19, 0.10, 0.0675

41 (c) $c_0 = 0,\ c_1 = \frac{3}{2},\ c_2 = 0,\ c_3 = -\frac{7}{8}$

42 (c) $c_0 = \frac{1}{4},\ c_1 = \frac{1}{2},\ c_2 = \frac{5}{16},\ c_3 = 0$

46 (b) $c_1 = 0,\ c_2 = \sqrt{(2\pi)},\ c_3 = 0$, MSE = 0

4.9 Review exercises

1 $f(t) = \dfrac{1}{6}\pi^2 + \displaystyle\sum_{n=1}^{\infty}\frac{2}{n^2}(-1)^n\cos nt + \sum_{n=1}^{\infty}\left[\frac{\pi}{2n-1} - \frac{4}{\pi(2n-1)^3}\right]\sin(2n-1)t - \sum_{n=1}^{\infty}\frac{\pi}{2n}\sin 2nt$

Taking $T = \pi$ gives the required sum.

2 $f(t) = \dfrac{1}{9}\pi + \dfrac{2}{\pi}\displaystyle\sum_{n=1}^{\infty}\frac{1}{n^2}\left\{\cos\frac{1}{3}n\pi - \frac{1}{3}[2 + (-1)^n]\right\}\cos nt,$

$\frac{2}{9}\pi$

3 (a) $f(t) = \dfrac{2T}{\pi^2}\displaystyle\sum_{n=1}^{\infty}\frac{(-1)^{n+1}}{(2n-1)^2}\sin\frac{2(2n-1)\pi t}{T}$

(b) $-\frac{1}{4}T$;
(c) Taking $t = \frac{1}{4}T$ gives $S = \frac{1}{8}\pi^2$

5 $f(t) = \dfrac{4}{\pi}\displaystyle\sum_{n=1}^{\infty}\frac{(-1)^n\sin(2n-1)t}{(2n-1)^2}$

8 $f(x) = \dfrac{4}{\pi}\displaystyle\sum_{n=1}^{\infty}\frac{(-1)^{n+1}}{(2n-1)^2}\sin(2n-1)x$

$f(x) = \dfrac{1}{4}\pi - \dfrac{2}{\pi}\displaystyle\sum_{n=1}^{\infty}\frac{\cos 2(2n-1)x}{(2n-1)^2}$

10 (a) $f(t) = \displaystyle\sum_{n=1}^{\infty}\frac{2}{n}\sin nt$

(b) $f(t) = \dfrac{1}{2}\pi + \dfrac{4}{\pi}\displaystyle\sum_{n=1}^{\infty}\frac{1}{(2n-1)^2}\cos(2n-1)t$

13 (a) $f(t)=\frac{1}{2}\pi-\frac{4}{\pi}\sum_{n=1}^{\infty}\frac{1}{(2n-1)^2}\cos(2n-1)t$

(b) $g(t)=\frac{4}{\pi}\sum_{n=1}^{\infty}\frac{1}{2n-1}\sin(2n-1)t$

15 (a) $v(t)=\frac{10}{\pi}+5\sin\frac{2\pi t}{T}-\frac{20}{\pi}\sum_{n=1}^{\infty}\frac{1}{4n^2-1}\cos\frac{4n\pi t}{T}$

(b) 2.5 W, 9.01%

16 $g(t)=\frac{4}{\pi}\sum_{n=1}^{\infty}\frac{1}{2n-1}\sin(2n-1)t$

$f(t)=1+g(t)$

18 (b) $\frac{\sin\omega t-\omega\cos\omega t}{1+\omega^2}$ $\frac{4}{\pi}\sum_{n=1}^{\infty}\frac{\sin\alpha t-\alpha\cos\alpha t}{(2n-1)(1+\alpha^2)}$

$\alpha=(4n-2)\pi/T$

19 (c) $T_0=1,\ T_1=t_1,\ T_2=2t^2-1,\ T_3=4t^3-3t$

(d) $\frac{1}{16}T_5-\frac{5}{8}T_4+\frac{33}{16}T_3-\frac{5}{2}T_2+\frac{95}{5}T_1-\frac{79}{8}T_0$

(e) $\frac{33}{4}t^3-5t^2+\frac{91}{16}t-\frac{59}{8},\ \frac{11}{16},\ t=-1$

CHAPTER 5

Exercises

1 $\frac{2a}{a^2+\omega^2}$

2 $AT^2\mathrm{j}\omega\,\mathrm{sinc}^2\frac{\omega T}{2}$

3 $AT\,\mathrm{sinc}^2\frac{\omega t}{2}$

4 $8K\,\mathrm{sinc}\,2\omega,\ 2K\,\mathrm{sinc}\,\omega,\ 2K(4\,\mathrm{sinc}\,2\omega-\mathrm{sinc}\,\omega)$

5 $4\,\mathrm{sinc}\,\omega-4\,\mathrm{sinc}\,2\omega$

7 $\frac{\omega_0}{(a+\mathrm{j}\omega)^2+\omega_0^2}$

10 $F_s=\frac{x}{x^2+a^2},\ F_c=\frac{x}{x^2+a^2}$

12 $\frac{1}{(1-\omega^2)+3\mathrm{j}\omega}$

13 $4\,\mathrm{sinc}\,2\omega-2\,\mathrm{sinc}\,\omega$

14 $\frac{1}{2}T[\mathrm{sinc}\,\frac{1}{2}(\omega_0-\omega)T+\mathrm{sinc}\,\frac{1}{2}(\omega_0+\omega)T]$

15 $\frac{1}{2}T\mathrm{e}^{-\mathrm{j}\omega T/2}[\mathrm{e}^{\mathrm{j}\omega_0 T/2}\mathrm{sinc}\,\frac{1}{2}(\omega-\omega_0)T$
$+\mathrm{e}^{-\mathrm{j}\omega_0 T/2}\mathrm{sinc}\,\frac{1}{2}(\omega+\omega_0)T]$

16 $\mathrm{j}[\mathrm{sinc}(\omega+2)-\mathrm{sinc}(\omega-2)]$

18 $4AT\cos\omega\tau\,\mathrm{sinc}\,\omega T$

19 High-pass filter

20 $\pi\mathrm{e}^{-a|\omega|}$

21 $T[\mathrm{sinc}(\omega-\omega_0)T+\mathrm{sinc}(\omega+\omega_0)T]$

26 $\frac{1}{2}\pi\mathrm{j}[\delta(\omega+\omega_0)-\delta(\omega-\omega_0)]-\frac{\omega_0}{\omega_0^2-\omega^2}$

28 {2, 0, 2, 0}

29 {2, 0, 2, 0}

5.9 Review exercises

1 $\frac{\sin\omega}{\omega^2}-\frac{\cos2\omega}{\omega}$

2 $-\frac{\pi\mathrm{j}}{\omega}\mathrm{sinc}\,2\omega$

7 (a) $\frac{1}{a-b}(\mathrm{e}^{at}-\mathrm{e}^{bt})H(t)$

(b) (i) $t\mathrm{e}^{2t}H(t)$ (ii) $(t-1+\mathrm{e}^{-t})H(t)$

8 (a) $-\sin\omega_0(t+\frac{1}{4}\pi)$ (b) $\cos\omega_0 t$

(c) $\mathrm{je}^{\mathrm{j}\omega_0 t}$ (d) $-\mathrm{je}^{-\mathrm{j}\omega_0 t}$

17 (a) $\frac{a+2\pi s}{a^2+4\pi^2s^2}$

(b) $\frac{1}{2\pi s}(\sin2\pi sT-\cos2\pi sT+1)$

CHAPTER 6

Exercises

1 (a) (762, 798) (b) 97

2 76.1, (65.7, 86.5)

3 (8.05, 9.40)

4 (71.2, 75.2), accept

5 (2.92, 3.92)

6 (24.9, 27.9)

7 95% confidence interval (53.9, 58.1), criterion satisfactory

8 (−1900, 7500), reject

9 90%: (34, 758), 95%: (−45, 837), reject at 10% but accept at 5%

10 90%: (0.052, 0.089), 95%: (0.049, 0.092), reject at 10% but accept at 5%. Test statistic leads to rejection at both 10% and 5% levels, and is more accurate

11 203, (0.223, 0.327)

12 90%: (–0.28, –0.08), 95%: (–0.30, –0.06), accept at 10% but reject at 5%

13 (0.003, 0.130), carcinogenic

14 (a) X: (0.34, 0.53, 0.13), Y: (0.25, 0.31, 0.44)
(b) 0.472, (c) $E(X) = 1.79$, $\text{Var}(X) = 0.426$, $E(Y) = 2.19$, $\text{Var}(Y) = 0.654$, $\rho_{X,Y} = -0.246$

17 (a) 0.552, (b) 0.368

18 0.934

19 0.732

20 (0.45, 0.85)

21 (0.67, 0.99)

22 0.444, 90%: (0.08, 0.70), 95%: (0.00, 0.74), just significant at 5%, rank correlation 0.401, significant at 10%

23 (a) 6, (b) 0.484,
(c) $f_X(x) = 6(\frac{1}{2} - x + \frac{1}{2}x^2)$, $f_Y(y) = 6(1 - y)y$

24 0.84

25 $a = 1.22$, $b = 2.13$

26 $a = 6.315$, $b = 14.64$, $y = 226$

28 (a) $a = 343.7$, $b = 3.221$, $y = 537$;
(b) (0.46, 5.98), reject; (c) (459, 615)

29 $a = 0.107$, $b = 1.143$, (14.4, 17.8)

31 120 Ω

32 $\lambda = 2.66$, $C = 2.69 \times 10^6$, $P = 22.9$

33 $a = 7533$, $b = -1.059$, $y = 17.9$

34 $\chi^2 = 2.15$, accept

35 $\chi^2 = 12.3$, significant at 5%

36 $\chi^2 = 1.35$, accept Poisson

37 $\chi^2 = 12.97$, accept Poisson

39 $\chi^2 = 1.30$, not significant

40 $\chi^2 = 20.56$, significant at 5%

41 $\chi^2 = 20.7$, significant at 0.5%

42 $\chi^2 = 11.30$, significant at 5% but not at 1%, for proportion 95%: (0.111, 0.159), 99%: (0.104, 0.166), significant at 1%

43 $c = 4$, $M_X(t) = 4/(t - 2)^2$, $E(X) = 1$, $\text{Var}(X) = \frac{1}{2}$

45 0.014

46 0.995

48 Warning 9.5, action 13.5, sample 12, UCL = 11.4, sample 9

49 UK sample 28, US sample 25

50 Action 2.93, sample 12

51 Action 14.9, sample 19 but repeated warnings

52 (a) sample 9, (b) sample 9

53 (a) sample 10, (b) sample 12

54 sample 10

55 sample 16

56 (a) Repeated warnings, (b) sample 15, (c) sample 14

58 sample 11

59 Shewhart, sample 26; cusum, sample 13; moving-average, sample 11

60 0.132

61 0.223, 0.042

63 (a) $\frac{1}{4}$, (b) $2\frac{1}{4}$, (c) 0.237,
(d) 45 min, (e) 0.276

65 Mean costs per hour: A, £200; B, £130

66 6

67 Second cash desk

68 29.4%

69 Sabotage

70 $P(C\,|\,\text{two hits}) = 0.526$

71 $\frac{1}{2}$

72 (a) 0.0944, (b) 0.81

73 (a) $\frac{3}{4}$, (b) $[1 + (\frac{1}{3})^k 2^{n-k}]^{-1}$

74 AAAA

75 1.28:1 in favour of Poisson

77 2.8:1 in favour of H_2

78 12.8:1 in favour of H_1

6.12 Review exercises

1 $Z = 0.27$, accept

2 (0.202, 0.266)

3 $(96.1 \times 10^6, 104.9 \times 10^6)$

4 $\chi^2 = 3.35$ (using class intervals of length 5, with a single class for all values greater than 30), accept exponential

5 Outlier 72 significant at 5%, outlier included (7.36, 11.48); excluded (7.11, 10.53)

6 $\chi^2 = 20.0$, significant at 2.5%

7 Operate if $p > \frac{4}{13}$

8 Cost per hour: A, £632.5; B, £603.4

9 (a) $P(\text{input } 0 | \text{output } 0) = \dfrac{\bar{p}\alpha}{\bar{p}\alpha + p\bar{\alpha}}$ etc.

(b) $p < \alpha < 1 - p$

Index

Emboldened page references indicate where an entry has been defined in the text.

D

Q

R

S

T

U

V

W

Z